SCIENCE AND TECHNOLOGY (ST)
ENVIRONMENTAL SCIENCE AND TECHNOLOGY (EST)
APPLIED SCIENCE AND TECHNOLOGY (AST)
SCIENCE AND THE ENVIRONMENT (SE)

OBSERVATORY

THE ENVIRONMENT

STUDENT BOOK
Second Year of Secondary Cycle Two

Marie-Danielle Cyr
Dominique Forget
Jean-Sébastien Verreault

ÉDITIONS DU RENOUVEAU PÉDAGOGIQUE INC.
5757, RUE CYPIHOT
SAINT-LAURENT (QUÉBEC)
H4S 1R3
TÉLÉPHONE : 514 334-2690
TÉLÉCOPIEUR : 514 334-4720
erpidlm@erpi.com

English Edition

Managing editor
Yzabelle Martineau

Translation
Jane Wilson
Freeman Translation
Kelli Ann Ferrigan
Patricia Hynes

Project editor and copy editor
Patricia Hynes

Proofreader
My-Trang Nguyen

Photo research and permissions
Marie-Chantal Masson

Art director
Hélène Cousineau

Graphic design coordinator
Sylvie Piotte

Electronic publishing
Interscript

Cartography
Dimension DPR

Consultants
Samira Cohen Spain, ST teacher, New Frontiers School Board
Gloria Cuccarolo, ST teacher, Sir Wilfrid Laurier School Board
Danielle Hamel, ST teacher, Eastern Townships School Board
Alison Hurst, ST teacher, Sir Wilfrid Laurier School Board
Mary Lum, ST teacher, New Frontiers School Board
Gilles Roussin, ST teacher, West Island College
Valérie Vien, ST teacher, West Island College

Registration of copyright – Bibliothèque et Archives nationales du Québec, 2009
Registration of copyright – Library and Archives Canada, 2009

Printed in Canada 567890 HLN 12 11
ISBN 978-2-7613-2863-0 11128 BCD CM12

Original French Edition

Managing editor
Monique Boucher

Project editors and copy editors
Marielle Champagne
Carole Lambert
Hélène Pelletier
Sylvie Racine

Copy editor
Luc Asselin

Proofreader
Pierre-Yves L'Heureux

Photo research and permissions
Marie-Chantal Masson

Art director
Hélène Cousineau

Graphic design coordinator
Sylvie Piotte

Cover design
Claire Senneville

Graphic design
Valérie Deltour
Frédérique Bouvier

Electronic publishing
Valérie Deltour

Illustrations
Michel Rouleau

Cartography
Dimension DPR

Writers
Hélène Crevier (INFO features)
Dominique Forget (newspaper article adaptations)
Danielle Ouellet (FOLLOW-UP features)

Consultants
Annie Châteauneuf, ST teacher, Polyvalente Chanoine-Armand-Racicot, Commission scolaire des Hautes-Rivières
Chantale Dionne, ST teacher, Polyvalente de Jonquière, Commission scolaire de la Jonquière

Science content reviewers
Luce Boulanger, clinical biochemist
Josée Brisson, chemist and professor at Université Laval
Normand Brunet, biologist and assistant professor at Institut des sciences de l'environnement, UQAM
Éric Duchemin, biologist, geologist, chemist and specialist in environmental science
Richard Gagnon, physicist
Richard Mathieu, biologist and teacher at Cégep de Drummondville
Guy Olivier, engineer and professor at École Polytechnique de Montréal
Bruno Tremblay, climatologist and assistant professor in the Department of Atmospheric and Oceanic Sciences, McGill University

These programs are funded by Québec's Ministère de l'Éducation, du Loisir et du Sport, through contributions from the Canada-Québec Agreement on Minority-Language Education and Second-Language Instruction.

TABLE OF CONTENTS

This textbook covers the four programs in Science and Technology:
- Science and Technology (ST)
- Environmental Science and Technology (EST)
- Applied Science and Technology (AST)
- Science and the Environment (SE)

The abbreviations beside the entries in the table of contents indicate the source programs for the section content. These abbreviations also appear beside each heading in the main text.

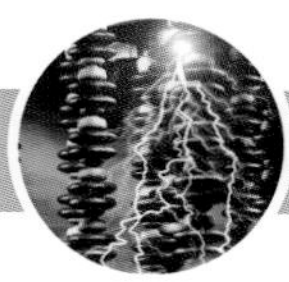

CHAPTER 2

CHAPTER 3

CHAPTER 4

CHAPTER 5

THE EARTH AND SPACE

CHAPTER 6

CHAPTER 7

CHAPTER 8

CHAPTER 9

CHAPTER 10

CHAPTER 11

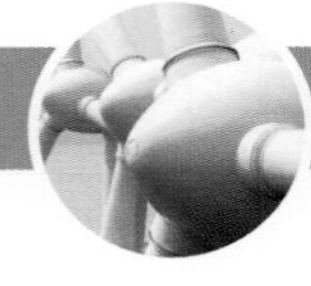

CHAPTER 12

CHAPTER 13

CHAPTER 14

OBSERVATORY

AT A GLANCE

OPENING PAGE OF AN AREA

The title of the area

A brief presentation of the area

THE LIVING WORLD

AT THIS POINT IN HISTORY, THE EARTH IS THE ONLY KNOWN PLACE IN THE UNIVERSE WHERE LIFE AS WE PERCEIVE IT HAS EVOLVED.

Life can be sustained almost anywhere on Earth, even in the harshest conditions: on the glacial expanses of Antarctica, in the depths of an ocean abyss, among the endless dunes of a sandy desert or on the rocky, snow-blown slopes of a mountain.

Of all living species, ours seems to be the one whose actions have the greatest repercussions for other species and for the Earth's resources. To grasp the full extent of the impact of our actions, we need to study how living beings form groups, how they interact with one another and with their environment and how the traits of a living organism are passed on to its descendants.

CONTENTS

288 289

The contents of the chapters in the area

CHAPTER FEATURES

An **introduction** makes concrete connections between the subject of the chapter and the environment which is the program theme for the second year of Secondary Cycle Two.

A **timeline**, from the beginnings of human history to the present day, presents discoveries and inventions related to the concepts covered in the chapter.

The **Concept review** feature lists the relevant concepts in the programs for Secondary Cycle One and the first year of Secondary Cycle Two.

Program abbreviations—ST (Science and Technology), EST (Environmental Science and Technology), AST (Applied Science and Technology) and SE (Science and the Environment)—appear beside each heading. These abbreviations indicate the source programs for the section content.

Definitions of the program concepts appear in colour. They also appear in the glossary.

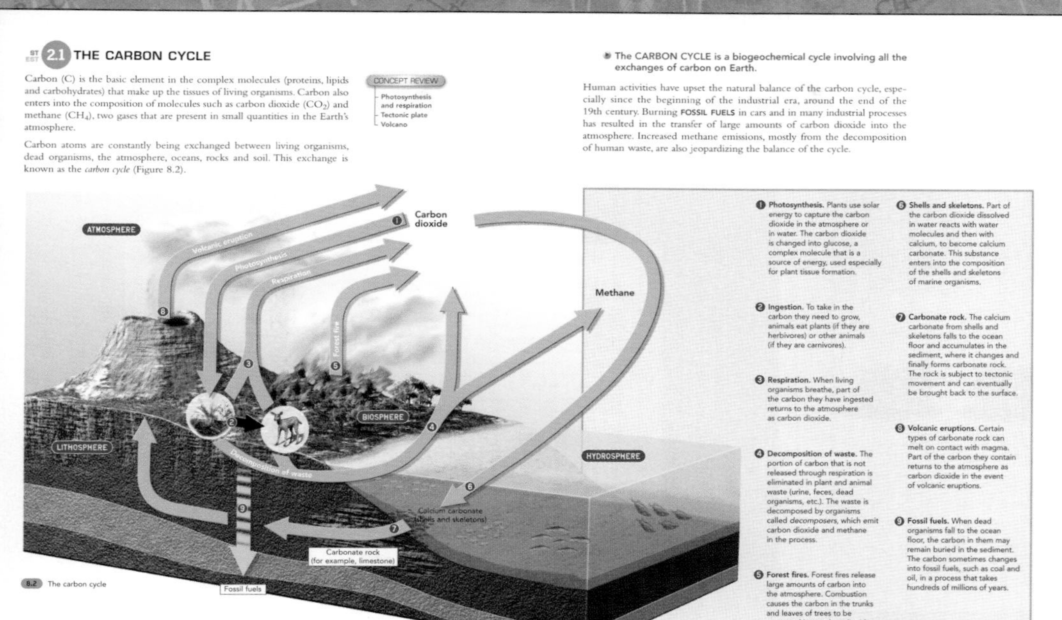

ST EST 2.1 THE CARBON CYCLE

Carbon (C) is the basic element in the complex molecules (proteins, lipids and carbohydrates) that make up the tissues of living organisms. Carbon also enters into the composition of molecules such as carbon dioxide (CO_2) and methane (CH_4), two gases that are present in small quantities in the Earth's atmosphere.

CONCEPT REVIEW
- Photosynthesis and respiration
- Tectonic plate
- Volcano

Carbon atoms are constantly being exchanged between living organisms, dead organisms, the atmosphere, oceans, rocks and soil. This exchange is known as the *carbon cycle* (Figure 8.2).

The CARBON CYCLE is a biogeochemical cycle involving all the exchanges of carbon on Earth.

Human activities have upset the natural balance of the carbon cycle, especially since the beginning of the industrial era, around the end of the 19th century. Burning **FOSSIL FUELS** in cars and in many industrial processes has resulted in the transfer of large amounts of carbon dioxide into the atmosphere. Increased methane emissions, mostly from the decomposition of human waste, are also jeopardizing the balance of the cycle.

8.2 The carbon cycle

1 Photosynthesis. Plants use solar energy to capture the carbon dioxide in the atmosphere or in water. The carbon dioxide is changed into glucose, a complex molecule that is a source of energy, used especially for plant tissue formation.

2 Ingestion. To take in the carbon they need to grow, animals eat plants (if they are herbivores) or other animals (if they are carnivores).

3 Respiration. When living organisms breathe, part of the carbon they have ingested returns to the atmosphere as carbon dioxide.

4 Decomposition of waste. The portion of carbon that is not released through respiration is eliminated in plant and animal waste (urine, feces, dead organisms, etc.). The waste is decomposed by organisms called decomposers, which emit carbon dioxide and methane in the process.

5 Forest fires. Forest fires release large amounts of carbon into the atmosphere. Combustion causes the carbon in the trunks and leaves of trees to be converted into carbon dioxide.

6 Shells and skeletons. Part of the carbon dioxide dissolved in water reacts with water molecules and then with calcium, to become calcium carbonate. This substance enters into the composition of the shells and skeletons of marine organisms.

7 Carbonate rock. The calcium carbonate from shells and skeletons falls to the ocean floor and accumulates in the sediment, where it changes and finally forms carbonate rock. The rock is subject to tectonic movement and can eventually be brought back to the surface.

8 Volcanic eruptions. Certain types of carbonate rock can melt on contact with magma. Part of the carbon they contain returns to the atmosphere as carbon dioxide in the event of volcanic eruptions.

9 Fossil fuels. When dead organisms fall to the ocean floor, the carbon in them may remain buried in the sediment. The carbon sometimes changes into fossil fuels, such as coal and oil, in a process that takes hundreds of millions of years.

256 CHAPTER 8 — The biosphere 257

Diagrams support student understanding of the concepts.

These icons show that a related **science lab** (LAB) or **technological lab** (TECH) is available as a reproducible handout.

Many **maps, photos** and **tables** illustrate the text.

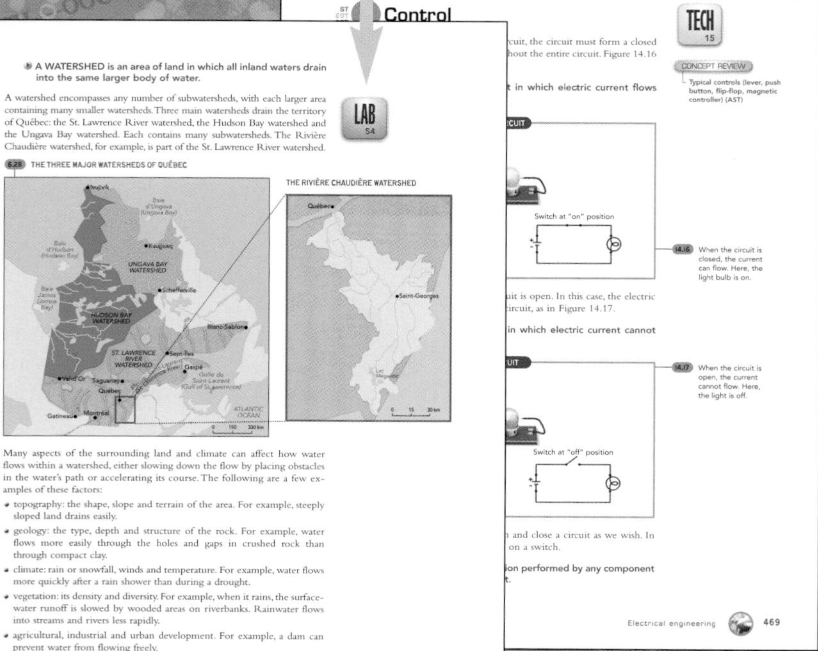

A WATERSHED is an area of land in which all inland waters drain into the same larger body of water.

LAB 54

A watershed encompasses any number of subwatersheds, with each larger area containing many smaller watersheds. Three main watersheds drain the territory of Québec: the St. Lawrence River watershed, the Hudson Bay watershed and the Ungava Bay watershed. Each contains many subwatersheds. The Rivière Chaudière watershed, for example, is part of the St. Lawrence River watershed.

8.28 THE THREE MAJOR WATERSHEDS OF QUÉBEC

THE RIVIÈRE CHAUDIÈRE WATERSHED

Many aspects of the surrounding land and climate can affect how water flows within a watershed, either slowing down the flow by placing obstacles in the water's path or accelerating its course. The following are a few examples of these factors:
- topography: the shape, slope and terrain of the area. For example, steeply sloped land drains easily.
- geology: the type, depth and structure of the rock. For example, water flows more easily through the holes and gaps in crushed rock than through compact clay.
- climate: rain or snowfall, winds and temperature. For example, water flows more quickly after a rain shower than during a drought.
- vegetation: its density and diversity. For example, when it rains, the surface-water runoff is slowed by wooded areas on riverbanks. Rainwater flows into streams and rivers less rapidly.
- agricultural, industrial and urban development. For example, a dam can prevent water from flowing freely.

202 CHAPTER 6

ST EST Control

TECH 15

CONCEPT REVIEW
- Typical controls (lever, push button, flip-flop, magnetic controller) (AST)

Switch at "on" position

14.16 When the circuit is closed, the current can flow. Here, the light bulb is on.

Switch at "off" position

14.17 When the circuit is open, the current cannot flow. Here, the light is off.

Electrical engineering 469

EST **2.4 THE LAW OF SEGREGATION OF ALLELES**

Gametes are formed during sexual reproduction through a phenomenon of cell division called **MEIOSIS**. This cell division leads to the creation of gametes containing half the chromosomes normally present in the cells of the organism. Instead of carrying pairs of chromosomes, gametes thus contain only one chromosome from each pair. Consequently, only one allele is present instead of two.

Since an offspring results from the fusion of a gamete from the father and a gamete from the mother, half of its chromosomes will come from the father, and the other half, from the mother. However, even if half the genes in the offspring's chromosomes come from one parent, and the other half, from the other parent, the offspring will not *half* resemble the father and *half* resemble the mother. Why not?

Without even knowing about meiosis, Mendel's research nonetheless led him to formulate the law of segregation of alleles. This law states that the two alleles for a particular character trait separate when gametes are formed. Half of the gametes thus receive one of the two alleles, and the other half receive the second allele. For example, in the case of flower colour (Figure 11.19), homozygous individuals produce gametes—shown here in circles—that all have the same allele, while in a heterozygous individual, 50 percent of the gametes carry the *P* allele, and 50 percent, the *p* allele.

Segregation comes from the Latin segregare, meaning "to set apart."

1902
1992

Barbara McClintock

This scientist focused her research on the structure of the corn genome. She developed techniques to visualize the behaviour of chromosomes and their genes during gamete formation. Her work earned her a Nobel Prize in 1983.

Phenotype	Purple flowers	Purple flowers	White flowers
Genotype	Homozygote PP	Heterozygote Pp	Homozygote pp
Gametes	P 50% / P 50%	P 50% / p 50%	p 50% / p 50%

11.19 Alleles for flower colour as they occur in gametes, according to the different genotypes possible and the law of segregation of alleles.

366 CHAPTER 11

Short **biographies** highlight the contribution of various personalities to the advancement of knowledge on the subject in question.

ST EST AST **2.4 PLASTICS**

TECH 3

Plastics are materials developed mainly from petroleum and natural gas. From these **FOSSIL FUELS**, basic units called monomers are extracted industrially and used in the synthesis of plastics. Monomers are arranged in chains to form polymers. Plastics are thus made up of different polymers, which vary with the type of plastic. The most widely used plastics are presented in Appendix 5, at the end of this textbook.

Various substances can be added to polymers to produce plastics with certain desirable properties.

Monomer comes from the Greek words monos, meaning "single," and meros, meaning "part."

Polymer comes from the Greek words polus, meaning "many," and meros, meaning "part."

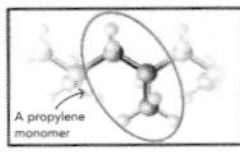

12.21 Polypropylene is a polymer formed from an arrangement of many propylene monomers. It is often used to make food containers.

ENVIRONMENT EXTRA

Plastic bags: good for shopping, bad for the environment

When Quebeckers go shopping, they usually leave the store with a plastic bag. Most plastic bags are made of low-density polyethylene, a recyclable thermoplastic. Few of them are actually recycled, however, and few are even reused, which means that roughly a billion bags end up in Québec landfills every year. Since the bags are hardly biodegradable, they take many years to decompose. They pile up in landfills, where the wind often catches them and blows them away, scattering them about the environment, even as far as the Arctic. In the wild, animals, especially marine species, may swallow the bags and die.

There are alternatives to using low-density polyethylene bags. Bags made of paper or fabric are two examples. Increasing numbers of biodegradable plastic bags are also becoming available, but the decomposition of these bags produces methane, a powerful greenhouse gas. All plastic bags may therefore be harmful to the environment in some way. The clearest path to reducing their environmental impact is to reuse them as many times as possible before throwing them away.

Many of the plastic bags piling up in dumps are scattered by the wind, littering the environment.

396 CHAPTER 12

The **Environment extra** feature informs students about current environmental issues.

AN END IN SIGHT FOR MINIATURIZATION?

In the world of microelectronics, small means powerful. Manufacturers are engaged in a fierce competition to miniaturize transistors, the building blocks of microprocessors. In 2001, a transistor measured 0.25 microns (micrometres, or 10^{-6} m), which was already tiny. In 2007, transistor size was down to only 0.065 microns, or 65 nanometres. Soon the figure will be 45 nanometres, and then 32. The principle is simple: the more transistors a manufacturer manages to install on a microchip, the lighter and more powerful the product.

Miniaturization has its limits, however. The technology behind transistor manufacture is highly complex; the transistors are engraved directly onto the silicon chip. At such small scales, it becomes increasingly difficult to etch perfect transistors without damaging those on either side.

Scientists now foresee the day when production techniques will become too complex and expensive to be worth the effort. Will transistors become as small as 12, 10 or even 6 nanometres? Scientists have their doubts.

The technical difficulties involved in manufacturing microchips increase as the chips become ever smaller.

All electrical devices contain an electrical circuit. Some circuits are very simple, while others are highly complex. However, they all contain at least the following three components:

- a power supply to create a potential difference (measured in volts)
- one or more elements that use electrical energy, such as a light bulb or a heating element (Their resistance is measured in ohms.)
- wires that carry the charges from the power supply to the elements and then from the elements back to the source (The current intensity in these wires is measured in amperes.)

Diagrams and symbols are often used to represent electrical circuits. The current direction shown in a diagram usually corresponds to the conventional current direction.

When a circuit contains two or more elements, the components can be connected in different ways. Series circuits and parallel circuits are two types of connections.

HOW TO DRAW A DIAGRAM - SYMBOLS
HOW TO DRAW A DIAGRAM - CIRCUIT DIAGRAM

ST EST AST **SERIES CIRCUITS**

In a series circuit, components are connected end to end. Since the circuit does not branch out at any point, the current can follow only one path.

Electricity and magnetism 157

Summaries of actual newspaper and magazine **articles** deal with concepts in the chapter in the light of current and historical events.

This icon indicates a reference to **Toolbox**, a companion volume that shows students how to process information, conduct a scientific experiment or carry out a technological activity.

Words in capital letters in the text are defined in the glossary.

LAB 57

The air surrounding the Earth is in constant motion. It rises in the atmosphere above the warm, humid regions at the equator (low-pressure zones), heads toward the poles and then descends over cold, dry regions (high-pressure zones). At the same time, the cold polar air makes its ... of CONVECTION helps distribute the solar energy the Earth receives. Without atmospheric circulation, the differences in temperature between the equator and the poles would be much greater.

ATMOSPHERIC CIRCULATION is the global-scale movement of the layer of air surrounding the Earth.

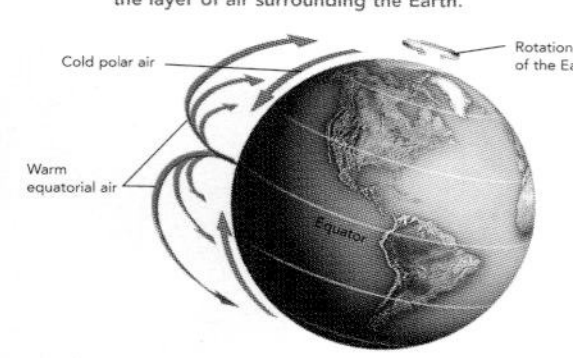

7.5 Air that has been warmed at the equator becomes lighter and less dense; it moves toward the poles. It is replaced by the heavier cold air coming from the poles.

THE DOLDRUMS
The doldrums is a name for an equatorial region of light or no winds. In the past, sailing ships were sometimes becalmed there for weeks on end. To conserve their freshwater supplies, sailors would throw their horses overboard.

The **Info** feature briefly describes surprising phenomena from daily life and enables students to make connections with the world around them. The icon indicates that a relevant activity is available as a reproducible handout.

Theoretically, air masses should move in a straight line from north to south or from south to north. However, the rotation of the Earth changes their trajectories through what is called the CORIOLIS EFFECT. Discovered by the French engineer and mathematician Gaspard-Gustave Coriolis in 1835, this effect operates when a body moves in an environment that is itself in rotation, directing the body in a course perpendicular to its original movement. The Coriolis effect causes winds to deviate to the right in the Northern Hemisphere and to the left in the Southern Hemisphere, thus affecting the trajectories of air masses.

Hemisphere comes from the Greek words *hêmi*, meaning "half," and *sphaira*, meaning a "spherical object."

Initial course
Perpendicular deviation
Rotation of the Earth

7.6 Due to the rotation of the Earth, the Coriolis effect causes a deviation in wind direction.

These movements of air occur in the troposphere and play an important role in meteorological phenomena. For example, they are responsible for the formation of cold fronts, warm fronts and the subsequent clouds, which occurs when air masses of different properties come into contact.

226 CHAPTER 7

Etymological notes help students understand more abstract or difficult words.

The **Checkup** section contains questions that cover all the chapter content. The section always ends with **review questions,** which encourage students to apply knowledge they acquired from the chapter.

CHECKUP

ST 1–5, A and D. CST 1–7, 9, 11, 14, A, B and D. AST 1–14 and A–D. SE None.

1 Materials (pp. 386–390)

1. Depending on how they are used, technical objects are likely to be subjected to stress. Name the constraint at work in the part of the object indicated in the photos below.

A B C D E

2. When manufacturing a technical object, it is often necessary to define the mechanical properties of different materials in order to make the most suitable choice. Which mechanical property is sought in each of the following examples?
a) a plastic that keeps its shape even when twisted
b) wooden flooring that resists indentation by pointed objects, such as shoe heels
c) a metal that stretches well to make wire
d) a boat hull that resists shocks caused by running into shoals
e) a material that bends easily, without breaking, to make eavestroughing

2 Categories of materials and their properties (pp. 390–401)

3. Identify the category of material used to make the following objects. Choose from the following categories (each category may be used only once):
– wood and modified wood
– plastics
– composites
– metals and alloys
– ceramics
a) coins
b) a sheet of plywood
c) a pane of glass
d) a soft-drink bottle
e) a bulletproof vest

4. Which category of material would you suggest to meet the following needs? Choose from the same categories as in question 3 (each category may be used only once).

418 CHAPTER 12

review questions

A. The photo below shows a handsaw, a tool often used to saw wood. The cutting part of this tool is made out of steel, while the handle is made of acrylonitrile butadiene styrene (ABS).
a) Which category of material does the cutting part belong to?
b) Since ABS can be remoulded when heated, which subcategory of plastics does this material belong to?
c) When the saw is used, the blade sometimes bends and then returns to its original shape. Which constraint is this part being subjected to and which mechanical property allows it to return to its original shape?
d) One of the important features of the handle is that it is difficult to deform permanently. Which mechanical property does the handle exhibit?

B. The steel used to manufacture the blade of the saw in question A has been quenched. What was the purpose of this treatment?

C. Look at the drawing opposite.
a) What type of drawing is it?
b) Make a technical diagram for the handsaw.
c) Can the handsaw be considered a machine tool? Explain your answer.
d) At which stage of the manufacturing process is this tool mainly used?

D. Prepare your own summary of Chapter 12 by building a concept map.

HOW TO BUILD A CONCEPT MAP

Manufacturing technical objects 421

The **Follow-up** feature presents a particular environmental problem and the solutions that have been implemented to deal with the issue.

FOLLOW-UP

FIGHTING ACID RAIN IN QUÉBEC

A large part of Québec is vulnerable to acid rain. Soil on the Canadian Shield contains few carbonates—minerals that can neutralize excess acid—so our environment is more sensitive to acid fallout than other parts of the country, like the western provinces. By 1990, one lake in five in Québec was considered too acidic, which means that its plant and animal populations are at risk. Forestry is also affected: development in half of Québec's forest regions has been slowed by acid rain. The plight of sugar maple stands, in particular, has attracted media attention. Acid rain also damages buildings and works of art that are exposed to the open air.

CHAPTER 2

REDUCING AIR POLLUTION

The Québec government decided to deal with the problem of acid rain by focusing on its cause: emissions of sulphur and nitrogen compounds, which acidify rain.

Sulphur emissions come mainly from industrial activity (metal works, oil- and coal-fired power plants, etc.). The nitrogen compounds are produced primarily by fossil fuel combustion and discharged, for example, in motor vehicle exhaust.

Between 1980 and 1994, Québec managed to reduce its sulphur compound emissions by 70 percent through measures such as installing purification systems in polluting factories, setting up energy conservation programs and installing catalytic converters in motor vehicles. Meanwhile, refineries have reduced the sulphur content of gasoline by 90 percent over the past 10 years, to respect Canadian regulations.

Atmospheric pollutants can travel far, however—so much so that three quarters of all emissions affecting Québec do not actually originate in the province. The mobility of pollutants explains the importance of negotiating agreements with our neighbours.

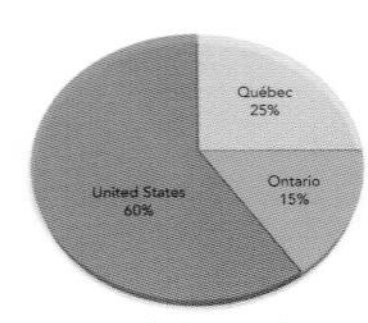

Origin of sulphur compounds affecting Québec

During the period between 1980 and 1994, Ontario also reduced its sulphur emissions by 70 percent. In addition, an agreement currently exists between Canada and the United States, requiring the Americans to reduce their sulphur compound emissions to levels 40 percent below 1980 levels by the year 2010.

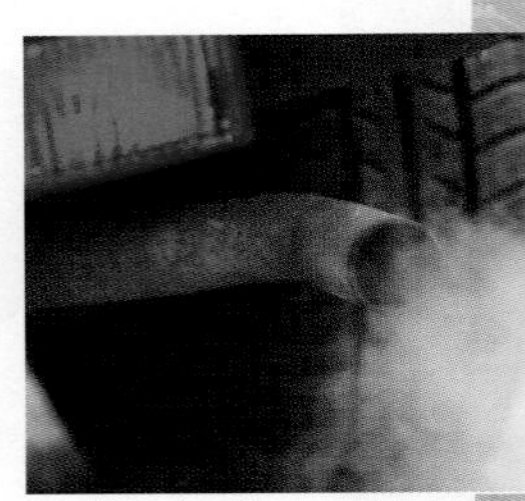

Motor vehicle exhaust is one of the main sources of the nitrogen compounds that cause acid rain.

Thanks to all these measures, total emissions of sulphur compounds, which represented the main cause of acid rain in the early 1980s, have now been cut in half. Further improvement is expected by 2010. Already, during the last decade, the pH of certain lakes has increased, suggesting that they are beginning to recover.

NEGOTIATING FURTHER REDUCTIONS

Despite efforts to reduce them, nitrogen compound emissions have remained practically the same since the 1980s. Recent studies show that, in some places, the acidification of lakes continues to be a problem.

In a report issued in 2004, a group of scientists declared that further reductions of 75 percent of polluting emissions would be needed to solve the problem of acid rain. A new round of negotiations is called for, involving the governments of Québec, Ontario, the Atlantic provinces and the United States.

1. To fight air pollution, we must reduce our reliance on fossil fuel combustion. What can each person do to contribute to this reduction?
2. Describe some consequences of acid rain in your region.

Molecules and solutions  67

The **Science at work** feature raises student awareness of employment possibilities. It presents a workplace with environmental significance and some of the employees who work there.

THE *SEDNA IV*

To study climate change, researchers can adopt no better approach than going directly into the field and observing the impact on one of the world's most fragile ecosystems: Antarctica. From September 2005 to November 2006, a dozen scientists, cinematographers and other adventurers lived on board the *Sedna IV*. Their mission was to measure the impact of the warming and to share their discoveries with the general public all around the world.

Let's meet a few members of the crew.

Stevens Pearson, mechanic and diver

Pascale Otis, biologist

Joëlle Proulx, cook

Jean Lemire, expedition leader, producer and director

Mariano Lopez, mental health worker

Geneviève Lagacée, communications officer

Occupation	Education	Length of study	Main tasks
Film director	Bachelor's degree in cinematography	3 years	• Prepare, organize and coordinate film production • Know and use a variety of film-making techniques and equipment
Mental health worker	Bachelor's degree in psychology	3 years	• Understand human behaviour • Treat and try to prevent problems of adaptation for a person with respect to his or her environment
Communications officer	DCS in media arts and technology	3 years	• Research, process and communicate information • Design and produce messages
Mechanic	DVS in marine mechanics	1350 hours	• Adjust and repair various marine engines • Install or remove injection pumps
Biologist	Bachelor's degree in biology	3 years	• Work to protect the environment • Ensure the conservation of natural resources
Cook	DVS in professional cooking	1350 hours	• Use cooking equipment safely • Prepare well-balanced meals

286 CHAPTER 8

287

ENVIRONMENTAL ISSUES

486

A summary of **six environmental issues** appears after the chapters in the textbook. The following issues are discussed: climate change, drinking water, deforestation, energy, residual materials and food production.

Deforestation

Forests are among the most precious natural resources on Earth. They are home to a large proportion of the planet's plants and animals. They also help to stabilize the climate because their abundant plant life captures carbon dioxide (CO_2), thus reducing the concentration of greenhouse gases in the atmosphere.

Forests provide other benefits: they prevent soil erosion and reduce the risks of natural disasters, such as floods, avalanches and desertification. Meanwhile, more than 300 million people live in forests and depend directly on their resources.

EI.14 CHANGES IN FOREST AREA FROM 1990 TO 2005

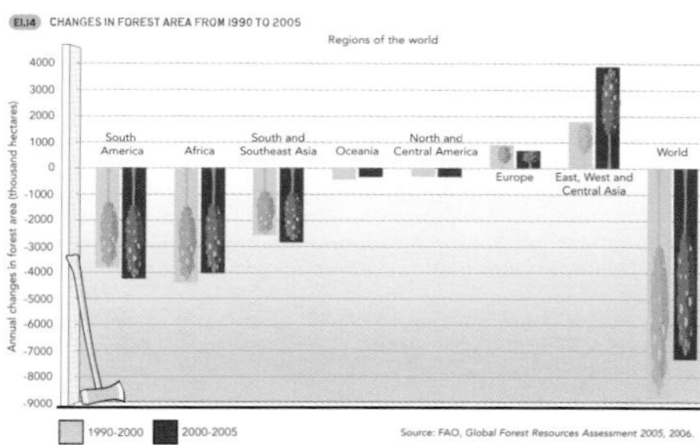

Source: FAO, *Global Forest Resources Assessment 2005*, 2006.

RECEDING FORESTS

Forests cover nearly four billion hectares—approximately 30 percent of dry land on Earth. More than half of the forests are concentrated in Russia, Brazil, Canada, the United States and China. However, forest area decreased at an average rate of 7.3 million hectares worldwide per year between 2000 and 2005. Since 1990, three percent of global forest cover has disappeared.

CAUSES

Many human activities, as well as natural causes, are responsible for the loss of forest area. The main factors are explained on the following page.

496 ENVIRONMENTAL ISSUES

Clearing land for farming

In certain tropical regions, as much as 45 percent of deforestation is caused by migrant farmers who burn small areas of the forest to plant subsistence crops, such as soybean or sorghum. After a few years, the soil is no longer fertile enough to produce a good crop, so the farmers move on to a new area of the forest.

EI.15 In order to work the land, farmers in some African and South American countries burn large areas of the tropical forest. This is known as *slash-and-burn agriculture*.

Logging

Harvesting forests for the pulp-and-paper or lumber industries poses a serious threat to the resource. In the Québec forest industry alone, 33 million cubic metres of lumber are cut annually. Replanting cannot keep pace with the rate of harvesting. Of particular concern is the practice of clear-cutting, which involves cutting down all the trees in an area, completely destroying certain wildlife habitats.

EI.16 An example of clear-cutting

Monoculture

Monoculture is an agricultural or forestry practice in which a single crop or species of tree is planted over a large area. In warm climates, for example, huge stands of eucalyptus are planted to supply newsprint mills. Such plantations are sometimes called "green deserts," and their environmental impact is significant. Trees become more vulnerable to harmful insects because single-species planting does not encourage **BIODIVERSITY**, which would usually include the insects' natural predators. Monoculture also results in **SOIL DEPLETION** because the crop draws constantly on the same nutrients.

EI.17 Plantation of eucalyptus near Coimbra, Portugal

Deforestation 497

The different facets of each issue are explained in just a few pages of concise texts, illustrations and diagrams.

APPENDIXES

APPENDIX I

PERIODIC PROPERTIES OF THE ELEMENTS IN THE PERIODIC TABLE (AT 20°C AND 101.3 kPa)

Atomic number	Chemical symbol	Melting point (°C)	Boiling point (°C)	Density (g/mL)	Atomic radius (10^{-12} m)	First ionization energy (eV)	Electronegativity (Pauling scale)
1	H	-259	-253	0.000 084	79	13.60	2.1
2	He	-272	-269	0.000 17	89	24.58	-
3	Li	180	1342	0.53	179	5.39	1.0
4	Be	1278	2970	1.85	127	9.32	1.5
5	B	2300	2550	2.34	100	8.30	2.0
6	C	3650	4827	2.25	91	11.26	2.5
7	N	-210	-196	0.001 7	73	14.53	3.0
8	O	-219	-183	0.001 33	65	13.62	3.5
9	F	-219	-188	0.001 58	64	17.42	4.0
10	Ne	-249	-246	0.000 84	51	21.56	-
11	Na	98	883	0.97	188	5.14	0.9
12	Mg	649	1107	1.74	166	7.65	1.2
13	Al	660	2467	2.70	163	5.98	1.5
14	Si	1410	2355	2.32	132	8.15	1.8
15	P	44	280	1.82	108	10.48	2.1
16	S	113	444	2.5	107	10.36	2.5
17	Cl	-101	-35	0.002 95	97	12.97	3.0
18	Ar	-189	-186	0.001 66	131	15.76	-
19	K	63	760	0.86	252	4.34	0.8
20	Ca	839	1484	1.54	210	6.11	1.0
21	Sc	1541	2831	3.0	185	6.54	1.3
22	Ti	1660	3287	4.51	172	6.82	1.5
23	V	1890	3380	5.96	162	6.74	1.6
24	Cr	1857	2672	7.20	155	6.77	1.6
25	Mn	1244	1962	7.20	152	7.43	1.5
26	Fe	1535	2750	7.86	148	7.87	1.8
27	Co	1495	2870	8.90	146	7.86	1.8
28	Ni	1455	2730	8.90	143	7.63	1.8
29	Cu	1083	2567	8.92	142	7.73	1.9
30	Zn	419	907	7.14	143	9.39	1.6
31	Ga	30	2403	5.90	152	6.0	1.6
32	Ge	937	2830	5.35	137	7.90	1.8
33	As	613	817	5.72	129	9.81	2.0
34	Se	217	685	4.81	169	9.75	2.4
35	Br	-7	59	0.003 12	112	11.81	2.8
36	Kr	-157	-152	0.003 48	103	14.00	-

514 APPENDICES

The **appendixes** contain useful reference tables for studying certain concepts. The **periodic table of the elements** appears on the inside back cover of the textbook.

GLOSSARY

A page number in bold type indicates that the same definition can be found on that page.

A

Abiotic factors: ecological factors of physical or chemical origin. (p. **300**)

Acid: substance that releases H^+ ions in an aqueous solution. (pp. **58**, 394)

Acid-base neutralization: chemical change involving the reaction of an acid with a base, producing a salt and water. (p. **119**)

Acid rain: rainwater with a very low pH (lower than 5.6) caused mainly by the transformation of sulphur dioxide and nitrogen oxides. (pp. 197, 200, 235, 498)

Adhesion: the phenomenon by which two surfaces tend to remain in contact with each other without slipping. (p. **433**)

Air: the mixture of gases, especially nitrogen and oxygen, that makes up the atmosphere. (p. **222**)

Air mass: large expanse of the atmosphere with relatively uniform temperature and humidity. (p. **229**)

Allele: possible form of a gene. Different alleles have different nucleotide sequences. (p. **362**)

Alloy: mixture of a metal with one or more other substances, which may be metallic or nonmetallic. (p. **394**)

Alternating current: electric current in which the electrons move back and forth in a regular pattern. (p. **461**)

Amino acid: molecule that can combine with other amino acids to form proteins. (p. **356**)

Annealing: heat treatment that restores the original properties of steel after it has been deformed, for example, after welding. (p. 395)

Anticyclone: area of atmospheric circulation surrounding a high-pressure centre. The air turns clockwise in the Northern Hemisphere and counterclockwise in the Southern Hemisphere. (p. **231**)

Aqueous solution: solution in which the solvent is water. (p. **51**)

Archimedes' principle: principle stating that an object immersed in a fluid is subjected to a buoyant force equal to the weight of the fluid displaced by the object. (p. **95**)

Assembling: set of techniques by which various parts are united to form a complete technical object. (p. **417**)

Atmosphere: the layer of air surrounding the Earth. (pp. **222**, 254)

Atmospheric circulation: the global-scale movement of the layer of air surrounding the Earth. (p. **226**)

Atmospheric pressure: the pressure of the air in the atmosphere. (p. **224**)

Atom: the smallest particle of matter. It cannot be divided chemically. (p. **7**)

Atomic number: number representing the number of protons in the nucleus of an atom. It distinguishes one element from another. (p. **24**)

Autotroph: organism that can feed itself without ingesting other organisms. Autotrophs are the base of any food chain. (p. 320)

Avogadro's number: number representing the number of entities in a mole. It equals 6.02×10^{23} of those entities. (pp. **31**, 54)

B

Balancing a chemical equation: process consisting in placing a coefficient before each reactant and product so that the number of atoms of each element on the reactant side is equal to the number of atoms of each element on the product side. (p. **111**)

Base: substance that releases OH^- ions in an aqueous solution. (pp. **59**, 394)

Bending: machining technique in which a material is curved into a certain shape. (p. **415**)

Bernoulli's principle: principle stating that the higher the speed of a fluid, the lower its pressure, and vice versa. (p. **98**)

Bioaccumulation: the tendency among certain contaminants to accumulate over time in the tissues of living organisms. (p. **335**)

Bioconcentration: (also *bioamplification*) phenomenon by which the concentration of a contaminant in the tissues of living organisms tends to increase with each trophic level. (p. **336**)

Biodegradation: the breaking down of organic matter into inorganic matter by microorganisms. (p. **337**)

Biodiversity: term describing the variety of species living in a community. (pp. 200, 265, **303**, 497)

Biogeochemical cycle: set of processes by which an element passes from one environment to the next and eventually returns to its original environment, in an infinite loop of recycling. (p. **255**)

Biological cycle: cycle composed of alternating periods of rise and fall in the size of a population. These periods are of fixed duration and are repeated continually. (p. **301**)

Biomass: the total mass of organic matter in an ecosystem at any given time. (p. **326**)

Biomes: large regions of the world with distinctive climates, wildlife and vegetation. (p. **262**)

Bioremediation: biotechnology for cleaning up a polluted site, using microorganisms that decompose the contaminants. (p. **337**)

Biosphere: the layer around the Earth containing all living organisms. (p. **254**)

534 GLOSSARY

The **glossary** defines terms that are essential to understanding the concepts covered in the textbook.

INDEX

A

B

C

546 INDEX

The **index** contains key words, with references to the pages where the words appear.

THE MATERIAL

WORLD

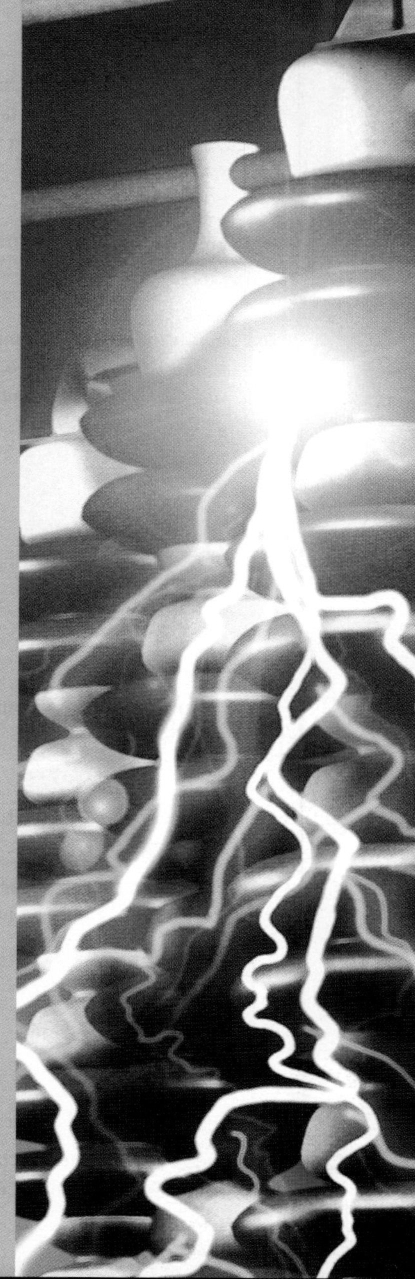

FROM THE COPPER ATOM IN AN ELECTRICAL WIRE to the water molecule so essential to our survival, and in every life-sustaining beam of sunlight, the structure, changes and behaviour of matter and energy are both fascinating and complex.

From the many and varied experiments and discoveries in the course of human history, we have gained a better understanding of the organization of matter. With progress, we have learned to use matter to obtain the food, energy and resources we need to satisfy our needs and desires.

Today's world calls on us to meet many environmental challenges. To understand the issues behind these challenges, we must take into account the properties of matter and energy and assess the impact of their use on the environment.

CONTENTS

- 2008 — Inauguration of the Large Hadron Collider, the largest particle accelerator in the world, used to study atomic structure
- 1991 — Discovery of carbon nanotubes
- 1981 — Invention of the scanning tunnelling microscope, providing the first images at the atomic level
- 1943 — Invention of the colour television
- 1932 — Discovery of the neutron
- 1925 — Transmission of the first black and white television images
- 1919 — Discovery of the proton
- 1911 — Discovery of the atomic nucleus
- 1897 — Discovery of the electron and measurement of its mass
- 1869 — Discovery of cathode rays
- 1854 — Invention of the Geissler tube, ancestor of neons and cathode ray tubes
- 1661 — Modern definition of the elements
- CIRCA 600 — Invention of gunpowder

Fireworks explode in a magnificent burst of colour because they contain a variety of elements: potassium for violet, barium for green, sodium for yellow, strontium for red and so on. Each element has its own characteristic properties, including the particular colour of light it gives off when it burns. To understand these properties and use them responsibly, we must begin with the atom. What do atoms look like? How do scientists study them? What can the periodic table tell us about the organization of elements? How can studying atoms help us meet environmental challenges? These are a few of the many questions we will try to answer in this chapter.

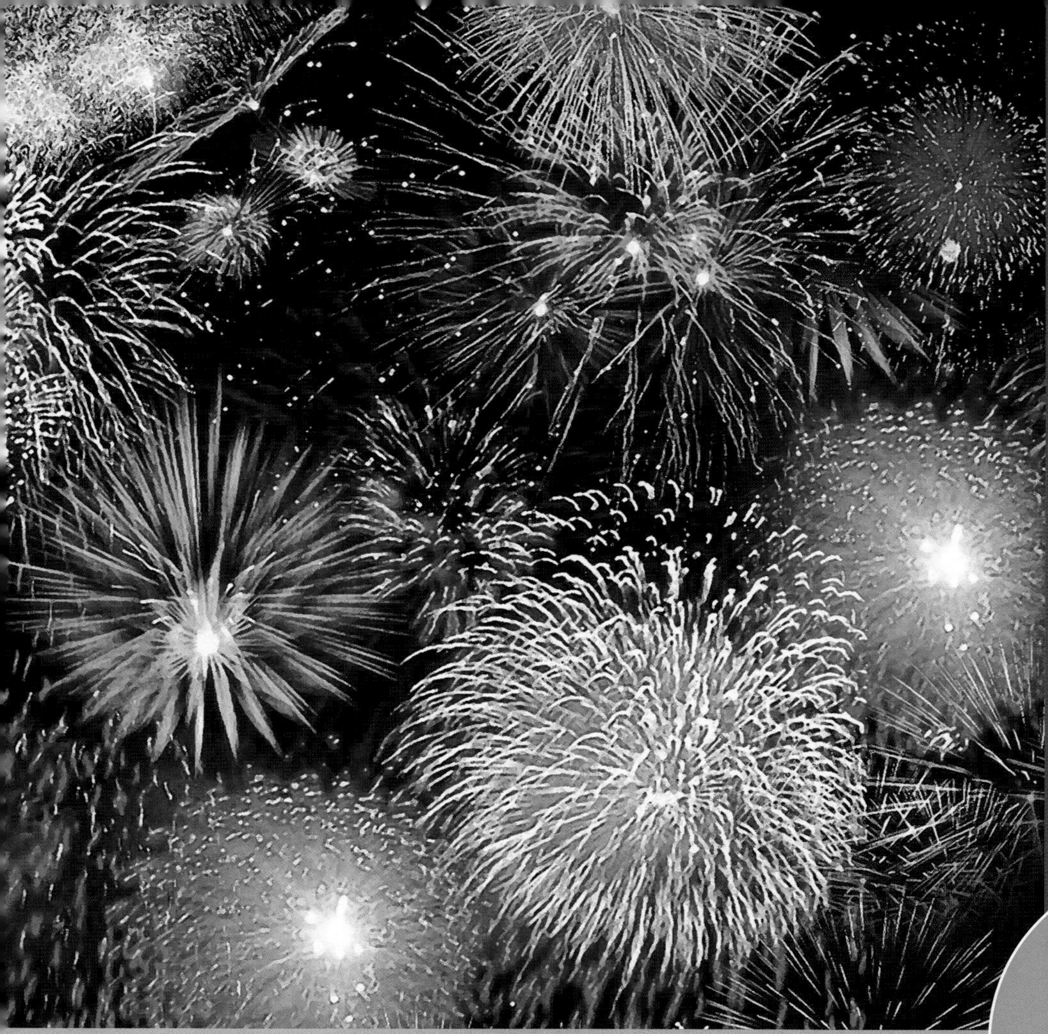

1

Atoms and elements

CONTENTS

ST EST SE 1 What is an atom?

CONCEPT REVIEW
- Atom

Humans have been wondering about the nature of matter for thousands of years. Ancient Greek philosophers had varying ideas on the subject. Aristotle (384–322 BCE), for example, believed that matter was infinitely divisible. Democritus (460–370 BCE), on the other hand, maintained that matter was made up of tiny indivisible particles like grains of sand on a beach. Democritus named these particles *atoms*. The two theories were philosophical rather than scientific because there was no way to test them experimentally at that time. Until the 19th century, Aristotle's theory was the most widely accepted.

Atom comes from the Greek *atomos*, meaning "indivisible."

We know today, however, that Democritus was right: the atom is the basic unit of matter. Atoms fit together, somewhat like building blocks, to form all the substances in our environment.

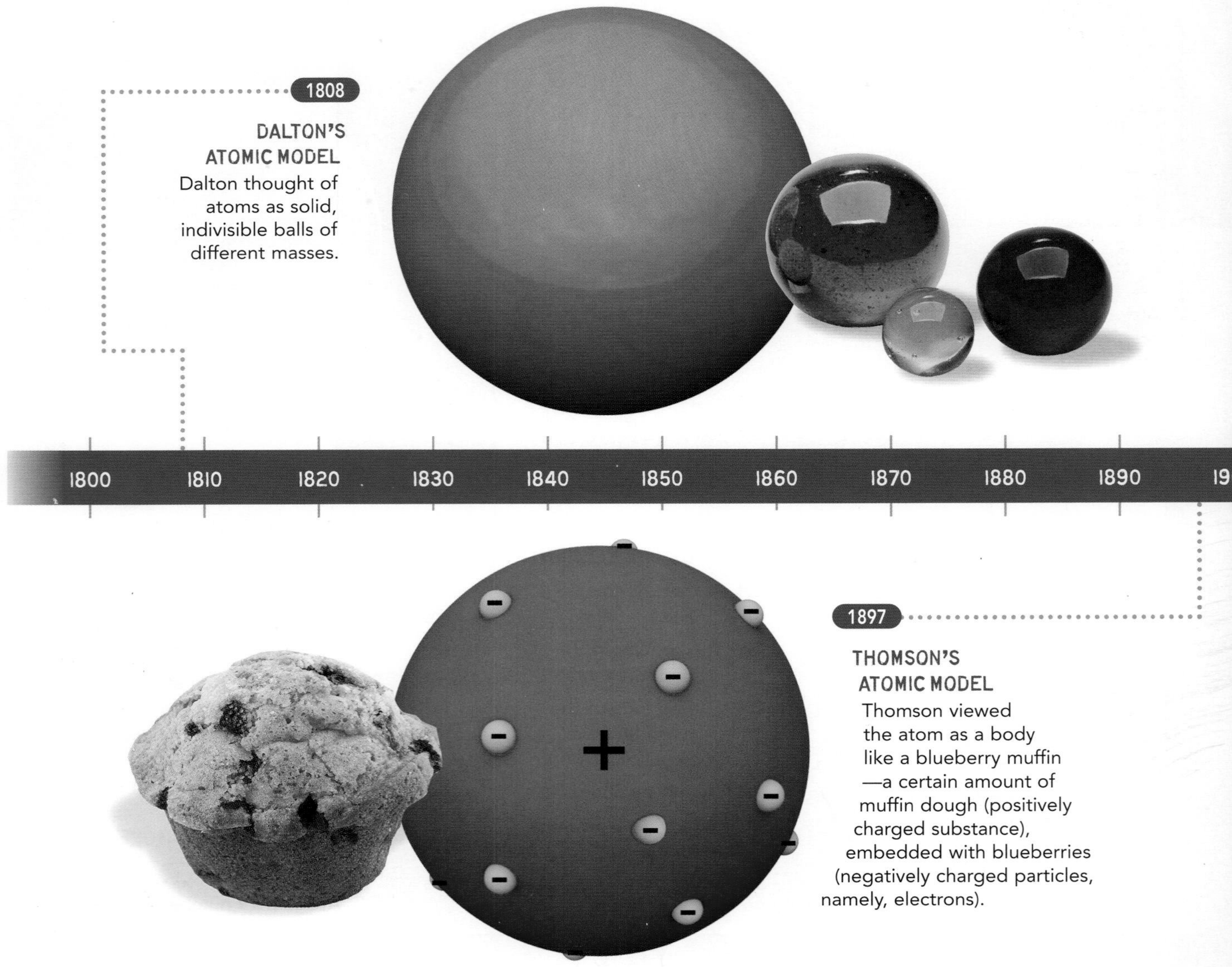

An ATOM is the smallest particle of matter. It cannot be divided chemically.

An atom is very small. How small? Consider the following examples:

- A sheet of paper is about a million atoms thick.
- A drop of water can contain as many as 10 sextillion (10^{22}) atoms.
- The diameter of the period at the end of this sentence is the length of at least 50 trillion atoms lined up in a row.

Because atoms are too small to be examined directly, scientists have devised various models to represent them. These models have been adapted over time and continue to change today, as researchers take recent discoveries into account.

Figure 1.1 outlines the main stages in the evolution of the atomic model. In the coming pages, we will see how scientists arrived at these different representations.

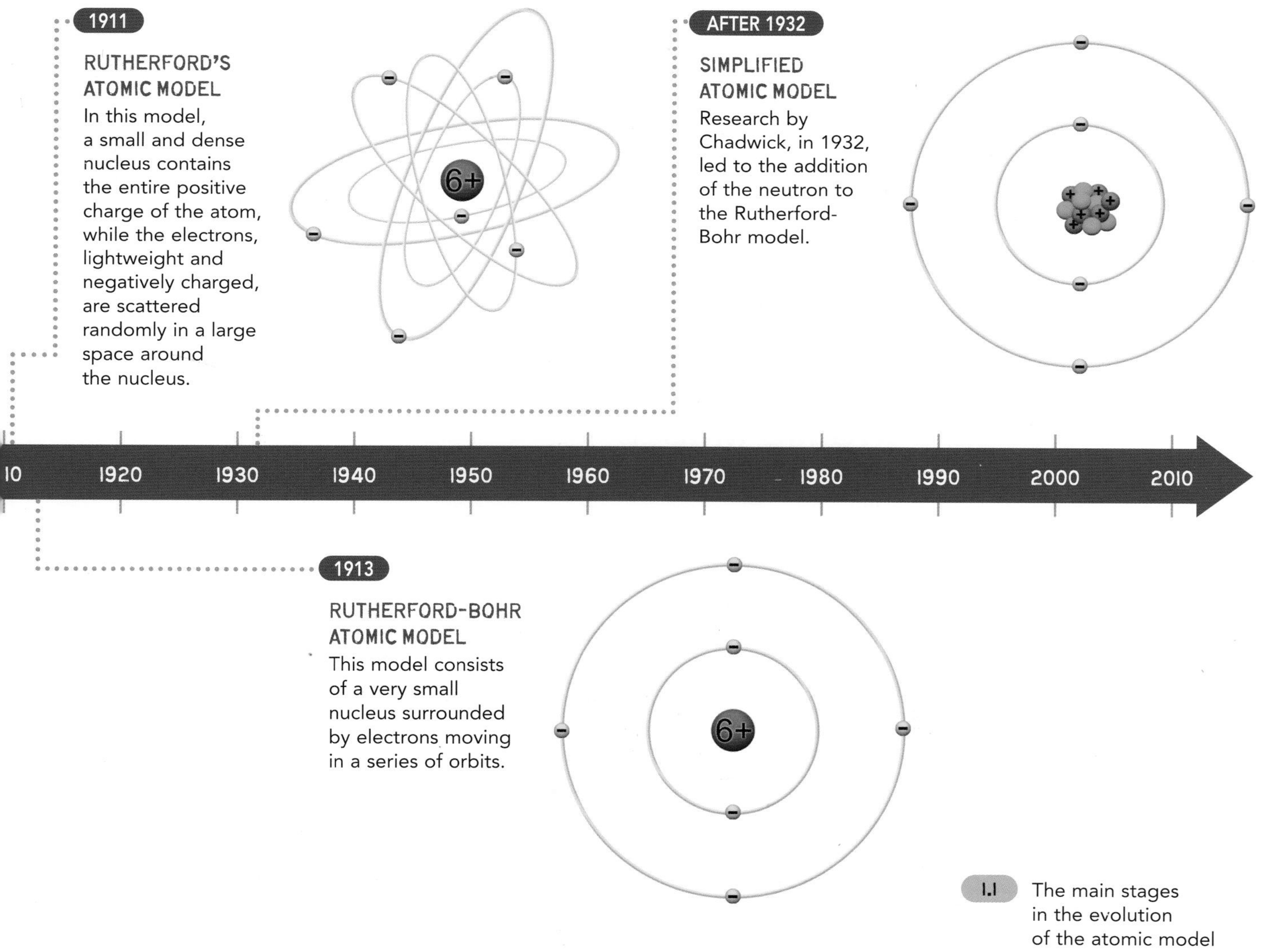

1.1 The main stages in the evolution of the atomic model

ST EST SE 1.1 DALTON'S ATOMIC MODEL

Chemistry became a true science during the 18th century, when the first laws based on experimental results were formulated. For example, the law of conservation of mass, stated by Antoine Laurent de Lavoisier (1743–1794), stipulates that the total mass of reactants is always equal to the total mass of their products.

CONCEPT REVIEW
- Conservation of matter
- Element
- Compound

The first scientist to formulate a theory on the nature of matter based on these laws was John Dalton (1766–1844), an English researcher and teacher. In 1808, Dalton theorized that matter was composed of indivisible particles, as Democritus had believed, and that these particles could be distinguished by their masses.

Dalton's atomic model is based on the following principles:

- Matter is composed of extremely small and indivisible particles called *atoms.*
- All the atoms of a single element are identical (same mass, same size, same chemical properties). For example, all carbon atoms are identical.
- The atoms of one element are different from those of another element. For example, oxygen atoms are different from carbon atoms.
- Atoms of different elements can combine, in fixed proportions, to form compounds. For example, carbon and oxygen can combine in a ratio of 1:1 to produce carbon monoxide (CO) or in a ratio of 1:2 to produce carbon dioxide (CO_2).
- Chemical reactions result in the formation of new substances. However, during a chemical reaction, no atom is created, divided or destroyed. For example, carbon dioxide is formed through the following reaction:
  $C + O_2 \rightarrow CO_2$

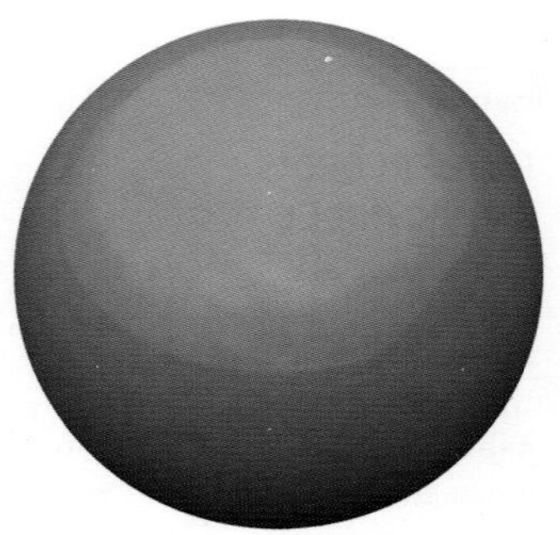

1.2 According to Dalton, the atom is like a billiard ball—solid and indivisible.

ST EST SE 1.2 THOMSON'S ATOMIC MODEL

The second half of the 19th century and the beginning of the 20th century formed a period of unprecedented scientific progress. One after another, fresh discoveries stimulated researchers in their efforts to explain the nature of matter and, especially, of the atom. The development of new technologies, such as high-voltage power supplies and more efficient vacuum pumps, cleared the way for studying how electric currents behave in tubes called *gas discharge tubes.* Figures 1.3 to 1.5 explain how these tubes work.

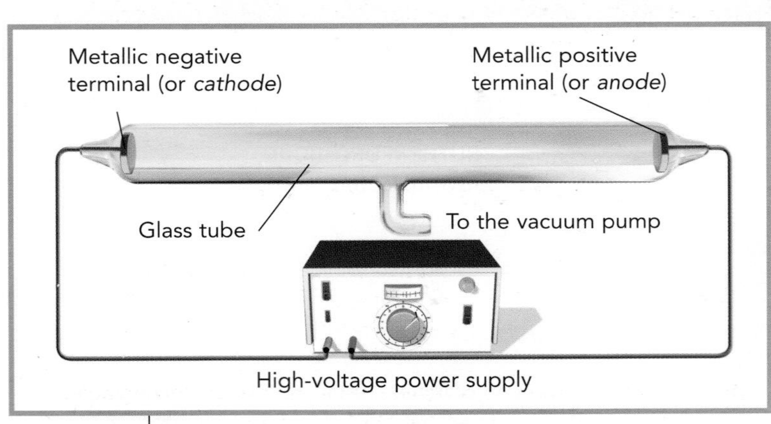

1.3 A gas discharge tube consists of a gas-filled tube with two metal terminals, or *poles*—a cathode and an anode—placed at opposite ends.

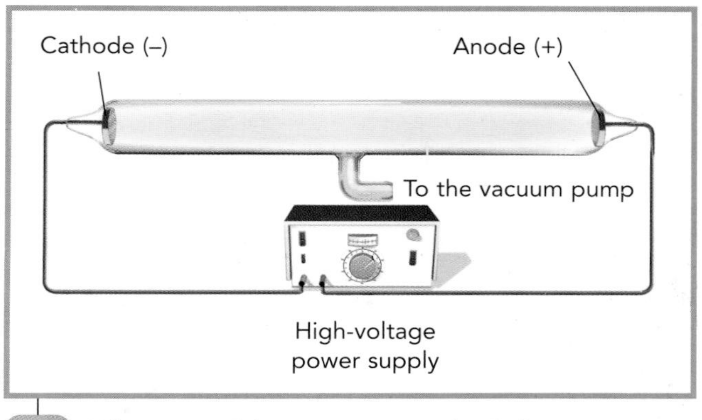

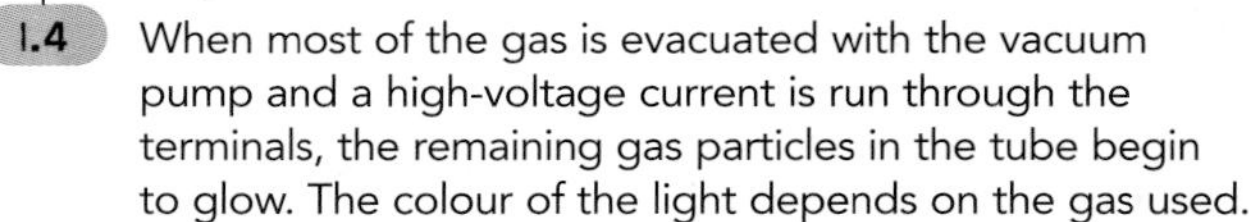

1.4 When most of the gas is evacuated with the vacuum pump and a high-voltage current is run through the terminals, the remaining gas particles in the tube begin to glow. The colour of the light depends on the gas used.

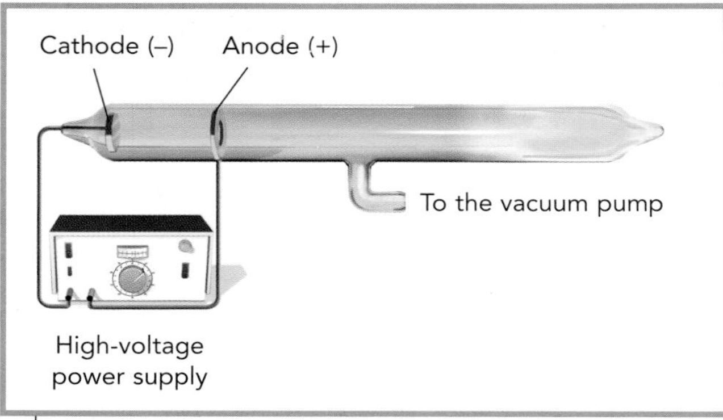

1.5 If almost all the gas in this tube is evacuated, the light gradually disappears. However, the end of the tube opposite the cathode begins to glow green.

Figure 1.4 shows how fluorescent tubes and neon lights work (except that these types of lights involve sealed tubes). Fluorescent tubes are widely used for lighting public areas, and neon lights are used in commercial signs. Red light in neons is made with neon gas. Argon mixed with neon gives off a green light, while argon mixed with xenon produces violet light, and argon and mercury combined glow yellow.

Given that the tube is practically empty in the situation illustrated in Figure 1.5, researchers concluded that the negative pole, the cathode, must emit an unknown type of ray and that the rays somehow interacted with the glass. The rays seemed to come from the cathode, so they were named *cathode rays*.

Until the appearance of liquid crystal and plasma technologies, cathode ray tubes were used to make television and computer screens. Today, they are still found in radiographic equipment and electron microscopes.

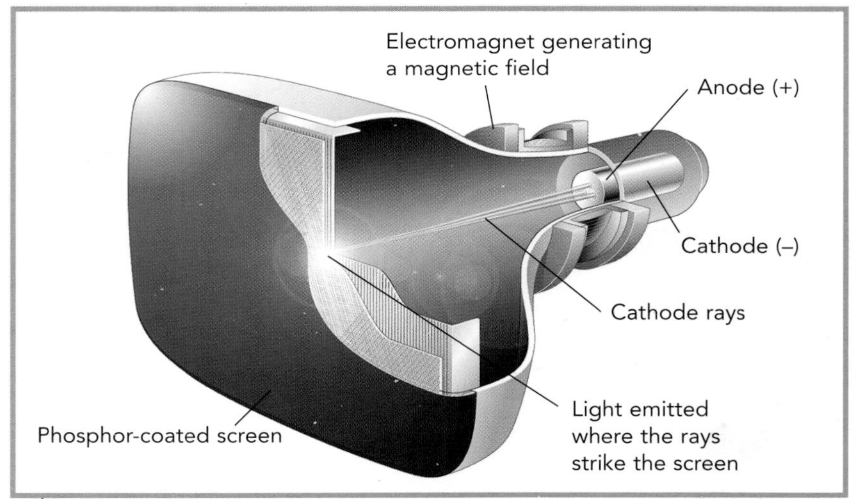

1.6 Before the invention of liquid crystal and plasma technologies, televisions generally contained cathode ray tubes. When cathode rays hit the phosphor-coated glass of a television screen, they create fluorescent light. A magnetic field diverts the cathode rays toward different points on the screen. Altogether, these glowing points form a television image.

1888
1946

John Logie Baird

Television was developed through a series of discoveries and inventions. In 1925, John Logie Baird, a Scottish engineer and inventor, created the first clear television image.

ENVIRONMENT EXTRA

The power of lightning

Clouds that cause thunderstorms are typically large clouds full of moisture. That is why they appear so dark.

As it forms, a thundercloud accumulates a positive electrical charge at its top, and a negative charge at its base. Meanwhile, the ground gradually acquires a positive charge. Obviously, this state of imbalance cannot last long. When the attraction between the opposing charges becomes too strong, an electrical discharge occurs, and the charges cancel each other. The result is a flash of lightning followed by a loud sound wave—a clap of thunder.

Nearly 80 percent of lightning is discharged within a single cloud or between two neighbouring clouds. The remaining 20 percent travels from cloud to ground.

Storm clouds are powerful generators of electricity. In fact, lightning can discharge as much as 10 000 amperes. It also reaches temperatures that exceed 30 000°C—five times the temperature on the surface of the sun.

Lightning has several features in common with gas discharge tubes: both involve high-voltage discharges in a low-pressure atmosphere (partial vacuum). The visible flash of lightning is produced by the heated air along the channel of the electrical discharge.

ST EST SE

THE ELECTRON

In 1897, an English physicist by the name of Joseph John Thomson (1856–1940) experimented with cathode rays. Figures 1.7 to 1.9 summarize his main findings.

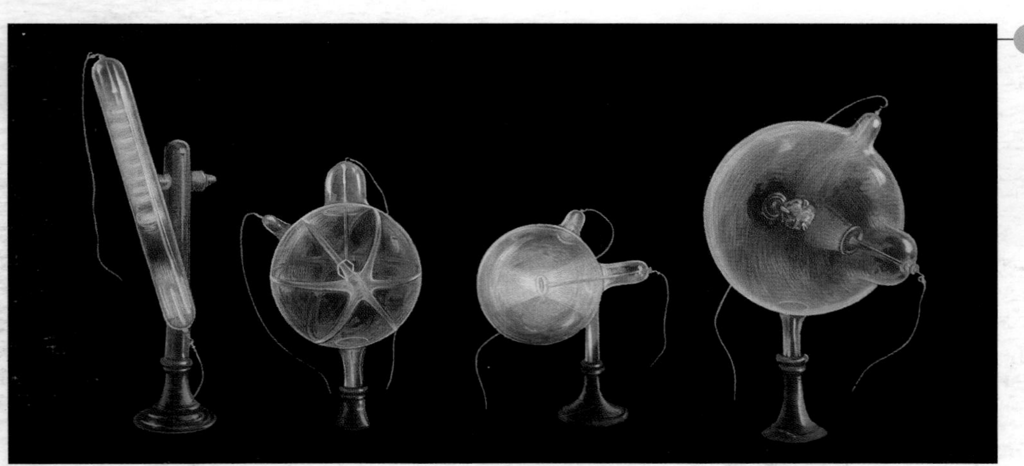

1.7 Cathode rays are identical regardless of the metal used to make the cathode. Thomson concluded that they are therefore common to all elements.

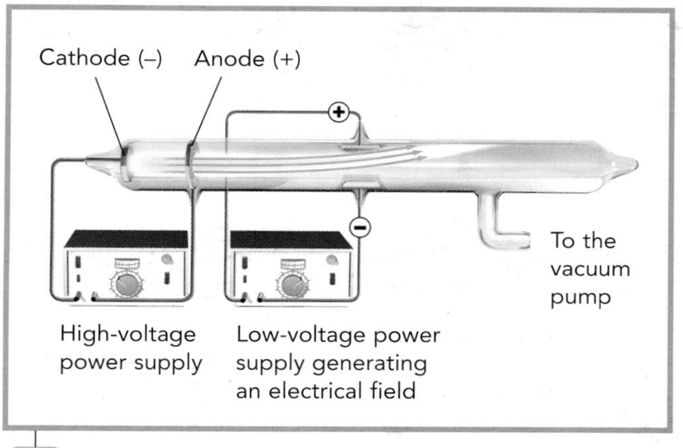

1.8 Cathode rays are attracted to the positive pole of an electrical field. Since positive charges attract negative charges, Thomson concluded that cathode rays are negatively charged.

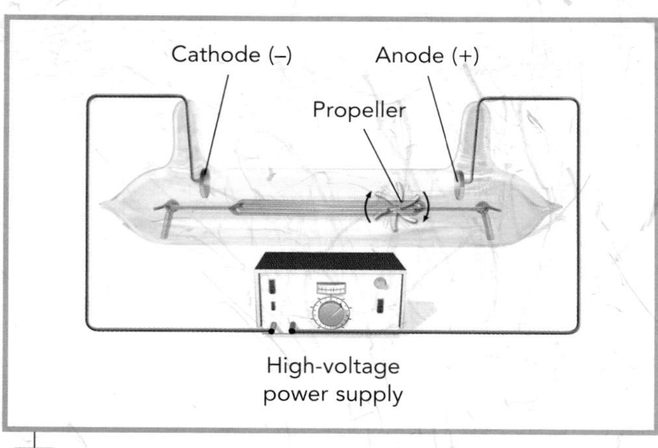

1.9 Cathode rays can cause a small propeller inserted inside the tube to spin, thereby demonstrating that they are made up of particles.

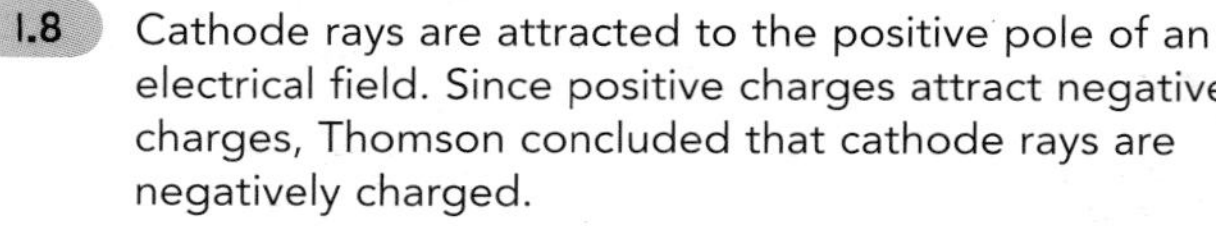

The particles emitted by the cathode were called *electrons*. According to Thomson, the electron had to be a negative particle that was part of an atom but that could detach itself from the rest of the atom with relative ease. Atoms were therefore not indivisible, as Dalton had suggested.

The ELECTRON is one of the particles that make up an atom. It is negatively charged.

In order to explain the behaviour of cathode rays, Thomson modified Dalton's atomic model to include electrons (Figure 1.10).

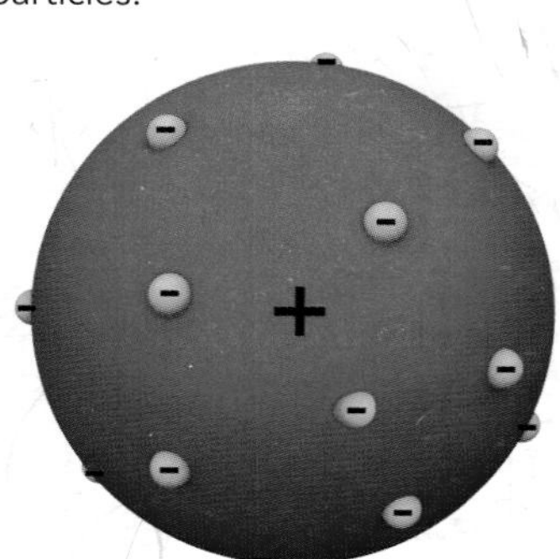

1.10 Thomson modified Dalton's atomic model by describing the atom as a positively charged ball embedded with small negatively charged particles, namely, electrons. Thomson's version is often referred to as the *plum pudding model*.

ST EST SE

1.3 RUTHERFORD'S ATOMIC MODEL

The study of cathode ray tubes led to other important scientific advances: the discovery of X-rays by Wilhelm Conrad Röntgen (1845–1923) in 1895 and the discovery of radioactivity by Henri Becquerel (1852–1908) in 1896.

ST EST SE

THE ATOMIC NUCLEUS AND THE PROTON

In 1911, a New Zealand physicist called Ernest Rutherford (1871–1937) became interested in the effect of radioactivity on matter. At that time, scientists had discovered that radioactive substances could emit three types of radiation: alpha (which is positively charged), beta (which is negatively charged) and gamma (which is electrically neutral).

Rutherford wanted to learn more about the distribution of electrons in atoms. He decided to bombard a sheet of gold foil with a stream of alpha particles.

Rutherford expected that most of the alpha particles would pass easily through the gold foil because it was extremely thin (only 160 atoms thick—very much thinner than a sheet of paper). Rutherford predicted that only a few of the alpha particles would be deflected slightly through contact with an electron.

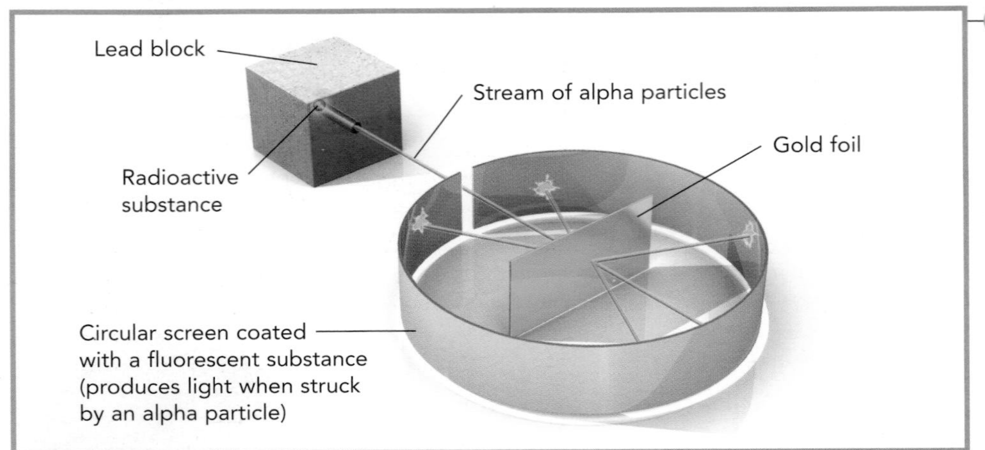

1.11 Rutherford performed his gold foil experiment with an apparatus like this.

To Rutherford's great surprise, a few alpha particles bounced back when they hit the gold foil. On examining the results of his experiment, he is said to have exclaimed, "It was almost as incredible as if you had fired a 15-inch shell at a piece of tissue paper and it came back and hit you!"

Given that the alpha particles are positive and that identical charges repel each other, Rutherford came to the conclusion that the entire positive charge of an atom must be concentrated in a very small area. An atom had to have a small, dense and positive nucleus, with electrons revolving around it in a relatively large space. Most of an atom is thus empty space.

ERNEST RUTHERFORD IN MONTRÉAL

From 1898 to 1907, Rutherford taught physics at McGill University, in Montréal. He continued his research on the atom there, focusing particularly on the radiation from radioactive substances. 

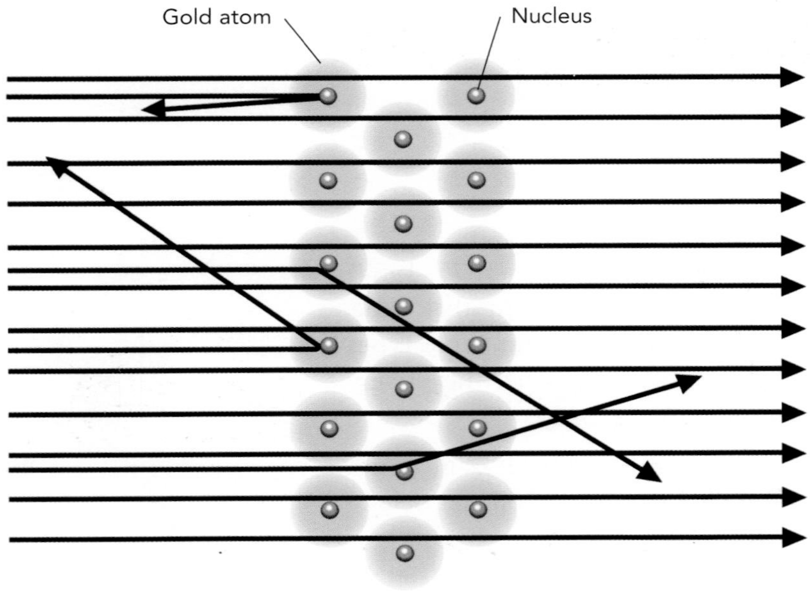

1.12 In Rutherford's experiment, a few of the alpha particles directed at the gold foil were strongly deflected or even bounced back.

1.13 RUTHERFORD'S OBSERVATIONS AND CONSEQUENT CONCLUSIONS

Observation	Conclusion
Most of the alpha particles pass through the gold foil without being deflected.	• An atom is mostly empty space.
Some alpha particles are strongly deflected or bounce back.	• An atom contains a very dense and very small nucleus. • The nucleus of an atom is positively charged.

1.14 Rutherford modified Thomson's atomic model by imagining the entire positive charge of the atom in the form of a small but massive nucleus. The negatively charged electrons circle the nucleus.

Rutherford also formulated the hypothesis that the nucleus is made up of positively charged particles, which he called *protons.* Since an atom is electrically neutral (neither positively nor negatively charged), there must be as many protons in the nucleus as there are electrons circling it for the charges to cancel each other.

The PROTON is one of the particles that make up an atom. It is found in the nucleus and carries a positive charge.

1.15 According to Rutherford's model, if an atom were the size of Montréal's Olympic Stadium, the nucleus would be no bigger than an insect at midfield, while the electrons would be flecks of dust whirling about randomly in the stadium space.

ST EST SE 1.4 THE RUTHERFORD-BOHR ATOMIC MODEL

The Rutherford model did not fully explain atomic structure, according to some scientists of the day. Since opposite charges attract each other, Rutherford's detractors argued, how could electrons hold their positions around the nucleus without crashing into it?

Only two years later, in 1913, the Danish physicist Niels Bohr (1885–1962) published an improved version of Rutherford's atomic model.

CONCEPT REVIEW
Electromagnetic spectrum

To understand Bohr's contribution, we must first remember that white light (from the sun or electric light bulbs) can be decomposed using a prism or a spectrometer. The resulting image represents all light wavelengths, or its **ELECTROMAGNETIC SPECTRUM**, as shown in Figure 1.16.

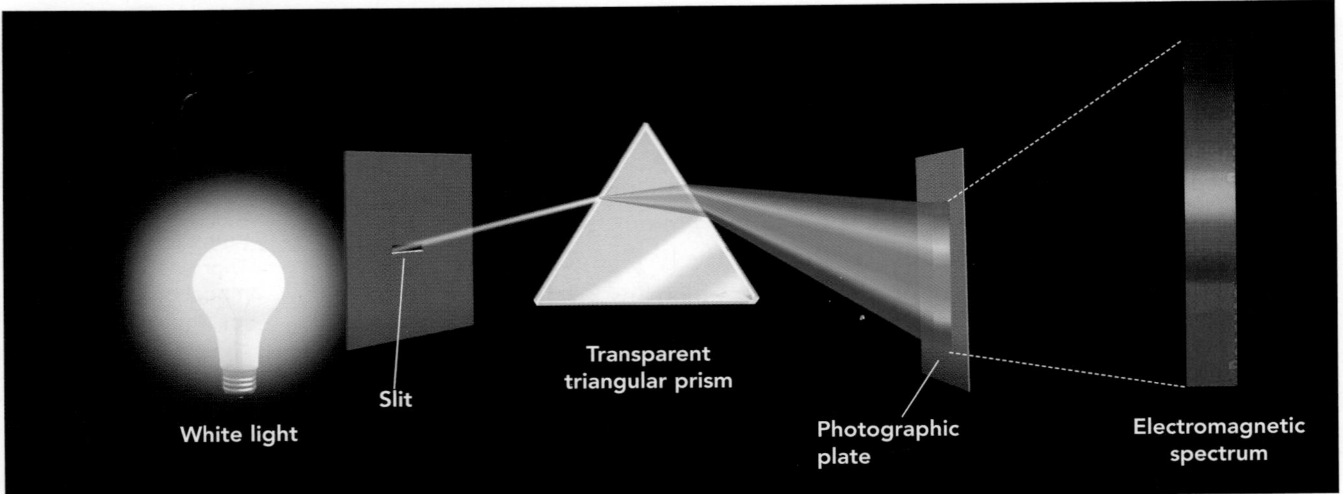

1.16 White light can be broken down into its electromagnetic spectrum.

When chemical elements are heated, they also emit light, but only at certain wavelengths (Figure 1.17).

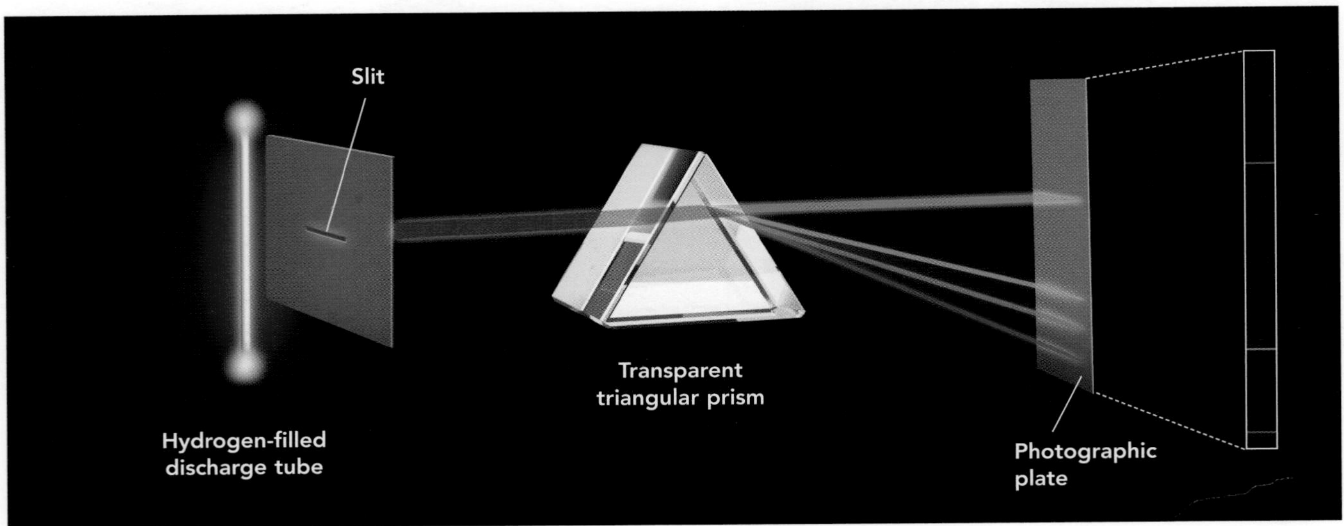

1.17 The visible emission spectrum of hydrogen contains four bands of colour.

Bohr studied the light emitted by different elements in gas discharge tubes (Figure 1.4, page 9). He focused particularly on the emission spectrum of hydrogen. To explain the presence of specific colours, Bohr modified Rutherford's atomic model as follows:

- He assumed that electrons were not randomly distributed but that they occupied specific areas of the atom, which he called *orbits* because they resembled planetary orbits in the solar system. Unlike planets, however, electrons could jump from one orbit to another.

- Each orbit corresponds to a level of energy. While it stays in its original orbit, an electron does not lose energy. This stability keeps it in the same orbit and prevents it from crashing into the nucleus.
- When an electron receives energy—for example, when it is heated, or stimulated by an electrical discharge—it becomes "excited" and can jump to an orbit farther from the nucleus.
- The electron returns rapidly to its original orbit, releasing the absorbed energy in the form of light.

The RUTHERFORD-BOHR ATOMIC MODEL is a representation of the atom as a very small nucleus made up of positively charged protons, surrounded by negatively charged electrons moving in defined orbits.

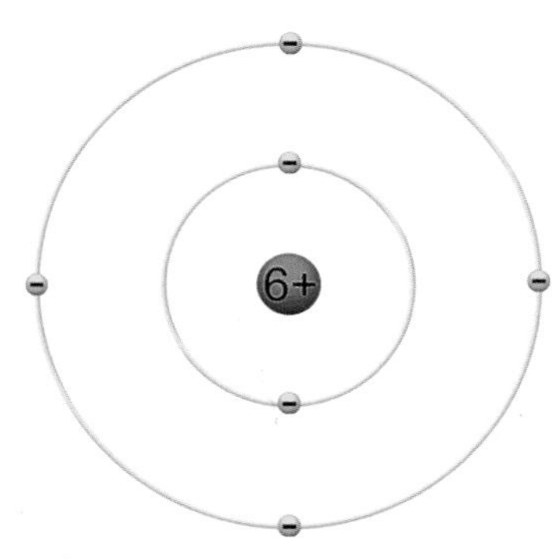

1.18 Bohr modified Rutherford's atomic model by describing the orbits in which electrons move.

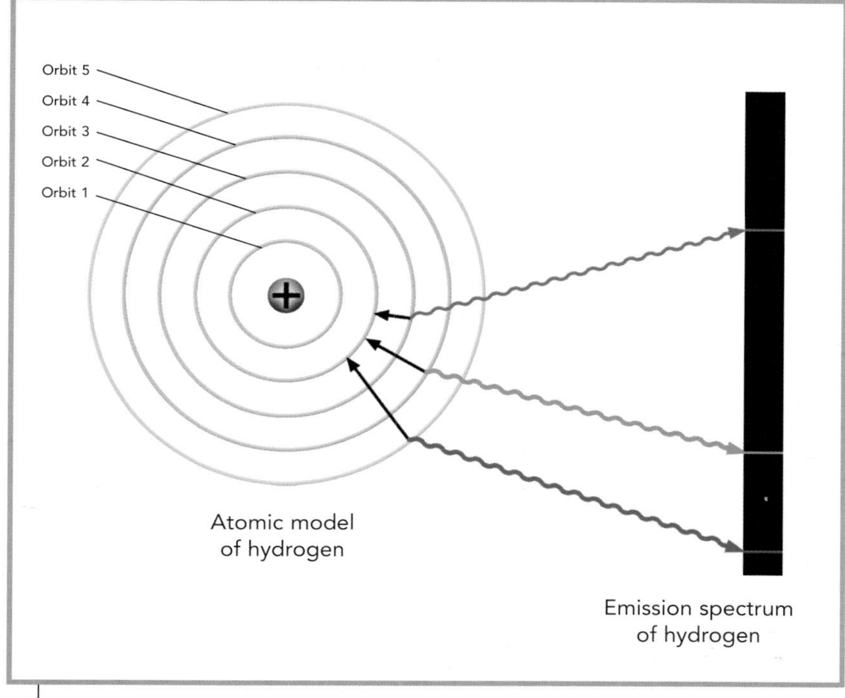

1.19 When an atom receives energy, its electrons become excited. They can then jump to a higher orbit (farther from the nucleus) for a short period of time. When they return to their original orbits, they release the energy they had accumulated, giving off light.

1906
1972

Maria Goeppert-Mayer

This American physicist of German origin received the 1963 Nobel Prize in Physics for her research on atomic nuclei. Her findings proved particularly useful in applications of laser technology, developed nearly 30 years later. Her research has thereby contributed to the fields of biomedical imagery, three-dimensional computer graphics and microfabrication.

EST SE 1.5 THE SIMPLIFIED ATOMIC MODEL

The Rutherford-Bohr model also met with criticism, since it did not provide an answer to a crucial question: "Why does the nucleus not explode, given that it is made up entirely of positively charged particles?"

THE NEUTRON

EST SE

In 1932, the British physicist James Chadwick (1891–1974) found the answer to the question raised by the Rutherford-Bohr model. Chadwick discovered a new particle in the nucleus of the atom, the neutron, whose role is to hold the protons together. As its name implies, the particle is neutral, which means it has no charge.

Neutron comes from the Latin *neuter*, meaning "neither one nor the other."

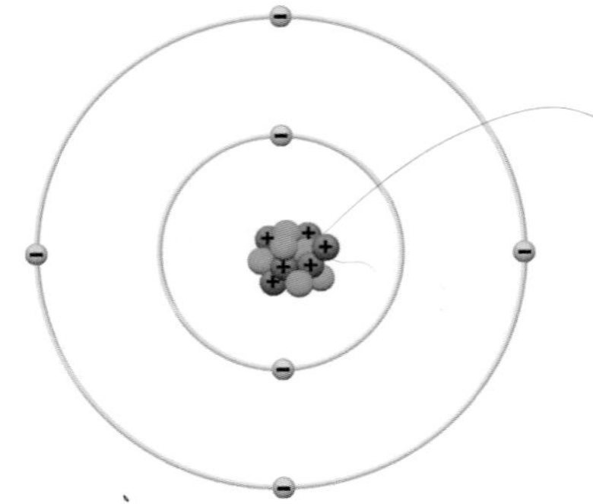

1.20 The simplified atomic model refines the Rutherford-Bohr model by adding the neutron, discovered by Chadwick.

The NEUTRON is one of the particles that make up an atom. With the proton, it forms the nucleus. It has no electrical charge, so it is neutral.

The simplified atomic model is a representation of the atom that takes into account the presence of the neutron in the nucleus. It is considered "simplified" in comparison with other current but highly complex models.

The SIMPLIFIED ATOMIC MODEL is a representation of the atom indicating the number of protons and neutrons in the nucleus and the number of electrons in each of the electron shells.

NANOTECHNOLOGIES: THE MIND-BOGGLINGLY SMALL

Nanotechnologies have quietly made their way into our daily lives. Since the invention of the scanning tunnelling microscope in 1981, scientists have been able to visualize the atoms that make up matter and to move them around at will. The technology gave rise to "Lilliputian engineering," in which nano-objects can be designed, atom by atom. At this scale, materials can take on new properties, becoming more resistant, transparent, etc.

Every major manufacturing sector has been affected by this revolutionary technology. For example, the Daimler-Benz automobile manufacturer sells cars with brakes and engines equipped with carbon nanotubes that are 100 times more resistant than steel, at only one sixth of its weight. IBM produces transistors 100 000 times finer than a human hair. And the cosmetic industry adds titanium oxide nanoparticles to sunscreen lotions to filter out ultraviolet rays.

Source: Adapted from Dorothée Benoit-Browaeys, "Nanotechnologies, le vertige de l'infiniment petit," *Le Monde diplomatique* 624 (March 2006), p. 22. *[Translation]*

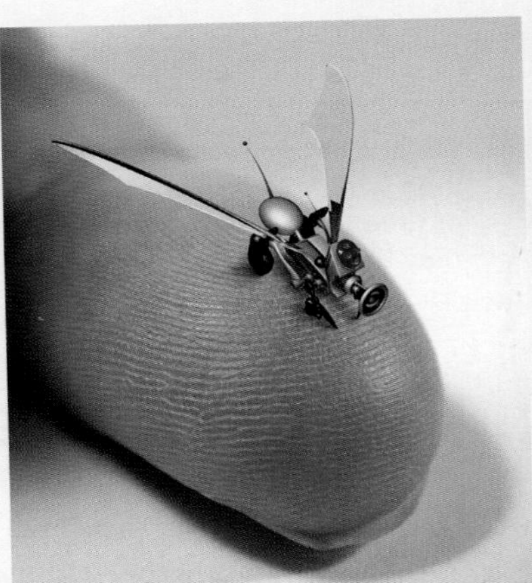

Researchers hope one day to create nanorobots like this fly robot but even smaller—as small as a red blood cell.

Table 1.21 summarizes some of the characteristics of electrons, protons and neutrons. As we can see, the respective masses of a proton and a neutron are similar and much greater than the mass of an electron. In fact, an electron is about 2000 times lighter than a proton or neutron (the precise figure is 1836 times). For this reason, the contribution of electrons to the total mass of an atom is often considered negligible.

1.21 CHARACTERISTICS OF ATOMIC PARTICLES

Particle	Symbol	Electrical charge	Mass (g)	Mass (u)*
Electron	e^-	Negative	9.109×10^{-28}	0.000 55
Proton	p^+	Positive	1.673×10^{-24}	1.007
Neutron	n	Neutral	1.675×10^{-24}	1.008

* The atomic mass unit (u or amu) is explained on page 24.

ST EST SE 2 The periodic classification of the elements

CONCEPT REVIEW
- Periodic table

It is often helpful to organize facts or objects into groups to identify tendencies or make predictions. For example, a system of weeks and months makes it easier to identify the day when the weekend begins or the date of your next science class.

The existence of more than 60 different elements led 19th-century scientists to look for a way to classify the elements according to certain patterns in their properties. This type of classification is called a *periodic classification*.

A PERIODIC CLASSIFICATION is a way to group the elements according to certain properties.

Several different classification systems have been proposed. The best-known and the most widely used is the system devised in 1869 by the Russian chemist Dmitri Mendeleev (1834–1907). Figure 1.22 (pages 18–19) shows a modern version of Mendeleev's periodic table. In the following pages, we will see how this table helps us understand the elements and their properties.

The PERIODIC TABLE OF THE ELEMENTS is a visual presentation of the elements in groups according to their physical and chemical properties.

1834
1907

Dmitri Ivanovich Mendeleev

This Russian chemist created his periodic classification of the elements while writing a chemistry textbook. The book was hugely successful. Numerous editions were published, and it was widely translated.

SQUARE

Each square represents an element. From top to bottom, the square contains the atomic number of the element, its chemical symbol, its name and its relative atomic mass.

ATOMIC NUMBER

The elements are arranged in order of increasing atomic number.

PERIOD

Each row is called a *period*. Note that periods do not all have the same length. They are numbered from 1 to 7.

GROUP

Each column is called a *group*. Groups are numbered in two ways: from 1 to 18 and with a combination of Roman numerals and the letters A and B.

Period	1 IA	2 IIA	3 IIIB	4 IVB	5 VB	6 VIB	7 VIIB	8 VIIIB	9 VIIIB
1	1 H Hydrogen 1.01								
2	3 Li Lithium 6.94	4 Be Beryllium 9.01							
3	11 Na Sodium 22.99	12 Mg Magnesium 24.31							
4	19 K Potassium 39.10	20 Ca Calcium 40.08	21 Sc Scandium 44.96	22 Ti Titanium 47.88	23 V Vanadium 50.94	24 Cr Chromium 52.00	25 Mn Manganese 54.94	26 Fe Iron 55.85	27 Co Cobalt 58.93
5	37 Rb Rubidium 85.47	38 Sr Strontium 87.62	39 Y Yttrium 88.91	40 Zr Zirconium 91.22	41 Nb Niobium 92.91	42 Mo Molybdenum 95.94	43 Tc Technetium 98	44 Ru Ruthenium 101.07	45 Rh Rhodium 102.91
6	55 Cs Cesium 132.91	56 Ba Barium 137.33	57-71	72 Hf Hafnium 178.49	73 Ta Tantalum 180.95	74 W Tungsten 183.84	75 Re Rhenium 186.21	76 Os Osmium 190.23	77 Ir Iridium 192.22
7	87 Fr Francium 223	88 Ra Radium 226.03	89-103	104 Rf Rutherfordium 261	105 Db Dubnium 262	106 Sg Seaborgium 263	107 Bh Bohrium 262	108 Hs Hassium 265	109 Mt Meitnerium 266

57 La Lanthanum 138.91	58 Ce Cerium 140.12	59 Pr Praseodymium 140.91	60 Nd Neodymium 144.24	61 Pm Promethium 145	62 Sm Samarium 150.36
89 Ac Actinium 227.03	90 Th Thorium 232.04	91 Pa Protactinium 231.04	92 U Uranium 238.03	93 Np Neptunium 237.05	94 Pu Plutonium 244

To make the table easier to read, elements 57 to 71 and elements 89 to 103 are placed under the table even though they belong to Periods 6 and 7, respectively.

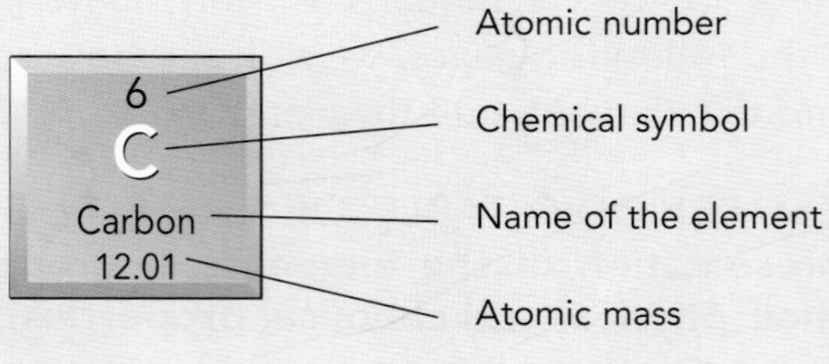

6 C Carbon 12.01

Atomic number

Chemical symbol

Name of the element

Atomic mass

1.22 A modern version of Mendeleev's periodic table

STAIRCASE

This staircase-shaped dividing line separates metals (to the left) from nonmetals (to the right) and helps to locate the metalloids.

10 VIIIB	11 IB	12 IIB	13 IIIA	14 IVA	15 VA	16 VIA	17 VIIA	18 VIIIA
								2 He Helium 4.00
			5 B Boron 10.81	6 C Carbon 12.01	7 N Nitrogen 14.01	8 O Oxygen 16.00	9 F Fluorine 19.00	10 Ne Neon 20.18
			13 Al Aluminum 26.98	14 Si Silicon 28.09	15 P Phosphorus 30.97	16 S Sulphur 32.07	17 Cl Chlorine 35.45	18 Ar Argon 39.95
28 Ni Nickel 58.69	29 Cu Copper 63.55	30 Zn Zinc 65.39	31 Ga Gallium 69.72	32 Ge Germanium 72.61	33 As Arsenic 74.92	34 Se Selenium 78.96	35 Br Bromine 79.90	36 Kr Krypton 83.80
46 Pd Palladium 106.42	47 Ag Silver 107.87	48 Cd Cadmium 112.41	49 In Indium 114.82	50 Sn Tin 118.71	51 Sb Antimony 121.76	52 Te Tellurium 127.60	53 I Iodine 126.90	54 Xe Xenon 131.29
78 Pt Platinum 195.08	79 Au Gold 196.97	80 Hg Mercury 200.59	81 Tl Thallium 204.38	82 Pb Lead 207.20	83 Bi Bismuth 208.98	84 Po Polonium 209	85 At Astatine 210	86 Rn Radon 222
110 Ds Darmstadtium 281	111 Rg Roentgenium 280	112 Uub 285	113 Uut 284	114 Uuq 285	115 Uup 288	116 Uuh 293		

Until they are assigned official names, elements 112 to 116 have been given names and symbols that describe their atomic numbers in Latin. For example, element 112 is called *ununbium*, which means "one-one-two."

63 Eu Europium 151.97	64 Gd Gadolinium 157.25	65 Tb Terbium 158.93	66 Dy Dysprosium 162.50	67 Ho Holmium 164.93	68 Er Erbium 167.26	69 Tm Thulium 168.93	70 Yb Ytterbium 173.04	71 Lu Lutetium 175.07
95 Am Americium 243	96 Cm Curium 247	97 Bk Berkelium 247	98 Cf Californium 251	99 Es Einsteinium 254	100 Fm Fermium 257	101 Md Mendelevium 258	102 No Nobelium 259	103 Lr Lawrencium 260

Standard state (at 25°C)

Gas

Solid

Liquid

Synthetic solid

Al Metals

C Nonmetals

B Metalloids

ST EST SE

2.1 METALS, NONMETALS AND METALLOIDS

LAB 1

The elements can be classified into three categories: metals, nonmetals and metalloids. The staircase-shaped line that crosses the right side of the table helps to locate and identify these categories. They can be briefly described as follows:

- Metals are generally good conductors of electricity and heat. They are often ductile and malleable, so they are easily shaped into wires or flattened into sheets. They are usually shiny. All metals are solids at room temperature, except mercury, which is a liquid. Many react with acids. In the periodic table, metals are found to the left of the staircase.
- Nonmetals are generally poor conductors of electricity and heat. Many of them are gases at room temperature. The solid nonmetals can easily be reduced to powder. In the periodic table, nonmetals are to the right of the staircase, except hydrogen, which is traditionally placed above the first column of the table.

ENVIRONMENT EXTRA

Batteries: heavy on metals

Nickel-cadmium, lithium, silver-zinc . . . batteries are made mostly of metals. Each year in Québec, we use more than 50 million batteries, of which approximately 97 percent are of the single-use type. Cellphones, laptops and MP3 players are just a few examples of the portable electronic devices that depend on this source of energy. Batteries in and of themselves are not dangerous to users. But what is their overall impact on the environment?

Manufacturing a battery requires 50 times more energy than it supplies, using rare and expensive nonrenewable raw materials.

Used batteries not only add to the volume of our waste but also leave dangerous residues. The heavy metals in batteries can enter animal and human food chains, causing allergies, cancers or disorders of the reproductive and nervous systems. Once in the food chain, they are very difficult to eliminate.

Batteries are hazardous waste and should never be disposed of with regular garbage. They should be recycled in a proper facility.

- Metalloids (also called *semimetals*) form a category of seven elements with properties of both metals and nonmetals. For example, metalloids are sometimes good conductors of electricity and sometimes poor conductors, depending on conditions. For this reason, they are used to make **SEMICONDUCTORS**—important materials for transistors, integrated circuits and lasers. In the periodic table, metalloids are found along both sides of the staircase.

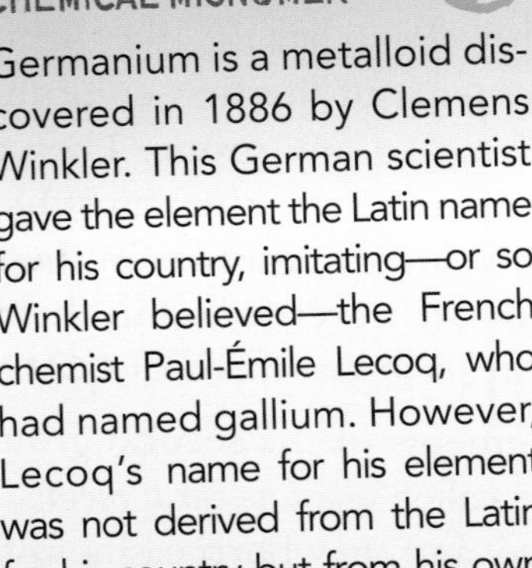

CHEMICAL MISNOMER

Germanium is a metalloid discovered in 1886 by Clemens Winkler. This German scientist gave the element the Latin name for his country, imitating—or so Winkler believed—the French chemist Paul-Émile Lecoq, who had named gallium. However, Lecoq's name for his element was not derived from the Latin for his country but from his own name. *Gallus* is the Latin word for "rooster," or *coq* in French.

ST EST 2.2 THE GROUPS OF THE PERIODIC TABLE

The elements in a column of the periodic table form a group. They have similar chemical properties, which means that they react in the same way in the presence of certain substances. To understand this similarity more clearly, consider three elements from the first column of the table, illustrated below in Figure 1.23. As we can see, each of these elements has the same number of electrons in its outer shell.

The electrons that are farthest from the nucleus are important because they are more frequently involved in the atom's chemical reactions. These electrons of the outermost shell are called *valence electrons*.

- **A VALENCE ELECTRON is an electron in the outermost shell of an atom.**

- **A GROUP corresponds to a column of the periodic table. The elements in a particular group have similar chemical properties because they all have the same number of valence electrons.**

The Roman numeral beside the letter A or B at the top of each column corresponds to the number of valence electrons in each element of the group. The elements in Group IA, such as those illustrated in Figure 1.23, all have only one valence electron. The elements of Group VIA, such as oxygen, have six valence electrons.

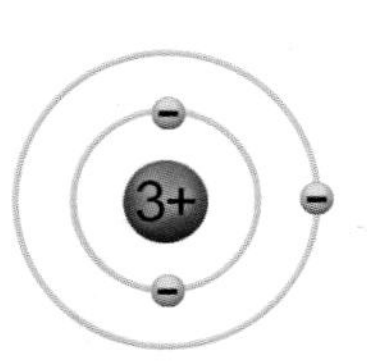

Lithium

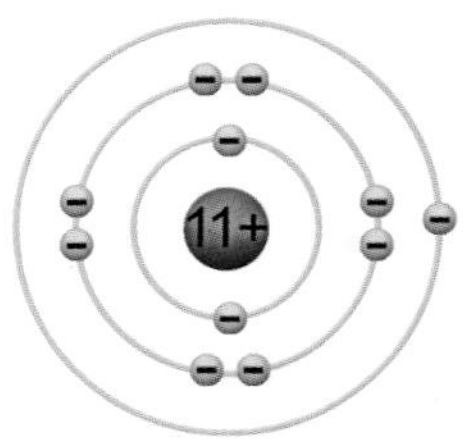

Sodium

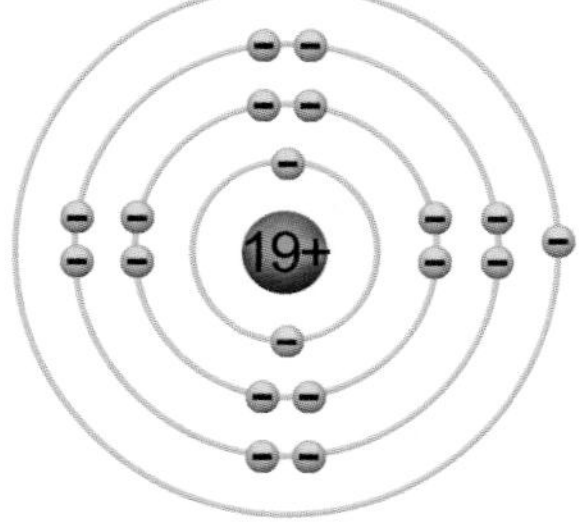

Potassium

1.23 Lithium, sodium and potassium belong to the same group in the periodic table. They all have only one valence electron.

Certain groups have specific names:

- The *alkali metals*, like lithium and sodium, include all the elements of the first column except hydrogen, which does not belong to any group. They are soft, highly reactive metals. In their pure state, they must be stored in oil because they react on exposure to moisture in the air. Because of their high reactivity, they are never found in their elemental state in nature but exist instead in the form of **COMPOUNDS**.
- Elements of the second group, such as magnesium and calcium, are called *alkaline earth metals*. They are highly malleable and reactive, and they burn easily in the presence of heat. Like Group IA elements, they are not found in their elemental state in nature; however, unlike the alkali metals, they can be exposed to the air. They form many compounds found in rocks or earth, which is where they get their name. Calcium carbonate ($CaCO_3$), for example, contains the alkaline earth metal calcium.
- The *halogens*, such as chlorine and iodine, are elements in the second-last column. They are non-metals that react easily to form compounds, including salts. Several are powerful disinfectants; chlorine, for example, is used to treat the water in swimming pools.

Halogen comes from the Greek words *halo*, meaning "salt," and *gene*, meaning "creator."

- The *noble gases* (also called *rare gases* or *inert gases*) include helium and argon and make up the final column of the periodic table. They are very stable, which means they react minimally with other elements. For this reason, they can be found in their elemental state in nature.

Argon comes from the Greek *argos*, meaning "lazy" or "inactive."

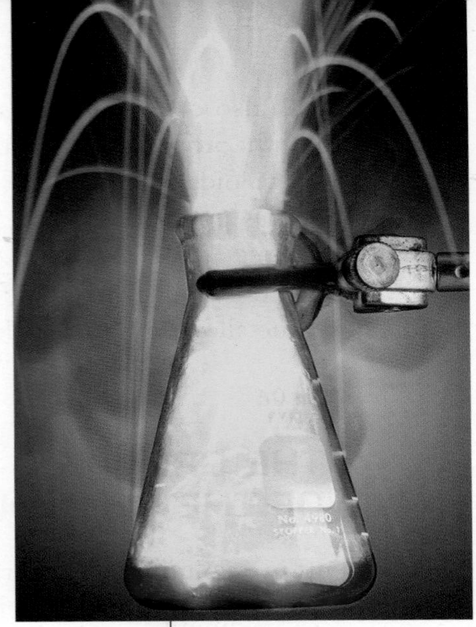

1.24 Alkali metals and halogens react violently with each other. This photo shows the explosive reaction that occurs when sodium comes into contact with bromine.

ST EST 2.3 THE PERIODS OF THE PERIODIC TABLE

Figure 1.25 shows the elements of the second row of the periodic table. We can see that they all have the same number of shells around the nucleus. The period number corresponds to the number of electron shells.

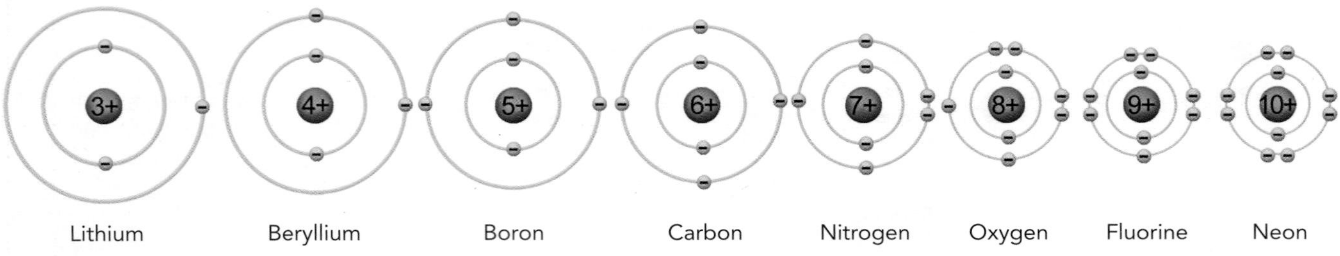

1.25 All these elements belong to the second period of the periodic table. Their atoms all have two electron shells.

▶ **A PERIOD corresponds to a row of the periodic table. All the elements in a period have the same number of electron shells.**

EST

THE PERIODICITY OF PROPERTIES

Electrical conductivity, density and melting point are a few examples of properties that can be determined for each of the elements of the periodic table.

How do these properties vary within a period? Let's go back to Figure 1.25 (page 22). As the numbers of protons and electrons increase, the protons' power of attraction for the electrons also increases. This causes the atom to shrink. The atomic radius thus generally decreases from the first to the last element in the period.

The graph in Figure 1.26 shows how the length of the atomic radius varies in a similar way from one period to another. This repetition of a pattern is referred to as *periodicity of a property*.

CONCEPT REVIEW

- Characteristic properties
- Melting point
- Boiling point
- Density

1.26 THE ATOMIC RADIUS OF ELEMENTS 1 TO 86

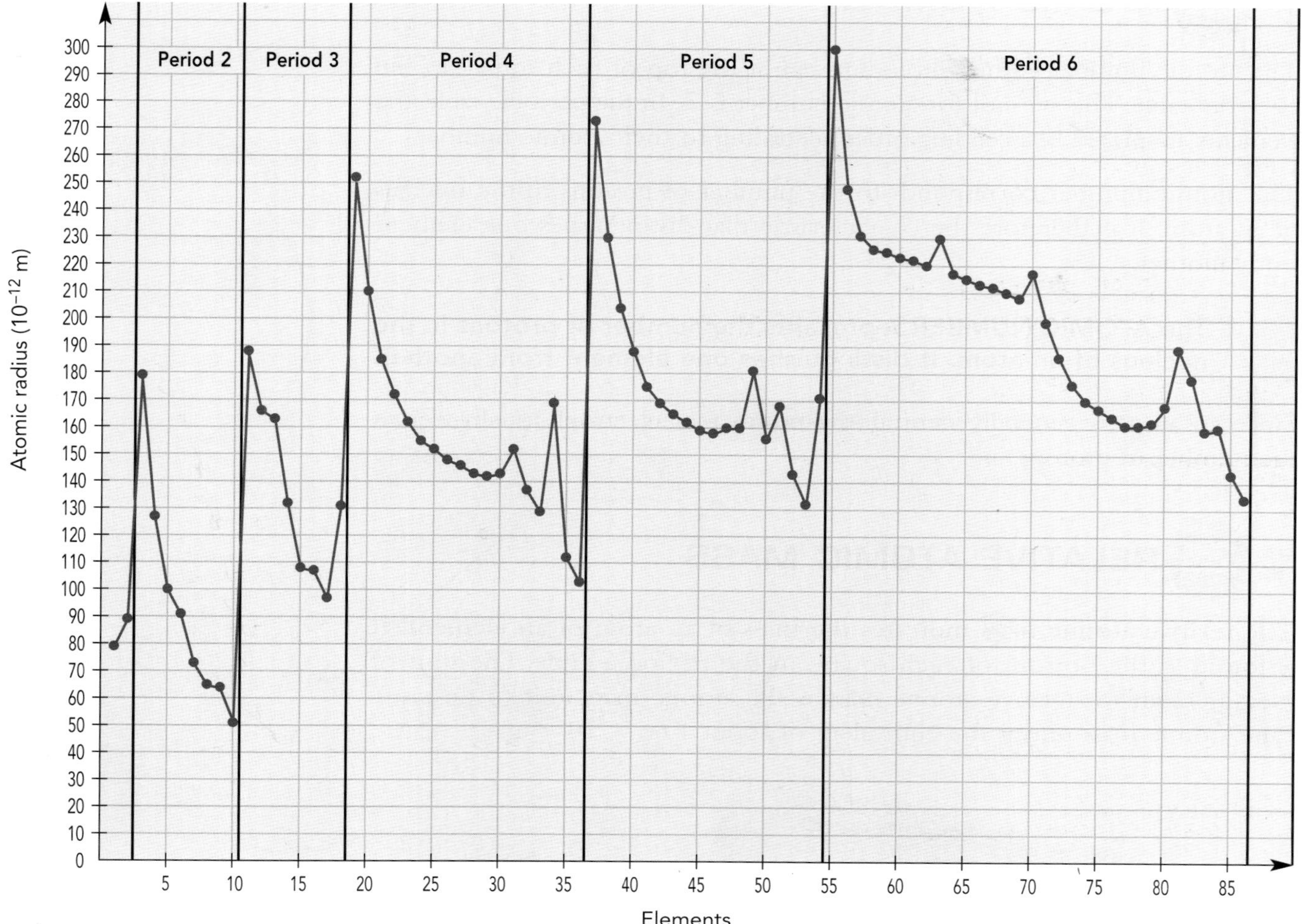

The PERIODICITY OF PROPERTIES is the repetition of patterns in properties from one period to another.

Appendix 1, at the end of this textbook, presents several characteristic properties of the elements, namely:

- melting point: temperature at which a solid becomes a liquid (or vice versa)
- boiling point: temperature at which a liquid becomes a gas (or vice versa)
- density: mass per unit of volume
- atomic radius: distance from the centre of the atom to its outermost electron
- first ionization energy: energy required to remove the outermost electron from an atom
- electronegativity: measure of the ability of an atom to attract electrons to form a chemical bond

MATTER FOR PREDICTION

Thanks to the periodicity of properties, Mendeleev was able to predict not only the existence of elements unknown in his day but also several of their properties. These elements were later discovered, and their properties proved to be astonishingly similar to the Russian scientist's predictions. 2

EST 2.4 ATOMIC NUMBER

The atomic number is the whole number at the top of each square in the periodic table. The symbol for atomic number is Z. In the periodic table, the elements are placed in ascending order according to their atomic numbers.

The atomic number corresponds to the number of protons in the nucleus of an atom. It is therefore the characteristic that distinguishes one element from another.

The ATOMIC NUMBER represents the number of protons in the nucleus of an atom. It distinguishes one element from another.

Since an atom is generally neutral, the number of electrons usually equals the number of protons.

EST SE 2.5 RELATIVE ATOMIC MASS

The relative atomic mass indicates the mass of an atom of an element. It is found at the bottom of each square in the periodic table. The unit of measurement for relative atomic mass is the atomic mass unit (u or amu). One atomic mass unit is the equivalent of about 1.66×10^{-24} g.

NEW ELEMENT BRINGS WEIGHT TO THE TABLE

A team of American and Russian scientists have announced the discovery of a new element, the heaviest to date. Provisionally named *ununoctium*, the "newborn" element does not exist naturally; it was created in a laboratory. In the periodic table, it is the 118th element.

Theoretically, there is no natural element with more than 92 protons, the number in uranium. However, scientists have found a way to produce heavier elements, using particle accelerators. They force a collision between the atomic nuclei of two elements and hope that they will bond to form a super-heavy nucleus. About 20 artificial elements have been created in this way.

To produce ununoctium ("one-one-eight" in Latin), scientists bombarded a californium target (Z=98) with atoms of calcium (Z=20). After billions of collisions, three atoms with nuclei containing 118 protons were created. The atoms were very unstable: they survived 0.9 milliseconds before disintegrating.

To discover new elements, scientists cause existing elements to collide. They then examine the debris from the collisions.

The mass of an atom is very small, so it is difficult to measure directly. Scientists therefore first established the atomic mass of a reference element. In 1961, at an international chemistry conference in Montréal, it was agreed that the atomic mass of carbon-12 (a form of carbon containing precisely six protons and six neutrons) would be exactly 12 u. Thus, one atomic mass unit (1 u) equals one twelfth of the mass of a carbon-12 atom—about the same mass as one proton or neutron. The masses of all the other atoms were then measured in relation to this standard.

The RELATIVE ATOMIC MASS is the mass of an atom measured by comparison with a reference element, carbon-12.

EST SE

MASS NUMBER

The mass number is a whole number indicating the sum of the numbers of protons and neutrons in an atom. Its symbol is A. It is found by rounding the relative atomic mass to the nearest whole number.

Atoms are often identified by an $^{A}_{Z}E$ formulation, in which A is the mass number, Z is the atomic number and E is the symbol of the element.

When the mass number and the atomic number of an atom are known, it is easy to calculate the number of its neutrons by subtracting Z from A. For example, $^{12}_{6}C$ represents a carbon atom containing six neutrons (12 – 6).

EST SE 2.6 ISOTOPES

All the atoms of an element have the same number of protons but not necessarily the same mass. For example, hydrogen can occur in three different forms:

- In its most common form, hydrogen contains one proton, one electron and no neutrons. Its mass number is one.
- Heavy hydrogen, or *deuterium,* contains one proton, one electron and one neutron. Its mass number is two.
- Super-heavy hydrogen, or *tritium,* owes its extra mass to the two neutrons in its nucleus. Its mass number is three.

The three forms of hydrogen differ only in their mass numbers. They are called *isotopes* of hydrogen. The number of protons and electrons in the different isotopes of an element always remains the same. Consequently, all the isotopes of an element have the same chemical properties. However, since they have different numbers of neutrons, isotopes have different physical properties.

Isotope is derived from two Greek words: *isos,* meaning "equal" or "the same," and *topos,* meaning "place." Isotopes do, in fact, all occupy "the same place" in the periodic table.

An ISOTOPE is an atom of an element with the same number of protons as another atom of the same element but with a different number of neutrons.

Isotopes are identified by their mass numbers. For example, tritium, the super-heavy isotope of hydrogen, is also called *hydrogen-3.* Isotopes can also be identified with a notation indicating their mass numbers and atomic numbers; for hydrogen, the isotopes are thus ${}^{1}_{1}H$, ${}^{2}_{1}H$ and ${}^{3}_{1}H$.

The atomic masses that appear in the periodic table are mean masses based on the proportions of different isotopes of the elements as they occur in nature. This explains why the relative atomic mass of carbon is 12.01 u, and not exactly 12 u.

HOW OLD DO YOU THINK I AM?

Certains isotopes are naturally radioactive. Carbon-14, for example, is present in fossils and makes it possible to date them.

1897
1956

Irène Joliot-Curie

In 1934, Irène Joliot-Curie (daughter of Pierre and Marie Curie) and her husband, Frédéric Joliot, discovered a technique for producing artificial radioactive isotopes. By bombarding aluminum foil with alpha particles, they created phosphorus-30, a radioactive isotope of phosphorus-31. Radioactive isotopes are particularly useful in nuclear medicine.

ST EST SE 3 Representing atoms

Atoms can be represented in different ways. In this section, four representations are described: Lewis notation, the Rutherford-Bohr atomic model, the simplified atomic model and the "ball-and-stick" atomic model.

As a general rule, electrons seek to fill the shells nearest the nucleus before occupying a farther shell. To find the maximum number of electrons in the shells of the first 20 elements of the periodic table, the following conditions apply:

- The innermost shell can contain a maximum of two electrons.
- The second shell can contain a maximum of eight electrons.
- The third shell can contain up to 18 electrons. However, once the third shell contains eight electrons, the next electrons begin to fill the fourth shell before returning to the third. In this way, the number of valence electrons always corresponds to the group number of the element in question.

LEWIS NOTATION

Lewis notation, or *electron dot notation,* was devised by the American chemist Gilbert Newton Lewis (1875–1946). It is a simplified representation of the atom, in which only the valence electrons are illustrated. They are represented by dots placed around the chemical symbol of the element.

LEWIS NOTATION is a simplified representation of the atom, in which only the valence electrons are illustrated.

In this notation, valence electrons are placed one by one around the symbol, like the four points on a compass. When these four positions are filled, the electrons are then doubled to form pairs (Figure 1.27).

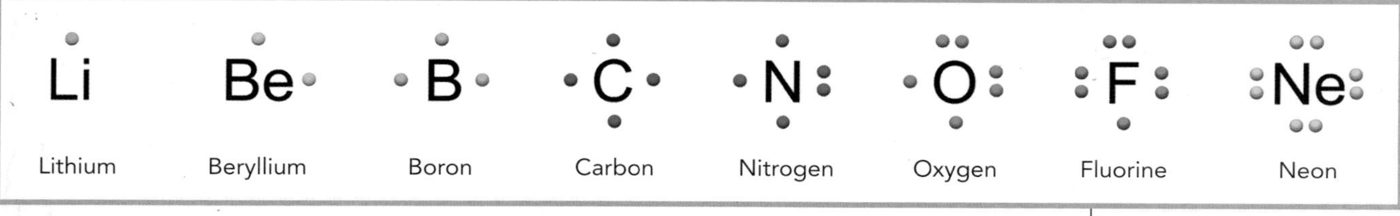

1.27 Representations of the Period 2 elements in Lewis notation

REPRESENTING AN ATOM ACCORDING TO THE RUTHERFORD-BOHR MODEL

To represent an atom correctly according to the Rutherford-Bohr model, three facts about the element must be known: the period, the group and the atomic number. This information can be obtained from the periodic table.

- The period indicates the number of electron shells in the atom; in other words, the number of the period corresponds to the number of shells.

- The group indicates the number of valence electrons—the number of electrons in the outermost shell.
- The atomic number indicates the total number of electrons, and of protons, in the atom.

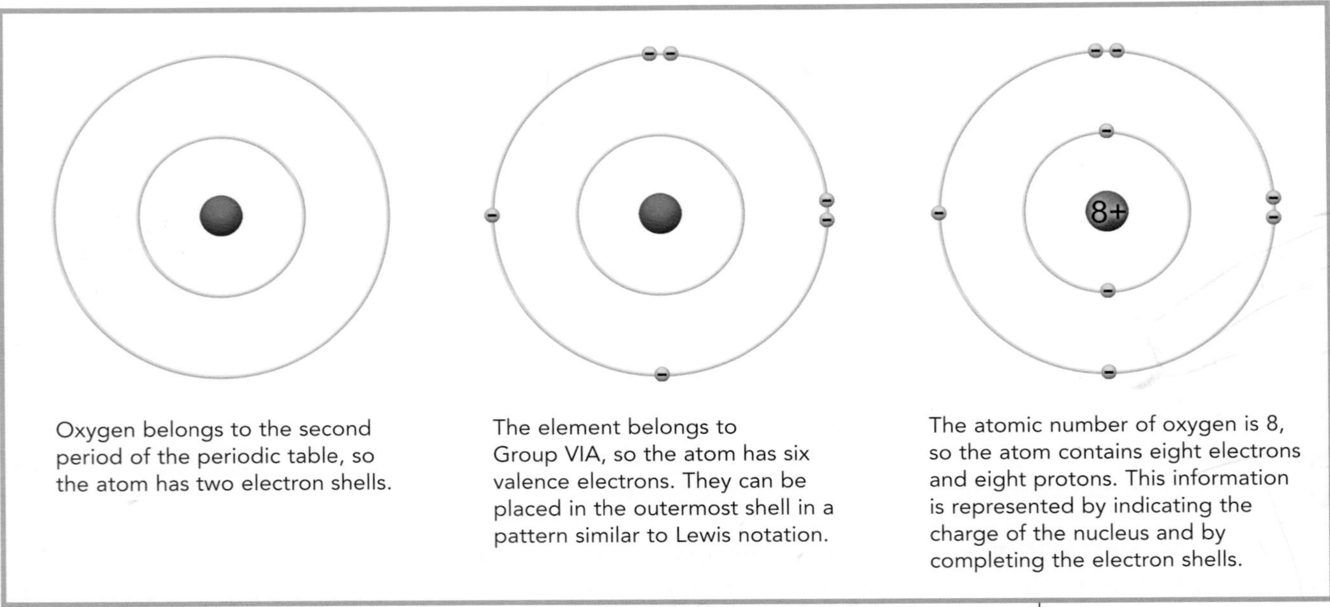

1.28 Representation of an oxygen atom according to the Rutherford-Bohr model

3.3 REPRESENTING AN ATOM ACCORDING TO THE SIMPLIFIED ATOMIC MODEL

Atoms are represented in the simplified model with numbers, symbols and arcs. This representation clearly shows the number of protons and neutrons in an atom. It also shows the number of electrons in each shell.

Electrons and protons are placed in the same way as in the Rutherford-Bohr model. To include the number of neutrons, we refer to the periodic table to find the relative atomic mass of the element. For example, the relative atomic mass of chlorine is 35.45 u. We round this number to the nearest whole number to obtain the mass number (the mass number of chlorine is thus 35) and then subtract the atomic number from the mass number (35 − 17 = 18 neutrons). Figure 1.29 shows several examples of elements represented with this kind of model.

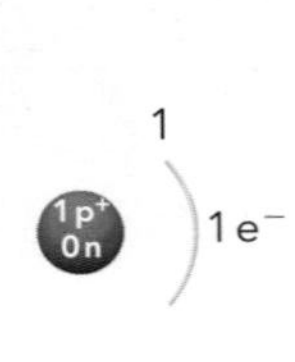

Hydrogen ($^{1}_{1}H$)

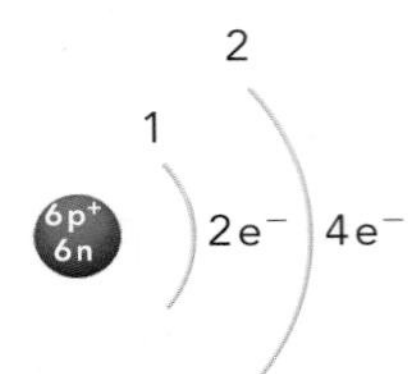

Carbon ($^{12}_{6}C$)

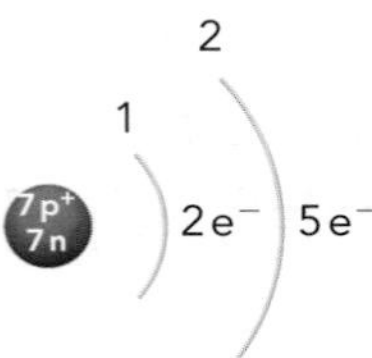

Nitrogen ($^{14}_{7}N$)

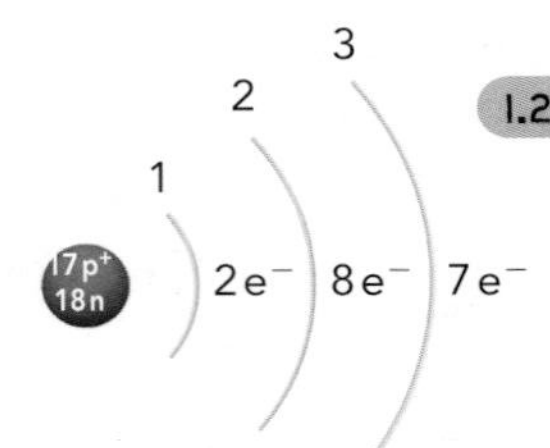

Chlorine ($^{35}_{17}Cl$)

1.29 The atoms of several elements according to the simplified atomic model

ST EST SE

3.4 THE "BALL-AND-STICK" ATOMIC MODEL

In this model, the atom is depicted as a ball, and its bonds with other atoms are shown with sticks. The size of the ball is generally proportional to the number of electron shells in the atom.

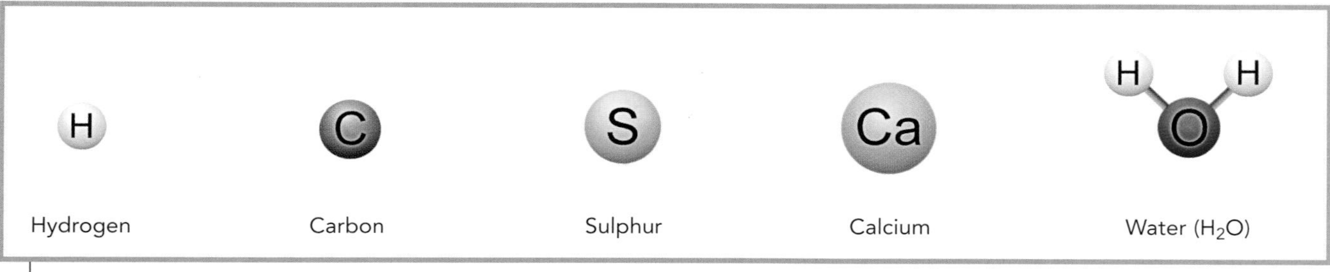

1.30 Representations of several atoms and a molecule according to the "ball-and-stick" model

UNRAVELLING THE UNIVERSE

Scientists have known for more than 100 years that atoms are the building blocks of matter, making up molecules. They eventually discovered that an atom contains a nucleus and electrons. And then they found out that the nucleus contains particles, too: neutrons and protons. How much longer will they continue breaking down matter into ever-smaller particles?

Thanks to particle accelerators, physicists' answer to this question is gradually becoming clearer. These machines propel particles at incredibly high speeds and then cause them to collide. Traces of matter and energy from the collision are collected and studied. In just a few decades, physicists have observed all sorts of strange little scraps of matter: pions, muons, gluons, mesons, bosons . . . more than 300 different particles in all!

Like paleontologists faced with a pile of bones, physicists now have to sort out their discoveries and find how these building blocks fit together. One important discovery they have made is that protons and neutrons are each made up of three quarks.

With a circumference of 27 km, the Large Hadron Collider, on the border between France and Switzerland, is currently the largest particle accelerator in the world.

According to the standard model, which was developed in the 1970s and still holds today, there are 12 elementary particles: six leptons, including the electron, and six quarks. Other particles also exist, such as gluons, which bind the quarks together.

The universe still holds many mysteries to unravel. And the hunt for new particles goes on!

Source: Adapted from Valérie Borde, "La recette de l'Univers, c'est pour bientôt," *L'Actualité* 30, 17 (November 1, 2005), p. 34. *[Translation]*

EST SE 4 The concept of mole

Atoms and molecules are extremely small. A minuscule sample of matter may contain billions of them. Chemists sometimes need to know the number of atoms or molecules in a substance. Since they cannot count atoms one by one, they have developed the concept of a mole.

A mole represents a quantity of matter. By definition, one mole equals the number of atoms in exactly 12 g of carbon-12. Just as we can talk about a dozen eggs, a hundred hats or a thousand days, scientists can quantify matter as a mole of atoms, a mole of pencils or a mole of anything else.

A MOLE is a quantity equal to the number of atoms in exactly 12 g of carbon-12. Its symbol is mol.

EST SE 4.1 MOLAR MASS

We have explained that, by definition, an atom of carbon-12 has a mass of exactly 12 u (page 25). We have also just specified that a mole of carbon has a mass of exactly 12 g. The mass of a mole of carbon is thus numerically equal to its relative atomic mass. However, the molar mass is expressed in g/mol rather than in atomic mass units. The mass of a mole of a substance is called its *molar mass.*

The MOLAR MASS of a substance is the mass of one mole of that substance.

... has a mass of 4.00 g because one atom of helium ... ilarly, one mole of molecular oxygen (O_2) has ... ise one atom of oxygen has a mass of 16.00 u and ... ygen in each molecule. This last example shows that ... of all the atoms in a molecule can simply be added ... iole of that molecule.

1.31 SOME EXAMPLES OF MOLAR MASS

Substance	Relative atomic mass (u)	Molar mass (g/mol)
Carbon (C)	C = 12.01	12.01
Neon (Ne)	Ne = 20.18	20.18
Calcium (Ca)	Ca = 40.08	40.08
Molecular hydrogen (H_2)	H = 1.01	1.01 + 1.01 = 2.02
Table salt (NaCl)	Na = 22.99 Cl = 35.45	22.99 + 35.45 = 58.44
Glucose ($C_6H_{12}O_6$)	C = 12.01 H = 1.01 O = 16.00	(6 × 12.01) + (12 × 1.01) + (6 × 16.00) = 180.18

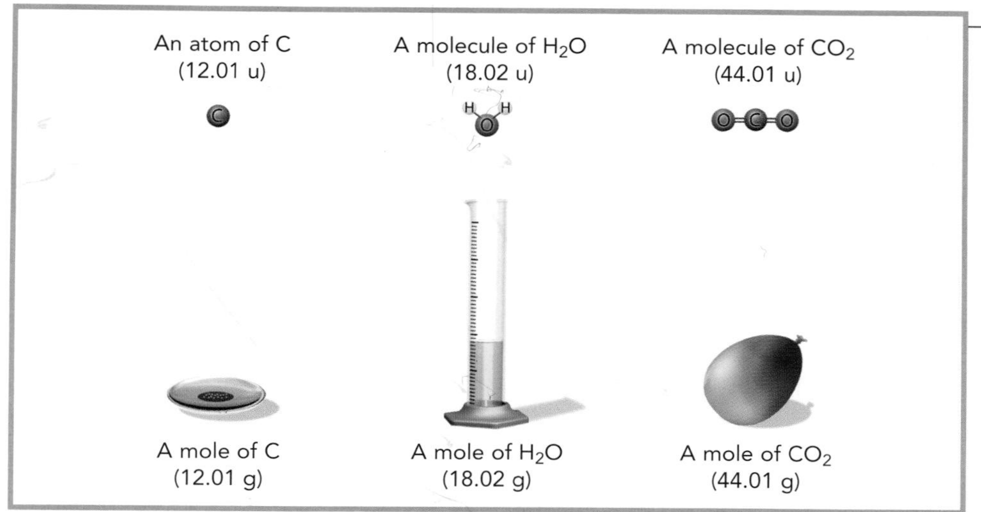

1.32 The mole relates microscopic and macroscopic quantities of a substance.

The following formula relates molar mass to mass so that one or the other may be used in calculations:

$M = \frac{m}{n}$ where M is the molar mass (in g/mol)
m is the mass (in g)
n is the number of moles (in mol)

For example, the number of moles in 100 g of carbon can be calculated as follows:

$$n = \frac{m}{M} = \frac{100 \text{ g}}{12.01 \text{ g/mol}} = 8.33 \text{ mol}$$

There are 8.33 mol in 100 g of carbon.

EST 4.2 AVOGADRO'S NUMBER

The number of atoms in 12 g of carbon-12 was determined through a series of experiments. It is equal to 6.02×10^{23} atoms. This quantity is also known as *Avogadro's number* (or the *Avogadro constant*), in honour of Amedeo Avogadro (1776–1856), the first physicist to fully realize the usefulness of the concept of a mole.

▶ **AVOGADRO'S NUMBER represents the number of entities in a mole. It equals 6.02×10^{23} of those entities.**

Like the mole, Avogadro's number is a quantity that can be applied to any entity to be measured. For example, we can say that a mole of carbon contains 6.02×10^{23} atoms of carbon just as we can say that a mole of eggs represents 6.02×10^{23} eggs.

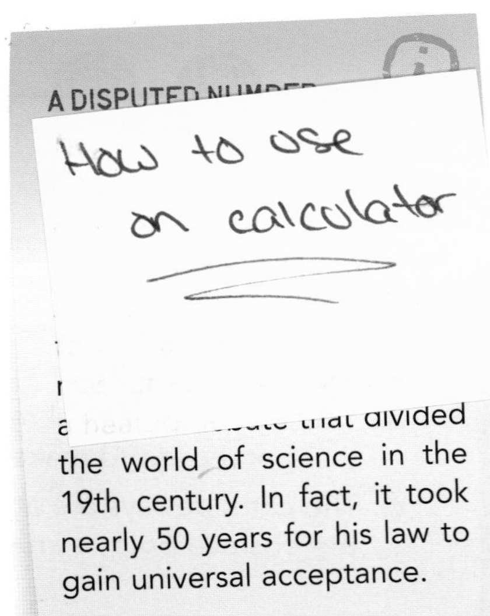

CHECKUP

ST 1–9, 13–18, 28–31, A and C.

EST 1–38 and A–C.

AST None.

SE 1–13, 23–36, B and C.

1 What is an atom? (pp. 6–17)

1. Why is it useful to represent an atom with a model?

2. Look at the two photos below.

A 

B 

a) Which photo represents a model in which matter can be infinitely divided? Explain your answer.

b) Which photo represents a model in which matter cannot be infinitely divided? Explain your answer.

3. Here is a representation of a molecule of water (H_2O). Does it respect the principles behind Dalton's atomic model? Explain your answer.

4. What conclusion did Thomson draw from each of the following observations?

a) The cathode rays cause a small propeller inside the tube to turn.

b) The rays are identical regardless of the metal used to make the cathode.

c) The cathode rays are attracted to the positive pole of an electrical field.

5. What type of radiation did Rutherford use for his research on atomic structure?

6. Look at the illustration below. Each letter corresponds to an observation made by Rutherford. Describe each observation and match it with one of Rutherford's conclusions.

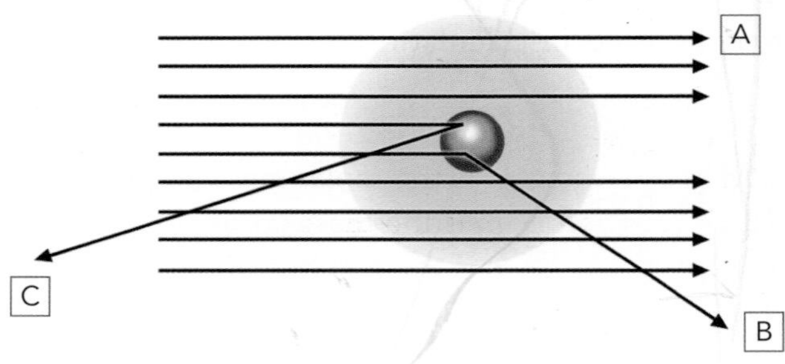

7. Which positively charged particle is found in the nucleus?

8. The bright colours of fireworks amaze and delight us. Each colour is the result of the combustion of a specific substance. For example, potassium chloride produces a purple flame, and sodium chloride, an orange-yellow flame. Which theory, proposed by Bohr, explains this phenomenon?

9. Match a characteristic of the Rutherford-Bohr atomic model with each of the following statements.

a) An atom contains as many protons as electrons.

b) Alpha particles pass easily through gold foil.

c) Alpha particles are strongly repelled by the nucleus.

d) A heated gas emits light waves of a specific length.

10. What is the neutron's function in the atom?

11. Which particles of the atom account for most of its mass?

12. Which is the lightest particle of the atom?

2 The periodic classification of the elements (pp. 17–26)

13. Where are the nonmetals in the periodic table?

14. What do elements of the same group have in common?

15. Hydrogen is a nonmetal, but it is in the same column as the alkali metals. Why?

16. What are the elements in the second column of the periodic table called? What do they have in common?

17. In the atomic model of potassium below, which letter represents a valence electron? Explain your answer.

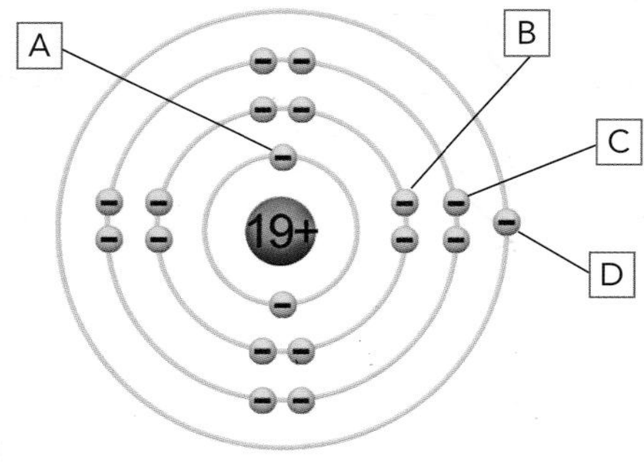

Potassium

18. What do elements of the same period have in common?

19. The atomic radius is a periodic property of the elements. Explain how the atomic radius varies within a period.

20. How does the melting point vary within a period? Draw a graph showing the melting point as a function of the atomic number to explain your answer. Refer to the data in Appendix 1.

21. The table in Appendix 1 shows the first ionization energy of the elements of the periodic table.
   a) How does this property vary within a period?
   b) How does this property vary within a group?

22. What does the atomic number of an element represent?

23. What is the relative atomic mass of an element?

24. An atom of argon contains 18 protons, and its mass number is 40. How many neutrons does it contain?

25. An atom has 25 protons, 25 electrons and 27 neutrons. What is its mass in atomic mass units? Round your answer to the nearest whole number and explain your calculation.

26. Among the elements below, which are isotopes of the same element? Explain your answer.

27. Which of these representations is impossible? Explain your answer.

3 Representing atoms (pp. 26–29)

28. How is Lewis notation useful?

29. Are the atomic representations below correct Lewis structures? If not, explain why.

Magnesium Argon Chlorine

30. Represent the following atoms in Lewis notation.

a) aluminum

b) iodine

c) barium

31. Are the atomic representations below correct according to the Rutherford-Bohr model? If not, explain why.

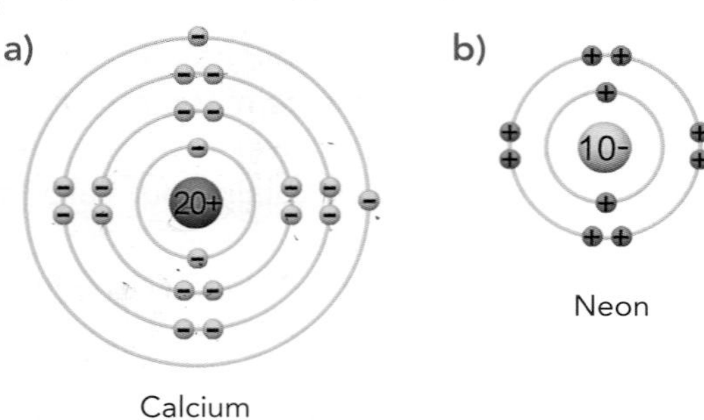

Calcium Neon

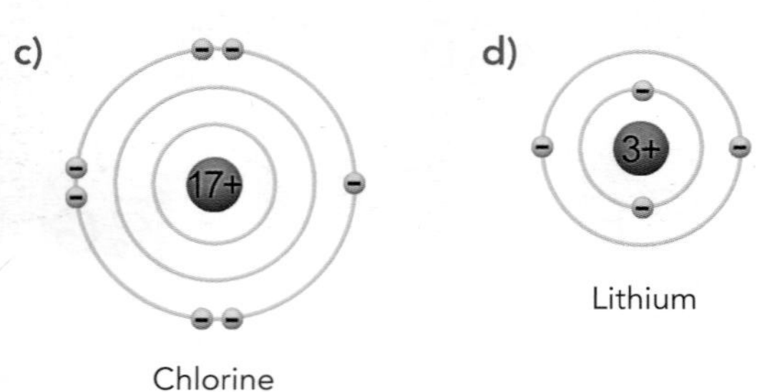

Chlorine Lithium

32. Are the following representations correct according to the simplified atomic model? If not, explain why.

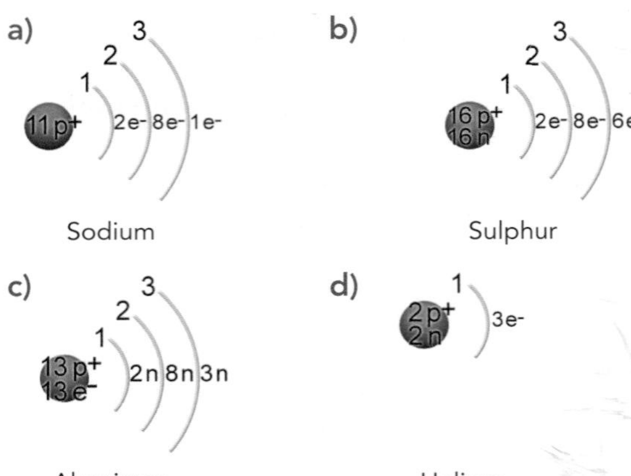

Sodium Sulphur

Aluminum Helium

33. Draw an atom of fluorine according to the simplified atomic model.

4 The concept of mole (pp. 30–31)

34. How many moles are there in each of the following samples of matter?

a) 12 g of carbon

b) 20 g of calcium

c) 80 g of argon

d) 10 g of sodium

35. What is the molar mass of each of the following molecules?

a) LiBr

b) CO_2

c) H_2SO_4

d) $Mg(NO_3)_2$

36. A 0.25-mol sample of a certain substance has a mass of 10 g.

a) What is the molar mass of this substance?

b) Which element has the same molar mass?

37. What is the mass, in grams, of 6.02×10^{23} atoms of gold?

38. How many particles are there in a sample of matter that contains three moles of particles?

review questions

A. The chemical reactivity of elements depends on their ability to give up their valence electrons. The most reactive metal in the periodic table is francium. Explain why, using the Rutherford-Bohr atomic model.

B. Different models of the atom have been proposed over time. The changes from one model to the next reflect recent experimental findings. In certain contexts, however, an older model may still apply. From this point of view, which model—Dalton's model, Thomson's model, the Rutherford-Bohr model or the simplified atomic model—is the most relevant to an explanation of each of the following phenomena?

a) Cathode ray screens depend on the emission of rays from the cathode of a gas discharge tube.

b) When magnesium burns, it emits a bright light. For this reason, it was previously used in camera flashes.

c) In a nuclear reaction, neutrons are frequently emitted.

d) If you rub a balloon on your head, it gives off electrons (onto your hair), creating static electricity.

e) Iron combines with oxygen in a ratio of 2:3 to form rust (Fe_2O_3).

f) Atoms are mostly empty space.

g) The atomic mass of helium is 4 u.

C. Prepare your own summary of Chapter 1 by building a concept map.

HOW TO BUILD A CONCEPT MAP

FOLLOW-UP

MERCURY CONTAMINATION IN THE AMAZON

During the 1980s, a Brazilian cardiologist working in a village at the junction of the Amazon and Tapajós rivers detected some cardiac anomalies in his patients. His subsequent research showed a connection between the level of mercury in the villagers' hair and a variety of neurological disorders, such as problems with speech and coordination and a limited field of view. Mining activities in the region, which discharged large amounts of mercury into the environment, came under immediate suspicion.

THE SOURCE OF THE PROBLEM

Between 1980 and 1995, the workers who collected gold from the streams and rivers often used mercury to extract the gold even though the technique is illegal in Brazil. Gold dissolves on contact with mercury, so these "gold panners" simply had to burn the gold-laden mercury afterwards to recover the precious metal. Unfortunately, when mercury evaporates or finds its way into a river, it changes chemically and becomes toxic to humans.

Before condemning local mining, however, authorities had to confirm the source of the problem. Researchers from Québec worked together with Brazilian scientists to study the contamination. They found, to their surprise, that no matter how far from the gold mining and processing sites their samples were taken, the levels of mercury in the environment remained the same. They concluded that there must be another source of pollution. They eventually realized that clearing land for agriculture was releasing the mercury contained in the soil, which was then washed into rivers by the tropical rain. It was the first time that scientists established a relationship between deforestation and mercury contamination in rivers. In fact, deforestation was found to account for 90 percent of the contamination of the Tapajós River, while only 10 percent was due to mining. The news made headlines around the world.

At the same time, a Québec researcher named Donna Mergler determined that the neurological disorders observed among the villagers appeared at much lower doses of mercury than predicted by the World Health Organization.

In an effort to reduce the effects of the contamination, Brazilian and Canadian scientists met with representatives of local communities. They first suggested changes to the local diet, in which fish was the main source of protein. They advised people to eat more herbivorous fish and fewer predator fish because the mercury levels of predators were higher than those of their prey. The population was also encouraged to identify and avoid areas where the fish contained the most mercury.

Clearing land for farming releases the mercury in the soil.

Some women from the village recorded everything they ate for over a year. Mercury levels were found to be lower among those women who ate more fruit, which suggested another way to modify the local diet. In addition, to help contain the mercury in the soil, new trees were planted, particularly fruit trees.

MONITORING DEFORESTATION

Solving the problem of land clearing remains the long-term priority. Although the rate of deforestation in the Brazilian Amazon dropped by 50 percent between 2004 and 2006, it subsequently rose again—to an even higher rate. Satellite images show that deforestation increased by 75 percent in 2007. Land clearing must be closely monitored in the future, and further action is needed to protect the environment and help local populations.

1. The Amazon is not the only place affected by mercury contamination. Relatively high concentrations can also be found in Québec landfills. Name three commonplace objects that you use that might contain mercury. Explain your answers.
2. Mercury is a heavy metal. Using atomic models and the periodic table of the elements, explain why it belongs to this category of elements.

1916 Description of the concept of the covalent bond
Formulation of the octet rule

1909 Description of the pH scale

1894 Discovery of the first noble gas, argon

1845 Artificial synthesis of acetic acid, or vinegar

1838 Invention of a method of photography using silver salts

1815 Discovery of polyatomic ions

1800 Invention of the electric cell (battery)

1787 Description of the first set of rules for naming chemical substances

CIRCA 1750 First definition of acids, bases and salts

1625 Development of a method for preparing sulphuric and hydrochloric acids

CIRCA -590 Proposal of the theory that the universe is made up of four fundamental elements: earth, water, fire and air

Thousands of different substances make up the world around us, and new ones are constantly being created. Some are hard, while others are malleable. Some conduct electricity, but others do not. Many dissolve in water. Behind this incredible diversity of substances lies the ability of atoms to combine in different ways. Why and how do atoms form chemical bonds? Why are certain substances soluble in water and others not? What are the properties of solutions? These are a few of the questions that we will discuss in this chapter.

THE MATERIAL WORLD

2

Molecules and solutions

CONTENTS

ST
EST
SE

1 What is a molecule?

CONCEPT REVIEW
- Atom
- Element
- Periodic table
- Molecule

Only a few elements, such as gold and helium, exist naturally on Earth in uncombined form. The atoms of most elements tend to bond with atoms of other elements to form molecules.

A MOLECULE is a group of two or more chemically bonded atoms.

Why do atoms tend to bond with other atoms? One answer to this question is that atoms generally try to acquire an electron configuration similar to that of the noble gases because it makes them more stable.

The **NOBLE GASES**, which make up the VIIIA **GROUP** of the periodic table, are extremely stable. It is very difficult to make a noble gas react with other elements. This distinctive feature is due to the fact that the electron shell farthest from the nucleus—the shell containing the **VALENCE ELECTRONS**—is complete.

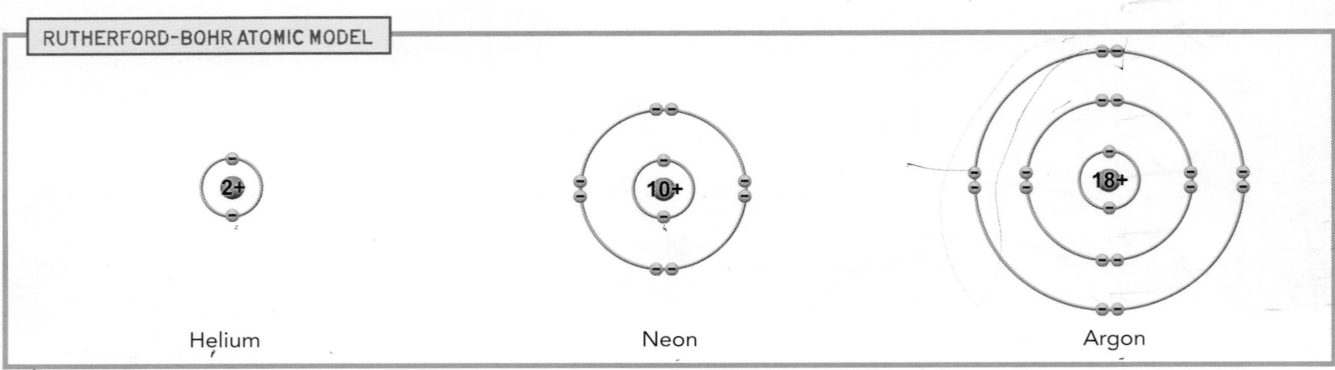

2.1 Electron configurations of three noble gases. The first shell of any atom can contain a maximum of two electrons. The second and third shells can contain up to eight valence electrons. The electron shell farthest from the nucleus in a helium, neon or argon atom is thus complete.

Now let's look at an element that is not a noble gas: fluorine, for example. This element has seven valence electrons. The simplest way for a fluorine atom to acquire the electron configuration of a noble gas would be to gain an additional electron. Its configuration would then be similar to that of neon. Fluorine is thus an element that tends to gain an electron.

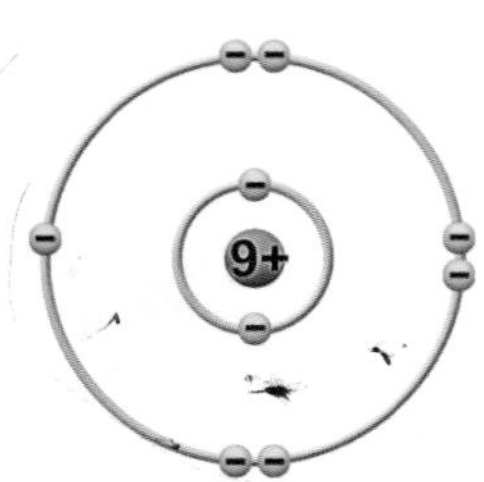

Fluorine

2.2 An atom of fluorine needs to gain only one electron to achieve the configuration of neon.

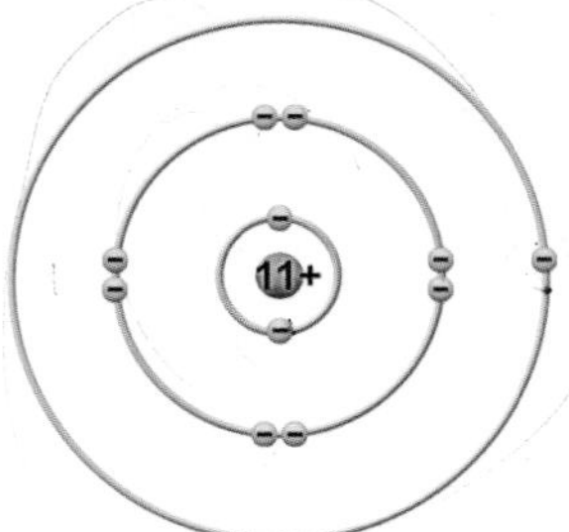

Sodium

2.3 If sodium had one less electron, it would have the same configuration as neon.

Now consider sodium. The electron shell farthest from the nucleus of this element contains only one electron. A sodium atom could try to gain seven electrons to match the configuration of argon, but there is an easier way to resemble a noble gas: giving up an electron. Sodium thus achieves the same electron configuration as neon. It is therefore an element that tends to lose an electron.

The periodic table helps to predict the tendency of elements to gain or lose electrons. All the alkali metals (the elements in Group IA) have one valence electron, so they all tend to lose an electron. Meanwhile, all the halogens (the elements in Group VIIA) contain seven valence electrons, so they need only one more to achieve the electron configuration of a noble gas with eight valence electrons.

2.4 THE TENDENCY TO GAIN OR LOSE ELECTRONS AMONG GROUP A ELEMENTS

Group number	IA	IIA	IIIA	IVA	VA	VIA	VIIA	VIIIA
Example element	Li	Be	B	C	N	O	F	Ne
Number of valence electrons	1	2	3	4	5	6	7	8 (except He)
Tendency	Lose 1 e^-	Lose 2 e^-	Lose 3 e^-	Gain or lose 4 e^-	Gain 3 e^-	Gain 2 e^-	Gain 1 e^-	None (stable)

Elements tend to acquire the configuration of the noble gas closest to them in the periodic table. Since the valence shell of all noble gases except helium contains eight electrons, elements are said to follow the *octet rule*.

Octet comes from the Latin *octo*, meaning "eight."

Lithium, beryllium and boron tend to acquire a configuration like that of helium, that is, with one electron shell containing two electrons. These elements are said to follow the *duet rule*.

Hydrogen is a special case. In certain circumstances, it tends to lose its only electron, while in other cases, it tends to gain a second electron.

ST EST SE 1.1 IONS

LAB 3

In general, atoms are electrically neutral. They have as many protons as they have electrons. Since each proton carries a positive charge and each electron carries a negative charge, the charges cancel each other, and the atom is neutral.

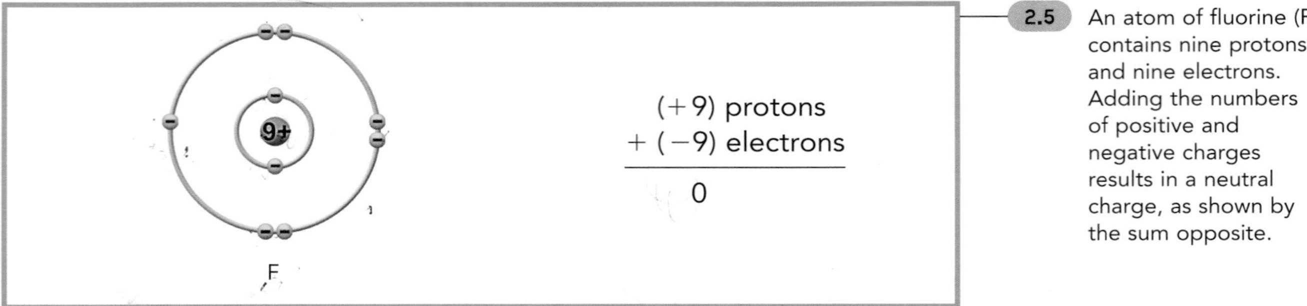

2.5 An atom of fluorine (F) contains nine protons and nine electrons. Adding the numbers of positive and negative charges results in a neutral charge, as shown by the sum opposite.

As mentioned previously (page 40), fluorine tends to gain an electron. When this happens, it acquires a negative charge, as shown in Figure 2.6.

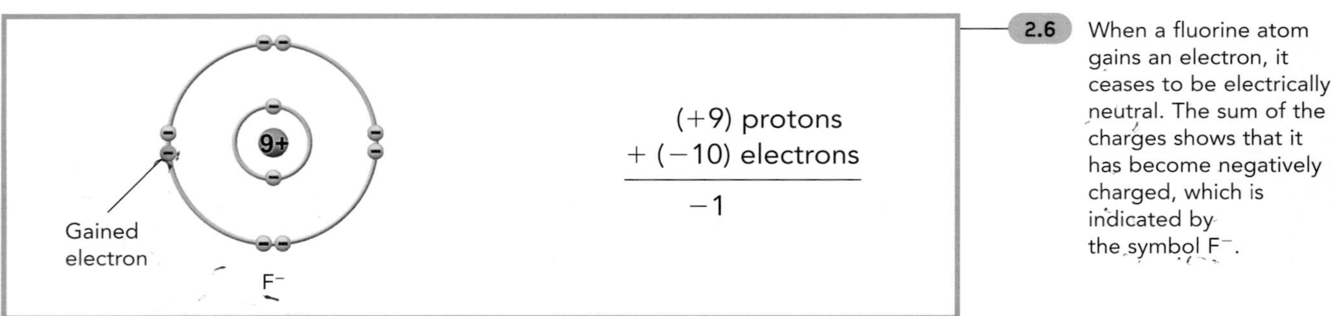

2.6 When a fluorine atom gains an electron, it ceases to be electrically neutral. The sum of the charges shows that it has become negatively charged, which is indicated by the symbol F^-.

Magnesium is an element that tends to lose two electrons. When this happens, magnesium carries a charge of +2, as shown in Figure 2.7.

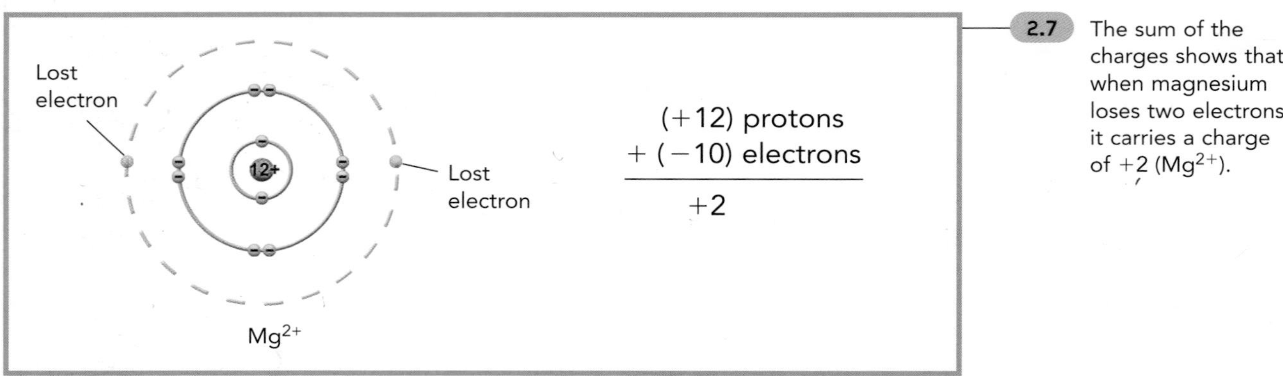

2.7 The sum of the charges shows that when magnesium loses two electrons, it carries a charge of +2 (Mg^{2+}).

Figures 2.6 and 2.7 demonstrate that, when they fulfill their tendency to gain or lose electrons, atoms acquire electrical charges. An atom that is no longer electrically neutral is called an *ion*.

An ION is an atom that has become electrically charged by losing or gaining one or more electrons.

It is important to note that when an ion is formed, the number of protons remains unchanged, preserving the nature of the element. Only the number of electrons changes.

When an atom gains one or more electrons, it forms a negative ion, and its charge corresponds to the number of electrons gained. For example, if sulphur gains two electrons, it acquires two negative charges. It thus becomes S^{2-}.

In contrast, when an atom loses one or more electrons, it forms a positive ion. Since positive ions have fewer electrons than protons, they carry a positive charge corresponding to the number of electrons lost. For example, if aluminum loses three electrons, it carries a charge of +3 (Al^{3+}).

2.8 CHARACTERISTICS OF IONS

Negative ion	Positive ion
Atom that has gained one or more electrons	Atom that has lost one or more electrons
More electrons than protons	Fewer electrons than protons
Negative net charge	Positive net charge

THE ACROPOLIS: CHEMISTRY TO THE RESCUE

A Greek chemist thinks he has found a way to protect the Acropolis of Athens from the pollution that is eating away at it. Pollutants in the surrounding air, especially sulphur dioxide (SO_2), have been transforming the marble of the monuments into gypsum, a very common sort of plaster.

The SO_2 molecules degrade the marble by stripping it of electrons, thus producing calcium ions. The process is similar to the way in which steel rusts, losing electrons to create iron ions.

Theodore Skoulikidis, Professor of Chemistry at the Athens Polytechnic School, has developed a transparent paint containing molecules that can supply large quantities of ions. Once applied to the monuments, the paint can "give" the electrons from its ions to the SO_2 molecules, and the marble can keep its own electrons.

Source: Adapted from Didier Kunz, "La chimie des métaux au secours des marbres du Parthénon," *Le Monde*, November 2, 1996. *[Translation]*

Unfortunately, 10 years later, the efforts of Professor Skoulikidis had not proven sufficient to save the Acropolis marble. In 2007, more than 300 statues and sculpted blocks were removed to a new museum and placed behind glass.

The periodic table can be used to predict the most probable form of ion for an element. For example, when the alkali metals lose their only valence electron, they acquire a positive charge. When the halogens gain an additional electron, they become negatively charged. Of course, the noble gases do not tend to form ions.

2.9 THE MOST PROBABLE IONS FOR GROUP A ELEMENTS

Group number	IA	IIA	IIIA	IVA	VA	VIA	VIIA	VIIIA
Most probable form of ion	E^{+}	E^{2+}	E^{3+}	E^{4+} or E^{4-}	E^{3-}	E^{2-}	E^{-}	None
Example	Li^{+}	Be^{2+}	B^{3+}	C^{4+} or C^{4-}	N^{3-}	O^{2-}	F^{-}	–

EST SE

POLYATOMIC IONS

Ions can be formed not only from individual atoms but also from certain groups of atoms. Sodium sulphate, for example, is formed from two ions, one positive and one negative, as shown in the following equation:

$$Na_2SO_4 \rightarrow 2\ Na^{+} + SO_4^{2-}$$

The negative ion SO_4^{2-} is composed of five chemically bonded atoms (one sulphur atom and four oxygen atoms). The group is referred to as a *polyatomic ion*.

Polyatomic comes from the Greek words *polus*, meaning "many," and *atomos*, meaning "indivisible."

A POLYATOMIC ION is a group of two or more chemically bonded atoms that has become electrically charged by losing or gaining one or more electrons.

2.10 EXAMPLES OF COMMON POLYATOMIC IONS

Chemical formula	Name	Chemical formula	Name
CH_3COO^{-}	Acetate	OH^{-}	Hydroxide
NH_4^{+}	Ammonium	NO_3^{-}	Nitrate
HCO_3^{-}	Bicarbonate	NO_2^{-}	Nitrite
CO_3^{2-}	Carbonate	PO_4^{3-}	Phosphate
ClO_3^{-}	Chlorate	SO_4^{2-}	Sulphate
CrO_4^{2-}	Chromate	SO_3^{2-}	Sulphite

EST SE 1.2

THE NATURE OF CHEMICAL BONDS

We have seen that most atoms, except those of noble gases, have a natural tendency to gain or lose one or more electrons. When two atoms come together, they will form a chemical bond whenever a bond can satisfy their respective tendencies.

There are two main types of chemical bond: ionic bonds, in which one or more electrons are transferred from one atom to another, and covalent bonds, in which one or more electron pairs are shared. The two types of bond will be discussed in greater detail in the following pages.

> **A CHEMICAL BOND is the union of two atoms through the transfer or sharing of one or more electrons.**

1875
1946

Gilbert Newton Lewis

In 1916, this American physicist and chemist proposed a theory describing chemical bonds, especially covalent bonds. He also created a form of chemical notation that shows the valence electrons of atoms; today these diagrams are referred to as *Lewis structures*.

EST SE

IONIC BONDS

Certain elements, such as metals, tend to give up their electrons. Other elements, often nonmetals, tend to gain electrons. When an atom that is ready to lose electrons comes in contact with an atom that is ready to accept them, under the right conditions, the atoms will react and form a chemical bond—an *ionic bond*. Figure 2.11 explains how an ionic bond is formed.

RUTHERFORD-BOHR ATOMIC MODEL

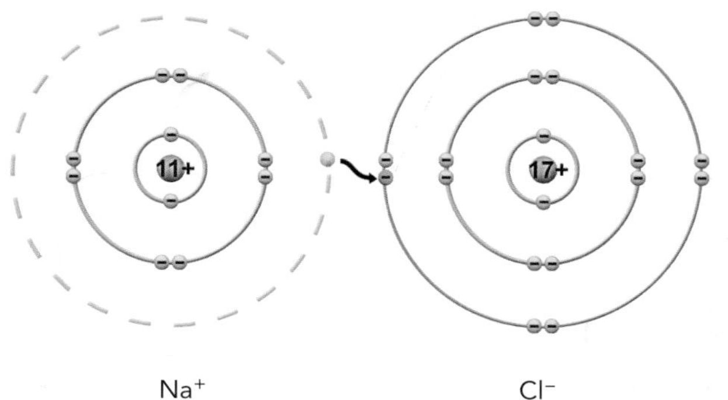

Na^+ Cl^-

When a sodium atom comes in contact with a chlorine atom, the sodium atom gives up an electron. Both atoms thus acquire an electron configuration similar to that of a noble gas. The sodium atom becomes a positive ion (Na^+), and the chlorine atom, a negative ion (Cl^-).

"BALL-AND-STICK" ATOMIC MODEL

NaCl

Since positive and negative charges attract each other, the positive sodium ion and the negative chloride ion tend to come together to form a neutral whole.

2.11 The formation of an ionic bond

An IONIC BOND is the result of a transfer of one or more electrons from one atom (usually a metal) to another atom (usually a nonmetal).

The formation of an ionic bond can be represented with **LEWIS STRUCTURES**. Figure 2.12 uses this type of notation to show what happens when magnesium reacts with chlorine.

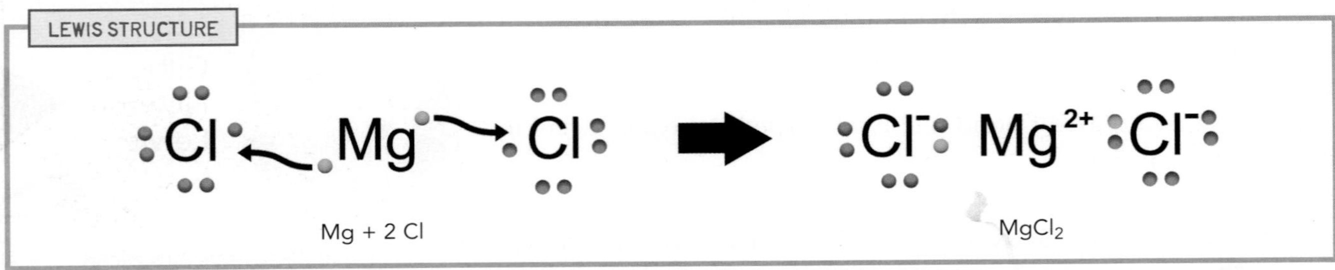

2.12 Magnesium needs to give up two electrons, while chlorine can accept only one. Each magnesium atom therefore reacts with two chlorine atoms, resulting in two ionic bonds.

EST SE

COVALENT BONDS

An electron "receiver" can also react with another receiver. Examples of this type of bonding are numerous, in fact: molecular oxygen, water, ammonia, methane, etc. Figure 2.13 shows what happens in this case.

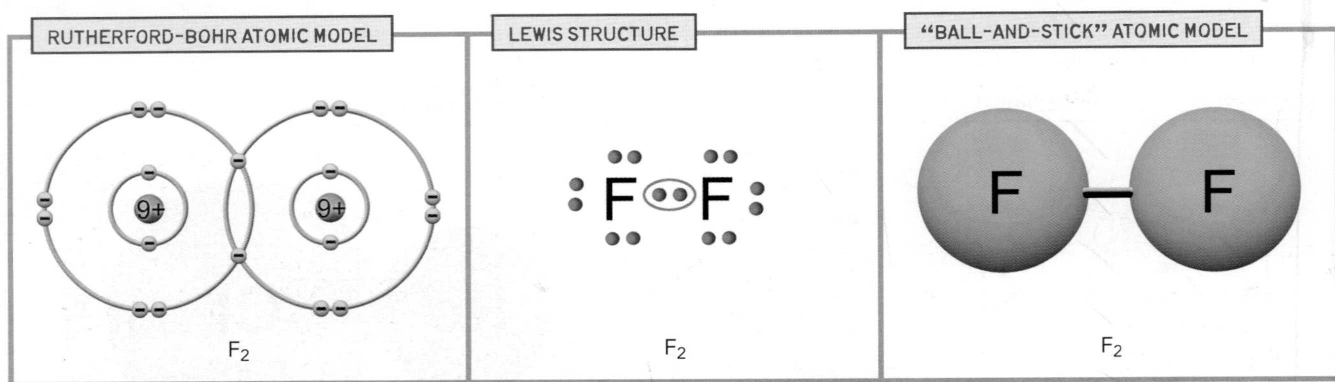

2.13 When molecular fluorine (F_2) is formed, each atom shares an electron with another fluorine atom so that both have the electron configuration of a noble gas. In the Lewis structure, the shared electron pair is circled; in the "ball-and-stick" model, it is represented by the stick.

When one or more pairs of electrons are shared by two atoms, the resulting chemical bond is called a *covalent bond*.

Covalent contains the prefix *co-*, meaning "joint," and the Latin word *valentia*, meaning "power."

A COVALENT BOND is the result of the sharing of one or more electron pairs between two atoms (usually two nonmetals).

Sometimes two atoms share more than one electron pair. In molecular oxygen (O_2), for example, each oxygen atom needs two more electrons to achieve the configuration of a noble gas, so two oxygen atoms tend to share two electron pairs. Oxygen atoms are thus linked in a **DOUBLE BOND**. Triple bonds, between atoms of other elements (such as nitrogen), are also possible.

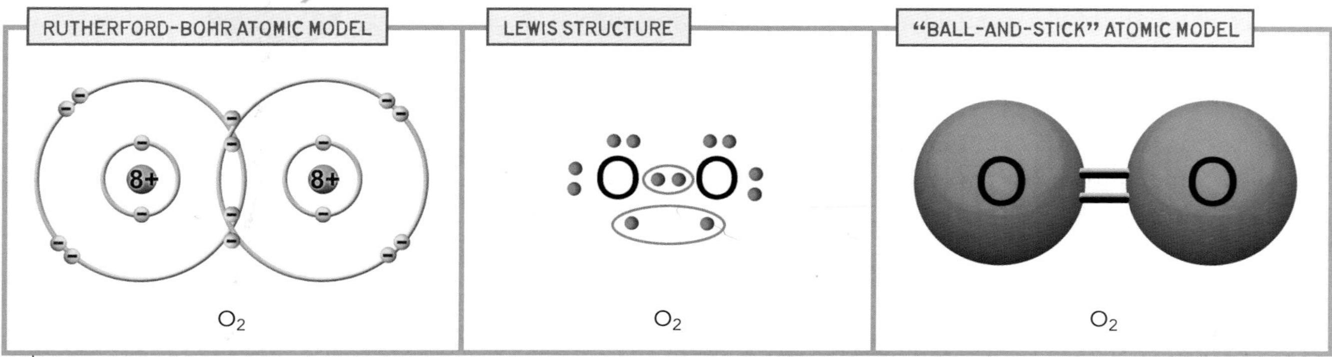

2.14 Each oxygen atom shares two electron pairs with another oxygen atom. Two covalent bonds are thus formed between the two atoms—a double bond.

THE CAR OF THE FUTURE

The future is almost at our doorstep, humming with the power of hydrogen. But don't run out to your local dealer just yet, for the hydrogen car exists only in the form of prototypes. Nonetheless, many scientists see it as the car of the future.

Like electric cars, the hydrogen car is powered by a battery. Inside the battery, hydrogen molecules (H_2) transmit their electrons to pure oxygen (O_2) to form water (H_2O). This exchange of electrons creates an electric current strong enough to allow rapid acceleration.

Since water is the only by-product of the reaction, the hydrogen car is a "clean" means of transportation. Several problems persist, however, and prevent its widespread use. At room temperature and pressure, hydrogen is a gas, which is difficult to store in the tank of a car. Once this problem is solved, a new network of service stations will be needed to distribute hydrogen along our roads.

Source: Adapted from Geneviève Dorval-Douville, "Vers la voiture de demain," *Le Soleil*, January 7, 2007. *[Translation]*

Prototype of a car that runs on liquid hydrogen

Two atoms do not always share electron pairs equally. Some atoms have a stronger force of attraction for electron pairs than others. For example, in a water molecule, the oxygen atom attracts the electrons more than the two hydrogen atoms do. This causes a certain degree of electrical polarity, with the oxygen atom carrying a slightly negative charge and the hydrogen atoms, a slightly positive one. The charges are only a fraction of a total charge, so they do not turn water into an ionic compound. The unequal covalent bonds are referred to as *polar covalent bonds*.

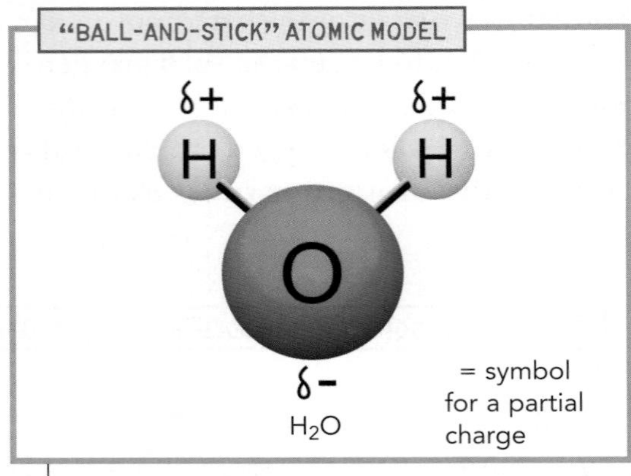

2.15 In a water molecule, electron pairs are not shared equally in the bonds; they are more attracted to the oxygen than to the hydrogen. The imbalance creates a partial negative charge near the oxygen atom ($^-$) and partial positive charges near the hydrogen atoms ($^+$).

Water can dissolve many substances because of the polarity of its molecules and so has earned its reputation as the “universal solvent.” We will focus on solutions and solvents in Section 2 (page 51).

EST SE 1.3 THE RULES OF CHEMICAL NOTATION AND NOMENCLATURE

The rules of chemical notation and nomenclature are used to name many substances. They also identify the elements that make up these substances, and their ratios. The following rules apply mainly to binary molecules, which are molecules formed from two different elements.

EST SE THE RULES OF NOTATION

A chemical formula is the symbolic representation of a molecule. It indicates which elements make up the compound and how many atoms of each element are present.

Three rules must be followed when writing the chemical formula of a molecule:

- First, find the symbol of each element in the molecule by referring to the periodic table.
- Next, determine the order of the symbols. If a binary molecule contains a metal and a nonmetal, the symbol for the metal comes first. In all other cases, symbols are written in the following order: B, Ge, Si, C, Sb, As, P, N, H, Te, Se, S, I, Br, Cl, O and F.
- Finally, add subscripts after symbols to specify the number of atoms or ions of each element in the molecule. Note that no subscript is used when only one atom (or ion) of an element is present.

To determine the correct subscripts for a formula, the number of atoms in the molecule must be adjusted so that each atom forms all the bonds it needs to achieve the configuration of a noble gas. Thus, hydrogen and all the alkali metals will usually form one bond; oxygen and all the other elements in Group VIA will form two. Similarly, nitrogen (and all the Group VA elements) will form three bonds, carbon (and other elements in the same group) will form four, etc.

The following example shows how to determine the formula of a molecule (in this case, an ionic compound) resulting from the reaction of beryllium and chlorine.

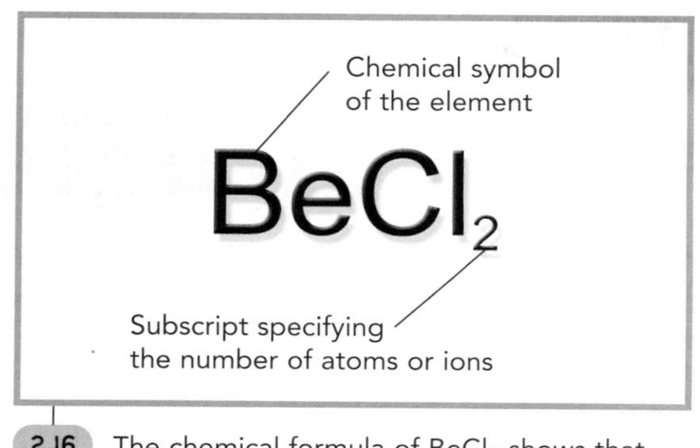

2.16 The chemical formula of $BeCl_2$ shows that each molecule is composed of one beryllium ion and two chloride ions.

- The chemical symbol for beryllium is Be. The symbol for chlorine is Cl.
- Beryllium is a metal, while chlorine is a nonmetal. The symbol for beryllium is therefore written first.
- Beryllium atoms tend to give up two electrons, while chlorine atoms tend to gain one. Since beryllium seeks to form two bonds, and chlorine, only one, two atoms of chlorine will be needed for each beryllium atom, to achieve a satisfactory configuration.

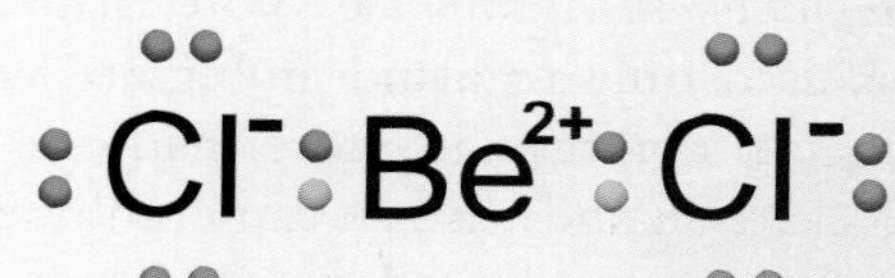

The formula for the molecule resulting from the reaction of beryllium and chlorine is therefore $BeCl_2$.

EST SE

THE RULES OF NOMENCLATURE

Chemists have developed certain rules of nomenclature for the different substances they use.

Nomenclature comes from the Latin *nomenclator*, a person who accompanied a Roman official to tell him people's names.

The nomenclature rules for binary covalent compounds are as follows:

- Name the first element.
- Change the name of the second element according to the indications in Table 2.17 (page 50).
- Add, when applicable, a prefix or prefixes to specify the number of atoms of each element (Table 2.18, page 50).

2.17 SOME NAMES FOR THE SECOND ELEMENT IN A BINARY MOLECULE

Name of the element	Name used in nomenclature
Bromine	Bromide
Carbon	Carbide
Chlorine	Chloride
Fluorine	Fluoride
Hydrogen	Hydride
Iodine	Iodide
Nitrogen	Nitride
Oxygen	Oxide
Phosphorus	Phosphide
Sulphur	Sulphide

2.18 PREFIXES INDICATING THE NUMBER OF ATOMS OF AN ELEMENT IN A BINARY COVALENT COMPOUND

Number of atoms	Prefix
One	Mono-
Two	Di-
Three	Tri-
Four	Tetra-
Five	Penta-
Six	Hexa-
Seven	Hepta-
Eight	Octa-
Nine	Nona-
Ten	Deca-

If these rules of nomenclature are applied to the molecule ClF_3, it becomes clear why it is called *chlorine trifluoride*. Similarly, the compound P_2S_3 is called *diphosphorus trisulphide*. Note that the prefix *mono-* is used only to avoid ambiguity when two elements can combine in more than one way. For example, carbon and oxygen can combine to form either a CO molecule, called *carbon monoxide*, or a CO_2 molecule, called *carbon dioxide*.

2.19 EXAMPLES OF COMPOUND NAMES

Chemical formula	Type of compound	Name
N_2O_4	Covalent compound	Dinitrogen tetroxide
CaI_2	Ionic compound	Calcium iodide
$Mg(NO_3)_2$	Ionic compound containing a polyatomic ion	Magnesium nitrate

In ionic formula units, the positive ion precedes the negative ion. An important difference in the nomenclature rules for ionic compounds, compared to those for covalent compounds, is that the numerical prefixes listed in Figure 2.18 are not used.

When a substance is composed of more than two elements, it is more difficult to name it. Nevertheless, if a polyatomic ion is present, the rules of nomenclature may still be applied, using the name of the polyatomic ion, without modifying it (Table 2.10, page 44). For example, the name of NaOH is *sodium hydroxide*.

In practice, certain substances are called by different names than those dictated by these rules of nomenclature. For example, HCl is often referred to as *hydrochloric acid* rather than *hydrogen chloride* although the acid is actually a solution of hydrogen chloride gas in water.

ST EST SE 2 Properties of solutions

CONCEPT REVIEW
- Mixtures
- Solutions
- Solubility
- Concentration
- Solute
- Solvent
- Dissolution
- Dilution
- Acidity/Alkalinity

The atoms and molecules that make up different substances in our environment sometimes combine without undergoing a chemical reaction. Instead, they form a mixture. A mixture is made up of at least two different substances, which can always be isolated using physical **SEPARATION TECHNIQUES** (no chemical bonds need to be broken).

Solutions figure prominently among the various types of mixtures. Tap water, air and steel are everyday examples of solutions. A solution is a homogeneous mixture, which means that its component substances (solids, liquids or gases) cannot be distinguished, even with the aid of a magnifying glass or a light microscope. One of the components of a solution (the **SOLUTE**) is dissolved in the other (the **SOLVENT**).

A SOLUTION is a homogeneous mixture whose component substances cannot be distinguished, even with the aid of a magnifying instrument.

Solutions differ in their properties. In the following sections, we will take a closer look at some of these properties: solubility, concentration, electrical conductivity and pH.

Many substances can be dissolved in water. The resulting solution is called an *aqueous solution*.

Aqueous comes from the Latin *aqua*, meaning "water."

An AQUEOUS SOLUTION is a solution in which the solvent is water.

The polarity of the water molecule (Figure 2.15, page 48) makes it a versatile solvent. Figure 2.20 shows what happens, for example, when table salt is dissolved in water.

Generally, water easily dissolves molecules with an ionic bond (like table salt) and molecules with a certain polarity (like sugar). In contrast, non-polar molecules, such as oil, rarely dissolve well in water.

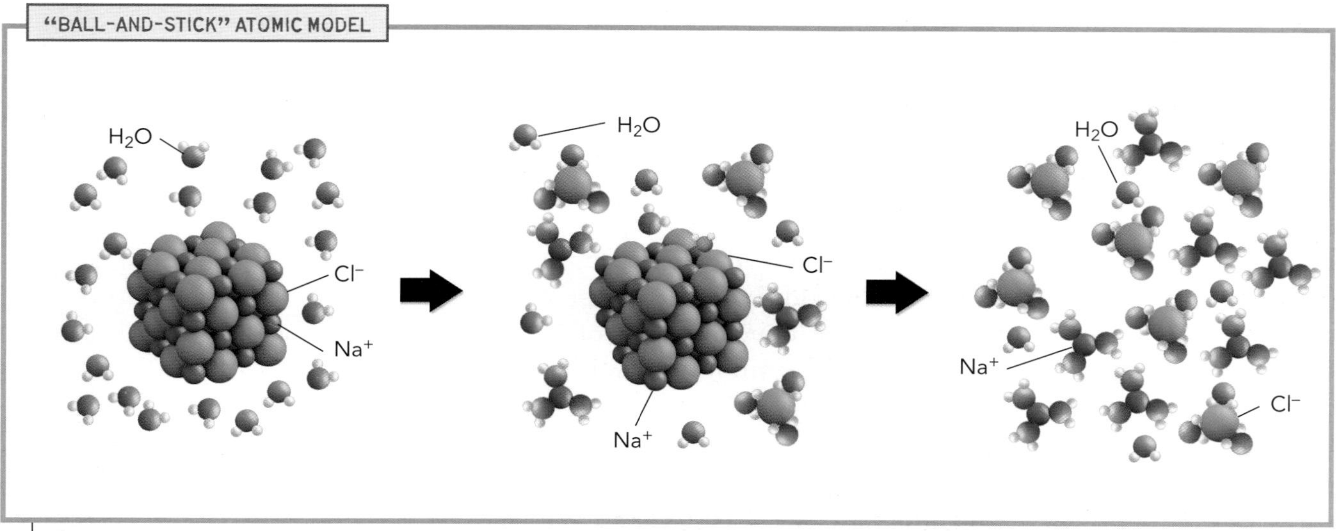

2.20 The positive poles of the water molecule (the "H" atoms) attract the negative ions (Cl^-) of the salt molecule, while the negative pole (the "O" atom) exerts a similar attraction on the positive ions (Na^+). The force of these attractions eventually detaches ions from the solid grain of salt, and they float freely in the water.

SE 2.1 SOLUBILITY

There is a limit to the amount of solute that can be dissolved in a given solvent. This limit represents the solubility of a solute in a solvent.

> **SOLUBILITY is the maximum amount of solute that can be dissolved in a certain volume of solvent.**

Many factors influence solubility, including the nature of the solute, the nature of the solvent, pressure (in the case of gaseous solutes) and temperature. For example, solids tend to become more soluble as the solvent temperature rises, while gases show the opposite tendency. Figure 2.21 shows that the solubility of molecular oxygen in water decreases as the temperature increases.

Appendix 2, at the end of this textbook, lists the solubility (and other characteristic properties) of many common substances.

2.21 SOLUBILITY OF MOLECULAR OXYGEN IN WATER AS A FUNCTION OF TEMPERATURE

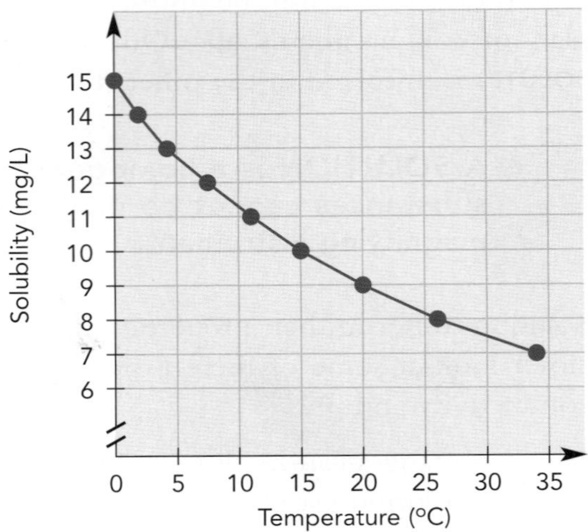

ST EST SE 2.2 CONCENTRATION

The relative proportion of solute to solvent varies greatly from one solution to another. Its precise value indicates the concentration of the solution.

> **The CONCENTRATION of a solution is the amount of solute in a given amount of solution.**

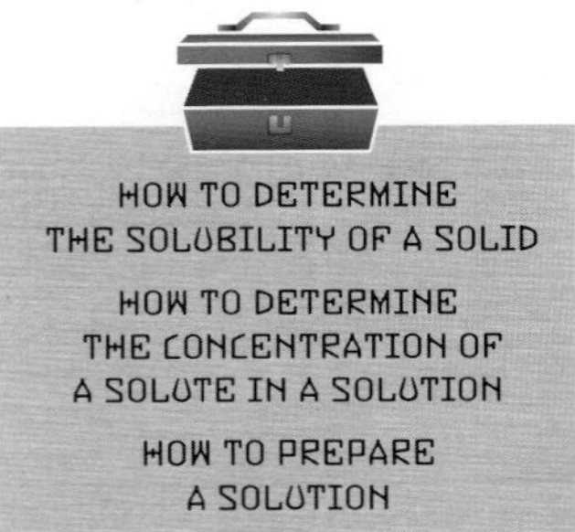

ST EST SE DILUTION AND DISSOLUTION

The concentration of a solution can be varied in different ways. For example, if water is added to a bowl of soup, the taste becomes less pronounced. The soup is diluted; in other words, the concentration of stock in the soup is reduced. Conversely, if chicken bouillon powder is added, the flavour becomes more intense. The addition and subsequent dissolution of solute increase the concentration of the solution. If evaporation takes place, the amount of solvent will be reduced, which will also have the effect of increasing the concentration.

2.22 EFFECTS OF VARIOUS CHANGES ON THE CONCENTRATION OF A SOLUTION

Change	Effect on the concentration
Dilution (addition of solvent)	Reduced concentration
Dissolution (addition of solute)	Increased concentration
Evaporation (reduction of solvent)	Increased concentration

The following are different ways of expressing concentration:

- number of grams of solute per litre of solution (g/L)
- number of grams of solute per 100 mL of solution, expressed as a percentage (% m/V)
- number of millilitres of solute per 100 mL of solution, expressed as a percentage (%V/V)
- number of grams of solute per 100 g of solution, expressed as a percentage (% m/m)

The following formula can be used to calculate concentration in g/L:

$$C = \frac{m}{V}$$ where C is the concentration (in g/L)
m is the mass of the solute (in g)
V is the volume of the solution (in L)

Concentration can be expressed in other ways, depending on the specific context. In the next two sections, we will describe concentration in ppm and molar concentration.

CONCENTRATION IN PPM

ST EST SE

When the amount of solute in a solution is extremely small, the concentration can be expressed in parts per million (ppm). Thus, 1 ppm is equivalent to 1 g of solute in 1 000 000 g of solution or to 1 mg of solute in 1000 g of solution. In aqueous solutions, 1 ppm corresponds to approximately 1 mg of solute per litre of solution.

The CONCENTRATION IN PPM ("parts per million") is the number of parts of solute in a million parts of solution.

$$1 \text{ ppm} = \frac{1 \text{ g}}{1\,000\,000 \text{ g}} = \frac{1 \text{ mg}}{1000 \text{ g}} = 1 \text{ mg/kg}$$

In aqueous solutions:

$$1 \text{ ppm} = \frac{1 \text{ g}}{1000 \text{ L}} = 1 \text{ mg/L}$$

A FINE SENSE OF SMELL

The only one of our five senses that allows us to detect substances in concentrations of just a few ppm is our sense of smell. For example, hydrogen sulphide (a gas known for its characteristic smell of rotten eggs) is toxic at a concentration of 10 ppm, but our noses can detect much smaller amounts—as little as 0.1 ppm.

2.23 Water in public swimming pools usually contains about 1 ppm of chlorine, to control bacterial growth.

MOLAR CONCENTRATION

Molar concentration is expressed in moles per litre (mol/L). It corresponds to a quantity of dissolved solute particles (in moles) per unit volume of solution (in litres). When studying changes in matter, molar concentration is a useful concept because it can be applied to compare different solutions with the same number of dissolved particles. Thanks to **AVOGADRO'S NUMBER**, we know, for example, that one litre of an aqueous salt solution with a concentration of 1 mol/L must contain 6.02×10^{23} molecules of sodium chloride per litre of solution.

MOLAR CONCENTRATION is the number of moles of solute in a litre of solution.

Molar concentration is symbolized by placing the chemical formula for the measured substance inside square brackets. For example, the expression [NaCl] = 0.5 mol/L means that the molar concentration of a sodium chloride solution equals 0.5 mol/L.

The molar concentration of a solution can be calculated using the following formula:

$C = \frac{n}{V}$ where C is the concentration (in mol/L)
n is the amount of solute (in mol)
V is the volume of solution (in L)

Let's look at an example. Suppose that 58.5 g of sodium chloride are dissolved in 500 mL of solution. The molar concentration of this solution is calculated in two steps.

- The first step is to transform the mass of NaCl into moles, using the following formula:

$M = \frac{m}{n}$ where M is the molar mass (in g/mol)
m is the mass (in g)
n is the number of moles (in mol)

The periodic table reveals that the molar mass of sodium is 22.99 g/mol and the molar mass of chlorine is 35.45 g/mol. The molar mass of NaCl is therefore 58.44 g/mol. By manipulating the preceding formula, we obtain:

$$n = \frac{m}{M} = \frac{58.5 \text{ g}}{58.44 \text{ g/mol}} = 1 \text{ mol}$$

- The molar concentration can then be calculated:

$$C = \frac{n}{V} = \frac{1 \text{ mol}}{0.5 \text{ L}} = 2 \text{ mol/L}$$

The molar concentration of the solution is 2 mol/L.

ST EST SE

2.3 ELECTRICAL CONDUCTIVITY

Pure water does not conduct electricity, yet we are often warned about the danger of electrocution when using electrical appliances near water. So how does water carry an electric current? In fact, it is not the water that conducts the electricity but substances dissolved in it. Certain substances, when dissolved in water or another solvent, allow an electric current to flow through the solution. These substances are called *electrolytes.* One example of an electrolyte is table salt.

2.24 The first electric cell was developed in 1800 by the Italian physicist Alessandro Volta. He made piles of alternating zinc and copper plates, between which he placed paper that had been soaked in an electrolytic solution (salt water). The arrangement is referred to as a *voltaic pile*.

- **An ELECTROLYTE is a substance that, when dissolved in water, allows an electric current to flow through the solution.**
- **The ELECTRICAL CONDUCTIVITY of a solution is a measure of its ability to allow an electric current to flow through it.**

Substances that are soluble in water but do not conduct electricity, such as sugar, are called *nonelectrolytes*.

Solutions that contain an electrolyte are **ELECTROLYTIC SOLUTIONS**. Electrolytes and electrolytic solutions have many applications. One example is the electric cell, more commonly known as a *battery*. Many batteries contain an electrolytic solution that conducts electricity between two poles, the electrodes.

Water in oceans, rivers and lakes contains electrolytes in varying concentrations. This difference in concentration is among the characteristics that distinguish the fresh water of rivers from the salt water of the sea. Many living organisms need the electrolytes in water to survive. Some fish have adapted to life in salt water and cannot live in fresh water; others thrive only in a freshwater environment.

1859
1927

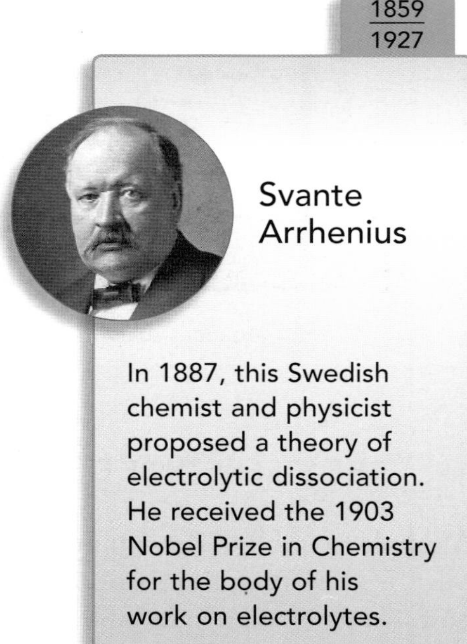

Svante Arrhenius

In 1887, this Swedish chemist and physicist proposed a theory of electrolytic dissociation. He received the 1903 Nobel Prize in Chemistry for the body of his work on electrolytes.

ST EST

ELECTROLYTIC DISSOCIATION

When an electrolyte is dissolved in water, it separates into two ions of opposite charges, one positive and one negative. For example, sodium chloride (NaCl) dissociates in water into a positive ion, Na^+, and a negative ion, Cl^-.

- **ELECTROLYTIC DISSOCIATION is the separation of a dissolved compound into two ions of opposite charges.**

Electrolytic dissociation is a physical change. In other words, it does not change the nature of the solute. For example, when sodium chloride is dissolved in water, it conserves all its properties. It can be recovered if the water evaporates.

The chemical equation for the electrolytic dissociation of sodium chloride is:

$$NaCl_{(s)} \xrightarrow{H_2O} Na^+_{(aq)} + Cl^-_{(aq)}$$

The subscripts in parentheses indicate the physical state of each substance involved. The *s* stands for "solid," and the *aq*, for "aqueous solution." The H_2O over the arrow indicates that the change takes place when the solute is placed in water.

CONDUCTORS OF LIFE

All the fluids in the human body are electrolytic solutions. One of their important functions is to allow the transmission of nerve impulses between neurons, the specialized cells of the nervous system. 3

When a nonelectrolyte is dissolved, no ions are produced. For example, when sugar is dissolved in water, its molecules remain intact although they become detached from one another. This dissolution is expressed as follows:

$$C_{12}H_{22}O_{11(s)} \xrightarrow{H_2O} C_{12}H_{22}O_{11(aq)}$$

The ions formed during electrolytic dissociation conduct electricity. When electrodes connected to a power supply are placed in an electrolytic solution, the positive ions migrate toward the negative electrode, and the negative ions migrate toward the positive electrode (Figure 2.25).

Ion comes from the Greek *ienai*, meaning "to go."

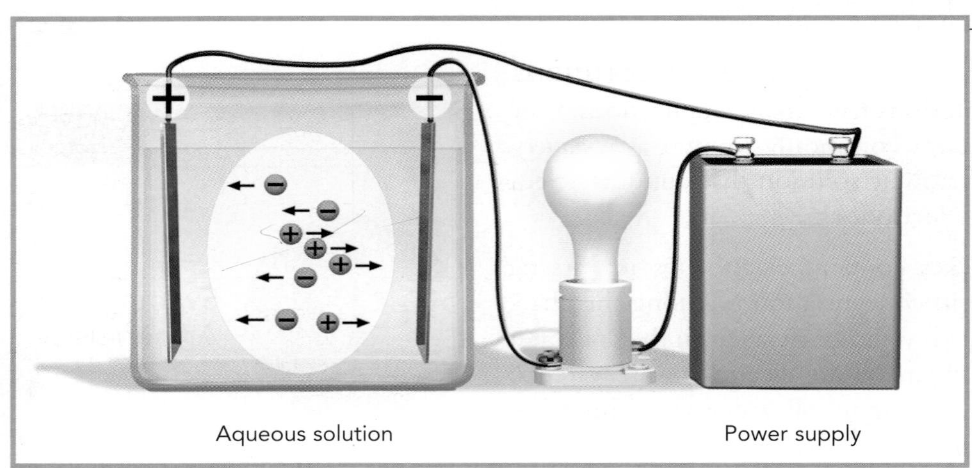

2.25 The movement of ions in an electrolytic solution allows an electric current to flow through it.

EST THE STRENGTH OF ELECTROLYTES

A simple method of determining whether a solute is an electrolyte is to dissolve it in water, place two electrodes in the solution, connect them to a power supply and a light bulb and then see if the bulb lights up. An apparatus like this shows that, at equal concentrations, all solutes in aqueous solutions will behave in one of three ways:

- The electric current flows through the solution, and the bulb produces a bright light.

- The electric current flows through the solution, and the bulb produces a dim light.
- The electric current does not flow through the solution, and the bulb does not light up.

The first case indicates that the solute is a "strong" electrolyte. On the atomic level, this means that practically all the molecules of this solute have dissociated in the water and formed ions. An example is the dissolution of sodium chloride.

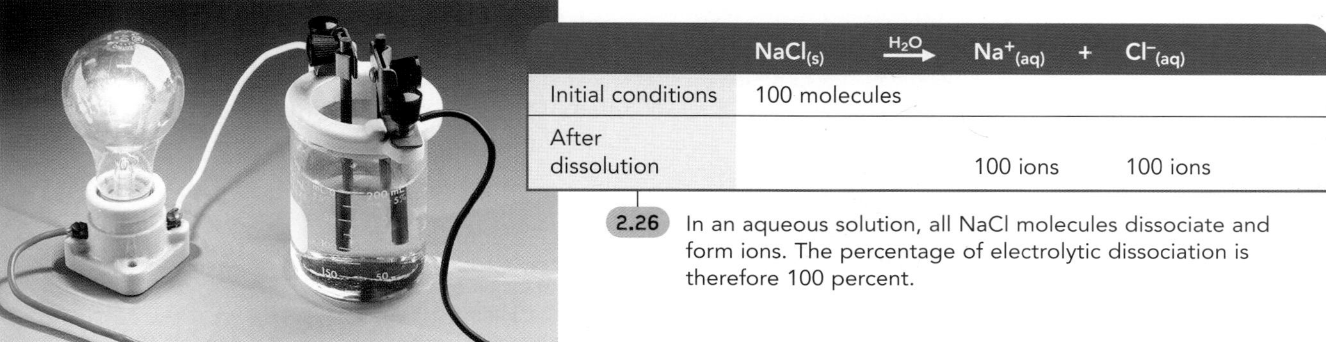

	$NaCl_{(s)}$	$\xrightarrow{H_2O}$	$Na^+_{(aq)}$	+	$Cl^-_{(aq)}$
Initial conditions	100 molecules				
After dissolution			100 ions		100 ions

2.26 In an aqueous solution, all NaCl molecules dissociate and form ions. The percentage of electrolytic dissociation is therefore 100 percent.

The second case involves a "weak" electrolyte. When the solute dissolves, only some of the molecules form ions. The others remain neutral (neither positively nor negatively charged). An example of this situation is the dissolution of hydrogen fluoride.

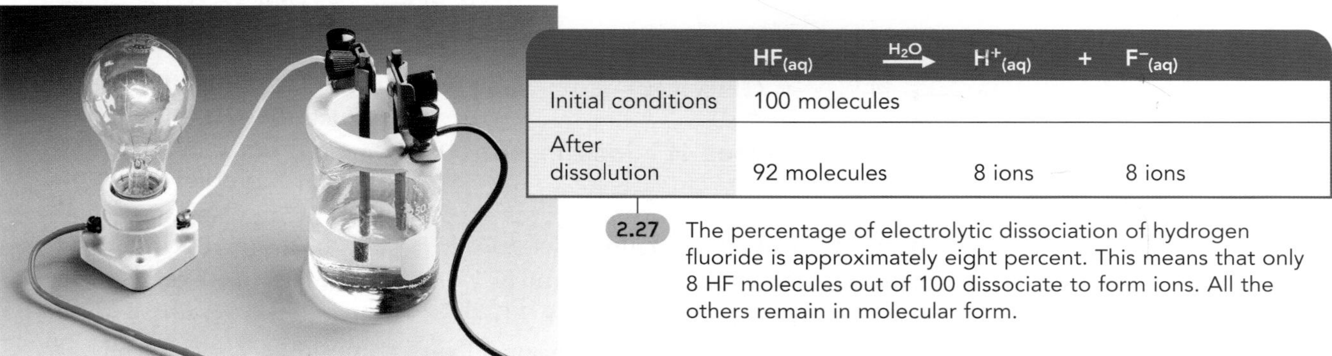

	$HF_{(aq)}$	$\xrightarrow{H_2O}$	$H^+_{(aq)}$	+	$F^-_{(aq)}$
Initial conditions	100 molecules				
After dissolution	92 molecules		8 ions		8 ions

2.27 The percentage of electrolytic dissociation of hydrogen fluoride is approximately eight percent. This means that only 8 HF molecules out of 100 dissociate to form ions. All the others remain in molecular form.

The third case describes the dissolution of a nonelectrolyte. This type of solute does not produce any ions. Sugar is an example of a nonelectrolyte.

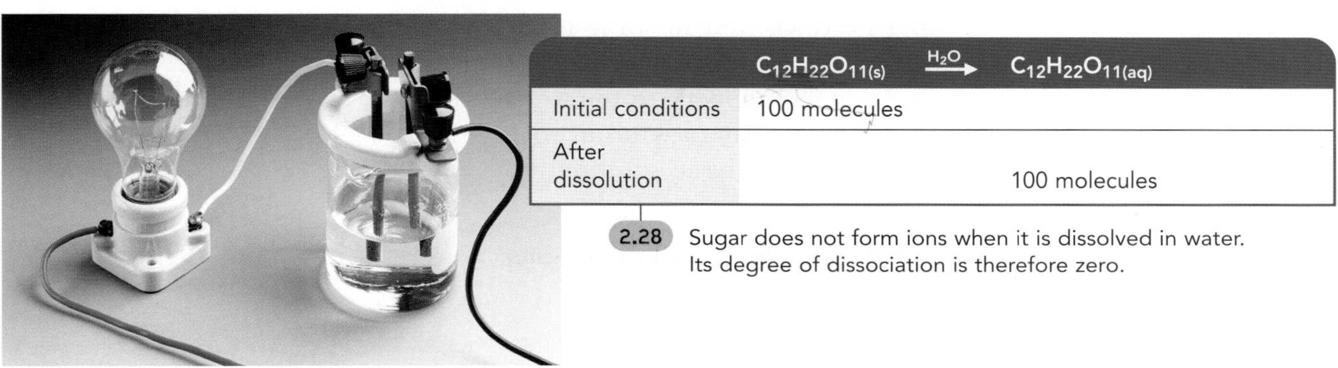

	$C_{12}H_{22}O_{11(s)}$	$\xrightarrow{H_2O}$	$C_{12}H_{22}O_{11(aq)}$
Initial conditions	100 molecules		
After dissolution			100 molecules

2.28 Sugar does not form ions when it is dissolved in water. Its degree of dissociation is therefore zero.

THE STRENGTH OF AN ELECTROLYTE is the degree to which it dissociates into ions. The higher the degree of dissociation, the stronger the electrolyte.

The strength of an electrolyte depends only on its degree of dissociation and not on its concentration. It is therefore possible that a strong but highly diluted electrolyte might not conduct electricity as well as a highly concentrated weak electrolyte.

ST EST SE

TYPES OF ELECTROLYTES

Acids, bases and salts are three important types of electrolytes. They each have their own specific properties.

Acids

Fruit juice, soft drinks and the gastric juices secreted by the human stomach are all acids. They can be identified by their sour taste. Certain tests can indicate the presence of an acid in a solution. For example, litmus paper turns red on contact with an acidic solution.

Acid comes from the Latin *acidus*, meaning "sour."

Acids are substances that release H^+ ions when dissolved in water. The following are a few examples of acid solutions:

- hydrochloric acid: $HCl_{(g)} \xrightarrow[H_2O]{} H^+_{(aq)} + Cl^-_{(aq)}$
- sulphuric acid: $H_2SO_{4(l)} \xrightarrow[H_2O]{} 2\ H^+_{(aq)} + SO_4{}^{2-}{}_{(aq)}$
- acetic acid: $CH_3COOH_{(l)} \xrightarrow[H_2O]{} H^+_{(aq)} + CH_3COO^-{}_{(aq)}$

An ACID is a substance that releases H^+ ions in an aqueous solution.

In addition to releasing one or more H^+ ions, an acid also releases a negative ion. An acid can usually be identified by its chemical formula. It often begins with the symbol for a hydrogen atom (H) followed by a nonmetal. Acetic acid (CH_3COOH), better known as vinegar, is an exception to this rule.

A DOUBLE-EDGED SWORD

You might not think that muscle cramps and dairy products have something in common, but they do: lactic acid. An ingredient in most dairy products, lactic acid also accumulates in human muscle during exercise and causes the pain people sometimes feel after an intense workout. Fortunately, eating yogurt does not have the same effect!

Bases

Bases are found in many cleaning products and in some heartburn medication. Blood and salt water are also slightly basic. Basic solutions have a bitter taste. They feel slippery to the touch because they react with oils in the skin, forming a kind of soap. When a strip of litmus paper is dipped in a basic solution, the paper turns blue.

Bases are substances that produce OH^- ions when dissolved in water.

The following are a few examples of basic solutions:

- sodium hydroxide: $NaOH_{(s)} \xrightarrow{H_2O} Na^+_{(aq)} + OH^-_{(aq)}$
- magnesium hydroxide: $Mg(OH)_{2(s)} \xrightarrow{H_2O} Mg^{2+}_{(aq)} + 2\ OH^-_{(aq)}$
- ammonium hydroxide: $NH_4OH_{(l)} \xrightarrow{H_2O} NH_4{}^+_{(aq)} + OH^-_{(aq)}$

A BASE is a substance that releases OH^- ions in an aqueous solution.

In addition to the OH^- ions, bases also release a positive ion. A base can usually be identified by its chemical formula. The formula often begins with a metal and usually ends with the group OH. Again, there are exceptions to the rule. Ammonia (NH_3), for example, is a base. When it is dissolved in water, it reacts with the water molecules in the following way: $NH_3 + H_2O \longrightarrow NH_4{}^+ + OH^-$. In water, ammonia thus behaves exactly like ammonium hydroxide, which can be considered an aqueous form of ammonia (usually a gas).

ANCIENT CLEANLINESS

Soap dates all the way back to antiquity, when it was first made in Alep, Syria, one of the oldest cities in the world. The first soaps were made with a few simple ingredients: olive oil, laurel berry oil, water and soda, a basic substance derived from the ashes of glasswort, a plant that grows along the seacoast.

Salts

Salts constitute a very large class of substances. They figure prominently in human diets because they enhance the taste of food. The best-known salt is obviously table salt.

Most salts are made up of a metal and one or more nonmetals. For example, sodium chloride (which is edible) contains one atom of sodium, a highly reactive metal, and one atom of chlorine, from the toxic gas Cl_2.

A SALT is a substance produced by the chemical bonding of a metallic ion and a nonmetallic ion (other than H^+ and OH^- ions).

In aqueous solutions, salts that are soluble in water dissociate into ions, allowing the flow of electric current. The following are a few examples of salts:

- sodium chloride: $NaCl_{(s)} \xrightarrow{H_2O} Na^+_{(aq)} + Cl^-_{(aq)}$
- silver nitrate: $AgNO_{3(s)} \xrightarrow{H_2O} Ag^+_{(aq)} + NO_3{}^-_{(aq)}$
- calcium chloride: $CaCl_{2(s)} \xrightarrow{H_2O} Ca^{2+}_{(aq)} + 2\ Cl^-_{(aq)}$

Not all salts dissolve easily in water. Calcium carbonate ($CaCO_3$), for example, is only slightly soluble.

Litmus tests do not reveal the presence of a neutral salt; they indicate only the acidity or basicity of a solution. Litmus paper does not change colour, therefore, on contact with many salts, pure water or a sugar-in-water solution.

Ions formed during the electrolytic dissociation of salts play an important role in maintaining the metabolism of living organisms. In fact, some of these ions are vital to our survival. For example, we are often advised to include a variety of minerals, such as magnesium and calcium, in our diets. The recommendation should really be to include daily portions of ions, such as Mg^{2+} and Ca^{2+}.

Ions are also important in maintaining healthy soil. When fertilizer is applied in a garden, it provides plants with the ions they need to grow.

2.4 pH

One property that distinguishes acidic, basic and neutral solutions is their pH. The pH of a solution can be measured in various ways. One way is to do a test using a pH indicator, which is a chemical compound that changes colour according to the pH of the solution. Universal indicator papers, for example, provide a measure of the pH value. An instrument called a *pH meter* can also be used.

THE pH SCALE

The pH scale ranges from 0 to 14. It indicates how acidic or basic a solution is. The following statements outline its broad classifications:

- If the pH < 7, the solution is acidic.
- If the pH $= 7$, the solution is neutral.
- If the pH > 7, the solution is basic.

ENVIRONMENT EXTRA

When lakes turn into vinegar

Rain and snow are naturally slightly acidic, with a pH of about 5.5. Rain is considered "acid rain" when its pH drops below 5. In Québec, the pH of the precipitation we receive tends to be about 4.5. The province thus suffers from a problem of acid rain.

The impact of this phenomenon on lakes is especially striking. Their acidification involves a series of highly visible changes.

The normal pH of a lake is between 8.5 and 6. When the pH drops from 6 to 5.5, certain acid-intolerant life forms begin to disappear, which may represent up to 25 percent of the fish species in the lake. Between 5.5 and 5, the changes become more dramatic. Up to 75 percent of the original fish species may be lost. In addition, many plants are replaced by different types of moss. Below a pH of 5, fish can no longer reproduce. Only a few adults remain, and they are often emaciated from lack of food.

A lake that is very acidic can become full of gelatinous and foul-smelling algae.

The pH scale is logarithmic, which means that a difference of one unit between two substances actually indicates that one of the substances is 10 times more acidic than the other. For example, a solution with a pH of 3 is 10 times more acidic than a solution with a pH of 4. Similarly, a solution with a pH of 9 is 100 times less basic than a solution with a pH of 11.

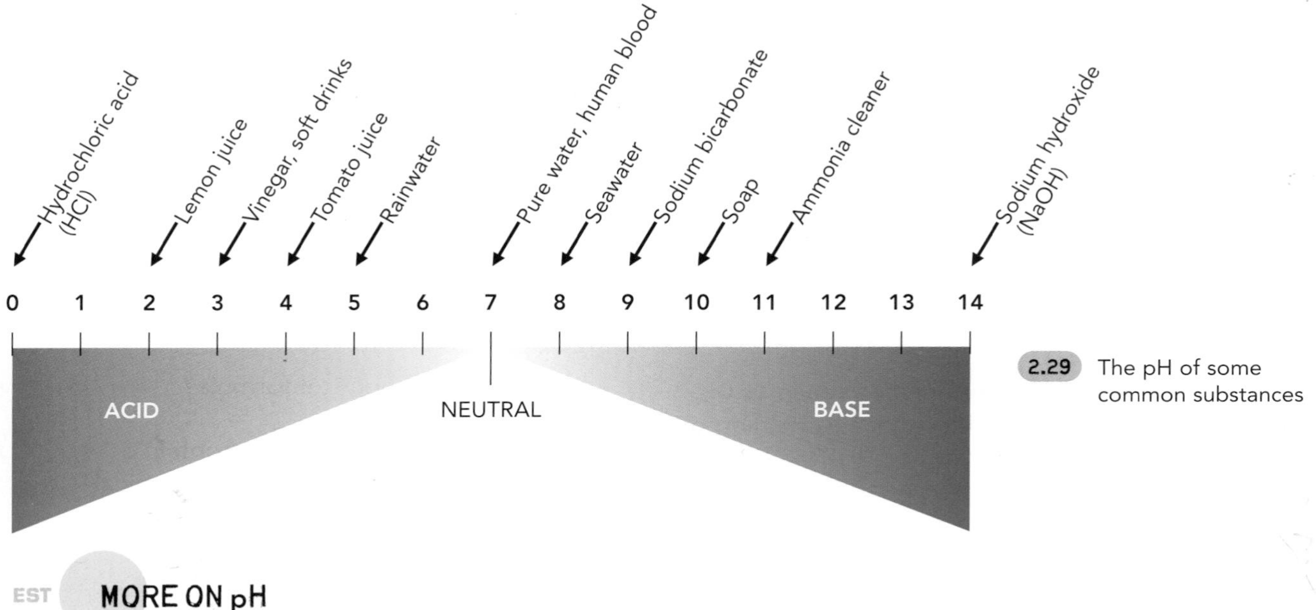

2.29 The pH of some common substances

MORE ON pH

The pH of a solution is actually an indication of the concentration of H^+ ions in that solution. Table 2.30 shows the correspondence between the concentration of H^+ ions and the pH scale.

2.30 CONCENTRATION OF H+ IONS AND CORRESPONDING pH

Concentration of H^+ ions (mol/L)	Concentration in scientific notation	pH
1.0	1×10^{0}	0
0.1	1×10^{-1}	1
0.01	1×10^{-2}	2
0.001	1×10^{-3}	3
0.000 1	1×10^{-4}	4
0.000 01	1×10^{-5}	5
0.000 001	1×10^{-6}	6
0.000 000 1	1×10^{-7}	7
0.000 000 01	1×10^{-8}	8
0.000 000 001	1×10^{-9}	9
0.000 000 000 1	1×10^{-10}	10
0.000 000 000 01	1×10^{-11}	11
0.000 000 000 001	1×10^{-12}	12
0.000 000 000 000 1	1×10^{-13}	13
0.000 000 000 000 01	1×10^{-14}	14

1868
1939

Søren Sørensen

In 1909, this Danish chemist introduced the concept of pH. Practical and easy to use, his scale was rapidly adopted by the scientific community.

CHECKUP

ST 1–6, 17–23, 27–29, 31–33, A and C.
EST 1–33 and A–C.
AST None.
SE 1–28, 31 and A–C.

1 What is a molecule? (pp. 40–50)

1. Are the following substances molecules? Why or why not?
   a) NaCl
   b) O_2
   c) Au
   d) Co
   e) CO
   f) H_2SO_4

2. What is the natural tendency of each of the following elements with regard to gaining or losing electrons?
   a) potassium
   b) oxygen
   c) aluminum
   d) krypton

3. Metals give up electrons. Consequently, do they tend to form positive or negative ions?

4. Calculate the sum of the charges for each of the following electron transfers, and indicate the net charge of the resulting ion.
   a) A calcium atom loses two electrons.
   b) A nitrogen atom gains three electrons.
   c) An iodine atom gains one electron.
   d) An aluminum atom loses three electrons.

5. Do the models below represent atoms or ions? Explain your answers.

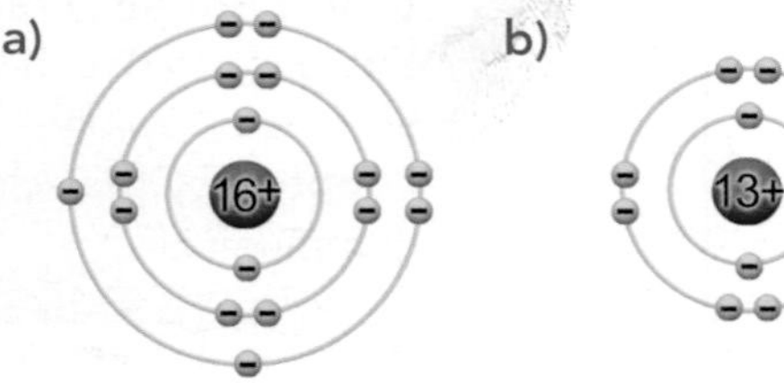

6. Iron has the ability to form one of two ions: Fe^{2+} or Fe^{3+}. How many protons and electrons does each of these ions contain?

7. Various soaps and detergents contain phosphates that contaminate the water in lakes and rivers. For this reason, many environmental groups encourage consumers to use phosphate-free cleansers.
   a) Is a phosphate an atom, a molecule or an ion?
   b) What is its chemical formula?

8. Do the following molecules contain a polyatomic ion? If so, write its chemical formula and its name according to the rules of nomenclature.
   a) NaOH
   b) $C_6H_{22}O_{11}$
   c) $MgSO_4$
   d) H_3PO_4

9. Which of the following substances contain at least one ionic bond?

   HCl, NaOH, CO_2, KBr, CaO, $AlCl_3$, NH_3

10. Draw a Lewis structure for each of the following molecules to show how their ionic bonds are formed.
    a) LiF
    b) $CaBr_2$
    c) Li_3N
    d) MgO

11. What is the charge of each of the ions in the following molecules?
    a) NaBr
    b) CaO
    c) Li_2S
    d) AlF_3

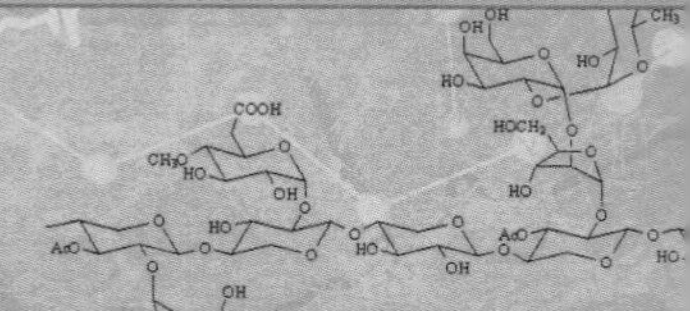

12. Which of the following substances contain at least one covalent bond?

CH_3COOH, CS_2, $CoCl_2$, Fe_2O_3, H_2O, CH_4, AgCl

13. Draw a Lewis structure for each of the following molecules to show how their covalent bonds are formed.

a) Cl_2

b) CBr_4

c) CO_2

d) HF

14. What does the subscript *2* mean in the molecule $MgCl_2$?

15. Write the chemical formula of the molecule resulting from the union of each of the following pairs of substances.

a) potassium and sulphur

b) chlorine and copper

c) chromium and fluorine

d) the ions Mg^{2+} and SO_4^{2-}

16. Apply the rules of nomenclature to name the following substances.

a) NaBr

b) PCl_5

c) $SiCl_4$

d) KN_3

e) Al_2O_3

2 Properties of solutions (pp. 50–61)

17. Name the substances that act as solvents and solutes in each of the following solutions.

a) Air is composed of approximately 80 percent nitrogen and 20 percent oxygen.

b) Steel is an alloy of iron with a small amount of carbon.

c) Seawater contains many mineral salts.

18. Fruit juices, body fluids and cleaning solutions for contact lenses are all examples of aqueous solutions. What is the solvent in these solutions?

19. Brine is a solution of sodium chloride (NaCl) at 18% m/V, which is used to preserve certain foods. To prepare 250 mL of brine, how much salt must be dissolved?

20. A technician prepares a solution, following the steps illustrated below. What is the concentration of this solution, in g/L?

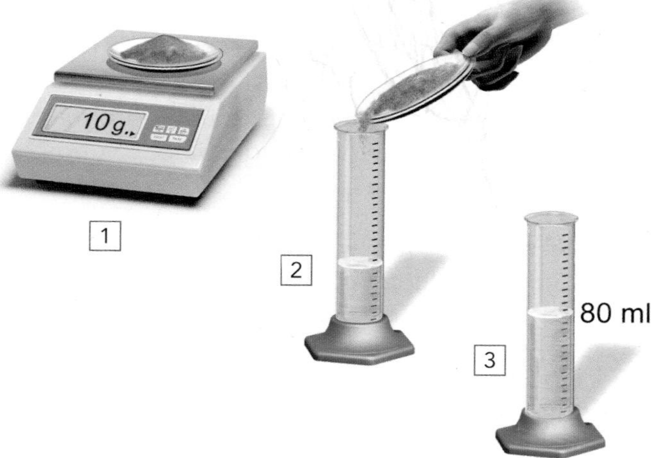

21. The label on a bottle of water says that the water contains 45 ppm of sodium.

a) What does this mean?

b) What is the concentration of sodium in g/L?

22. The water in a lake is contaminated. To determine the concentration of the contaminant, a technician takes a 50-mL sample of the water. After several tests, he concludes that the sample contains 3.75 mg of contaminant. Calculate the concentration of the contaminant, in ppm.

23. Certain minerals are essential to good health. For example, a person should take in approximately 350 mg of magnesium daily. Magnesium can be found in many foods, such as whole wheat bread, which contains about 850 ppm. Assuming that a slice of whole wheat bread has a mass of about 30 g, how many would a person have to eat to obtain the recommended daily dose of magnesium? Show your calculations.

24. A technician dissolves 50 g of potassium nitrate (KNO_3) in a small amount of water and then adds more water to obtain 500 mL of solution. What is the molar concentration of the solution?

25. For the purposes of an experiment, a student must take a sample of exactly 0.2 mol of copper sulphate ($CuSO_4$) from a 0.5 mol/L solution. What volume of solution must she measure?

26. A chemist must prepare 300 mL of a 1.5 mol/L solution of magnesium phosphate ($Mg_3(PO_4)_2$). What mass of the solute must she measure?

27. Which of the beakers below probably contains an electrolyte? Explain your answer.

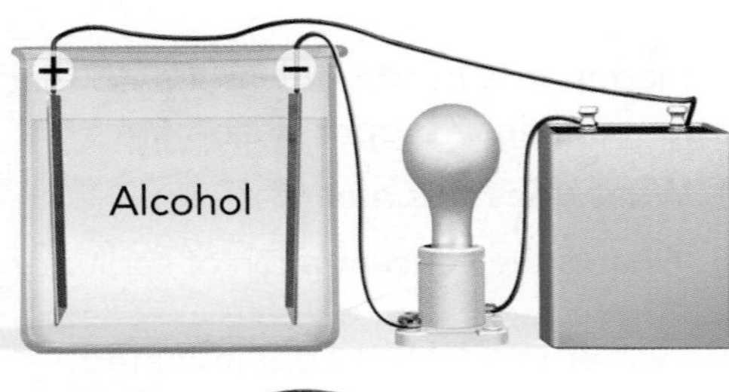

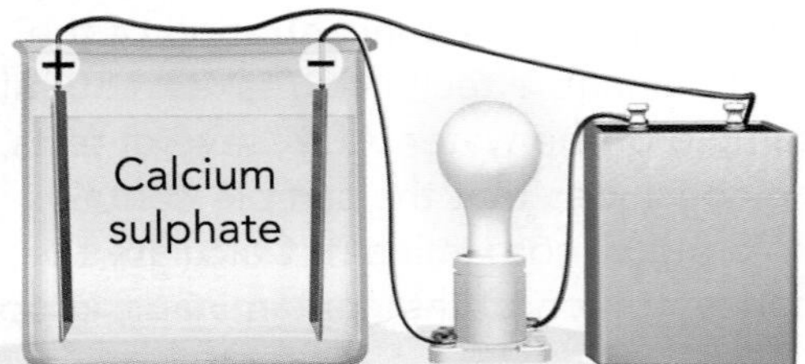

28. How does a solution conduct electricity?

29. Are the following equations of electrolytic dissociation written correctly? Explain your answers.

a) $MgO_{(s)} \xrightarrow{H_2O} Mg^{2+}_{(aq)} + O^{2-}_{(aq)}$
b) $CaBr_{2(s)} \xrightarrow{H_2O} Ca^{2+}_{(aq)} + Br^{-}_{(aq)}$
c) $LiH_{(s)} \xrightarrow{H_2O} Li^{+}_{(aq)} + H^{+}_{(aq)}$
d) $Al_2O_{3(s)} \xrightarrow{H_2O} 2\ Al^{3+}_{(aq)} + 3\ O^{2-}_{(aq)}$

30. What distinguishes a strong electrolyte from a weak one?

31. Is each of the following substances an acid, a base or a salt?

a) HBr
b) KOH
c) BaF_2
d) $ZnSO_4$
e) H_3PO_4
f) $Cu(OH)_2$

32. Look at the photo below.

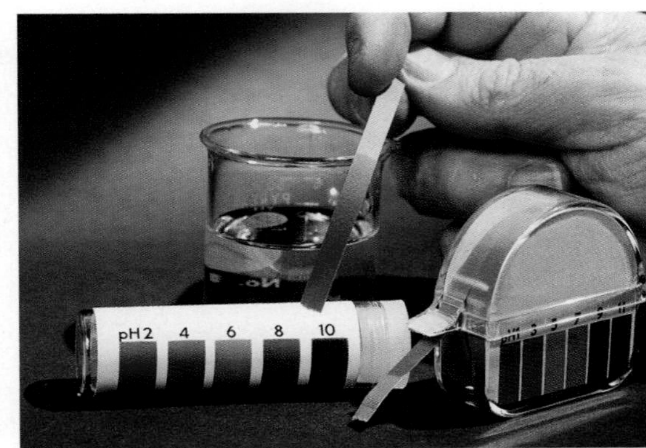

a) What is the pH of this solution?
b) Is the solution acidic, basic or neutral? Explain your answer.

33. Rain has a pH of about 5, while the pH of seawater is about 8. How many times more acidic is rainwater than seawater?

review questions

A. A coalition was formed recently to protest the use of dihydrogen monoxide. According to the coalition, the widespread use of this substance has harmful effects on human health and the environment.

Dihydrogen monoxide is both colourless and odourless. It exists as a solid, liquid and gas, but it is usually sold in liquid form. Certain precautions must be taken during its use. Its vapour can cause burns, while prolonged exposure to the compound in its solid form can cause frostbite. Inhaling it in its liquid form has resulted in many deaths.

a) What is the chemical formula for dihydrogen monoxide?

b) Dihydrogen monoxide is the main component of acid rain. Is it the solute or the solvent? Explain your answer.

c) In its pure state, this substance does not conduct electricity, yet it is used to manufacture batteries. Explain how this is possible.

d) Soil erosion by this substance dissolves the minerals in the soil and carries them into lakes and rivers. How does this affect the concentration of minerals in the lakes and rivers?

e) If the total concentration of dissolved matter in a lake is 500 mg/L, what is its concentration in ppm?

f) Should the use of dihydrogen monoxide be banned? Explain your answer.

B. Are the atoms in dihydrogen monoxide joined by ionic or covalent bonds? Explain your answer.

C. Prepare your own summary of Chapter 2 by building a concept map.

HOW TO BUILD
A CONCEPT MAP

FIGHTING ACID RAIN IN QUÉBEC

A large part of Québec is vulnerable to acid rain. Soil on the Canadian Shield contains few carbonates—minerals that can neutralize excess acid—so our environment is more sensitive to acid fallout than other parts of the country, like the western provinces. By 1990, one lake in five in Québec was considered too acidic, which means that its plant and animal populations are at risk. Forestry is also affected: development in half of Québec's forest regions has been slowed by acid rain. The plight of sugar maple stands, in particular, has attracted media attention. Acid rain also damages buildings and works of art that are exposed to the open air.

REDUCING AIR POLLUTION

The Québec government decided to deal with the problem of acid rain by focusing on its cause: emissions of sulphur and nitrogen compounds, which acidify rain.

Sulphur emissions come mainly from industrial activity (metal works, oil- and coal-fired power plants, etc.). The nitrogen compounds are produced primarily by fossil fuel combustion and discharged, for example, in motor vehicle exhaust.

Between 1980 and 1994, Québec managed to reduce its sulphur compound emissions by 70 percent through measures such as installing purification systems in polluting factories, setting up energy conservation programs and installing catalytic converters in motor vehicles. Meanwhile, refineries have reduced the sulphur content of gasoline by 90 percent over the past 10 years, to respect Canadian regulations.

Atmospheric pollutants can travel far, however—so much so that three quarters of all emissions affecting Québec do not actually originate in the province. The mobility of pollutants explains the importance of negotiating agreements with our neighbours.

Motor vehicle exhaust is one of the main sources of the nitrogen compounds that cause acid rain.

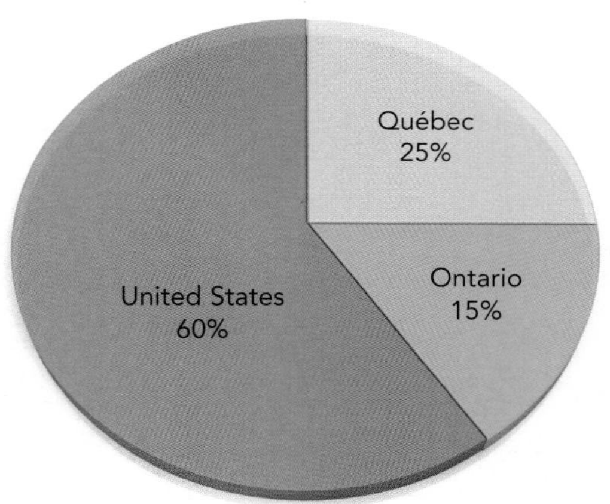

Origin of sulphur compounds affecting Québec

During the period between 1980 and 1994, Ontario also reduced its sulphur emissions by 70 percent. In addition, an agreement currently exists between Canada and the United States, requiring the Americans to reduce their sulphur compound emissions to levels 40 percent below 1980 levels by the year 2010.

Thanks to all these measures, total emissions of sulphur compounds, which represented the main cause of acid rain in the early 1980s, have now been cut in half. Further improvement is expected by 2010. Already, during the last decade, the pH of certain lakes has increased, suggesting that they are beginning to recover.

NEGOTIATING FURTHER REDUCTIONS

Despite efforts to reduce them, nitrogen compound emissions have remained practically the same since the 1980s. Recent studies show that, in some places, the acidification of lakes continues to be a problem.

In a report issued in 2004, a group of scientists declared that further reductions of 75 percent of polluting emissions would be needed to solve the problem of acid rain. A new round of negotiations is called for, involving the governments of Québec, Ontario, the Atlantic provinces and the United States.

1. To fight air pollution, we must reduce our reliance on fossil fuel combustion. What can each person do to contribute to this reduction?
2. Describe some consequences of acid rain in your region.

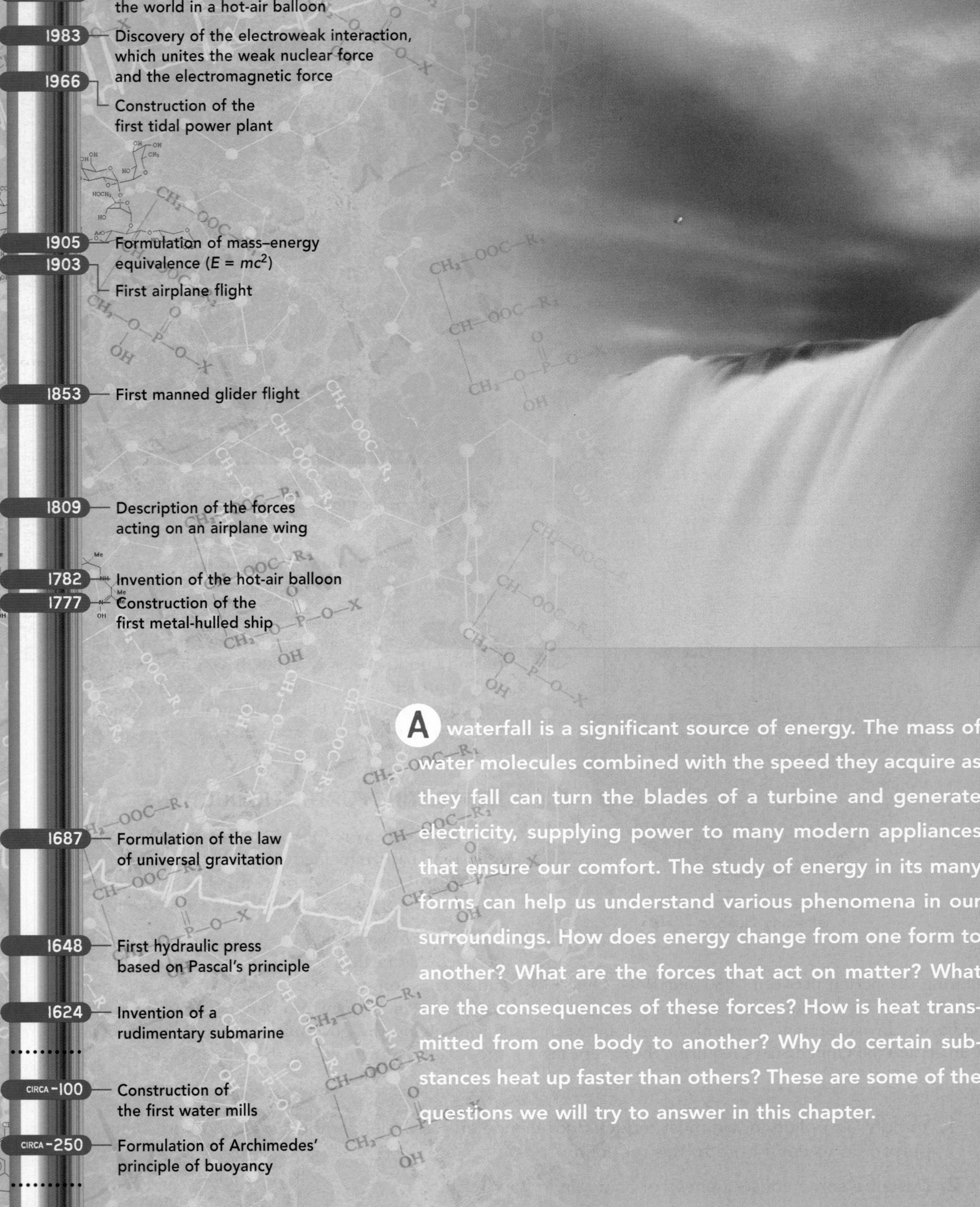

A waterfall is a significant source of energy. The mass of water molecules combined with the speed they acquire as they fall can turn the blades of a turbine and generate electricity, supplying power to many modern appliances that ensure our comfort. The study of energy in its many forms can help us understand various phenomena in our surroundings. How does energy change from one form to another? What are the forces that act on matter? What are the consequences of these forces? How is heat transmitted from one body to another? Why do certain substances heat up faster than others? These are some of the questions we will try to answer in this chapter.

THE MATERIAL WORLD

3

Different forms of energy

CONTENTS

ST
EST
AST
SE

1 What is energy?

Energy occurs in many forms and comes from a wide variety of sources. For example, to produce glucose, plants use solar energy—a combination of thermal energy and radiation resulting from nuclear reactions in the sun. Glucose itself is a source of energy. Living organisms can use the chemical energy it contains to release heat, for example, or to move their muscles. Table 3.1 describes some forms of energy, with examples of sources.

CONCEPT REVIEW

- Energy transformations
- Forms of energy (chemical, thermal, mechanical, radiation)
- Temperature
- Mass

3.1 FORMS OF ENERGY, WITH POSSIBLE SOURCES

Form of energy	Description	Examples of sources
Elastic energy	Energy stored in an object due to its compression or extension	• Compressed spring • Stretched elastic
Electrical energy	Energy resulting from the ordered movement of electrons from one atom to another	• Power plant • Battery • Generator
Thermal energy	Energy resulting from the random motion of all particles in a substance	• Fire • Heating element • Sun
Radiation energy	Energy contained in and transported by electromagnetic waves	• Light bulb • Microwave oven • Sun • Cellphone • Radiographic equipment • Fire • Radio • Television
Chemical energy	Energy stored in molecular bonds	• Apple • Candle wax • Fossil fuels
Wind energy	Energy resulting from the movement of air	• Wind
Sound energy	Energy contained in and transported by sound waves	• Sound • Music
Hydraulic energy	Energy resulting from the flow of water	• Waterfall • River
Nuclear energy	Energy stored in atomic nuclei	• Atomic nuclei • Sun

Energy is very useful. We use it to walk, lift a box and keep warm. In scientific terms, energy allows us to do work (such as walking or lifting a box), or it effects change (such as giving off heat to keep people warm).

ENERGY is the ability to do work or effect change.

In the International System of Units (SI), energy is expressed in joules (J). One joule corresponds to the energy required to move an object with the force of one newton over a distance of one metre. This relationship is expressed by the following equation:

$$1\ J = 1\ N \times 1\ m$$

1.1 THE LAW OF CONSERVATION OF ENERGY

Energy can be transported from one place to another. It can also change from one form to another. During **PHOTOSYNTHESIS**, for example, solar energy makes its way to plants, which absorb it. The solar energy is then transformed into chemical energy. The process is described as the *transfer* of energy from the sun to the plants and then the *transformation* of that energy into chemical energy.

ENERGY TRANSFER is the movement of energy from one place to another.

ENERGY TRANSFORMATION is the changing of energy from one form to another.

Our modern lifestyle depends heavily on a series of energy transfers and transformations. Figure 3.2 provides one example of this.

3.2 Hydraulic energy is transformed into mechanical energy when water spins the turbines of a power plant. This energy is then transformed into electrical energy by a generator, and the electrical energy is transferred to our homes. Various electrical appliances may, in turn, transform the energy into other forms (such as sound and light), depending on the particular mechanisms involved.

During the 19th century, many scientists contributed to the definition of a fundamental principle of physics: the law of conservation of energy. According to this law, energy can be neither created nor destroyed. The total amount of energy in an isolated system thus remains constant.

The LAW OF CONSERVATION OF ENERGY states that energy can be neither created nor destroyed; it can only be transferred or transformed. The total amount of energy in an isolated system always remains constant.

ST EST AST 1.2 ENERGY EFFICIENCY

Human beings can build machines or systems capable of changing energy from one form to another. However, a machine or system can rarely convert all the energy it consumes into a useful form. The rest is changed into another form or dispersed in the environment. For example, friction between parts in a car engine transforms some of the energy the engine burns into heat. Only 12 percent of the energy from gasoline is actually used to run the car (Figure 3.3). In an incandescent light bulb, only five percent of the electrical energy consumed is actually used to produce light.

The energy efficiency of a machine or system corresponds to the percentage of energy consumed that is effectively transformed as intended.

$$\text{Energy efficiency} = \frac{\text{Amount of useful energy}}{\text{Amount of energy consumed}} \times 100$$

ENERGY EFFICIENCY is the percentage of energy consumed by a machine or system that was transformed into useful energy.

ENERGY WELL SPENT

The bicycle is one of the most efficient means of transportation. Ninety percent of the energy provided by a cyclist's muscles is actually used to make the bicycle wheels turn. 4

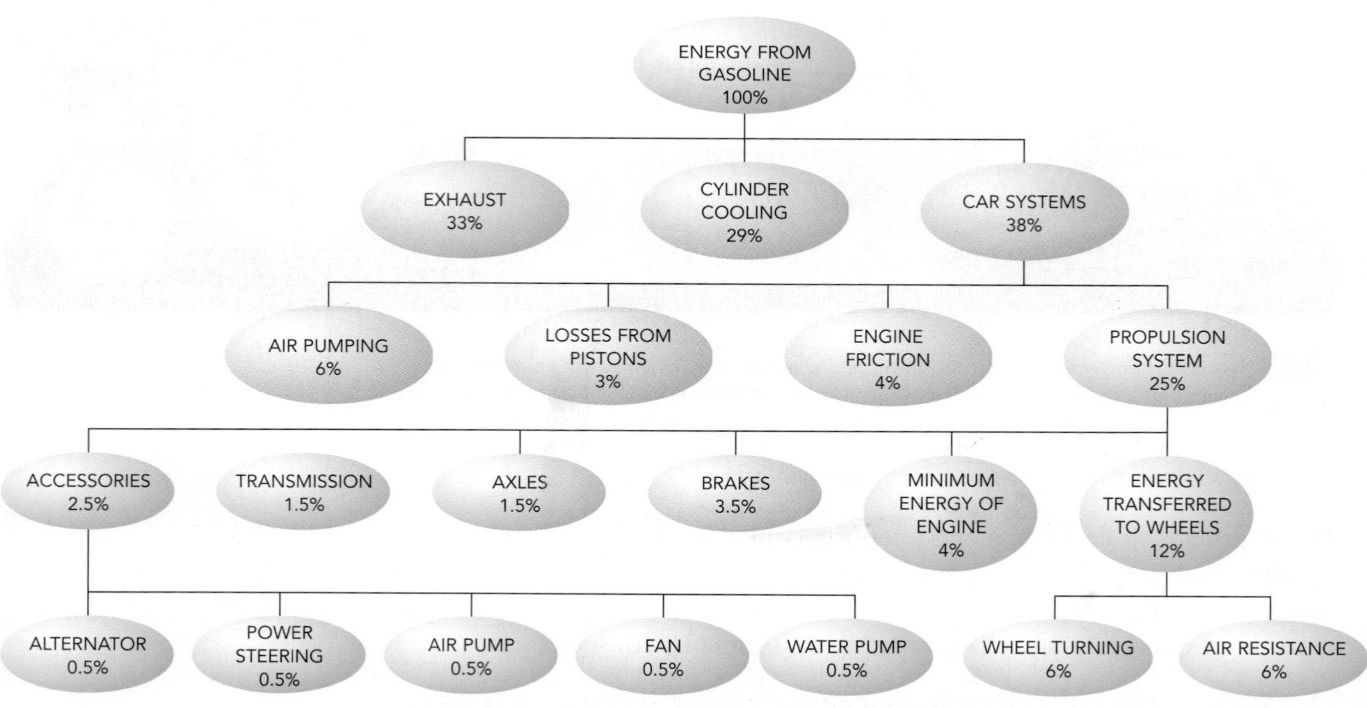

3.3 Only 12 percent of the chemical energy from gasoline is actually used by the wheels to make the car move.

ST EST AST SE

1.3 THERMAL ENERGY

Thermal energy results from the random movement of all the microscopic particles in a substance. The energy level reflects their degree of agitation. The amount of energy produced depends on the number of particles in the substance and its temperature.

3.4 FACTORS AFFECTING THE THERMAL ENERGY OF A SUBSTANCE

Factor	Factor variation	Result
Number of particles	More particles	Increased thermal energy
	Fewer particles	Reduced thermal energy
Temperature	Higher temperature	Increased thermal energy
	Lower temperature	Reduced thermal energy

THERMAL ENERGY is the energy contained in a substance, determined by the number of particles in the substance and their temperature.

Thermal energy can be transferred from an environment where the temperature is high to an environment where the temperature is lower until the two environments have the same temperature. This transfer of thermal energy is known as *heat*.

HEAT is the transfer of thermal energy between two environments with different temperatures. Heat always passes from the warmer to the cooler environment.

The relationship between heat and thermal energy is expressed in the following equation:

$Q = \Delta E_t$ where Q is the heat (in J)
ΔE_t is the variation in thermal energy (in J)

The Greek letter delta (Δ) is often used in science to symbolize a variation.

3.5 Water gives off heat, which the ice absorbs. This transfer of thermal energy causes the water temperature to fall and the ice to change state (melt).

ST EST AST

THE DISTINCTION BETWEEN HEAT AND TEMPERATURE

Heat and temperature are often confused. When the temperature is high, people say, "It's hot!" Yet even below its freezing point, a substance retains the ability to give off heat. Temperature takes into account only the speed of the particles in a substance. Heat, on the other hand, depends not only on the speed of the particles (their degree of agitation) but also on their mass (the number of particles).

TEMPERATURE is a measure of the degree of agitation of the particles of a substance.

EST SE

THE RELATIONSHIP BETWEEN HEAT, MASS, SPECIFIC HEAT CAPACITY AND TEMPERATURE VARIATIONS

When two different substances are heated, their temperatures increase but not necessarily at the same rate. The amount of heat that a substance must absorb to make its temperature rise by one degree is a characteristic property of that substance. This property is referred to as the *specific heat capacity* of the substance.

The SPECIFIC HEAT CAPACITY corresponds to the amount of thermal energy required to raise the temperature of one gram of a substance by one degree Celsius.

Table 3.6 (page 75) shows that water has a particularly high specific heat capacity. This explains why, on a sunny summer day, the sand on a beach can sometimes feel burning hot, while the nearby seawater feels freezing cold—even though the sand and sea are both receiving the same amount of thermal energy from sunlight.

1701
1744

Anders Celsius

In an effort to improve the accuracy of his meteorological observations, this Swedish astronomer and physicist developed a new temperature scale in 1742. The scale bears his name today and is used throughout the world.

ENVIRONMENT EXTRA

Water, the climate regulator

Water is unique by virtue of many of its properties, including its very high specific heat capacity. Water absorbs large amounts of thermal energy as it warms and releases large amounts as it cools. It can thus build up a significant store of heat during the day and gradually release it overnight. The presence of a large body of water in a region can thus moderate its climate, reducing local temperature variations. In contrast, very dry regions, such as deserts, experience wide variations in temperature between day and night.

Coastal regions generally enjoy a milder climate than areas far removed from water.

3.6 THE SPECIFIC HEAT CAPACITY OF SOME SUBSTANCES

Substance	Specific heat capacity $(\frac{J}{g°C})$	Substance	Specific heat capacity $(\frac{J}{g°C})$
Water	4.19	Glass	0.84
Ethanol	2.46	Sand	0.80
Ice	2.06	Iron	0.45
Vegetable oil	2.00	Copper	0.38
Wood	1.76	Silver	0.24
Air	1.01	Tungsten	0.13

It is possible to calculate the heat absorbed or released by a given substance. This quantity of thermal energy depends on the mass, the specific heat capacity and the change in temperature of the substance. The mathematical relationship is expressed by the following formula:

$Q = mc\Delta T$ where Q is the heat—in other words, the variation in thermal energy (in J)
m is the mass (in g)
c is the specific heat capacity (in J/g°C)
ΔT is the temperature variation (in °C)

$\Delta T = T_f - T_i$ where T_f is the final temperature (in °C)
T_i is the initial temperature (in °C)

Appendix 3, at the end of this textbook, contains all the mathematical formulas used throughout the book.

If the change in temperature is negative, we can conclude that the substance has lost thermal energy, which means that it has given off heat. If the change in temperature is positive, however, the substance has absorbed heat. Its thermal energy has therefore increased.

Let's see how the thermal energy of the following substances can vary:

- A beaker containing 100 g of water is heated from 20°C to 44°C.

  $Q = 100\ \cancel{g} \times 4.19\ \frac{J}{\cancel{g°C}} \times (44 - 20)\cancel{°C}$

  $= 10\ 056\ J$

- A beaker containing 100 g of vegetable oil is heated from 20°C to 44°C.

  $Q = 100\ \cancel{g} \times 2.00\ \frac{J}{\cancel{g°C}} \times (44 - 20)\cancel{°C}$

  $= 4\ 800\ J$

- A beaker containing 200 g of water is heated from 20°C to 44°C.

  $Q = 200\ \cancel{g} \times 4.19\ \frac{J}{\cancel{g°C}} \times (44 - 20)\cancel{°C}$

  $= 20\ 112\ J$

- A beaker containing 100 g of water is cooled from 44°C to 20°C.

  $Q = 100\ \cancel{g} \times 4.19\ \frac{J}{\cancel{g°C}} \times (20 - 44)\cancel{°C}$

  $= -10\ 056\ J$

These examples show that, even if the temperature variation is the same for each of the liquids, the amount of heat absorbed or released is different.

EST SE

1.4 KINETIC ENERGY

A moving object has the capacity to do work. For example, a marble rolling on a table can move another marble by hitting it. Running water from a waterfall can turn the blades of a turbine. In these examples, the marble and the waterfall contain energy because of their motion. This form of energy is called *kinetic energy*.

Kinetic comes from the Greek *kinēticos*, meaning "moving."

KINETIC ENERGY is the energy an object possesses due to its motion.

EINSTEIN'S EQUATION

Another relationship is known to exist between energy, mass and speed. It is expressed in Einstein's famous equation $E = mc^2$. (The *c* represents the speed of light.) While the kinetic energy equation describes the amount of energy available during physical and chemical reactions, Einstein's equation describes the amount of energy contained in atomic nuclei. This energy can be released only during nuclear reactions.

EST SE

THE RELATIONSHIP BETWEEN KINETIC ENERGY, MASS AND VELOCITY

The kinetic energy of an object depends on its mass and speed. The heavier a marble is and the faster it rolls, the more energy it possesses, and the greater is its capacity to do work.

The mathematical relationship between the kinetic energy of an object, its mass and its velocity (speed in a given direction) is expressed in the following equation:

$E_k = \frac{1}{2}mv^2$ where E_k is the kinetic energy of the object (in J)
m is the mass of the object (in kg)
v is the velocity of the object (in m/s)

Now let's calculate the kinetic energy of the following vehicles:

- A car weighing 2500 kg travels at 50 km/h (about 14 m/s).

$$E_k = \frac{1}{2}mv^2$$
$$= \frac{1}{2} \text{ x } 2500 \text{ kg x } (14 \frac{\text{m}}{\text{s}})^2$$
$$= 245\ 000 \text{ J}$$

- A car weighing 2500 kg travels at 100 km/h (about 28 m/s).

$$E_k = \frac{1}{2}mv^2$$
$$= \frac{1}{2} \text{ x } 2500 \text{ kg x } (28 \frac{\text{m}}{\text{s}})^2$$
$$= 980\ 000 \text{ J}$$

- A minivan weighing 5000 kg travels at 50 km/h.

$$E_k = \frac{1}{2}mv^2$$
$$= \frac{1}{2} \text{ x } 5000 \text{ kg x } (14 \frac{\text{m}}{\text{s}})^2$$
$$= 490\ 000 \text{ J}$$

The three examples above show that, when the mass of an object is doubled, its kinetic energy becomes twice as great. If its velocity is doubled, however, its kinetic energy is quadrupled. This explains in part why speeding is so often the cause of fatal accidents.

EST SE 1.5 POTENTIAL ENERGY

When people lift hammers or pull on bowstrings, they are doing work. The kinetic energy needed to do the work is transferred to the object as potential energy. It is considered an energy reserve because it must first be transformed into another type of energy to do the work. When a hammer falls, its potential energy is transformed into kinetic energy, and it can drive in the nail. Similarly, when an archer releases the bowstring, its potential energy is also transformed into kinetic energy, and it can dispatch an arrow.

> *Potential* comes from the Latin *potens*, meaning "able."

There are different ways to calculate potential energy. When the potential energy of an object is considered in terms of its mass and its height above a reference surface, the measure is called the *gravitational potential energy* of the object.

GRAVITATIONAL POTENTIAL ENERGY is the energy reserve of an object based on its mass and its height above a reference surface.

3.7 The work done in lifting a hammer is stored as potential energy. To hammer in the nail, the potential energy must be transformed into kinetic energy.

EST SE THE RELATIONSHIP BETWEEN GRAVITATIONAL POTENTIAL ENERGY, MASS, GRAVITATIONAL FIELD INTENSITY, AND HEIGHT

The gravitational potential energy of an object depends on its mass, the intensity of the gravitational field and the height of the object above a reference surface. The mathematical relationship between these values is expressed by the following formula:

$E_p = mgh$ where E_p is the gravitational potential energy (in J)
m is the mass of the object (in kg)
g is the gravitational field intensity (in N/kg), which is 9.8 N/kg at the Earth's surface
h is the height of the object above the reference surface (in m)

Let's look at the gravitational potential energy acquired by a rock in the following situations:

- A 1-kg rock raised to a height of 1 m
  $E_p = mgh$
  $= 1 \cancel{\text{kg}} \times 9.8 \frac{\text{N}}{\cancel{\text{kg}}} \times 1 \text{ m}$
  $= 9.8 \text{ J}$
- A 2-kg rock raised to a height of 1 m
  $E_p = mgh$
  $= 2 \cancel{\text{kg}} \times 9.8 \frac{\text{N}}{\cancel{\text{kg}}} \times 1 \text{ m}$
  $= 19.6 \text{ J}$
- A 1-kg rock raised to a height of 2 m
  $E_p = mgh$
  $= 1 \cancel{\text{kg}} \times 9.8 \frac{\text{N}}{\cancel{\text{kg}}} \times 2 \text{ m}$
  $= 19.6 \text{ J}$

These examples show that the gravitational potential energy doubles when either the mass or the height of the object is doubled.

EST SE 1.6 MECHANICAL ENERGY

The example of the hammer in Figure 3.7 (page 77) shows that kinetic energy can be transformed into potential energy, and vice versa. The sum of the kinetic and the potential energy is the **MECHANICAL ENERGY** of a system.

EST SE THE RELATIONSHIP BETWEEN MECHANICAL, KINETIC AND POTENTIAL ENERGY

The mathematical relationship between mechanical, kinetic and potential energy is expressed in the following equation:

$E_m = E_k + E_p$ where E_m is the mechanical energy (in J)
E_k is the kinetic energy (in J)
E_p is the potential energy (in J)

The law of conservation of energy states that, in a system without friction, mechanical energy always remains constant. Consider the example of a free-falling object. As it falls, its potential energy decreases, while its kinetic energy increases. Setting aside the effects of friction, the mechanical energy of the object remains constant throughout its fall.

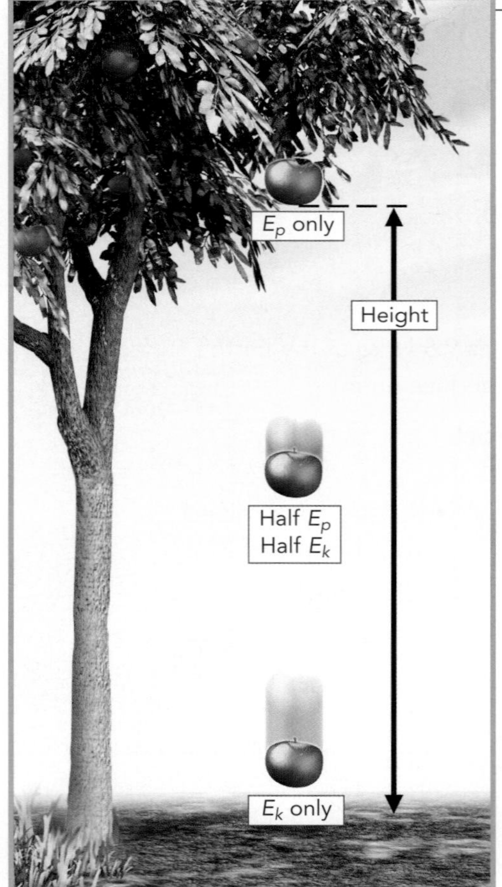

3.8 The mechanical energy of an object in free fall remains constant throughout the fall. The potential energy of the apple is gradually transformed into kinetic energy.

3.9 On a roller coaster, the potential energy of the cars is constantly transformed into kinetic energy, and vice versa.

EST AST SE 2 Motion and forces

The study of motion is one of the oldest branches of physics. Describing motion means explaining how an object travels in time and space. Physicists do not stop at a mere description of motion, however; they also try to understand its cause. In most cases, one or more forces are at work in the motion of an object.

CONCEPT REVIEW
- Effects of a force
- Universal gravitation

MOTION

The main variables in the description of motion are speed (or velocity), travel, time and acceleration.

In science, speed is defined in terms of distance travelled per unit of time (in m/s). The definition of velocity has an added element of direction: velocity is speed in a given direction. Acceleration is a change in velocity over time (in m/s^2). It is often useful to know the acceleration of an object because it is one of the main effects of applying a force.

AST THE RELATIONSHIP BETWEEN SPEED, DISTANCE AND TIME

The terms *average speed* and *instantaneous speed* can be used to describe the motion of an object travelling at a certain speed. Imagine a car travelling from Montréal to Québec. The instantaneous speed of the car is its speed at a precise moment in time, for example, when it is measured by radar. The average speed is the speed the car would have travelled at if it had maintained a constant speed for the entire trip. To determine the average speed, we need to know the distance travelled and the travelling time. The mathematical relationship between these values is expressed by the following formula (note that v is the symbol for *speed* as well as for *velocity*):

$$v = \frac{d}{\Delta t}$$

where v is the average speed (in m/s)
d is the distance travelled (in m)
Δt is the time variation—in other words, the travelling time (in s)

Consider, for example, the average speed of a car that travels 10 km (10 000 m) in 10 min (600 s):

$$v = \frac{d}{\Delta t} = \frac{10\,000 \text{ m}}{600 \text{ s}} = 16.67 \frac{\text{m}}{\text{s}}$$

The average speed of this car is 16.67 m/s (60 km/h).

EST AST SE 2.2 FORCES AND CHANGES IN MOTION

When we pull or push on an object, we are exerting a *force* on it. A force is a push or pull on an object that can change its motion. Sometimes forces change the motion of only a part of the object, resulting in its deformation.

A FORCE is an action that can change the motion of an object, or deform the object, by pushing or pulling on it.

3.10 By pushing on the pedals, the cyclist's feet exert a force that changes the motion of the entire pedal system.

3.11 The potter's hands exert a force that shapes the clay.

A force is always exerted by one body on another, and in one direction. It can be represented graphically with an arrow, taking into account the following four elements:

- the horizontal or vertical line of action, represented by a straight (dotted) line
- the direction of application, represented by the arrowhead
- the magnitude of the force, represented by the length or width of the arrow, or by a number
- its point of application, corresponding to the starting point of the arrow

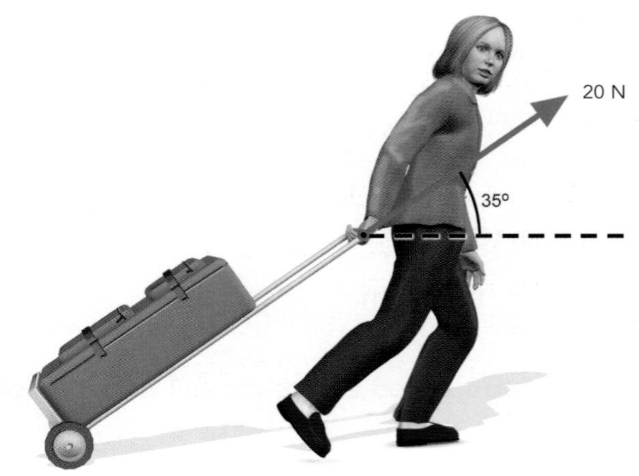

3.12 This woman is pulling her trolley (point of application and direction) with a force of 20 N (magnitude), at an angle of 35° to the horizontal (line of action).

Force is measured in newtons (N). By definition, a newton corresponds to the force required to make a one-kilogram object accelerate at a rate of 1 m/s^2. In mathematical terms, a newton is defined by the following equation:

$$1\ N = 1\ kg \times 1\ \frac{m}{s^2}$$

A force can change the motion of an object in different ways:

- A force can act on a stationary object by giving it a certain velocity. It can also increase the velocity of an object already in motion, when the force is exerted in the same direction as the motion of the object. In both cases, the object is said to *accelerate*.
- A force can also reduce the velocity of an object, either slowing it down or stopping it completely. This happens when the force is exerted in the opposite direction to the motion of the object. The object is then said to undergo *negative acceleration*, or *deceleration*.
- A force can also modify the trajectory of an object, setting it off course. For example, a force exerted on one side or the other of a moving object tends to divert it. Physicists regard a change in direction of a moving object as another form of acceleration.

EST AST 2.3 TYPES OF FORCES

Most scientists categorize forces into four types: gravitational force, electromagnetic force, strong nuclear force and weak nuclear force. These forces can act across a distance, without direct contact between two bodies.

EST AST GRAVITATIONAL FORCE

Gravitational force is a force of attraction acting between all objects as a result of their masses and the distances between them. The higher the product of the masses of two objects, the greater the force of attraction between them. Conversely, the greater the distance between two objects, the weaker the attraction between them.

Among the many objects in our surroundings, the Earth is the one with the largest mass. It is also very close to us. The force of gravity between the Earth and all the objects on its surface is therefore by far the greatest gravitational force acting on those objects.

For example, a free-falling body is subject to the Earth's gravitational force, causing the body to accelerate at a rate of 9.8 m/s^2. This acceleration is the same for all free-falling objects, regardless of their mass, as long as air resistance remains negligible (Figure 3.13, page 82).

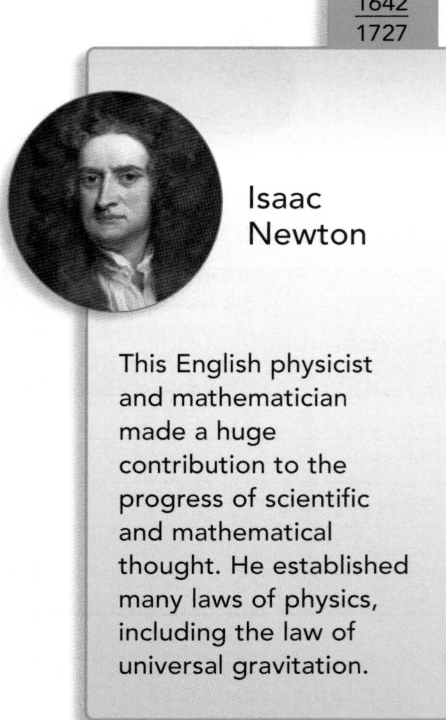

This English physicist and mathematician made a huge contribution to the progress of scientific and mathematical thought. He established many laws of physics, including the law of universal gravitation.

Gravitational force on Earth pulls toward the centre of the planet. Since this force decreases with distance, it is reasonable to assume that the gravitational field around the planet loses intensity the farther one travels from the centre of the Earth (Figure 3.14). From this perspective, the acceleration of objects inside the gravitational field can be considered a measure of its strength at a given distance from the centre of the planet. This acceleration is expressed in N/kg rather than m/s^2. The two measures are actually equivalent, as shown by the following calculation:

If $1\ N = 1\ \frac{kg \times m}{s^2}$, then:

$$9.8\ \frac{N}{kg} = 9.8\ \frac{\cancel{kg} \times m}{s^2 \times \cancel{kg}} = 9.8\ \frac{m}{s^2}$$

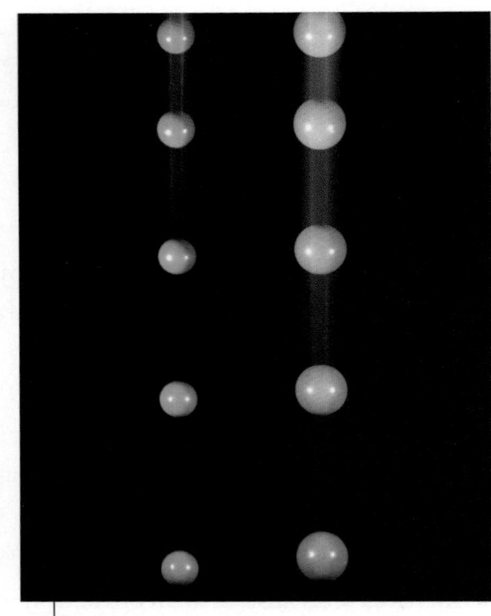

3.13 At the Earth's surface, all objects in free fall are subject to a force causing them to accelerate at a rate of 9.8 m/s^2. In other words, if we drop two objects with different masses from the same height, and if the air resistance is negligible, the objects will reach the ground at the same time.

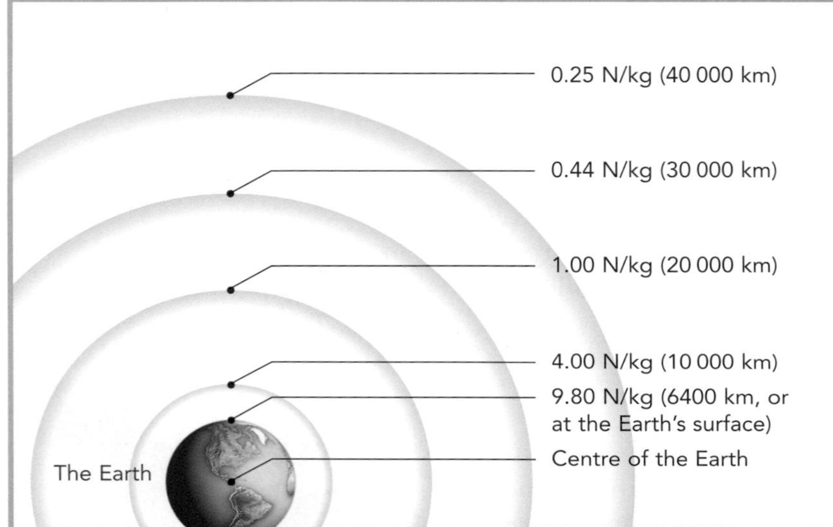

3.14 The intensity of the Earth's gravitational field at the surface is 9.8 N/kg. The field becomes weaker as the distance from the centre of the planet increases.

3.15 INTENSITY OF THE GRAVITATIONAL FIELD AT THE SURFACE OF BODIES IN THE SOLAR SYSTEM

Celestial body	Intensity of the gravitational field at the surface (N/kg)	Celestial body	Intensity of the gravitational field at the surface (N/kg)
Sun	273.95	Mars	3.72
Moon	1.67	Jupiter	25.87
Mercury	3.63	Saturn	11.27
Venus	8.62	Uranus	8.82
Earth	9.80	Neptune	11.56

THE EARTH'S MASS

The discovery of the law of universal gravitation by Newton led Henry Cavendish (1731–1810) to calculate the mass of the Earth for the first time, in 1798. Today, its mass is estimated to be 5.98×10^{24} kg.

Gravitational force explains not only falling objects but also other phenomena, such as the Earth's tides and the trajectories of celestial bodies.

The relationship between mass and weight

In everyday language, the words *mass* and *weight* are often used interchangeably. In science, however, these two words have different meanings.

Mass is a measure of the quantity of matter in an object. Its SI unit is the kilogram (kg). It is a value that does not depend on the place where it is measured. Thus, an object with a mass of one kilogram on Earth also has a mass of one kilogram on the Moon.

MASS is a measure of the quantity of matter in an object.

In contrast, the weight of this object will vary depending on where it is found. Its weight is actually an indication of the gravitational force acting on it.

WEIGHT is a measure of the gravitational force acting on an object.

Weight depends on the intensity of the gravitational field at the weighing site and on the mass of the object being weighed. The following mathematical formula relates weight, gravitational force and mass:

$w = F_g = mg$ where w is the weight (in N)
F_g is the gravitational force (in N)
m is the mass (in kg)
g is the gravitational field intensity (in N/kg)

THE RIGHT BALANCE FOR THE JOB

Balances with trays are used to measure the mass of objects, while spring balances are used to measure weight. Spring balances convert weight to mass according to a pre-established calibration.

3.16 Despite the heavy space suit, this astronaut can move around easily on the surface of the Moon because a person's weight there is six times lighter than on Earth. The astronaut's mass, however, remains the same as on Earth.

Thus, a one-kilogram object will weigh 9.8 N at the Earth's surface but only 1.67 N on the Moon, where the gravitational force is six times weaker than on our planet.

AST ELECTROMAGNETIC FORCE

Electromagnetic force is a force of attraction or repulsion between two objects with an **ELECTRICAL CHARGE** or with **MAGNETIC POLES**. This force is responsible for the bonds between the atoms of a molecule, for example, and for muscle tension, magnetic phenomena and the movement of charge in an electric current.

At the macroscopic level, electromagnetic force is also responsible for forces known as *contact forces*. A contact force is the result of acting directly on an object. For example, when we pull or push on a door handle, we apply force directly to it. An example of electromagnetic contact force occurs when we place a book on a table. The table resists the pressure of the book's weight by acting on the book with an equal, opposite force (Figure 3.18). At the microscopic level, electromagnetic contact forces can be explained by the force of the bonds between the atoms that make up matter.

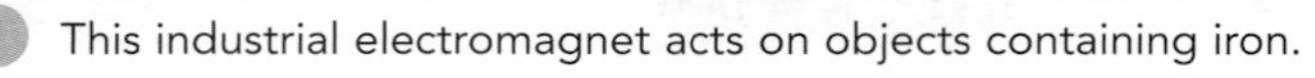

3.17 This industrial electromagnet acts on objects containing iron.

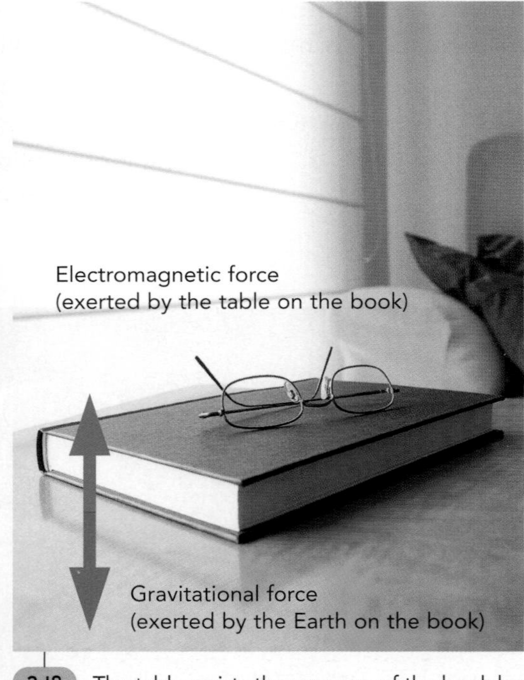

3.18 The table resists the pressure of the book by opposing it with an electromagnetic contact force equal to the weight of the book.

The force of friction

Friction is a form of contact force that we frequently encounter in our daily lives. It wears out machine parts, but it also allows us to walk. Without friction, our feet would slide over the ground as if we were walking on ice or a wet floor. Air resistance is also a force of friction.

Friction can occur between two objects whose surfaces are not perfectly smooth, when they come into contact. It is the opposite of the phenomenon of one object's slipping over another. To set or maintain an object in motion, friction must be overcome. For this reason, one object slipping over another ends up coming to a stop if no other force is applied to it. Friction thus always occurs in opposition to *slip*.

FRICTION is a force that prevents two objects from slipping over each other when they come into contact.

Friction depends on two factors:

- the nature of the surfaces in contact (the rougher the surfaces, the greater the friction)
- the intensity of the pressure of each surface on the other (the higher the pressure, the greater the friction)

3.19 Even if a metallic surface looks smooth to the naked eye, its unevenness becomes apparent when it is examined under a microscope.

3.20 The force of friction is opposite to slip.

AST STRONG AND WEAK NUCLEAR FORCES

Strong and weak nuclear forces both act within the nucleus of an atom. Their effect is thus extremely short-range—and practically nonexistent outside the nucleus.

The strong nuclear force is a high-intensity force of attraction that holds protons and neutrons together. It is responsible for the cohesion of atomic nuclei and becomes apparent in nuclear reactions.

FOLLOWING IN EINSTEIN'S FOOTSTEPS

An important part of current research in physics is devoted to the quest for the "theory of everything." Physicists are convinced that the four fundamental forces of nature (gravity, electromagnetic force and strong and weak nuclear forces) are actually different forms of a single force. Fifty years after Einstein failed in his attempt, however, scientists are still seeking a theory that can account for all physical phenomena.

The crux of the problem lies in the incompatibility between Einstein's general relativity (which takes into account the properties of gravitational force) and quantum mechanics (which integrates the other forces—electromagnetic and strong and weak nuclear forces).

The two theories hold up brilliantly as long as they are considered independently, each in its own field. Any attempt to unite quantum mechanics and general relativity, however, has led to absurd results, suggesting that a major error has been made.

String theory, discovered in 1984, inspired the belief that it could bring together the two pillars of fundamental physics, but this highly complex theory has met with huge problems, preventing the elaboration of a universal theory. Other physicists are re-examining current knowledge in the hope of finding new clues.

Source: Adapted from Pauline Gravel, "Einstein s'est-il trompé?" *Le Devoir*, April 14, 2007, p. A1. *[Translation]*

After publishing his special theory of relativity in 1905 and then his theory of general relativity in 1916, Albert Einstein (1879–1955) sought a theory that would unite all the findings of modern physics—but his efforts were in vain.

The weak nuclear force, as its name suggests, is a low-intensity force of attraction. It is responsible for certain phenomena related to radioactivity (especially beta radiation), and it plays a role in creating sunshine.

AST 2.4 THE EQUILIBRIUM OF TWO FORCES

When we look at an immobile object, we might think it is free of any force. On Earth, however, every object is constantly subjected to at least one force: gravity. If certain objects do not move, it is simply because other forces also act on them, and all these forces cancel one another.

It is very common for an object to be subjected to several forces at the same time. To determine the combined effect of a number of forces acting simultaneously on an object, we calculate the *resultant force*, or *net force*.

The RESULTANT FORCE is a virtual force whose action is equal to the combination of all the forces applied simultaneously to an object.

The resultant force is calculated in the following ways, depending on the situation:

- When two forces are applied in the same direction, along the same line of action (vertically or horizontally), the resultant force is the sum of the two (Figure 3.21).
- When two forces are applied along the same line of action but in opposite directions, the resultant force is the difference between the two (Figures 3.22 and 3.23).

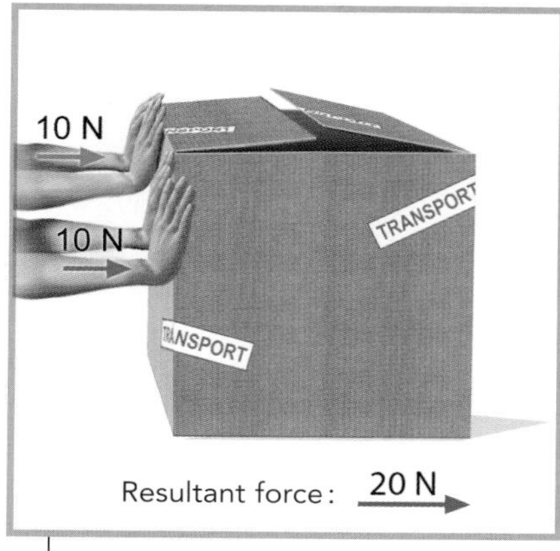

3.21 Since these two forces are both applied horizontally and in the same direction, they are added together for a resultant force of 20 N. The box is moved to the right.

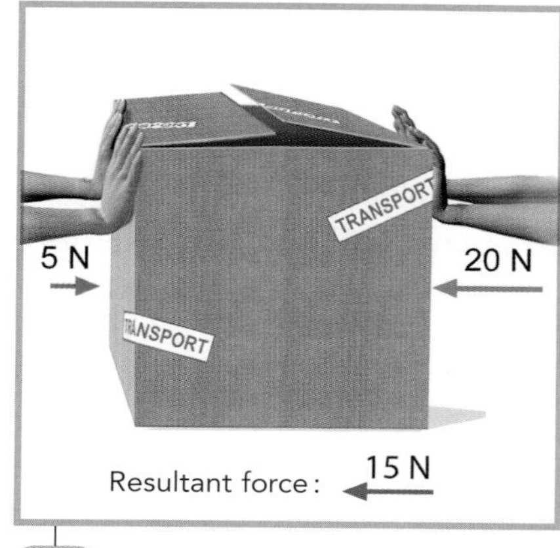

3.22 Since these two forces are applied horizontally but in opposite directions, they are subtracted. The resultant force of 15 N causes the box to move to the left.

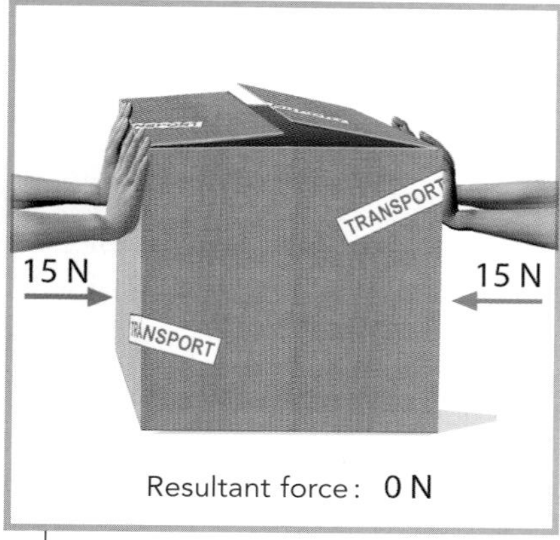

3.23 These two forces are applied horizontally but in opposite directions, so they are subtracted. Since they are equal, they cancel each other. The resultant force is zero, and the box does not move.

When the resultant force is zero, an object appears as if there were no force acting on it. It is said to be *in equilibrium*. If it is immobile, it will remain in its place. If it is in motion, it will continue to travel at a constant speed.

The EQUILIBRIUM OF TWO FORCES is achieved when the resultant force is zero. The motion of the object therefore remains constant.

3.24 In this example, the propulsion force achieved by the cyclist is just enough to cancel friction. The resultant force is therefore zero, and the bicycle travels at a constant speed.

EST SE 2.5 THE EFFECTIVE FORCE

LAB 22

When force is applied to an object, sometimes only a part of that force really acts on the object. Only one component of the force actually alters the motion of the object or deforms it. The rest of the force is insufficient to have a noticeable effect. The force component that affects the motion of an object is called the *effective force*.

The EFFECTIVE FORCE is the force component that alters the motion of an object. It is the component that is parallel to the movement of the object.

Consider the example of a person pulling a bag of soccer balls over a gymnasium floor with a force of 20 N and at an angle of 40° to the horizontal. The force can be broken down into two components: one parallel to the ground and the other perpendicular to it (Figure 3.25).

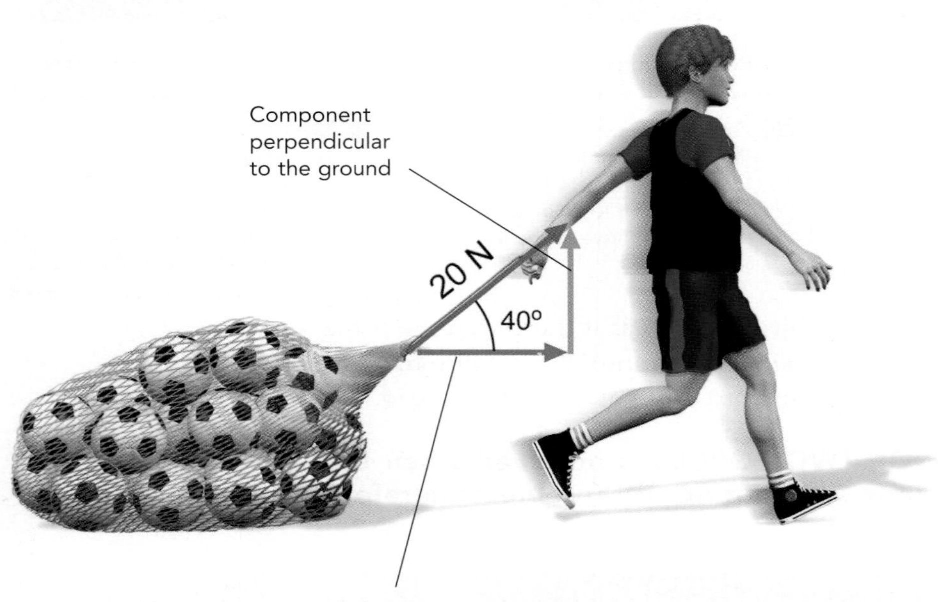

3.25 The force exerted by the person pulling the bag can be broken down into two components: one parallel to the ground and the other perpendicular to it.

If the bag moves along the floor, it is the horizontal force component that is acting on the bag. If the vertical component had been greater, the bag would also have been lifted off the floor.

To calculate the magnitude of the effective force, we can use a graph like the one in Figure 3.26. This graph refers to the example of Figure 3.25 above and shows that the magnitude of the horizontal force component is 15.3 N. The magnitude of the effective force can also be calculated using trigonometry.

3.26 THE VERTICAL AND HORIZONTAL FORCE COMPONENTS

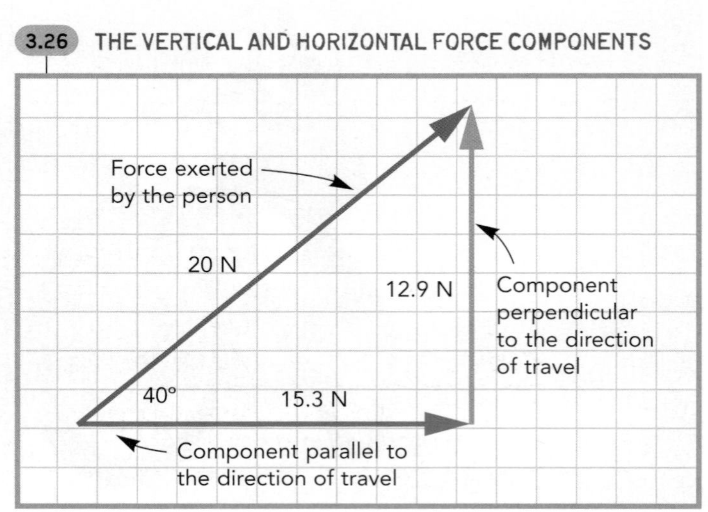

First, let's review a few principles of trigonometry. In a right triangle, we can calculate the sine (sin), cosine (cos) and tangent (tan) of any angle, represented here by the Greek letter theta (θ). These values are related in the following ways:

$$\text{Sin } \theta = \frac{\text{opposite side}}{\text{hypotenuse}}$$

$$\text{Cos } \theta = \frac{\text{adjacent side}}{\text{hypotenuse}}$$

$$\text{Tan } \theta = \frac{\text{opposite side}}{\text{adjacent side}}$$

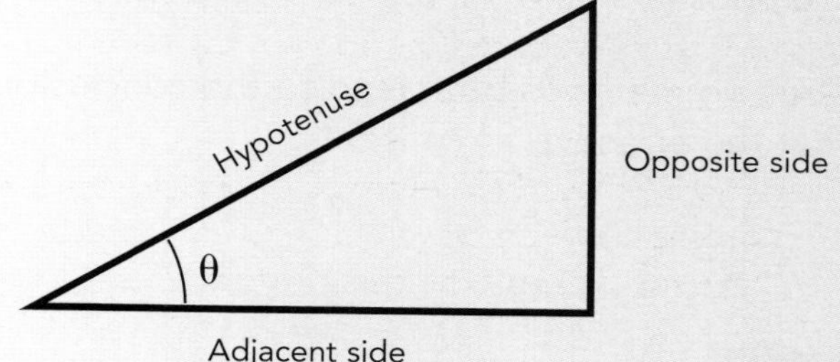

Now let's see how to apply these principles to calculate the effective force in the example of Figure 3.25. Since the bag is travelling horizontally, the effective force is the horizontal component of the 20-N force—in other words, the side adjacent to the 40° angle.

Adjacent side = cos (40°) x 20 N = 15.3 N

The effective force is therefore 15.3 N.

Now let's consider the case of an object sliding down an inclined plane.

A box weighing 10 N is placed on a plane inclined at an angle of 30°. To calculate the magnitude of the gravitational force component, which causes the box to slide down the plane, two methods are possible.

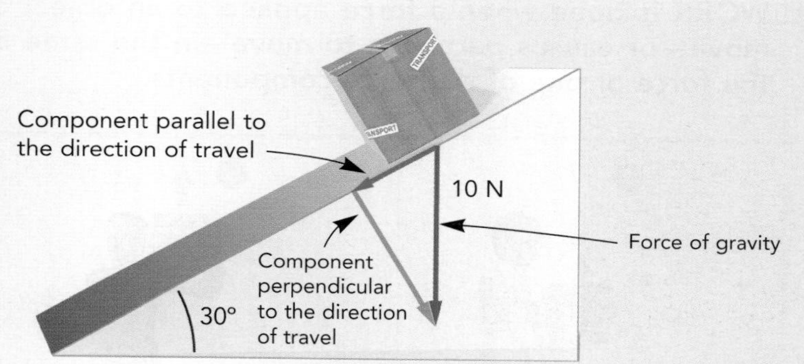

- Using a graph, we can calculate the magnitude of the component parallel to the plane as follows:

THE PARALLEL AND PERPENDICULAR FORCE COMPONENTS

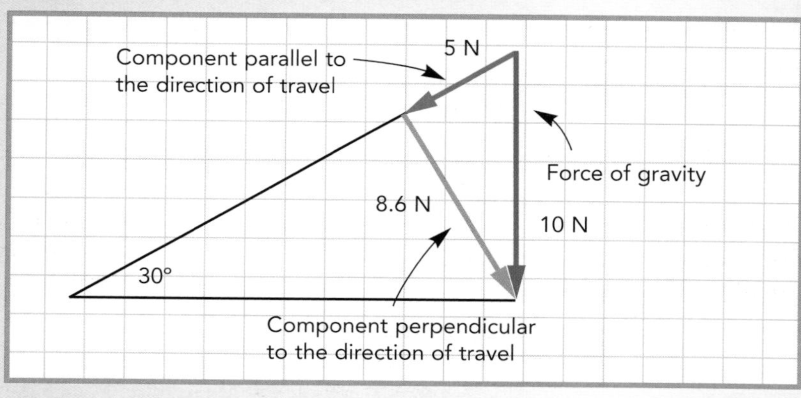

- Using trigonometry, we can calculate the magnitude of the component parallel to the inclined plane as follows:
  Opposite side = sin (30°) x 10 N = 5 N

The two methods both lead to the conclusion that the effective force is 5 N.

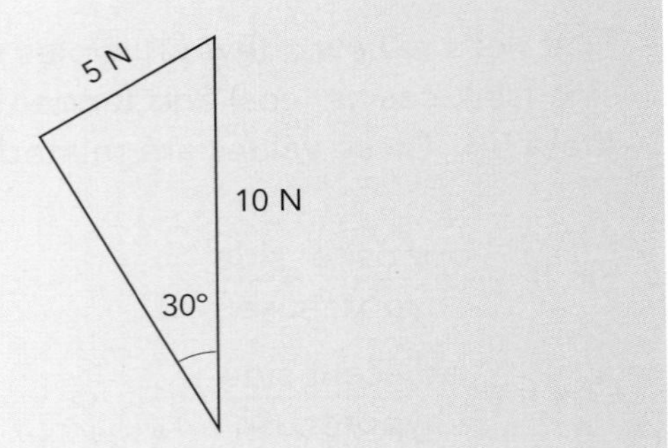

WORK

In science, the word *work* does not have the same meaning as in everyday life. Even if we push on an object with all our strength, we do not necessarily accomplish work from a scientific point of view. Work is done when a force applied to an object causes it to move in the same direction as the force or in the direction of one of the force components.

Work can also cause the deformation of an object. This happens when only a part of the object is forced into motion.

WORK is done when a force applied to an object causes it to move—or causes part of it to move—in the same direction as the force or one of the force components.

3.27 If we consider only the force of the person's arms on the box, then the person in situation A is the only one doing work because the box is moving in the same direction as the applied force. In B, the box is not moved by the force of the person's arms. And in C, the box moves perpendicular to the applied force, so the force component with the same direction as the actual movement is zero.

The scientific definition of the word *work* is particularly useful when combined with the concept of energy. Work in its scientific sense is a means of transferring energy from one place to another. Just as heat is a transfer of energy due to a difference in temperature, work is a transfer of energy due to travel. And like energy and heat, work is measured in joules.

EST SE THE RELATIONSHIP BETWEEN WORK AND ENERGY

At the beginning of this chapter, we defined energy as the ability to do work or effect change (page 71). In other words, when people do work or cause changes, they use energy. Since energy is neither lost nor created during work, it is transferred from one object or system to another and is usually transformed. For example, the work of turbines in a hydroelectric plant results in the transfer of hydraulic energy from water to the turbines, which transform it into electrical energy.

The relationship between work and energy can be expressed by the following formula:

$W = \Delta E$ where W is the work (in J)
ΔE is the variation in energy in an object or a system (in J)

An increase in the energy of an object or a system can thus be attributed to work that has been accomplished (or heat that has been absorbed). Conversely, the energy required to do work must come from an object or a system.

EST SE THE RELATIONSHIP BETWEEN WORK, FORCE AND TRAVEL

Work is calculated using the following mathematical relationship:

$W = F_{//}d$ where W is the work (in J)
$F_{//}$ is the force or the force component parallel to the direction of travel (in N)
d is the distance travelled by the object (in m)

- Suppose a person pushes a box with a force of 20 N and moves it 1 m.
  $W = F_{//}d$
  $= 20\ \text{N} \times 1\ \text{m} = 20\ \text{J}$
  The work applied to the box is 20 J.
- Now let's return to the example at the bottom of page 89 and suppose that the box moves 0.5 m. In this case, the force component parallel to the direction of travel is 5 N, as we saw on page 89.
  $W = F_{//}d$
  $= 5\ \text{N} \times 0.5\ \text{m} = 2.5\ \text{J}$
  The work applied to the box is 2.5 J.

AST 3 # Forces in fluids

In the preceding section, we discussed the general effect of forces. We will now focus on a specific case: the effect of forces on fluids.

First, let's review what a fluid is. A fluid is a substance of variable shape; it thus assumes the shape of its container. In addition, a solid can be immersed in a fluid because of the fluid's ability to spread out in even distribution around the solid. Liquids and gases display these characteristics, so they are both considered fluids.

CONCEPT REVIEW
- Pressure
- Density

HOW TO MEASURE PRESSURE

AST 3.1 ## PRESSURE IN FLUIDS

Since fluids can take different shapes, certain phenomena related to fluids, such as buoyancy or flight, cannot be properly explained using the concept of force. The concept of pressure is more useful in these cases.

Pressure is the amount of force applied perpendicularly to an object per unit of surface area. It is measured in pascals (Pa) and described by the following formula:

$$P = \frac{F}{A}$$

where P is the pressure (in Pa)
F is the force perpendicular to the surface (in N)
A is the surface area subjected to the force (in m^2)

One pascal thus represents the force of one newton applied perpendicularly to a surface of one square metre, or:

$$1 \text{ Pa} = \frac{1 \text{ N}}{1 \text{ m}^2}$$

AST ### PRESSURE IN A LIQUID

In a liquid, the pressure depends on two factors: the depth and the density of the liquid. Table 3.28 summarizes the effects of these two factors on pressure.

3.28 FACTORS INFLUENCING PRESSURE IN A LIQUID

Factor	Factor variation	Result
Depth	Increased depth in the liquid	Increased pressure
	Reduced depth in the liquid	Reduced pressure
Density	Higher liquid density	Higher pressure
	Lower liquid density	Lower pressure

3.29 The water pressure on the diver increases as he dives deeper. If he is in the sea, he will experience greater pressure than in fresh water because the density of seawater is higher than that of fresh water.

AST PRESSURE IN A GAS

In a gas, the pressure depends on the number of collisions between the gas particles. The more collisions, the greater the pressure, and vice versa. The number of collisions can be made to vary by changing any one of three factors: the temperature, the volume and the number of particles. Table 3.31 summarizes the effects of variations in these factors on pressure.

3.30 The atmospheric pressure on these balloons drops as they gain altitude because the number of gas particles in the atmosphere and their temperature both fall.

3.31 FACTORS INFLUENCING PRESSURE IN A GAS

Factor	Factor variation	Result
Temperature	Higher gas temperature	Increased pressure
	Lower gas temperature	Reduced pressure
Volume	Higher gas volume	Reduced pressure
	Lower gas volume	Increased pressure
Number of particles	Higher number of gas particles	Increased pressure
	Lower number of gas particles	Reduced pressure

AST 3.2 PASCAL'S PRINCIPLE

Blaise Pascal (1623–1662), the famous French physicist and mathematician, experimented widely with pressure applied to enclosed fluids. He noticed that, when pressure is applied at one point of such a fluid, the resulting rise in pressure is transmitted uniformly throughout the fluid and even to the container surfaces. In 1653, he stated the principle that still bears his name today.

> **PASCAL'S PRINCIPLE states that an increase in the pressure of an enclosed fluid is transmitted uniformly in all directions.**

Pascal's principle has been applied in many modern devices, from water pistols to hydraulic brakes and from syringes to artesian wells. In some of these applications, force is transmitted from one point to another, making it possible to do work across a distance. This is true of syringes and hydraulic brakes, for example (Figure 3.32). Other applications, such as hydraulic lifts, amplify the applied force (Figure 3.33).

A BARREL FULL OF PRESSURE

Pascal himself demonstrated his principle, using a barrel full of water in which he installed a small pipe. He then gradually added water to the barrel through the pipe. After a certain time, the barrel burst.

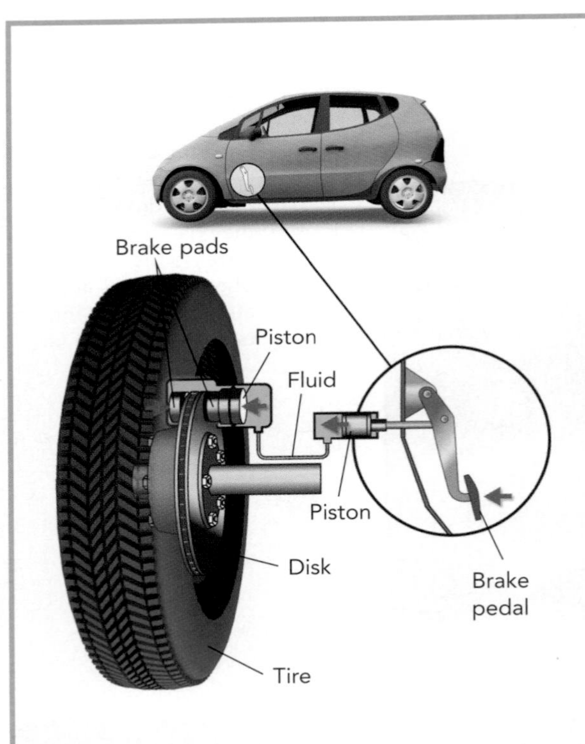

3.32 When a driver steps on the brake pedal, the pressure from his or her foot is transmitted through the brake fluid to the pads, which, in turn, act on the disks. Force is thus transmitted across a distance.

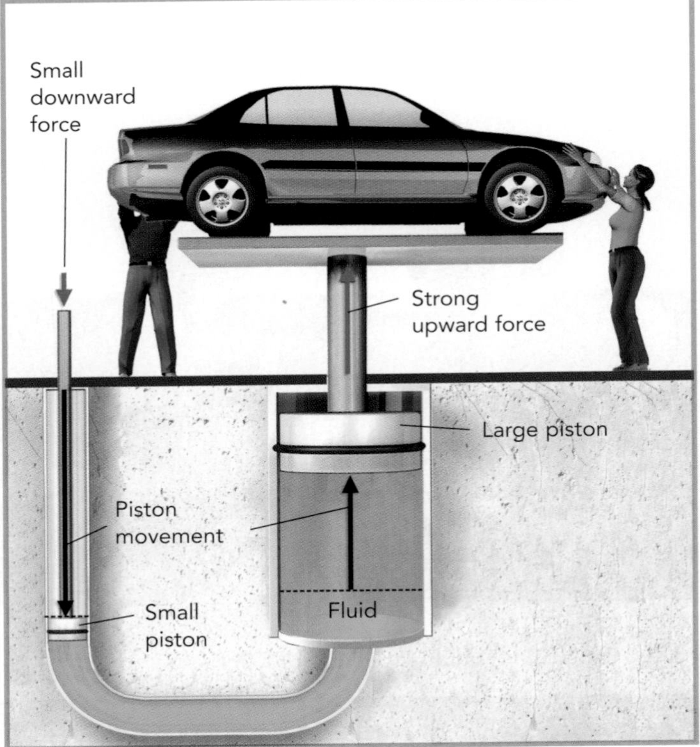

3.33 When the small piston is pressed, the resulting increase in pressure is distributed uniformly throughout the fluid. And because the surface area of the two pistons is different, a small force applied to the small piston generates a stronger force on the large piston. This mechanical advantage is used to lift heavy objects, such as cars. Note, however, that the large piston moves much less than the small piston.

AST 3.3 ARCHIMEDES' PRINCIPLE

LABS 24–27

An object dropped into a liquid can either sink, remain suspended at a certain depth or float on the surface. What determines whether an object sinks or floats? The ancient Greek scientist Archimedes (287–212 BCE) came up with an ingenious answer to this question.

First, Archimedes discovered that the volume of a solid can be determined by measuring the volume of water that the solid displaces when it is placed in a container filled to the brim. This is the overflow method of measuring volume.

Next, Archimedes knew that the pressure in a liquid increases with depth, creating an upward force called *buoyancy* (Figure 3.34). Finally, Archimedes discovered that the magnitude of this buoyant force was equal to the weight of the fluid displaced by the immersed object.

ARCHIMEDES' PRINCIPLE states that an object immersed in a fluid is subjected to a buoyant force equal to the weight of the fluid displaced by the object.

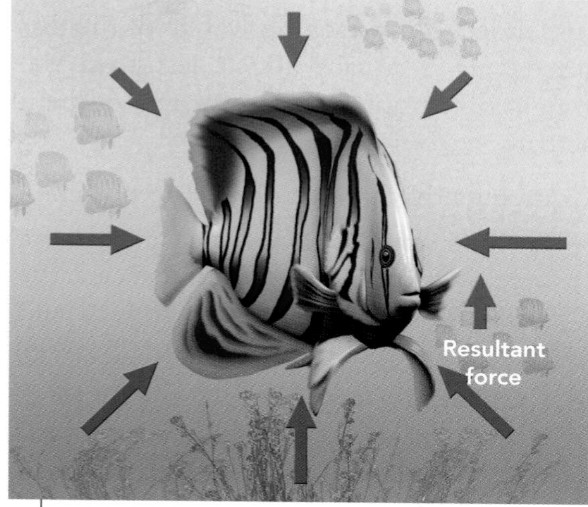

3.34 Since the pressure in a liquid increases with depth, the pressure at the base of an immersed object is greater than the pressure at the top. The pressure on each side of the object is equal, so its net effect is zero. The resultant force is thus directed upward.

THE RIGHT FIGURE FOR FLOATING

At the pool, some people swim like fish, and others sink like stones. The difference is not simply a question of mastering the techniques of the crawl or breaststroke. Swimming fast also depends on a person's body type.

"The greater a swimmer's buoyancy, the less energy he or she uses to stay afloat," says Didier Chollet, a sports scientist at Université de Rouen. People's buoyancy varies with their weight, its distribution in the body and the density of their muscles and bones. Ideally, a swimmer has a long, light body.

The French swimmer Laure Manaudou, winner of two gold medals, two silver and one bronze at the 2007 World Aquatics Championships in Melbourne, Australia, has the ideal body shape. "She's like a raceboat," says Georges Cazorla, a specialist in exercise physiology at Université de Bordeaux II.

Source: Adapted from Olivier Talles, "La force des nageurs, c'est leur silhouette," *La Croix*, March 29, 2007, p. 23. *[Translation]*

Body type can affect human buoyancy.

Archimedes' principle gives the impression that an object in a fluid is automatically "relieved" of a part of its weight, equivalent to the volume of displaced fluid. In fact, even air exerts an upward force on objects suspended in it. Since the weight of the displaced air is usually much less than the weight of the objects, however, few of them actually remain suspended.

Consequently, three situations are possible:

- The buoyant force (F_b) is weaker than the force of gravity ($F_b < F_g$). In this case, the resultant force is directed downward, and the immersed object sinks to the bottom.
- The buoyant force is equal to the force of gravity ($F_b = F_g$), so the resultant force is zero, and the object maintains the same depth.
- The buoyant force is greater than the force of gravity ($F_b > F_g$). In this case, the resultant force is directed upward, and the object rises to the surface.

3.35 When this anchor is dropped into the water, it displaces 2 L of water. The weight of this volume of water is 20 N. The buoyant force on the anchor is thus 20 N. Since the anchor weighs 150 N, it will sink to the bottom.

ENVIRONMENT EXTRA

David vs. Goliath

To assure their buoyancy, big ships often have ballast tanks that the crew can fill with water or empty, depending on the weight of the cargo. The tanks may also carry unwelcome visitors. Zebra mussels are thought to have been introduced into Canada in this way. The mussels' presence was first noted around 1990, in Lake St. Clair, Ontario.

Since then, the zebra mussel population has grown rapidly. Each female can lay up to a million eggs a year. The microscopic eggs can spread easily from one region to another. At a certain stage of their development, zebra mussels attach themselves to a solid surface with a bundle of filaments. Many types of surfaces are affected: rocks, aquatic plants, shells of other mollusk species, pipes, and boat motors and hulls. In sufficient numbers, the mussels can block pipes, choke motors and compromise ship buoyancy.

Even if adult zebra mussels are no more than a few centimetres long, they can cause significant damage if hundreds, even thousands, of them mass together on the same surface.

Ship designers apply Archimedes' principle by distributing the weight of a ship so that it displaces the largest possible volume of water. The weight of the vessel is thus equal to the weight of the displaced water. The ship achieves equilibrium and remains afloat.

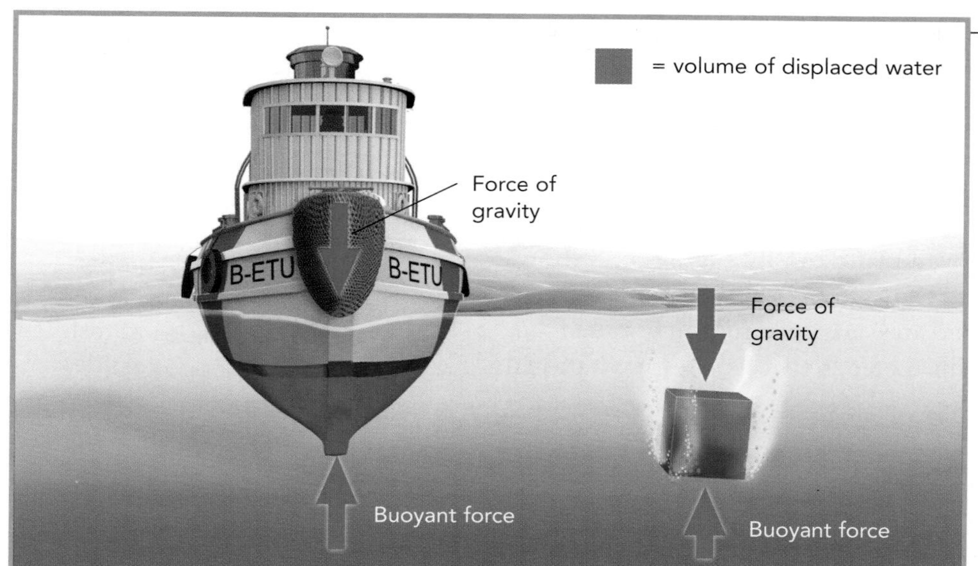

3.36 The two objects have the same weight. However, the boat floats, while the iron block sinks to the bottom because the boat displaces a much larger volume of water than the iron block does.

Submarines can adjust their own buoyancy with a system of ballast tanks, as explained in Figure 3.37.

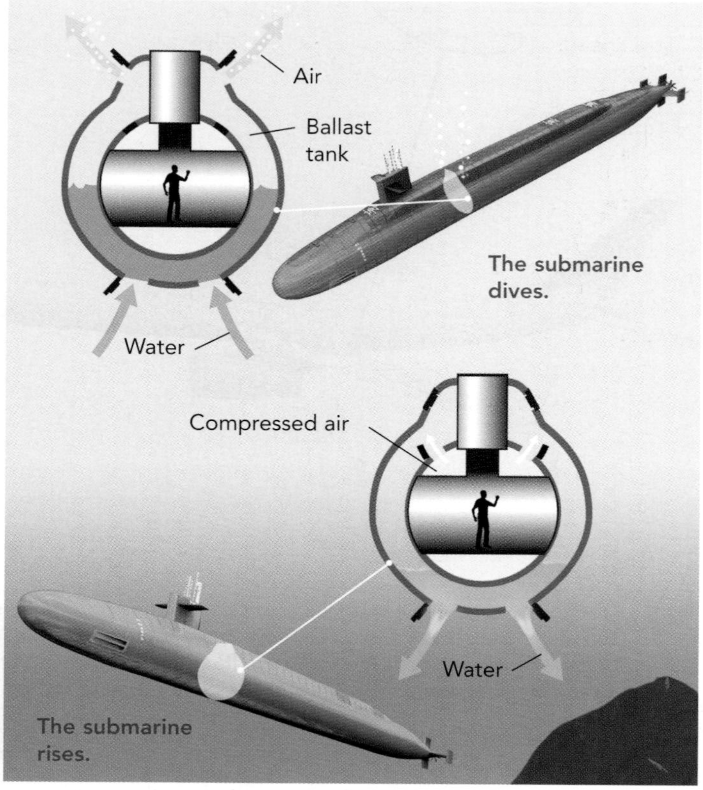

3.37 When the submarine crew decides to dive, the ballast tanks are filled with water. The vessel sinks because its weight has increased. To make the submarine rise again, the crew empties the ballast tanks, replacing the water with air from a compressed air tank. The submarine becomes lighter and rises to the surface.

AST 3.4 BERNOULLI'S PRINCIPLE

When a fluid is in motion, such as water running through pipes or the wind in the air, its pressure varies with its speed. The higher the speed of the fluid, the lower its pressure, and vice versa. This relationship between speed and pressure was established in 1738 by the Swiss mathematician and physicist Daniel Bernoulli (1700–1782).

> **BERNOULLI'S PRINCIPLE states that the higher the speed of a fluid, the lower its pressure, and vice versa.**

This principle helps explain how a plane can fly. Figure 3.38 shows that the drop in pressure above the wing combined with the rise in pressure below the wing creates an upward force called *lift*. When the magnitude of the lift exceeds that of the gravitational force, the plane rises into the air.

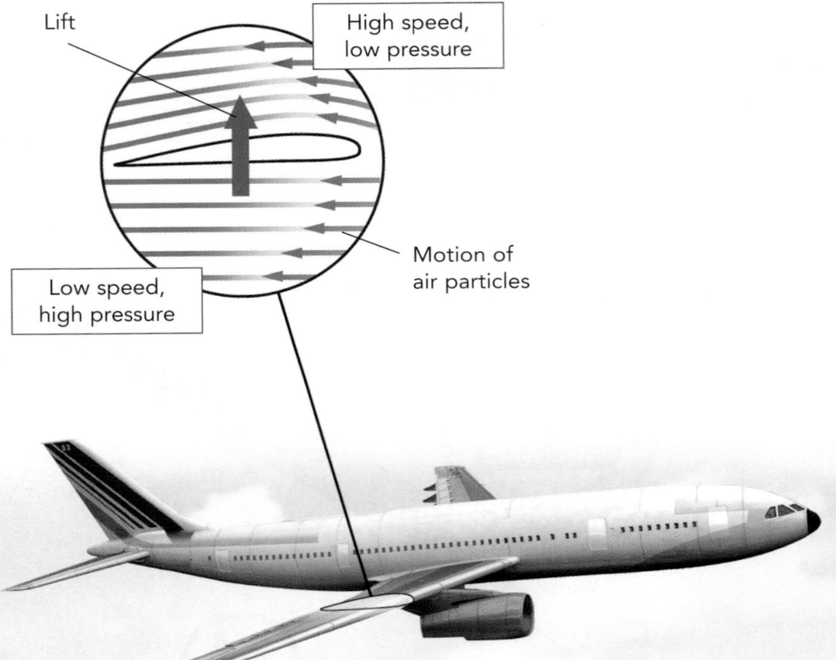

3.38 Due to the shape of a wing, air particles that pass over it, where the surface is curved, are forced to move more rapidly than those that pass below the wing, where the surface is flat. The pressure is thus greater below the wing than above, and the wing is subjected to an upward force called *lift*.

THE MYSTERY OF THE MOVING SHOWER CURTAIN

In the shower, the water spray causes a displacement of air particles. According to Bernoulli's principle, the particles in motion are at lower pressure than particles at rest. The pressure on opposite sides of the curtain thus becomes unequal, forcing the curtain to move toward the low-pressure area—inside the shower.

1773–1857

George Cayley

In 1809, this English engineer and inventor explained how a plane can fly, by defining the forces acting on the wings. Several years later, he designed the first prototype of an airplane—a nonmotorized glider.

CHECKUP

ST 1–6 and E.

EST 1–19, 25–29 and A–E.

AST 1–6, 13–24, 30–36 and E.

SE 1, 2, 6–14, 25–29 and B–E.

1 What is energy? (pp. 70–78)

1. Name the form or forms of energy in each of the following energy sources.

A

C

2. In each of the following examples, is energy used to do work or to cause a change?

a) a puddle of water evaporating in the sun

b) a burning log

c) a car moving along the road

d) a person climbing a staircase

3. Why is the amount of energy in the universe said to be constant?

4. Does each of the following situations describe a transfer or a transformation of energy, or both?

a) Solar energy makes photosynthesis in plants possible.

b) Energy from a heating system warms the air in a home.

c) Power plants generate electricity that is then delivered to our homes.

d) Food provides the energy we need to go about our daily lives.

5. To perform work equal to 2400 J, a machine consumes 12 000 J. What is the energy efficiency of this machine?

6. Can a cup of boiling water contain more thermal energy than a bucket of water at 50°C? Explain your answer.

7. Amanda applies the same amount of heat to four samples of matter:

– a piece of wood

– a piece of silver

– a piece of iron

– a piece of copper

If each sample has the same mass and the same initial temperature, which will experience the greatest temperature variation? Explain your answer.

8. Ravi puts a 100-g block of lead, heated to 155°C, in 100 mL of water at 19°C. The water temperature rises to 24°C. Assuming no energy has been lost to the surroundings, calculate the specific heat capacity of lead.

9. You pour 250 mL of water into a glass just out of the freezer. After a while, you notice that the temperature of the water has fallen from 18°C to 12°C.
   a) How much heat has been transferred between the water and the glass?
   b) Did the water give off or absorb energy? Explain your answer.
   c) Did the glass give off or absorb energy? Explain your answer.

10. A baseball pitcher throws a ball weighing about 150 g to another player. What is the kinetic energy of the ball if, at the moment it is caught, its velocity is 5 m/s?

11. An elevator carries a person weighing 60 kg from the ground to the eighth floor.
   a) If the eighth floor is 56 m above the ground, what is the potential energy acquired by the person?
   b) Where did the potential energy come from?

12. Jessica builds a model track for her little brother. She places a toy bus weighing 0.5 kg at point A and gives it a velocity of 2 m/s. The bus travels the entire route with no further addition of energy.

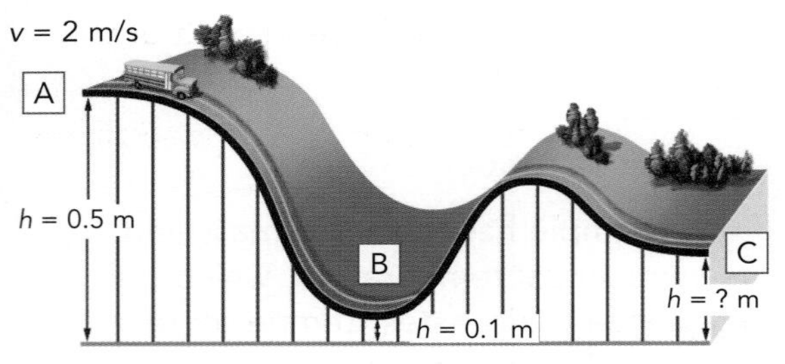

   a) Ignoring the effect of friction, calculate the mechanical energy, the potential energy and the kinetic energy of the bus at points A, B and C.
   b) Calculate the height of the bus at point C.

2 Motion and forces (pp. 79–91)

13. In each of the following situations, does the force involve pulling or pushing?
   a) the force of a dog on its leash
   b) the force of a person inserting a letter in an envelope
   c) the force of a magnet on a paper clip
   d) the force of a bowstring on an arrow

14. The illustration below represents the action of a force.

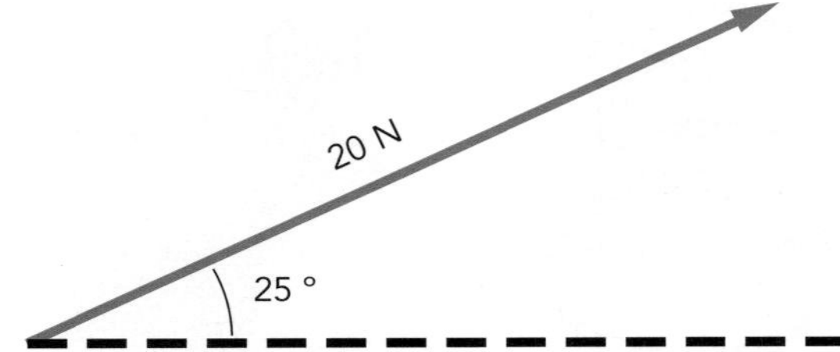

   a) Is the force applied horizontally or vertically?
   b) Which symbol indicates the direction of the force?
   c) What is the magnitude of the force?

15. How does the intensity of the Earth's gravitational field vary?

16. What distinguishes mass from weight?

17. Plasma or liquid crystal television sets are much lighter in weight than the old models with cathode ray screens. What is the weight of a television set that has a mass of 25 kg at the Earth's surface?

18. On the surface of which planet of the solar system would you be heaviest? Explain your answer.

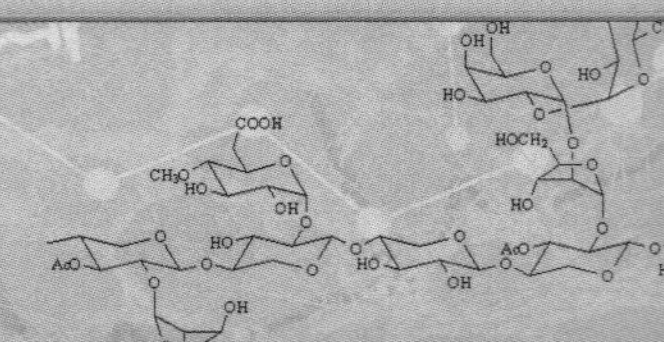

19. Look at the illustration below.

a) Will the mass of this explorer vehicle be the same on Earth and Mars? Explain your answer.

b) Will the weight of the explorer be the same on Earth and Mars? Explain your answer.

20. Name the type of force involved in each of the following examples.

a) pants that stick to our legs from static electricity

b) the force that holds together the particles in the nucleus of an atom

c) the friction between the gears of a watch

d) the string holding a helium-filled balloon

21. Find the resultant force in each of the following situations.

a)

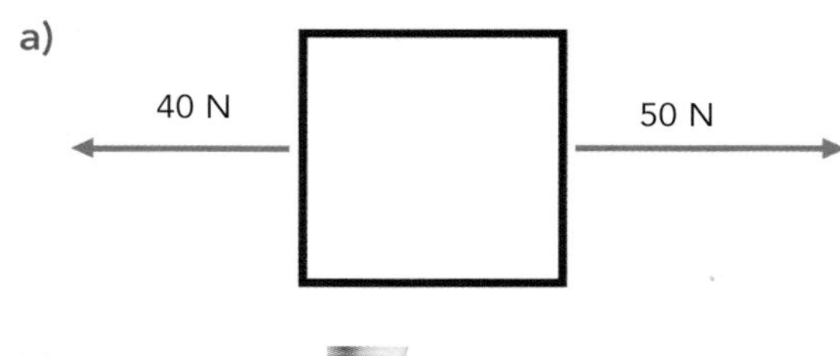

b)

22. Which of the following situations will have the same effect as a force of 50 N? Explain your answer.

a) two forces of 25 N applied along the same line of action but in opposite directions

b) two forces of 25 N applied along the same line of action and in the same direction

c) two forces of 25 N applied along different lines of action but in the same direction

23. The motor of a boat has a propulsion force of 75 N, while the frictional force of the water against the hull is 10 N. What is the resultant force of this system?

24. If you walk at a constant pace (speed), what is the resultant force of your travel?

25. Find the horizontal and vertical components of each of the following forces.

a)

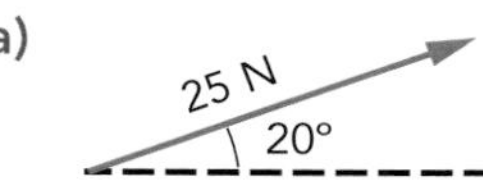

b)

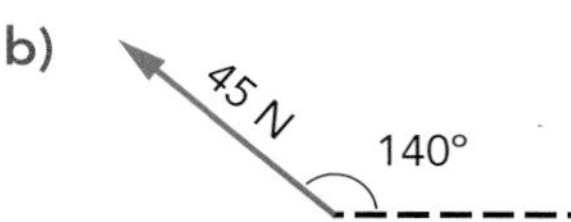

26. What is the effective force in each of the following situations?

a) The box slides down the inclined plane.

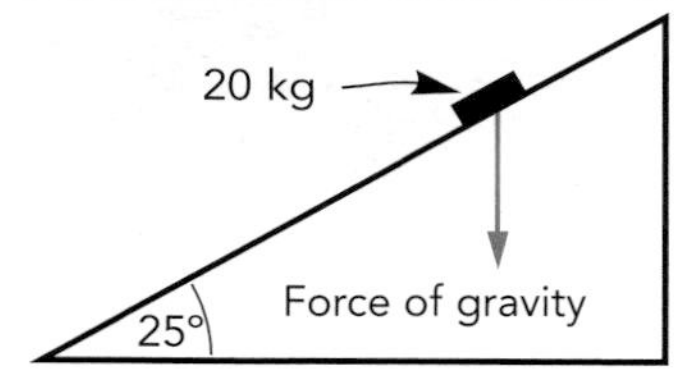

b) The box slides along the ground.

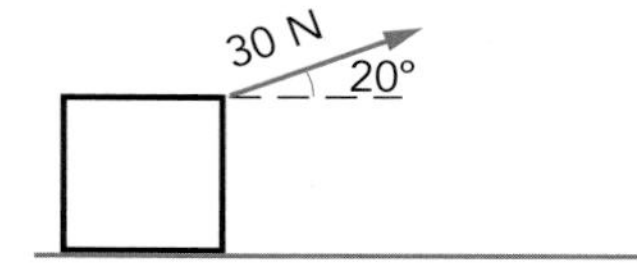

27. A person applies a force of 200 N to the side of a piano. How much work will it take to move the piano 5 m?

28. How much work does the gravitational force acting on this skier represent if the skier travels 4 m?

29. When work is done, energy is consumed. What happens to this energy? Explain your answer.

3 Forces in fluids (pp. 92–98)

30. a) What is a fluid?
    b) Name four examples of fluids.

31. Look at the photo below.

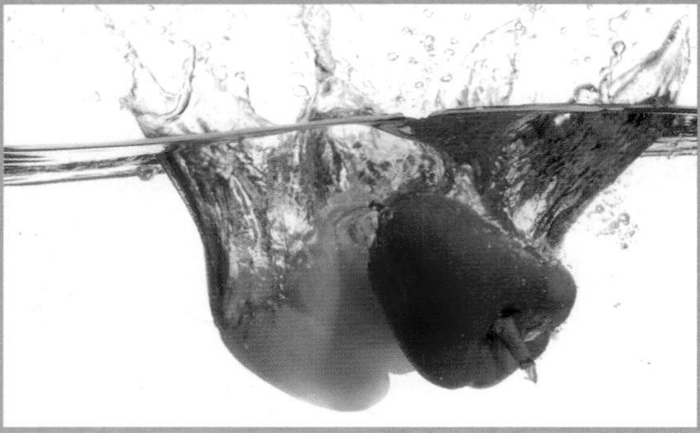

   a) How does water pressure act on these objects?
   b) Where is the pressure greatest? Explain your answer.
   c) If the water is replaced by a liquid of lower density, how will the pressure change?

32. Pressure is applied to the plunger of a syringe containing 30 mL of liquid. The plunger then exerts a pressure of 30 kPa on the liquid. If the initial pressure of the liquid was 2 kPa, what will be the pressure of the liquid expelled at the other end of the syringe? Explain your answer, specifying the principle of physics you used to determine the pressure.

33. What makes a boat float?

34. An object weighing 98 N is immersed in water.
   a) What weight of water must be displaced so that the object can float? Explain your answer.
   b) What is the volume of water displaced by the object, given that the density of water is 1 g/mL?
   c) The same object is immersed in a solution with a density of 0.8 g/mL. Given that the object displaces the same volume of liquid as in b), will it float or not? Show your calculations.

35. When the wind blows hard, what happens to the air pressure? Explain your answer.

36. Name the principle that explains each of the following situations.
   a) The hull of a submarine must be very thick, from top to bottom, to resist the pressure of the water.
   b) To float, a submarine must empty its ballast tanks.
   c) Force can be amplified with a hydraulic press.
   d) The action of the wind makes a flag fly.
   e) Warming the air in a hot-air balloon makes it rise into the air.
   f) Birds can fly partly because of the particular shape of their wings.

review questions

A. To boil water, Bassima uses a microwave oven.

a) How much energy does it take to boil 250 mL of water with an initial temperature of 20°C?

b) Bassima calculates that to boil the water, her oven used 100 000 J of electrical energy. What is the energy efficiency of the microwave oven?

B. James Prescott Joule designed many experiments involving thermal energy. In one of these experiments, he transformed the mechanical energy of an object into thermal energy, using the apparatus illustrated opposite, known today as *Joule's apparatus*.

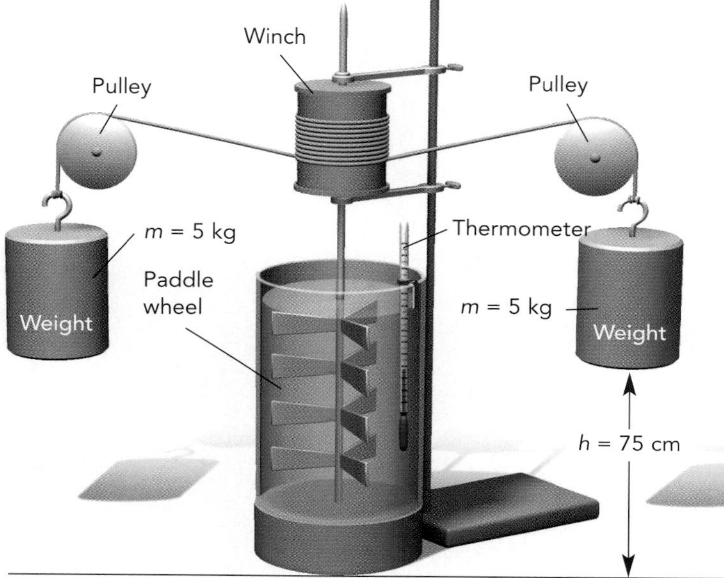

a) How much mechanical energy do the weights possess?

b) Given an initial quantity of one litre of water at 20°C in the container, what will be the final water temperature if the weights are lowered 20 times? The Joule apparatus is assumed to be 100-percent efficient, and the weights move 75 cm each time they fall.

C. A 10-kg chair is placed on a plane inclined at an angle of 25° to the horizontal. The plane exerts a frictional force of 30 N on the chair. Will the chair move? Explain your answer.

D. Fred lifts a 20-kg box to a height of 1 m.

a) How much work did Fred do to lift the box?

b) What form of energy did the box store?

E. Prepare your own summary of Chapter 3 by building a concept map.

JUGGLING WITH ENERGY EFFICIENCY

In Canada, buildings consume a huge share of our resources: about one third of the total energy used (including two thirds of the electricity) and one eighth of the water. Yet very few buildings are designed to reduce their energy use. The situation in Québec can be explained by two facts. First, electricity is relatively inexpensive, an advantage that obscures the need to reduce energy consumption. Second, companies have fallen into the habit of awarding construction contracts to the lowest bidder, leaving little room for projects that are more expensive to build but more economical in the long term. Despite this context, the Cité des arts du cirque, a centre for circus arts, did not hesitate to break the architectural mould. Its main building, called *La Tohu*, is a model of energy efficiency, both in Canada and around the world.

LA TOHU: GREEN TO THE CORE

La Tohu was built in the heart of Montréal, on the site of the former Miron quarry, which had long been a municipal landfill. Right from the start, the designers had a vision of an environmentally friendly building, both in its construction and its use.

To reduce heating costs, the organization reached an agreement with a neighbouring business that used methane from the landfill to generate electricity. Part of the water vapour from the methane combustion is diverted to La Tohu through a system of ducts. Heating the building thus takes 20 to 30 percent less energy than a conventional heating system.

The air-conditioning system for the theatre is also energy-efficient. It consists in an enormous "ice tray," which can be seen through a glass section of the floor in the main entrance hall. Air circulation in the theatre is also improved by an air shaft in the middle of the roof. Since hot air is less dense than cold air, the hot air naturally rises. Outdoor weather permitting, this method of hot-air evacuation represents a savings of up to 70 percent of the energy used in conventional ventilation systems.

Near the building, five geothermal wells were drilled to a depth of approximately 100 m, where the temperature remains around 10°C all year round. The wells provide heating in the winter and air conditioning in the summer.

La Tohu also features "green roofs." The roofs over the cloakroom, washrooms and north entrance are covered in vegetation. These green roofs help reduce the costs of air conditioning and heating by limiting temperature variations. They also reduce the greenhouse gas emissions from the building by recycling carbon dioxide.

In 2005, La Tohu was one of the first buildings in Canada to obtain LEED (Leadership in Energy and Environmental Design) certification, an international standard in environmentally sustainable construction.

A glass section in the floor of the main entrance hall gives visitors to the Tohu a glimpse of the 10 000-kg ice tray lying beneath it.

CHANGES IN THE CONSTRUCTION SECTOR

Environmental awareness is growing, and energy-efficient buildings are multiplying: the Lassonde building of École Polytechnique de Montréal, École de technologie supérieure, Cégep de Rimouski, the Biological Sciences building of Université du Québec à Montréal, and the Sûreté du Québec police station in Mont-Laurier are all examples of this new trend.

In 2007, the Société immobilière du Québec decreed that, in the future, all building projects of more than $2.5 million must obtain LEED certification. For the moment, however, few engineers and architects design buildings that meet this international standard. And even if the growing popularity of this certification brings hope of higher energy efficiency in new construction and in renovations, it will do nothing to improve energy efficiency in existing buildings.

1. Why is it important to reduce energy consumption?
2. Whether we own or rent our homes, we can all take steps to reduce our energy consumption. Give three examples of such steps.

2016 Scheduled start of testing at the future fusion power plant ITER, in France

1991 First controlled nuclear fusion

1986 Serious accident at the Chernobyl nuclear power plant, in Ukraine

1961 Development of scintigraphy, a technique for observing organs, using radioactive substances

1945 Development of the fission bomb (atomic bomb)

1896 Discovery of radioactivity

1866 Invention of dynamite

1840 Demonstration that all reactions are either endothermic or exothermic

1789 Formulation of the law of conservation of mass

1772 Demonstration that combustion results from the reaction of a substance with oxygen

CIRCA 1690 Demonstration that the reaction of an acid with a base produces a salt and water

CIRCA -3000 Discovery of petroleum

CIRCA -450 000 Taming of fire

Fire is at the root of profound changes. Sometimes it is destructive—when it sweeps through a forest, for example; sometimes it is beneficial, when people use it to cook food. Matter can be changed in other ways, too. In fact, the environment is subjected to a multitude of changes all interacting with one another. From photosynthesis in plants to the springtime melting of snow, every change in matter affects the balance of the world around us. How does matter change? What factors can alter these transformations? These are some of the questions we will try to answer in this chapter.

THE MATERIAL WORLD

4 Changes in matter

CONTENTS

ST
EST
AST
SE

1 What are changes in matter?

CONCEPT REVIEW
- Physical change
- Chemical change
- Atom
- Element

All matter is subject to change. When a tree loses a branch in strong winds, it changes shape. When snow melts in the sun, it changes state. When wood burns, it gives rise to new substances. When uranium reacts in a nuclear reactor, it transforms into other elements. Each of these examples involves a change in matter.

There are three types of changes in matter: physical changes, chemical changes and nuclear transformations.

If the **CHARACTERISTIC PROPERTIES** of matter remain the same after a transformation has occurred, the changes are called *physical changes*. The tree broken by the wind and the snow melting in the sun are examples of physical changes. In these cases, only the form or state of the matter is altered. The atoms and molecules that make up the matter do not change.

A PHYSICAL CHANGE alters neither the nature nor the characteristic properties of matter. The atoms and molecules of the substance do not change.

In other cases, such as burning wood, new substances with different characteristic properties are formed. Such changes are called *chemical changes*; they involve transformations in the nature of the matter. On the atomic level, the bonds between atoms are rearranged, which leads to the formation of different molecules.

A CHEMICAL CHANGE alters the nature and characteristic properties of matter. The bonds between atoms are rearranged, and new molecules are formed.

Nuclear transformations involve even more profound changes because they affect the very heart of the atom: the nucleus. For example, during uranium fission, the atoms split to form new elements, such as krypton and barium.

Nuclear comes from the Latin *nucleus*, meaning "kernel."

In a NUCLEAR TRANSFORMATION, the particles making up an atomic nucleus are rearranged, and new elements are formed.

In this chapter, chemical changes and nuclear transformations will be discussed in greater detail.

ST
EST
AST
SE

2 Chemical changes

During chemical changes, the chemical bonds between the atoms of the reactants (the substances involved) are broken, and new bonds are formed. As a result, new substances (products) emerge, with characteristic properties that are different from those of the original substances. The process is not instantaneous. Figure 4.1 shows that as a change is taking place, the reactants gradually disappear, giving way to products.

A number of signs point to the occurrence of a chemical change, including:

- the release of a gas
- the emission or absorption of heat
- the emission of light
- a change in colour
- the formation of a precipitate

4.1 QUANTITIES OF REACTANTS AND PRODUCTS OVER TIME

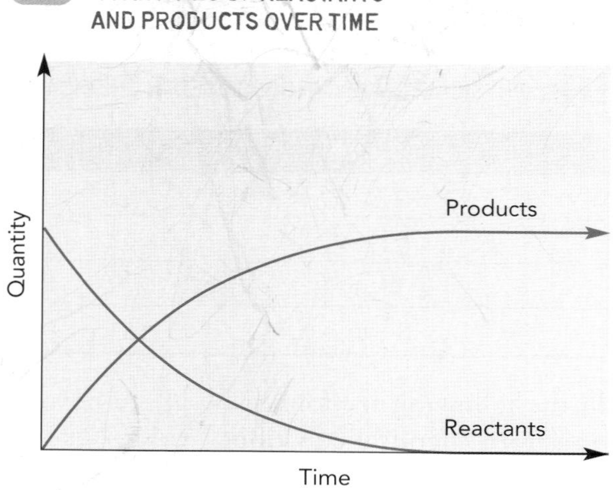

4.2 When methane (CH_4) burns, it releases heat and light. We can therefore deduce that a chemical change has occurred.

Chemical changes, which are also called *chemical reactions*, can be represented symbolically with chemical equations. Table 4.3 shows how to interpret (read) the equation for the reaction of methane with oxygen.

4.3 INTERPRETING A CHEMICAL EQUATION

Chemical equation	$CH_{4(g)}$	+	$2\ O_{2(g)}$	$\rightarrow$	$CO_{2(g)}$	+	$2\ H_2O_{(g)}$
Interpretation	Methane	reacts with	oxygen	to form	carbon dioxide	and	water vapour.

It is often useful to identify the physical state of the substances involved in a reaction, as in the equation of Table 4.3 (page 109). The state is indicated with a subscript symbol in parentheses to the right of the substance. For example, liquid water is written $H_2O_{(l)}$ in chemical equations. (In some texts, the physical state is not written as a subscript, but in standard print.)

4.4 PHYSICAL-STATE SYMBOLS USED IN CHEMICAL EQUATIONS

Symbol	Physical state
s	solid
l	liquid
g	gas
aq	aqueous (dissolved in water)

In the following sections, we will see how we can obtain further information from chemical equations.

ST EST SE 2.1 THE LAW OF CONSERVATION OF MASS

CONCEPT REVIEW
- Mass
- Conservation of matter

"Nothing is lost; nothing is created; everything is transformed." Antoine Laurent de Lavoisier (1743–1794) uttered this famous statement when he observed that the mass of a substance remained constant even after a chemical change. Indeed, when all the reactants and products involved in a reaction are taken into consideration, the total mass before and after the reaction does not vary. Scientists call this observation the *law of conservation of mass*.

When a sheet of paper is burned, for example, it seems to disappear. However, the sum of the mass of the gases released during combustion and the mass of the ashes left behind is exactly equal to the mass of the original paper and the oxygen used to burn it. The paper has not disappeared; it has been transformed.

On the atomic level, this law implies that the nature of the atoms involved in a chemical reaction is not altered by that reaction. Only the bonds between the atoms change.

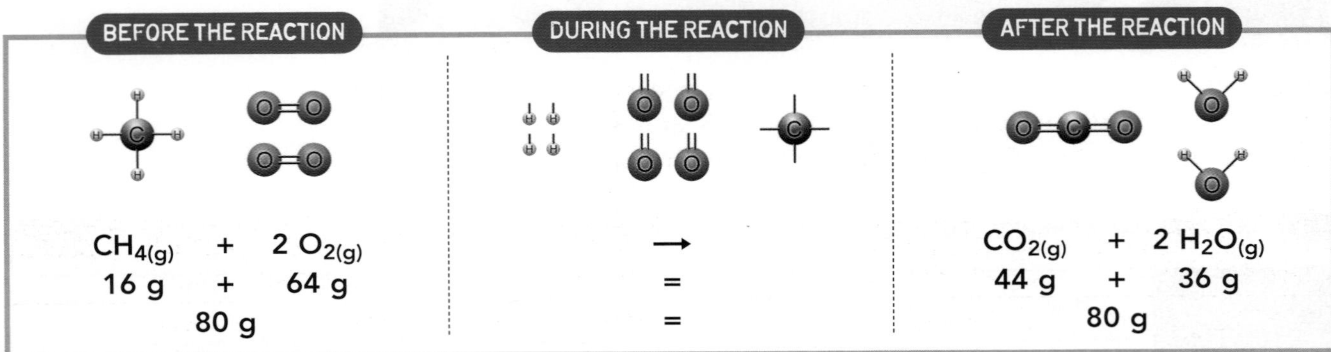

4.5 The combustion of methane does not change the nature of the carbon, hydrogen and oxygen atoms involved in the reaction. It changes only the way the atoms are arranged.

The LAW OF CONSERVATION OF MASS states that the total mass of reactants is always equal to the total mass of products.

ST EST SE 2.2 BALANCING CHEMICAL EQUATIONS

When we write a chemical equation, we first note the chemical formulas of all the reactants and products involved. Let's take the formation of ammonia as an example. Using the chemical formulas of the relevant substances, we can write a first version of the equation:

$$N_{2(g)} + H_{2(g)} \longrightarrow NH_{3(g)} \text{ (unbalanced equation)}$$

By counting the number of atoms of each element, as shown in Table 4.6, we can see that the the numbers are different before and after the reaction. To follow the law of conservation of mass, the number of molecules must be adjusted by adding the appropriate coefficient before each of the substances. This adjustment is known as *balancing a chemical equation*.

BALANCING A CHEMICAL EQUATION consists in placing a coefficient before each reactant and product so that the number of atoms of each element on the reactant side is equal to the number of atoms of each element on the product side.

1757
1836

Marie-Anne Lavoisier-Rumford

As the wife of Antoine Laurent de Lavoisier, this French woman of science worked with her husband, translating many scientific publications into French and drawing the illustrations for his treatise on chemistry. After Lavoisier's death, she had his memoirs published. Her second husband was the American scientist Benjamin Thompson, Count Rumford.

4.6 TOTAL NUMBER OF ATOMS OF EACH ELEMENT BEFORE AND AFTER THE REACTION

Before the chemical reaction		After the chemical reaction	
Reactants	Number of atoms	Product	Number of atoms
$N_2 + H_2$	2 nitrogen atoms 2 hydrogen atoms	NH_3	1 nitrogen atom 3 hydrogen atoms

The balanced chemical equation for ammonia synthesis is:

$$N_{2(g)} + 3\ H_{2(g)} \longrightarrow 2\ NH_{3(g)}$$

Note that a coefficient with a value of 1 is not written in an equation. We can now check whether this chemical equation is truly balanced, using Table 4.7.

4.7 TOTAL NUMBER OF ATOMS OF EACH ELEMENT BEFORE AND AFTER THE REACTION

Before the chemical reaction		After the chemical reaction	
Reactants	Number of atoms	Product	Number of atoms
$N_2 + 3\ H_2$	2 nitrogen atoms 6 hydrogen atoms	$2\ NH_3$	2 nitrogen atoms 6 hydrogen atoms

When balancing chemical equations, the following rules must be applied:

- Coefficients must be whole numbers.
- Coefficients must be as small as possible.
- New substances must never be added, nor existing substances removed.
- Subscripts in chemical formulas must never be changed.
- The final equation should always be checked by counting the number of atoms of each element on both sides.

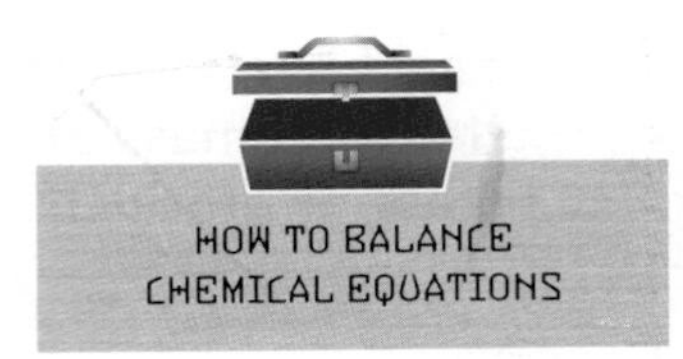

STOICHIOMETRY

Chemical equations contain valuable information that can be used to establish the precise quantities of reactants needed for a reaction to occur and to predict the resulting amounts of products. Chemicals can thus be used properly, and disastrous accidents can be avoided. This information is of the utmost importance in many areas, from the pharmaceutical laboratory to industry, and even to schools. To obtain this information from chemical equations, we apply the principles of stoichiometry.

Stoichiometry comes from the Greek *stoikheion*, meaning "element," and the suffix *-metry*, meaning "measure."

STOICHIOMETRY is the study of the quantities of reactants required for chemical reactions to occur and of the quantities of products that are thus formed.

To understand how stoichiometry can be useful, let's consider the following example from everyday life.

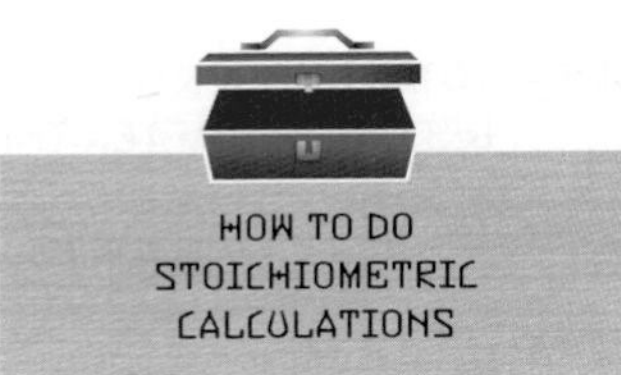

A box of pancake mix indicates that to prepare six pancakes, you must mix 250 mL of the powder with 500 mL of milk. However, you want only three pancakes. Since three is half of six, all you have to do is divide all of the amounts by two. So, to prepare three pancakes, you mix only 125 mL of powder with 250 mL of milk.

The same principle applies to chemical reactions. The proportions of the substances involved in a reaction are indicated by the related chemical equation. It is therefore possible to multiply or divide the amount of each of the substances by a given factor to obtain the desired result.

Now let's consider the equation for the synthesis of water:

$$2\ H_{2(g)} + O_{2(g)} \longrightarrow 2\ H_2O_{(l)}$$

Table 4.8 (page 113) provides several interpretations of this equation. The basic principle remains the same, however: the proportions of the substances must be maintained.

4.8 DIFFERENT INTERPRETATIONS OF THE CHEMICAL EQUATION FOR THE SYNTHESIS OF WATER

Chemical equation	$2\ H_{2(g)}$	+	$O_{2(g)}$	$\rightarrow$	$2\ H_2O_{(l)}$
Interpretation 1	Two hydrogen molecules	react with	one oxygen molecule	to form	two water molecules.
Interpretation 2	Two moles of hydrogen molecules	react with	one mole of oxygen molecules	to form	two moles of water molecules.
Interpretation 3	Four moles of hydrogen molecules	react with	two moles of oxygen molecules	to form	four moles of water molecules.

The mass of each substance can be calculated using the molar mass of its component elements (based on their atomic masses in the periodic table of the elements). Each of the masses can also be multiplied or divided by a given factor in various applications of the equation.

4.9 MASSES OF THE SUBSTANCES INVOLVED IN THE SYNTHESIS OF WATER

Reactants		Product
$2\ H_{2(g)}$	$O_{2(g)}$	$2\ H_2O_{(l)}$
$2\ \cancel{mol} \times (1.01 + 1.01)\ g/\cancel{mol} = 4.04\ g$	$1\ \cancel{mol} \times (16.00 + 16.00)\ g/\cancel{mol} = 32.00\ g$	$2\ \cancel{mol} \times (1.01 + 1.01 + 16.00)\ g/\cancel{mol} = 36.04\ g$

Table 4.9 shows the masses of the reactants and the product in the synthesis reaction. Based on this data, it is possible to calculate, for example, the mass of water produced by the reaction of exactly 1.00 g of hydrogen with a sufficient amount of oxygen.

$2\ H_{2(g)} + O_{2(g)} \rightarrow 2\ H_2O_{(l)}$

$2\ H_{2(g)}$	$2\ H_2O_{(l)}$
2 mol	2 mol
4.04 g	36.04 g
1.00 g	? g

$$\frac{1.00\ \cancel{g\ of\ H_2} \times 36.04\ g\ of\ H_2O}{4.04\ \cancel{g\ of\ H_2}} \approx 8.92\ g\ of\ H_2O$$

The reaction of 1.00 g of hydrogen with sufficient oxygen will produce approximately 8.92 g of water.

It is also possible to calculate the mass of a reactant based on the mass of another reactant. Referring to the previous example once again, the mass of oxygen needed to react completely with 1.00 g of hydrogen can be calculated as follows:

$2\ H_{2(g)} + O_{2(g)} \rightarrow 2\ H_2O_{(l)}$

$2\ H_{2(g)}$	$O_{2(g)}$
2 mol	1 mol
4.04 g	32.00 g
1.00 g	? g

$$\frac{1.00\ \cancel{g\ of\ H_2} \times 32.00\ g\ of\ O_2}{4.04\ \cancel{g\ of\ H_2}} \approx 7.92\ g\ of\ O_2$$

It takes approximately 7.92 g of oxygen to react completely with 1.00 g of hydrogen.

EST SE

2.4 ENDOTHERMIC AND EXOTHERMIC REACTIONS

LAB 31

Chemical reactions can be classified into two main categories, depending on whether they absorb or release energy. Since thermal energy is the most frequently encountered form of energy, reactions are described as *endothermic* or *exothermic*.

Exothermic comes from the Greek words *exō*, meaning "outside," and *thermos*, meaning "heat."

Endothermic contains the prefix *endo-*, from the Greek *endon*, meaning "within."

An ENDOTHERMIC REACTION is a chemical change that absorbs energy.

An EXOTHERMIC REACTION is a chemical change that releases energy.

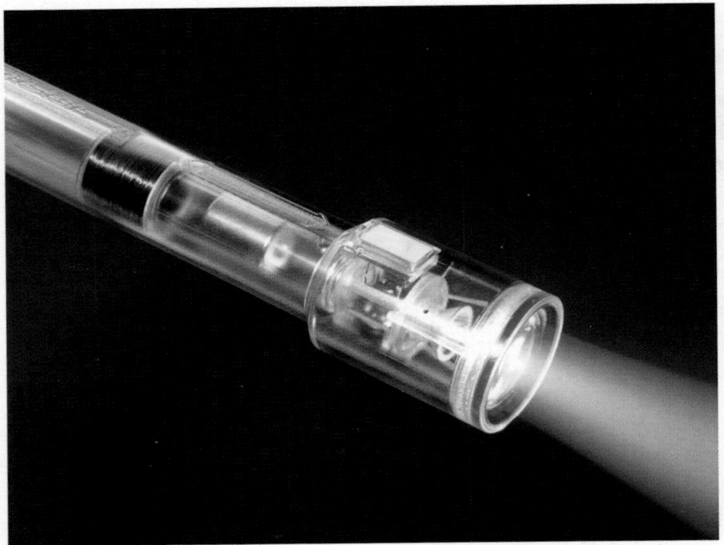

4.10 The flashlight works because the batteries in it produce electricity. The chemical reaction that occurs in the batteries is an exothermic reaction.

4.11 For a cake to bake, it must absorb heat from the oven. Baking the cake involves an endothermic reaction.

Endothermic reactions require a constant source of energy. For example, a cake will stop baking if it is taken out of the oven before it is ready. Exothermic reactions, on the other hand, need energy only to be initiated. They then continue on their own, using the energy they generate themselves. No additional energy is required. In fact, an exothermic reaction can be used as a source of energy for initiating other reactions.

The energy released by an exothermic reaction is absorbed by the surrounding environment, often causing the temperature to rise. Conversely, the energy absorbed by an endothermic reaction is taken from the surrounding environment, which often causes the temperature to drop. The two types of reaction can therefore usually be distinguished by measuring the variations in the environmental temperature before and after reactions.

Why does one reaction release energy, while another absorbs it? The type of reaction depends on several factors, including the energy in the bonds of the reactants and the products. Breaking a chemical bond always requires energy, while forming a chemical bond always releases energy. Calculating the difference between the total energy absorbed when bonds are broken and the total energy released when new bonds are formed is one way of determining whether a reaction is endothermic or exothermic.

Tables 4.12 and 4.13 present the amount of energy involved in breaking or forming certain chemical bonds, depending on whether they are **SINGLE BONDS** (Table 4.12) or **DOUBLE BONDS** and triple bonds (Table 4.13). Note that the energy required to break a bond is equal to that released during the formation of the same bond. However, the amount of energy differs from one bond to another.

AN EFFECTIVE DE-ICER

Calcium chloride ($CaCl_2$), which is sometimes scattered on roads in winter, makes ice melt and prevents it from freezing again. Dissolving $CaCl_2$ in water is a highly exothermic reaction, which makes the ice on the road melt. The solution also has a much lower freezing point than that of pure water, so it can remain liquid even during periods of intense cold. 5

4.12 SINGLE BOND ENERGIES, IN kJ/mol

H	C	N	O	F	Si	P	S	Cl	Br	I	
435	414	389	464	569	293	318	339	431	368	297	H
	347	293	351	439	289	264	259	330	276	238	C
		159	201	272	355	209	—*	201	243	—	N
			138	184	368	351	—	205	201	201	O
				159	540	490	327	255	197	273	F
					176	213	226	360	289	213	Si
						213	230	331	272	213	P
							213	251	213	—	S
								243	218	209	Cl
									192	180	Br
										151	I

* A dash means that the two elements do not tend to bond.

4.13 DOUBLE AND TRIPLE BOND ENERGIES

Type of bond	Energy (kJ/mol)
N=N	418
C=N	615
C=C	611
C=O	741
O=O	498
N≡N	946
C≡N	891
C≡C	741

Let's consider the example of methane reacting with oxygen.

As Figure 4.5 (page 110) shows, the methane molecule contains four carbon-hydrogen single bonds. Table 4.12 (page 115) indicates that these bonds each contain 414 kJ of energy. Meanwhile, oxygen is made up of two oxygen atoms joined by a double bond. Table 4.13 (page 115) shows that this bond contains 498 kJ of energy. The energy required to break the bonds of the reactants is therefore:

$CH_4 + 2\ O_2$

$(4 \times 414\ kJ) + (2 \times 498\ kJ) = 2652\ kJ$

This chemical reaction produces carbon dioxide and water. One molecule of carbon dioxide contains two carbon-oxygen double bonds. Water contains two hydrogen-oxygen single bonds. The energy released when these molecules form is therefore:

$CO_2 + 2\ H_2O$

$(2 \times 741\ kJ) + (4 \times 464\ kJ) = 3338\ kJ$

The amount of energy released or absorbed by a reaction can be estimated by calculating its reaction energy (also called its *Q value*), which is the difference between the energy absorbed when the bonds between the atoms of the reactants break and the energy released when the bonds between the atoms of the products form.

In the example of the methane reaction, the reaction energy is as follows:

- Energy absorbed by the reactants: 2652 kJ
- Energy released by the products: 3338 kJ
- Reaction energy: 2652 kJ – 3338 kJ = –686 kJ

The reaction of one mole of methane with two moles of oxygen therefore releases 686 kJ of energy. The negative result indicates that this reaction releases more energy than it absorbs, so it is an exothermic reaction. Note that this is an approximation. To obtain a more exact figure, other factors (whose measurement is more complex) must be taken into account.

Reaction energy also helps explain why some exothermic reactions do not take place spontaneously. For example, it takes approximately 2652 kJ of energy to burn one mole of methane. As long as this amount of energy has not been supplied, no reaction will occur.

Now let's look at an example of an endothermic reaction: the electrolysis of water.

- Chemical reaction of water electrolysis: $2\ H_2O \rightarrow 2\ H_2 + O_2$
- Energy absorbed by the reactants: 4 × 464 kJ = 1856 kJ
- Energy released by the products: (2 × 435 kJ) + (498 kJ) = 1368 kJ
- Reaction energy: 1856 kJ – 1368 kJ = +488 kJ

The electrolysis of two moles of water absorbs approximately 488 kJ of energy. The reaction is therefore endothermic.

4.14 ENERGY ABSORBED AND RELEASED AS THE REACTION OF METHANE WITH OXYGEN PROGRESSES

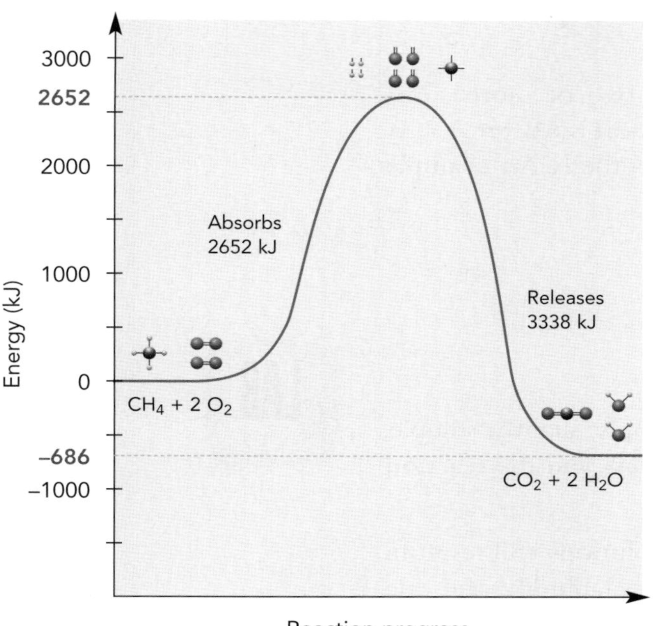

4.15 ENERGY ABSORBED AND RELEASED DURING WATER ELECTROLYSIS AS THE REACTION PROGRESSES

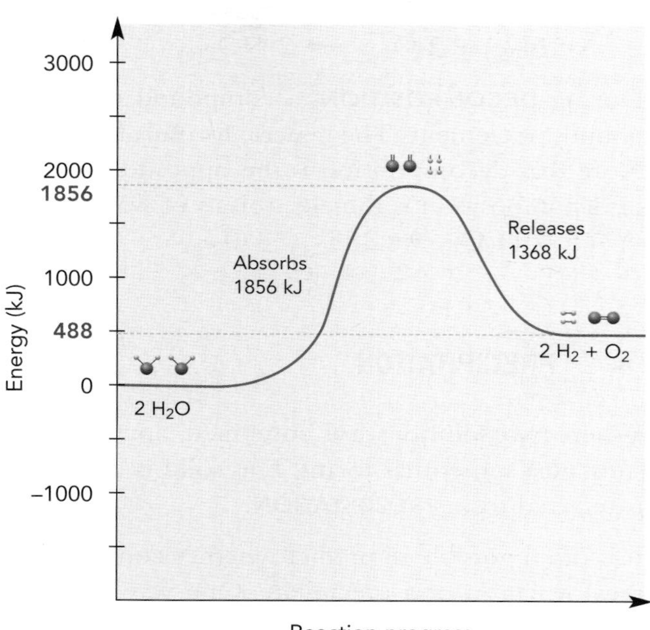

Based on the reaction energy and the principles of stoichiometry, the amount of energy resulting from the reaction of different quantities of matter can be estimated. For example, the amount of energy produced by the reaction of 32 g of methane with sufficient oxygen is calculated as follows:

$$CH_{4(g)} + 2\ O_{2(g)} \longrightarrow CO_{2(g)} + 2\ H_2O_{(g)} + 686\ kJ$$

1 mol	686 kJ
16.05 g	686 kJ
32.00 g	? kJ

$$\frac{32.00\ \cancel{g} \times 686\ kJ}{16.05\ \cancel{g}} = 1368\ kJ$$

The reaction of 32 g of methane with sufficient oxygen will produce approximately 1368 kJ of energy.

ST EST AST SE 2.5 TYPES OF CHEMICAL CHANGE

Chemical changes occur in a multitude of forms. Some types of change share certain characteristics, which makes it possible to predict their behaviour. In the coming sections, we will discuss the following types of chemical change: synthesis and decomposition, precipitation, acid-base neutralization, oxidation, cellular respiration and photosynthesis.

CONCEPT REVIEW

- Decomposition and synthesis
- Precipitation
- Acidity/alkalinity
- Oxidation
- Photosynthesis and respiration

SE SYNTHESIS AND DECOMPOSITION

SYNTHESIS is a reaction in which two or more reactants combine to form a new product. The generic formula for synthesis is A + B ⟶ AB. For example, the equation for the synthesis of nitrogen dioxide is:

$$N_{2(g)} + 2\ O_{2(g)} \longrightarrow 2\ NO_{2(g)}$$

During **DECOMPOSITION**, a compound separates into two or more compounds or elements. The generic formula for decomposition is AB ⟶ A + B. Note that decomposition is the opposite reaction to synthesis. An example of decomposition is the electrolysis of water:

$$2\ H_2O_{(l)} \longrightarrow 2\ H_{2(g)} + O_{2(g)}$$

SE PRECIPITATION

When two solutions are combined, an insoluble, or only slightly soluble, substance sometimes forms. This solid is called a *precipitate*, and the reaction is referred to as **PRECIPITATION**.

It is often possible to predict whether combining two solutions will result in the formation of a precipitate. One way is to refer to a table like the one below showing the solubility of various **IONIC COMPOUNDS**.

4.16 THE SOLUBILITY OF VARIOUS IONIC COMPOUNDS

Negative ions	Positive ions																
	NH_4^+	Li^+	Na^+	K^+	Mg^{2+}	Ca^{2+}	Ba^{2+}	Al^{3+}	Cu^{2+}	Fe^{2+}	Fe^{3+}	Ni^{2+}	Zn^{2+}	Hg^{2+}	Ag^+	Sn^{2+}	Pb^{2+}
CH_3COO^-	○	○	○	○	○	○	○	○	○	○	○	○	○	○	●	—	○
NO_3^-	○	○	○	○	○	○	○	○	○	○	○	○	○	○	○	○	○
Cl^-	○	○	○	○	○	○	○	○	○	○	○	○	○	○	●	○	●
Br^-	○	○	○	○	○	○	○	○	○	○	○	○	○	●	●	○	●
I^-	○	○	○	○	○	○	○	○	○	○	—	○	○	●	●	○	●
SO_4^{2-}	○	○	○	○	○	●	●	○	○	○	○	○	○	—	○	○	●
SO_3^{2-}	○	○	○	○	●	●	●	—	—	●	—	—	●	—	●	—	●
S^{2-}	○	○	○	○	—	—	—	—	●	●	●	●	●	●	●	●	●
CO_3^{2-}	○	●	○	○	●	●	●	—	●	●	—	●	●	—	●	—	●
OH^-	○	○	○	○	●	●	○	●	●	●	●	●	●	●	●	●	●
PO_4^{3-}	○	○	○	○	●	●	●	●	●	●	●	●	●	●	●	—	●
CrO_4^{2-}	○	○	○	○	○	○	●	—	●	—	●	●	●	●	●	—	●

○ = Soluble ● = Insoluble or only slightly soluble — = Does not form a compound

Let's look at an example. When a solution of sodium chloride (NaCl) is combined with a solution of silver nitrate ($AgNO_3$), the following ions come into contact: Na^+, Cl^-, Ag^+ and NO_3^-. Since positive ions tend to attract negative ions, the most likely compounds to result from the mixture are $NaNO_3$ and AgCl. Table 4.16 (page 118) indicates that the compound $NaNO_3$ is soluble, while the compound AgCl is insoluble or only slightly soluble. We can therefore predict that combining the two solutions will produce a solid precipitate of silver chloride (AgCl), based on the following reaction:

$$NaCl_{(aq)} + AgNO_{3(aq)} \longrightarrow AgCl_{(s)} + NaNO_{3(aq)}$$

ST EST SE

ACID-BASE NEUTRALIZATION

LABS 33–34

Acid-base neutralization is a reaction in which an acid and a base react to form a salt and water. The generic formula for a reaction of acid-base neutralization in an aqueous solution is:

$$\text{acid}_{(aq)} + \text{base}_{(aq)} \longrightarrow \text{salt}_{(aq)} + \text{water}_{(l)}$$

When the number of H^+ ions from the acid equals the number of OH^- ions from the base, the result is neutral, meaning that the pH of the solution is 7. For this reason, the acid is said to *neutralize* the base, or vice versa. When the numbers of H^+ and OH^- ions are different, the neutralization reaction is incomplete. The pH then depends on the concentration of surplus reactants in the solution.

ACID-BASE NEUTRALIZATION is a chemical change involving the reaction of an acid with a base, producing a salt and water.

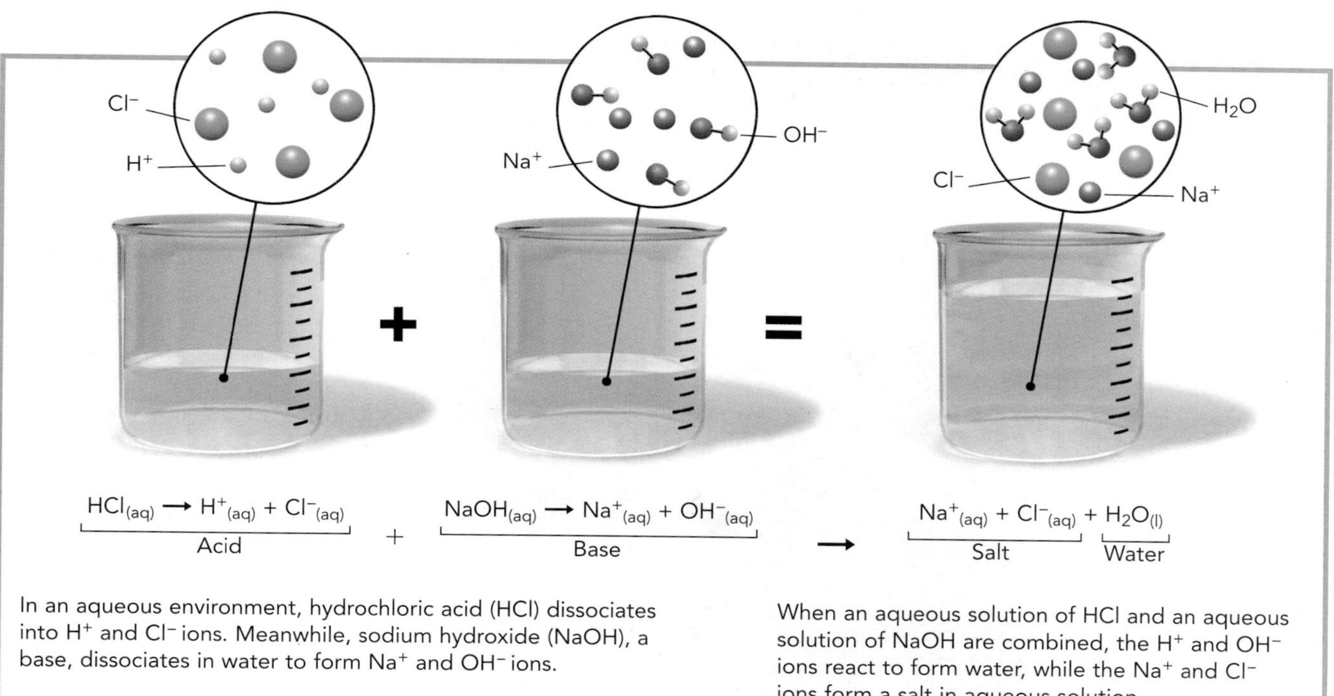

4.17 The neutralization reaction between hydrochloric acid and sodium hydroxide

The following equations show other examples of acid-base neutralization:

- $HF_{(aq)} + KOH_{(aq)} \rightarrow KF_{(aq)} + H_2O_{(l)}$
- $H_2SO_{4(aq)} + Mg(OH)_{2(aq)} \rightarrow MgSO_{4(aq)} + 2\ H_2O_{(l)}$
- $2\ HBr_{(aq)} + Ca(OH)_{2(aq)} \rightarrow CaBr_{2(aq)} + 2\ H_2O_{(l)}$

OXIDATION

Oxidation is a reaction that is fundamental to our existence. On the one hand, it keeps us alive (particularly through cellular respiration); on the other hand, it causes our cells to age. Many substances, such as metals and food, have the ability to oxidize because they react with the oxygen in the air.

Oxidation was originally defined as the reaction of any substance with oxygen. Present-day chemists have broadened the definition and now consider oxidation to be the reaction of a substance with oxygen or with any substance similar in properties to oxygen.

OXIDATION is a chemical change involving oxygen or a substance with properties similar to those of oxygen.

FIGHTING CORROSION WITH SHELLFISH

Crustaceans have a very special shell that could be used to prevent the corrosion that eats away at metals. Boat hulls and port facilities could thus be protected without contaminating the marine environment. Chitin, the main component of crustacean shells, lies at the root of this discovery. More specifically, researchers are interested in a derivative of chitin, called *chitosan*.

Crustacean shells could one day be used to protect boats from corrosion.

Chemist Caroline Dupont, from Université Laval, has demonstrated that chitosan has a high affinity for metals. It can adhere to metal surfaces, forming a protective coating. Once applied, chitosan delays corrosion by slowing the action of the chlorides in seawater. Chitosan also presents other advantages: it is not at all toxic to marine wildlife, it does not accumulate in the food chain, and it is biodegradable.

Source: Adapted from Pauline Gravel, "Des crustacés pour combattre la corrosion," *Le Devoir*, May 17, 2006, p. A6. *[Translation]*

Certain conditions promote oxidation reactions. For example, the presence of humidity in the air accelerates the formation of rust, an oxidation of iron. Light speeds up the oxidation of oils, altering their taste and making them unfit for consumption.

To combat some of the undesirable effects of oxidation, various processes or substances can be applied. For example, galvanization is a process that protects iron-based materials from rust by coating them with zinc. Similarly, antioxidants are preservatives added to food to prolong its shelf life.

COMBUSTION

Combustion is a form of oxidation that releases a large amount of energy. Burning wood, rusting iron and cellular respiration are examples of combustion.

4.18 Oxidation alters the appearance of the substance undergoing this type of chemical change.

ENVIRONMENT EXTRA

Burning fossil fuels

Fossil fuels and the products we obtain from them, such as natural gas, gasoline, heating oil and coal, play an important role in today's society. They are used to fuel cars, heat homes, operate power plants, etc.

When a fossil fuel burns, it reacts with the oxygen in the air to produce mainly carbon dioxide and water vapour. The reaction also usually releases energy, as indicated by the following equation:

fossil fuel + oxygen →
carbon dioxide + water + energy

Burning fossil fuels on a massive scale for human activities causes a constant increase in the level of carbon dioxide in the atmosphere, adding to the greenhouse effect.

Burning fossil fuels is likely to increase the greenhouse effect and the phenomenon of acid rain.

The increased production of carbon dioxide is not the only concern raised by fossil fuel combustion. When oxygen is not available in sufficient quantities, burning fossil fuels also emit carbon monoxide, a gas that is deadly to humans. In addition, some fossil fuels contain sulphur, so their combustion produces another gas, sulphur dioxide, which is partially responsible for acid rain.

COMBUSTION is a form of oxidation that releases a large amount of energy.

Three conditions must be fulfilled for combustion to take place: there must be fuel, there must be an oxidizing agent, and the ignition temperature must be reached. The interaction of these three conditions is illustrated below in the triangle of fire.

Combustion comes from the Latin *comburere*, meaning "to burn up."

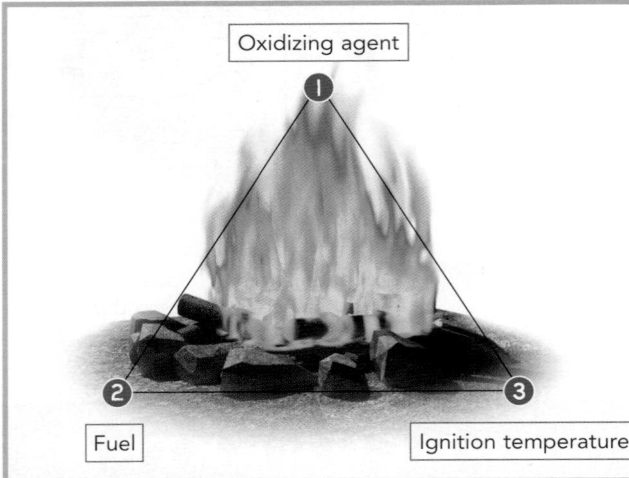

1. An oxidizing agent, or *oxidant*, is a substance that can cause a fuel to react. Oxygen is the most common oxidizing agent on Earth.
2. A fuel is a substance that releases a large amount of energy by reacting with an oxidizing agent. Wood and propane are excellent fuels.
3. The ignition temperature is the minimum temperature at which the energy present is sufficient to start combustion. Ignition temperatures vary from one fuel to another.

4.19 The triangle of fire illustrates the relationship between the three conditions for initiating and maintaining combustion. Firefighters study this relationship in order to control fires.

Combustion is categorized as one of three types: rapid combustion, spontaneous combustion and slow combustion.

- Rapid combustion is the most spectacular form of combustion. Within a short period of time, it releases a great deal of energy, mostly in the form of heat and light. A log fire, a burning candle and the controlled explosion of gasoline in an engine are examples of rapid combustion.
- Spontaneous combustion is rapid combustion in which the fuel reaches its ignition temperature without any energy from an outside source. It is often an unpredictable phenomenon and may have disastrous consequences. For example, in the summer, when it is very hot and the ground is very dry, wood can catch fire spontaneously, causing forest fires.
- Slow combustion occurs over a very long period of time. The energy emitted seems less considerable because it is released gradually into the environment. Decomposition, fermentation, cellular respiration and metal corrosion are examples of slow combustion.

4.20 This car can race along the highway thanks to the rapid combustion of gasoline in its engine.

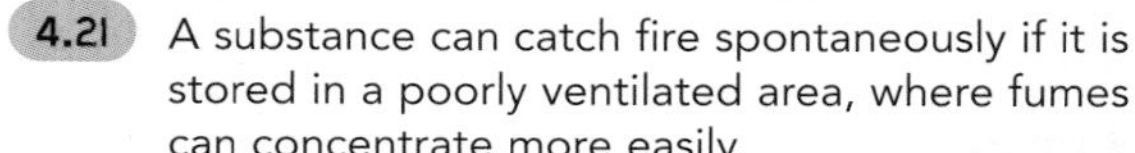
4.21 A substance can catch fire spontaneously if it is stored in a poorly ventilated area, where fumes can concentrate more easily.

4.22 Rust is an example of slow combustion.

ST EST SE

CELLULAR RESPIRATION AND PHOTOSYNTHESIS

Cellular respiration is a form of slow combustion. As with all types of combustion, it is an exothermic reaction. It takes place in the cells of most living organisms. Part of the energy released during cellular respiration disperses in the surrounding tissues in the form of heat. In humans, this process keeps our body temperature at around 37°C. The energy also enables cells to carry out the tasks that are essential to the organism's proper functioning.

CELLULAR RESPIRATION is a chemical change in which glucose and oxygen are used to generate energy. The reaction also produces carbon dioxide and water.

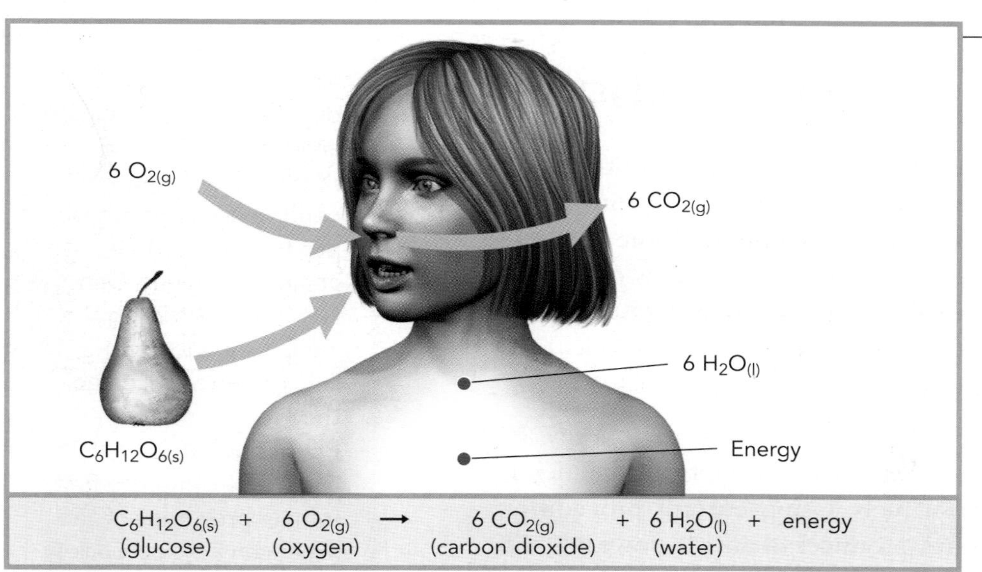

4.23 The fuel used in cellular respiration is glucose ($C_6H_{12}O_6$), a type of sugar.

Photosynthesis is the opposite reaction to cellular respiration, so it is an endothermic reaction. Through photosynthesis, plant cells use solar energy to manufacture glucose and oxygen from carbon dioxide and water. Glucose is a source of energy for plants and animals. Since photosynthesis also releases oxygen, the process is essential for maintaining oxygen levels in the air.

$$6\ CO_{2(g)}\ \text{(carbon dioxide)} + 6\ H_2O_{(l)}\ \text{(water)} + \text{solar energy} \longrightarrow C_6H_{12}O_{6(s)}\ \text{(glucose)} + 6\ O_{2(g)}\ \text{(oxygen)}$$

4.24 Through photosynthesis, plants manufacture glucose, a source of energy that can be used by all living organisms.

PHOTOSYNTHESIS is a chemical change that produces glucose and oxygen from solar energy, carbon dioxide and water.

Organisms that carry out photosynthesis form the basis of all **FOOD CHAINS**. These life forms are referred to as **PRODUCERS** because they use sunlight to produce the organic matter other living organisms need to survive.

1912
1997

Chien-Shiung Wu

This Chinese-born American physicist designed and conducted an experiment on radioactive decay, confirming a hypothesis put forward by her colleagues Tsung-Dao Lee and Chen Ning Yang. Lee and Yang subsequently received the Nobel Prize for Physics in 1957. In 1975, Dr. Wu became the first female president of the American Physical Society.

EST 3 Nuclear transformations

Nuclear transformations are reactions that occur in the nucleus of an atom. They result in a variation in the number of protons and neutrons, which alters the nature of the element. Some of these reactions are exothermic and release enormous amounts of energy. The nucleus of an atom is, in fact, a huge energy reserve. For example, the reaction of 1 kg of uranium can, *in theory*, release as much energy as the combustion of 2 500 000 kg of coal.

Various applications have been developed for nuclear energy. Its main use lies in generating electricity. Nuclear energy efficiency is much greater than that of fossil fuels. Using current procedures, the reaction of 1 kg of uranium produces as much power as the combustion of 20 000 kg of coal.

EST 3.1 NUCLEAR STABILITY

The nucleus of an atom is composed of protons and neutrons. Since each proton has a positive electrical charge and since charges of the same sign exert repulsive forces, protons tend to repel each other. As their name suggests, neutrons have no electrical charge. Most nuclei remain stable because a force of attraction greater than the forces of electrical repulsion between protons binds the particles of the nucleus together. This force is called the *nuclear force*.

> **NUCLEAR STABILITY refers to the state of a nucleus in which the nuclear force is greater than the forces of electrical repulsion between protons.**

The stability of the nucleus depends chiefly on two factors: its size and the number of neutrons it contains.

OUR "OTHER" SOURCE OF ELECTRICITY

Canada is the largest producer of uranium in the world. Our nuclear facilities consist of 22 reactors, in Québec, Ontario and New Brunswick. Nuclear energy currently meets half of the demand for electricity in Ontario.

4.25 THE RELATIONSHIP BETWEEN NUMBER OF NEUTRONS, ATOMIC NUMBER AND NUCLEAR STABILITY

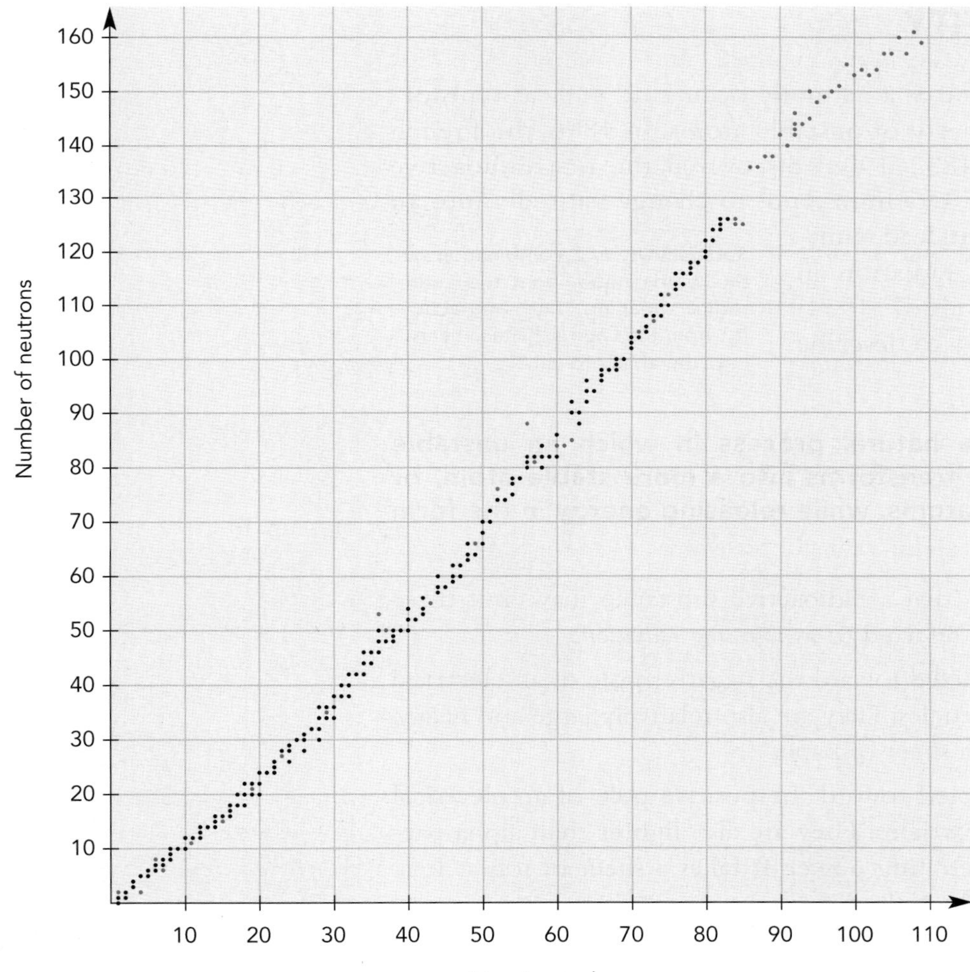

Legend
- Stable nucleus
- Unstable nucleus

Normally, the nuclear force is much greater than the forces of electrical repulsion. However, the nuclear force is effective only over very short distances. As a result, the larger a nucleus, the more difficult it becomes for the nuclear force to offset the forces of electrical repulsion. This limitation explains why all the atoms with an atomic number greater than 83 (the atomic number of bismuth) are unstable, which means they tend to decay into one or more atoms of smaller elements.

Almost all the elements have several **ISOTOPES**, with varying degrees of nuclear stability. Since the number of neutrons differentiates the various isotopes of a given element, it is reasonable to conclude that neutrons play a role in the stability of atomic nuclei.

Figure 4.25 (page 125) shows that unstable isotopes exist across the range of elements. (In this graph, the isotopes of each element appear as vertically aligned dots.) The graph also shows that all the elements with an atomic number greater than 83 are unstable.

SHORTAGE OF ISOTOPES IN HOSPITALS

The closure of a 50-year-old nuclear reactor in November 2007 led to a shortage of radioactive isotopes for nuclear medicine. Confronted with protests from specialists in the field, the federal government passed emergency legislation to force the reopening of the reactor for reasons of public health.

EST 3.2 RADIOACTIVITY

Radioactivity can be described as a naturally occurring nuclear transformation. It is therefore a property of unstable atoms. In 1896, the French physicist Henri Becquerel (1852–1908) discovered the first radioactive element, uranium, by chance. Uranium tends to change naturally into an atom of a more stable element, lead, emitting energy in the form of radiation in the process. Marie Curie (1867–1934) proposed the term *radioactivity* to describe this phenomenon.

Radioactivity is a combination of the words *radio*, from the Latin *radius*, meaning "ray," and *activity*, from the Latin *activitas*, meaning "the ability to act."

RADIOACTIVITY is a natural process in which an unstable atom spontaneously transforms into a more stable atom, or several more stable atoms, while releasing energy in the form of radiation.

Figure 4.26 (page 127) shows that a radioactive substance may emit three types of radiation, collectively referred to as *ionizing radiation*:

- Alpha (α) particles are deflected toward the negative pole of an electrical field, so they are positive particles. They are also relatively large and heavy. They can be stopped with a sheet of paper.
- Beta (β) particles are deflected toward the positive pole of an electrical field, so they are negative particles. They are also lighter than alpha particles and have greater penetrating power. It takes a sheet of foil at least three millimetres thick to block them.

- Gamma (γ) rays are not deflected by an electrical field; they are neutral. Moreover, these rays are not made up of particles, but only of energy. They have the greatest penetrating power among the three types of radiation, so a very dense material (such as lead or high-density concrete) is needed to block them. Obviously, they pass easily through the human body.

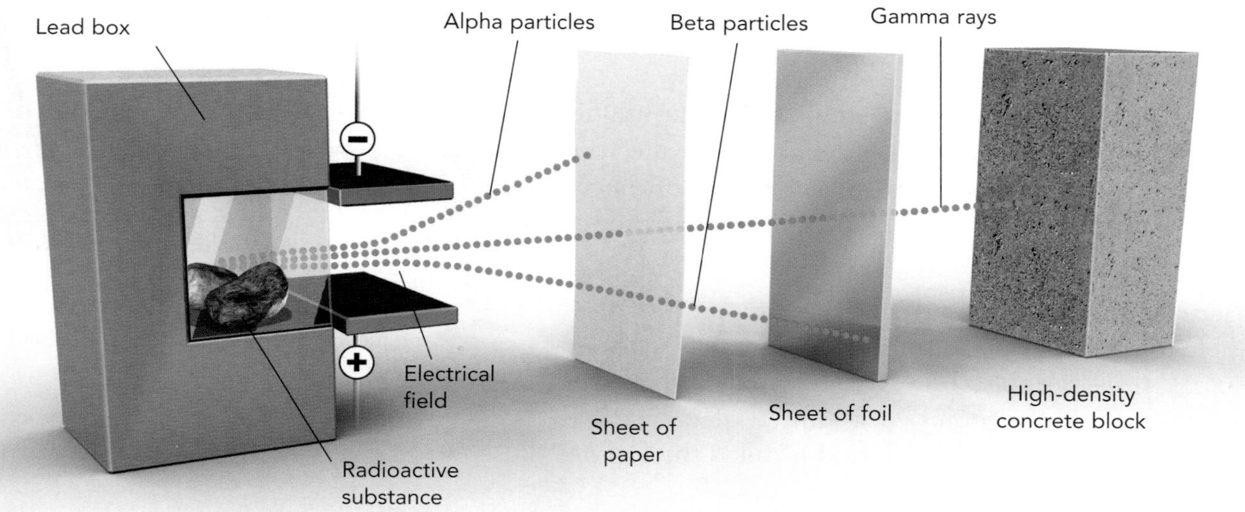

4.26 By directing the radiation from a radioactive substance between the poles of an electrical field, scientists can distinguish three types of radiation: alpha particles, beta particles and gamma rays. These types of radiation are different in their charges and their relative powers of penetration.

ENVIRONMENT EXTRA

Background radiation

We are constantly exposed to ionizing radiation and are even slightly radioactive ourselves. In fact, we absorb radioactive elements on a daily basis through our food and the air that we breathe. Radon, a gas released by decaying uranium in the ground, constitutes another important source of radioactivity. We are also exposed to ionizing radiation from the universe: cosmic rays. Finally, we can add to the list of sources the radiation from X-rays, watch batteries, smoke detectors, etc.

The damage caused by all this exposure is considerable. Fortunately, our cells are equipped with a defence mechanism that can eliminate and replace the cells damaged by low doses of ionizing radiation. However, the mechanism has its limits.

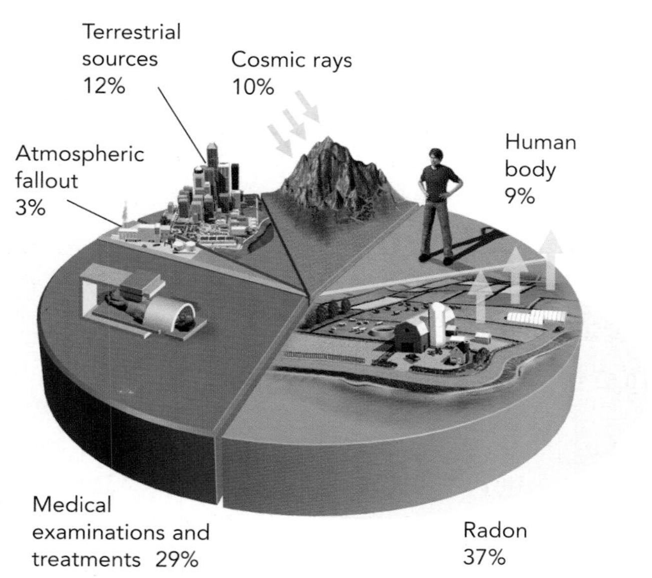

We are constantly exposed to ionizing radiation from a variety of sources. This is known as *background radiation*.

Ionizing radiation is capable of tearing electrons away from the atoms it encounters. This property can lead to the formation of new substances. Irradiation, which means exposure to ionizing radiation, has industrial applications. For example, it is possible to improve the quality of some materials by adding substances that harden under the effect of ionizing radiation. Irradiating food is also useful because it can increase the shelf life of fresh products.

However, exposure to ionizing radiation can be harmful to living organisms. The radiation has the ability to alter the DNA in cells, which can lead to the development of cancer cells. Paradoxically, during radiotherapy, ionizing radiation is used to kill cancer cells and thus treat the disease.

Radioactivity is a spontaneous and random process. It is impossible to predict which atoms will decay or when they will do so. It is possible, however, to predict the time required for half of the atoms in a sample of radioactive material to be transformed. This period is called the *half-life* of the isotope.

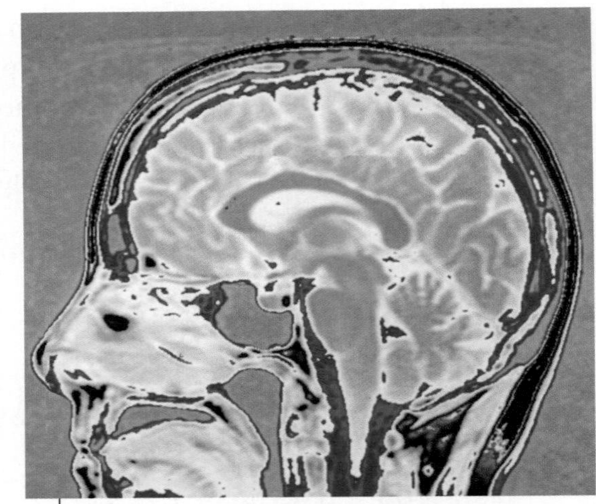

4.27 Thanks to radioactivity, it is possible to obtain images of an organ, like the brain, as it functions. This is the principle behind scintigraphy, an imaging technique in nuclear medicine.

The HALF-LIFE is the time it takes for half of the nuclei in a sample of radioactive material to decay.

4.28 AMOUNTS OF CARBON-14 OVER TIME

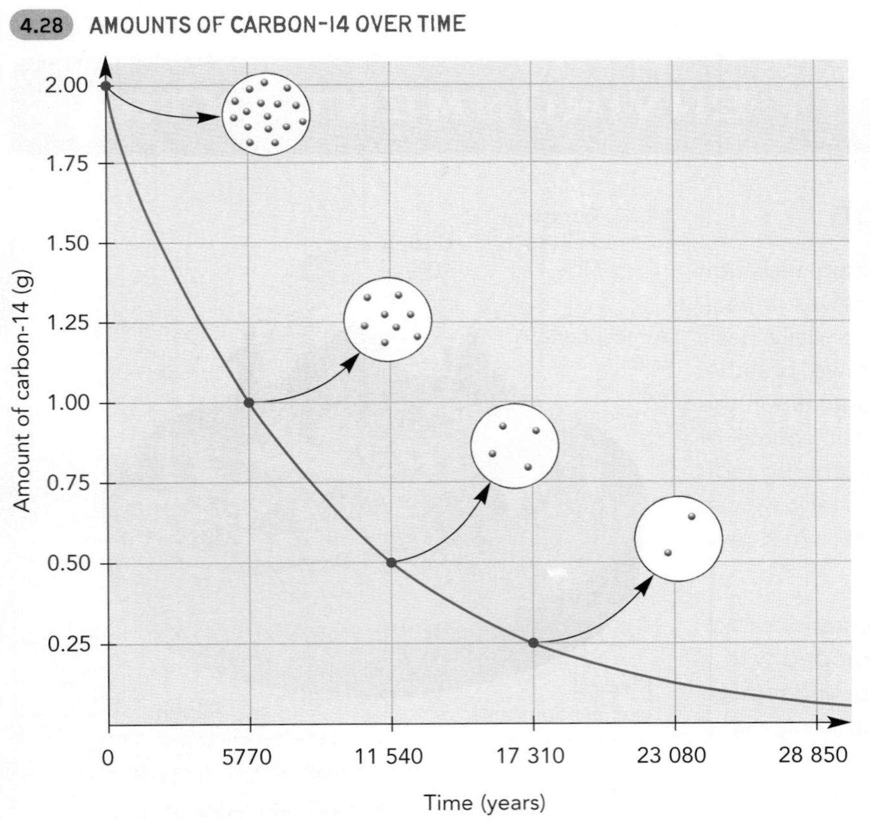

1890
1967

Hermann Joseph Muller

In 1946, this American geneticist won the Nobel Prize in Medicine for establishing the connection between irradiation and changes in DNA. He subsequently attempted to raise popular awareness of the dangers of the atomic bomb and of exposure to ionizing radiation.

Figure 4.28 (page 128) shows the half-life of carbon-14 (a carbon isotope containing eight neutrons) to be 5770 years. This means that, given a two-gram sample of carbon-14, only one gram of it would remain in 5770 years' time. After another period of 5770 years, only half a gram would remain, and so on.

The longer the half-life of an element, the longer it takes to eliminate that element from the environment. Long half-lives pose a considerable challenge in waste management for nuclear power plants.

4.29 THE HALF-LIVES OF SOME RADIOACTIVE ISOTOPES

Isotope	Half-life
Polonium-216	0.16 seconds
Sodium-24	15 hours
Iodine-131	8.1 days
Cobalt-60	5.26 years
Hydrogen-3	12 years
Strontium-90	28 years
Carbon-14	5 770 years
Plutonium-239	24 000 years
Uranium-235	710 000 000 years
Potassium-40	1 300 000 000 years

EST 3.3 TYPES OF NUCLEAR TRANSFORMATION

During the 20th century, humans discovered how to initiate nuclear reactions under artificial conditions. However, large amounts of energy are required to set these reactions in motion. They are triggered by bombarding atomic nuclei with particles or other nuclei moving at very high speed. Depending on the results, two types of nuclear reaction can be distinguished: nuclear fission and nuclear fusion.

EST NUCLEAR FISSION

Nuclear fission is the nuclear reaction most commonly used by humans. As its name suggests, the nucleus of the atom is split during nuclear fission to form two or more smaller nuclei.

Fission comes from the Latin *fissus*, meaning "split."

NUCLEAR FISSION is a nuclear reaction in which the nucleus of a large atom is split to form two or more lighter atomic nuclei.

1878
1968

Lise Meitner

This Austrian physicist focused her research on radioactivity and nuclear reactions. In 1939, she published the first article on nuclear fission, but her contribution was not recognized until 1966. Element 109, meitnerium, was named after her.

As shown in Figure 4.30 below, the nuclear fission of uranium-235 releases neutrons as well as lighter nuclei. These neutrons may then, in turn, bombard the nuclei of as many uranium atoms. A chain reaction ensues. If it is not controlled, it can cause a nuclear explosion like those in Hiroshima and Nagasaki, two Japanese cities struck by atomic bombs at the end of World War II. The bombs had disastrous consequences, destroying everything in their paths and leaving behind an enormous amount of radioactive waste.

By slowing down the neutrons released by nuclear fission, physicists can control the chain reaction. It then becomes possible to make use of the energy potential of fission to generate electricity. However, even controlled nuclear fission is not an entirely beneficial process. The nuclear reactors used for fission also produce large amounts of radioactive waste. Some of this waste can be used in nuclear medicine or for other applications, while the rest is usually buried.

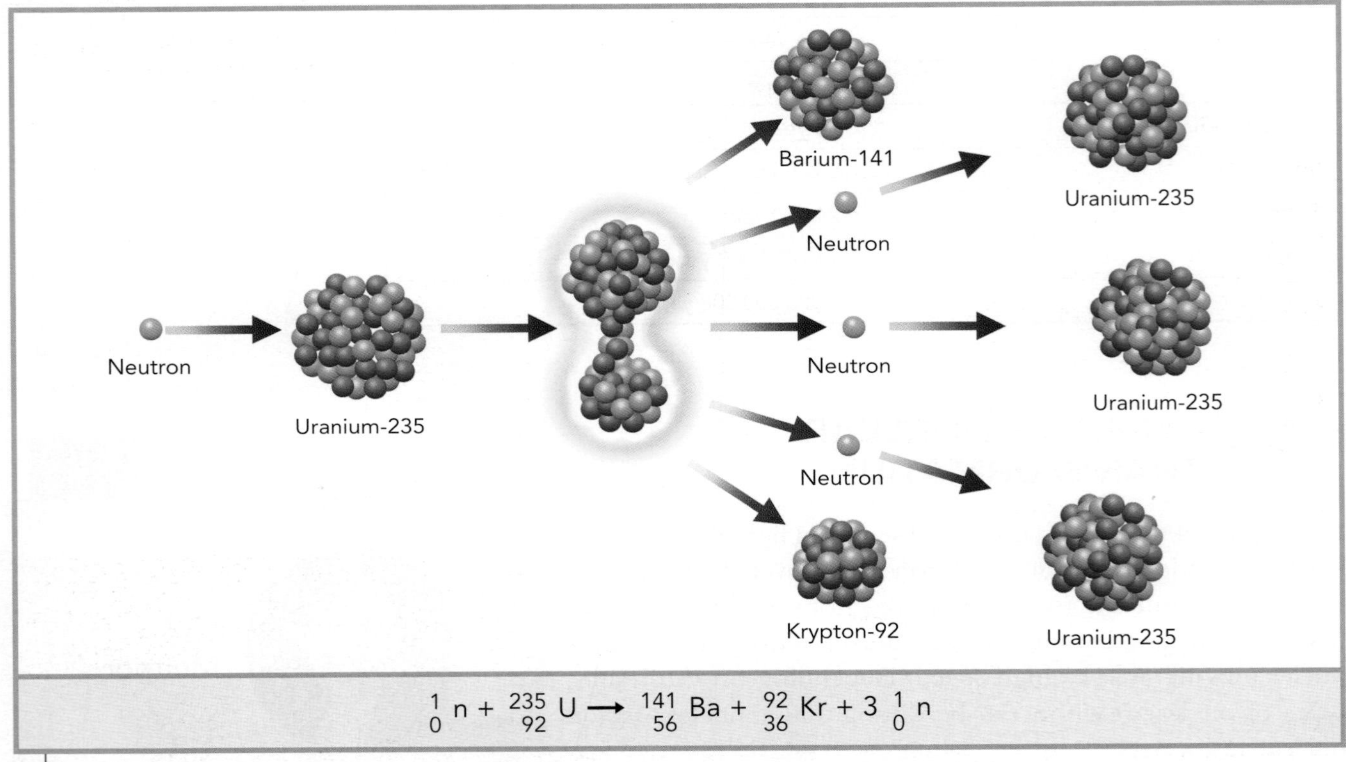

4.30 Bombarding the nucleus of a uranium-235 atom with a neutron causes nuclear fission to occur. Different products result from the reaction: for example, two lighter atomic nuclei (of the isotopes barium-141 and krypton-92) and three neutrons. These neutrons may, in turn, bombard other uranium-235 atoms, triggering a chain reaction.

EST NUCLEAR FUSION

Nuclear fusion is the principal source of energy in stars. It occurs when two small nuclei collide and unite to form one heavier nucleus.

NUCLEAR FUSION is a nuclear reaction in which two small atomic nuclei join together to form one heavier nucleus.

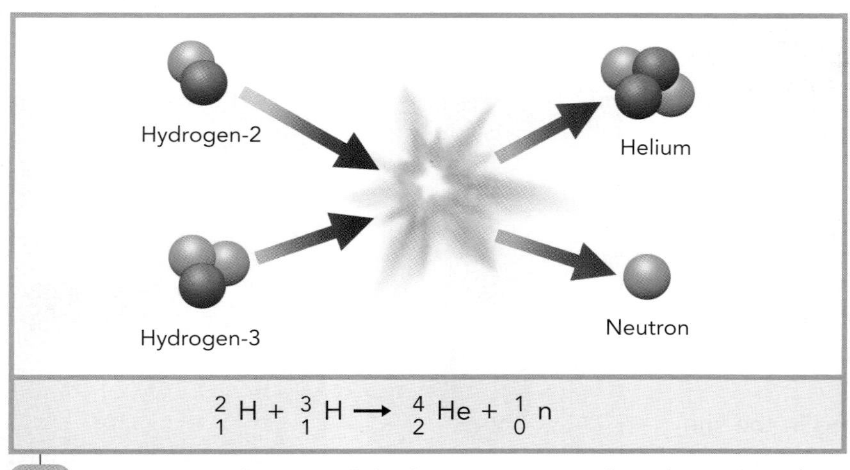

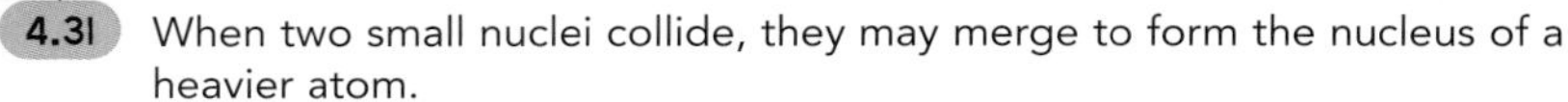
$$^{2}_{1}H + ^{3}_{1}H \longrightarrow ^{4}_{2}He + ^{1}_{0}n$$

4.31 When two small nuclei collide, they may merge to form the nucleus of a heavier atom.

4.32 The Sun generates its energy through a series of nuclear fusion reactions.

Nuclear fusion is a reaction that can be initiated and maintained only at very high temperatures, in the order of a million degrees Celsius. This condition explains why fusion is more difficult to recreate than fission. To date, very few applications have been found for nuclear fusion on Earth. The hydrogen bomb, also called the *H bomb*, is one example. In this type of bomb, nuclear fission is used to generate the energy required to start nuclear fusion.

Extensive research is underway so that, one day, nuclear fusion can be controlled. A number of reasons motivate this interest. First, the energy efficiency of nuclear fusion is much greater than that of nuclear fission. Second, nuclear fusion produces less radioactive waste, which makes it a more environmentally friendly source of energy.

4.33 A nuclear power plant, such as Gentilly-2 in Québec, generates electricity through nuclear fission.

4.34 A tokamak is a machine in which nuclear fusion can be achieved. However, this process is not yet cost-effective.

CHECKUP

ST 1–7, 17, 18, 20–23, C and E.
EST 1–28 and A–E.
AST 1–3, 19–22 and E.
SE 1–18, 23, A–C and E.

1 What are changes in matter? (p. 108)

1. Does each of the following phenomena describe a physical change, a chemical change or a nuclear transformation? Explain your answers.

a) a puddle of water evaporating in the sun
b) propane gas burning in a barbecue
c) a wooden plank being sawn in half
d) lead turning into gold

2 Chemical changes
(pp. 109–124)

2. For each of the situations in the following photos, name at least one sign that a chemical change is occurring.

A

B

C
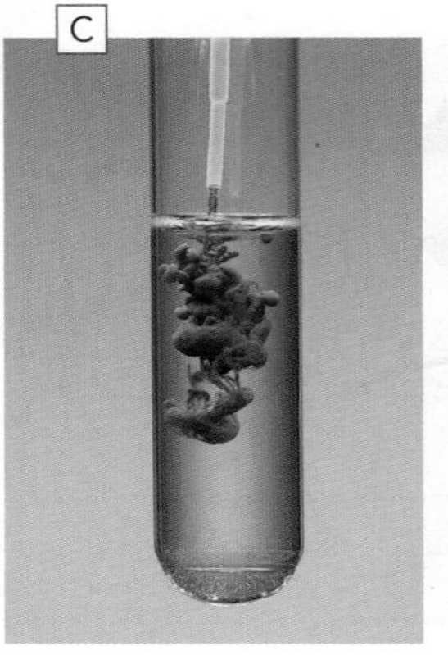

D

3. Represent each of the following reactions with a chemical equation. Specify the physical state of each substance.

a) A solid zinc atom reacts with two molecules of a solution of hydrochloric acid (HCl), to form one molecule of zinc chloride ($ZnCl_2$) in solution and one molecule of hydrogen gas.
b) Two atoms of solid sodium react with two molecules of liquid water to form two molecules of sodium hydroxide (NaOH) in solution and one molecule of hydrogen gas.
c) The reaction of one molecule of propane gas (C_3H_8) with five molecules of oxygen gas produces three molecules of carbon dioxide gas and four molecules of water vapour.
d) When two molecules of sodium chloride (NaCl) in solution are mixed with one molecule of barium nitrate ($Ba(NO_3)_2$) in solution, two molecules of sodium nitrate ($NaNO_3$) in solution are formed, as well as one molecule of barium chloride ($BaCl_2$) in the form of a solid precipitate.

4. The equation for the synthesis of water is:

$$2\ H_{2(g)} + O_{2(g)} \longrightarrow 2\ H_2O_{(l)}$$

If 2 g of hydrogen are made to react with 16 g of oxygen, what is the mass of the resulting water? Show your calculations.

5. When magnesium is made to react with hydrochloric acid, hydrogen gas is released. If the reaction occurs in an open beaker, what will happen to the mass of the beaker's contents? Explain your answer.

6. Is each of the following equations balanced or not? Explain your answers.

a) $Na + O_2 \longrightarrow Na_2O_2$
b) $C + O_2 \longrightarrow CO_2$
c) $2\ C_2H_2 + 5\ O_2 \longrightarrow 4\ CO_2 + 2\ H_2O$
d) $CH_4 + 2\ Cl_2 \longrightarrow CCl_4 + 4\ HCl$

7. Balance each of the following equations.

a) $Mg + O_2 \longrightarrow MgO$
b) $Fe + O_2 \longrightarrow Fe_2O_3$
c) $C_3H_8 + O_2 \longrightarrow CO_2 + H_2O$
d) $KOH + H_2SO_4 \longrightarrow K_2SO_4 + H_2O$

8. The equation for the formation of copper oxide (CuO) is:

$$2\ Cu + O_2 \longrightarrow 2\ CuO$$

If four moles of copper are made to react with a sufficient amount of oxygen, how many moles of copper oxide will be obtained? Show your calculations.

9. Consider the following reaction:

$$2\ Na + 2\ H_2O \longrightarrow 2\ NaOH + H_2$$

How many moles of sodium hydroxide will be produced if 46 g of sodium are made to react completely? Show your calculations.

10. The equation for the synthesis of ammonia is:

$$N_2 + 3\ H_2 \longrightarrow 2\ NH_3$$

Write the equation for the decomposition of ammonia.

11. When a solution of hydrochloric acid is mixed with sodium bicarbonate, carbon dioxide is released according to the following equation:

$$HCl_{(aq)} + NaHCO_{3(s)} \longrightarrow NaCl_{(aq)} + H_2O_{(l)} + CO_{2(g)}$$

Suppose that 200 mL of the hydrochloric acid solution are made to react with sufficient sodium bicarbonate. What should the molar concentration of the solution be to obtain 4.4 g of carbon dioxide? Show your calculations.

12. Iron rusts in the presence of oxygen according to the following equation:

$$4\ Fe_{(s)} + 3\ O_{2(g)} \longrightarrow 2\ Fe_2O_{3(s)}$$

To obtain 20 g of rust, what mass of iron must be transformed? Show your calculations.

13. Does each of the following phenomena describe an endothermic reaction or an exothermic reaction?

a) an egg cooking
b) the electrolysis of hydrochloric acid
c) a battery in use
d) $4\ Fe_{(s)} + 3\ O_{2(g)} \longrightarrow 2\ Fe_2O_{3(s)} + \text{energy}$
e) $6\ C_{(s)} + 3\ H_{2(g)} + \text{energy} \longrightarrow C_6H_{6(l)}$
f) wood burning

14. Ammonia synthesis is a reaction that is widely used in industry. Calculate the reaction energy of the process in order to estimate the amount of energy released or absorbed.

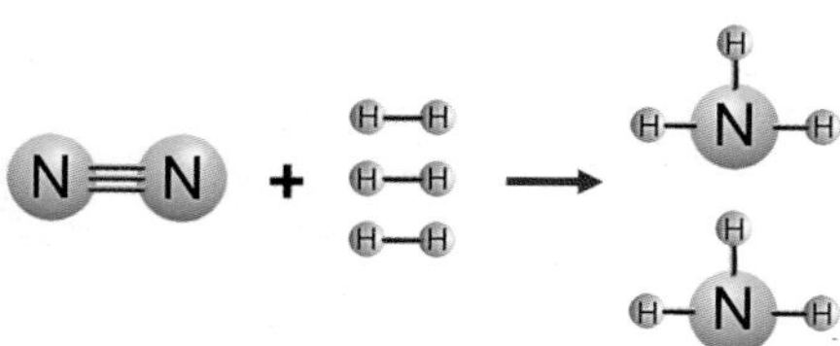

$$N_2 + 3\ H_2 \longrightarrow 2\ NH_3$$

15. The synthesis of nitrogen dioxide is an endothermic phenomenon. What amount of energy would be needed to produce six moles of NO_2?

$$N_{2(g)} + 2\ O_{2(g)} + 67.6\ kJ \longrightarrow 2\ NO_{2(g)}$$

Show your calculations.

16. The complete combustion of one mole of carbon releases 393.5 kJ of energy. To obtain 900 kJ of energy, what mass of carbon would have to be burned?

$$C_{(s)} + O_{2(g)} \longrightarrow CO_{2(g)} + 393.5\ \text{kJ}$$

Show your calculations.

17. When solutions of hydrochloric acid (HCl) and potassium hydroxide (KOH) are mixed, the substances react with each other.
   a) What type of chemical reaction is involved?
   b) Write the chemical equation for this reaction.

18. In an acid-base neutralization reaction, what happens to the pH of the acid solution? Explain your answer.

19. What is oxidation? Give two examples of oxidation.

20. To learn how to control fires, firefighters have to study the three necessary conditions for a fire to start. What are these conditions?

21. What is the difference between an oxidizing agent and a fuel? Give an example of each.

22. Does each of the following statements refer to rapid combustion, spontaneous combustion or slow combustion?
   a) A fire starts because of a gasoline-soaked rag.
   b) Iron rusts easily in damp environments.
   c) A campfire draws people together with its light and warmth.
   d) Many varieties of fruit rot quickly when cut and left in the open air.

23. What distinguishes photosynthesis from cellular respiration? Name at least five differences.

3 Nuclear transformations

(pp. 124–131)

24. Which type of ionizing radiation, though very harmful to human health, can be blocked with a simple sheet of paper?

25. Food irradiation is a process that kills harmful microorganisms and prolongs the shelf life of the food. Isotopes like cobalt-60 are used. Since ionizing radiation must travel a certain distance and penetrate the food completely, which type of radiation would be the most appropriate for this application? Explain your answer.

26. Scintigraphy is a method of medical imaging used to visualize certain organs as they are functioning. It involves a radioactive substance, which is injected into the patient. The radioactive substances used usually have a very short half-life. Explain why they are preferred over substances with longer half-lives.

27. Even though radioactivity can be harmful to human health, it nonetheless provides many advantages. Name two industrial applications of radioactivity.

28. Does each of the following nuclear reactions involve fusion or fission? Explain your answers.
   a) ${}^{235}_{92}\text{U} + {}^{1}_{0}\text{n} \longrightarrow {}^{140}_{54}\text{Xe} + {}^{94}_{38}\text{Sr} + 2\,{}^{1}_{0}\text{n}$
   b) ${}^{2}_{1}\text{H} + {}^{2}_{1}\text{H} \longrightarrow {}^{3}_{2}\text{He} + {}^{1}_{0}\text{n}$
   c) ${}^{6}_{3}\text{Be} + {}^{1}_{0}\text{n} \longrightarrow {}^{4}_{2}\text{He} + {}^{3}_{1}\text{H}$
   d) ${}^{14}_{7}\text{N} + {}^{4}_{2}\text{He} \longrightarrow {}^{17}_{8}\text{O} + {}^{1}_{1}\text{p}^{+}$
   e) ${}^{27}_{13}\text{Al} + {}^{4}_{2}\text{He} \longrightarrow {}^{30}_{15}\text{P} + {}^{1}_{0}\text{n}$

review questions

A. The combustion of one litre of gasoline provides approximately 30 MJ (3.0×10^7 J) of energy, while the reaction of one mole of zinc with oxygen provides approximately 350 kJ (3.5×10^5 J). What mass of zinc would be required to obtain as much energy as from the combustion of 20 L of gasoline?

B. Gasoline is composed mostly of octane (C_8H_{18}). When octane burns in a car engine, it reacts mainly according to the following equation:

$$C_8H_{18(l)} + O_{2(g)} \longrightarrow CO_{2(g)} + H_2O_{(g)}$$
(unbalanced equation)

a) Balance this equation.

b) If a car consumes, on average, 14 kg of gasoline per week, how many moles of carbon dioxide will it release into the air (on average) per week?

C. Dwindling oil reserves and climate change are spurring scientists to find alternative methods of fuelling cars. One method is to use metal powder. For example, zinc reacts with oxygen gas to produce solid zinc oxide (ZnO), releasing a large amount of energy in the process. Preliminary results for this method look promising.

a) Write a balanced equation for this reaction.

b) What type of chemical change is involved?

c) Normally, when a metal reacts with oxygen, the energy released is barely noticeable. Explain why.

d) Researchers believe that using metal powder to fuel cars would be less harmful to the environment than burning gasoline. Explain why.

D. Is the combustion of zinc powder an endothermic or exothermic reaction? Explain your answer.

E. Prepare your own summary of Chapter 4 by building a concept map.

THE CHILDREN OF CHERNOBYL

On April 26, 1986, the nuclear power plant in Chernobyl, Ukraine, exploded. It was the most serious nuclear accident in history. Nearly 70 percent of the radioactive fallout landed in Belarus, a neighbouring country. Russia was also affected. The entire food chain was contaminated with radioactive substances, including cesium-137. In the fall of 2007, 21 years after the incident, French scientists measured the radioactivity in the soil at Novozybkov, a historic Russian city that had been affected. Areas declared safe were few and far between. In many places, children are still being born with a variety of malformations. Their immune system is also often fragile, leading to illness and problems of all kinds.

CLEAN AIR AND HEALTHY FOOD

Opening one's home to a child from Chernobyl for just a few weeks a year can improve his or her health. With this goal in mind, various associations have been formed in many countries. *Les enfants de Tchernobyl*, for example, was founded in the French department of Haut-Rhin, near Alsace. Its members organize awareness campaigns and financing to send medicine to cities like Novozybkov or to support orphanages there. Its most important activity, however, is finding temporary homes for children for a few weeks in the summer, to give them a chance to breathe clean air and eat healthy food.

In Québec, the organization *Séjour santé enfants Tchernobyl* pursues similar goals. During the summer of 2007, Cathy Quinaux and Steve Plante, themselves parents of four children, welcomed eight-year-old Anastasia in their home in Saint-Victor de Beauce. By the end of the summer, Anastasia could understand French. As an only child, she enjoyed playing with the other children in the family. But most importantly, she gained nine pounds, her immune system was strengthened, and her level of cesium-137, a radioactive element, fell below levels considered dangerous to human health. The benefits of Anastasia's stay in Québec will persist throughout the year, and her hosts, who paid $2000 for her plane ticket, intend to bring her back to Québec in the summers to come.

Since 1991, thousands of children aged 8 to 16 have stayed with families in about 20 countries, often for several summers in a row.

THE DISASTER CONTINUES

Radioactive cesium is still present in the Chernobyl environment, especially in a 30-km radius around the site of the accident. Evidence of fallout has also been found far from the source of contamination: for example, in contaminated reindeer meat in Scandinavia and in incidences of thyroid cancer in Corsica. Decontamination is vital, but expensive. Money must also be found for prevention and health care. The leaders of the countries involved tend to minimize the damage, and the populations directly concerned are often poorly informed. Finally, the effects of radiation on future generations remain to be seen.

Even today, levels of radioactivity are abnormally high near the site of the Chernobyl accident.

Anastasia (on the right) with her Québec foster family

1. Why is it difficult to protect people from the radiation given off by radioactive elements? Why is this radiation harmful to human health?
2. Cesium-137 has a half-life of about 30 years. Is it normal that after more than 20 years, levels of radioactivity in the ground near Chernobyl are still very high? Explain your answer.

2003 Construction of a maglev train (a train supported by a magnetic field) in China

1986 Discovery of a ceramic superconductor

1882 Construction, in New York, of the first electrical distribution network

1827 Formulation of Ohm's law

1821 Invention of the first electric motor

1820 Invention of the electromagnet

1800 Invention of the electric cell (battery)

1785 Formulation of Coulomb's law

1752 Discovery of the electrical nature of lightning

1672 Construction of a machine that generates static electricity

1600 Discovery of the Earth's magnetic field

CIRCA 1120 Use of the compass for navigation

CIRCA −585 Discovery of magnetite, a natural magnet

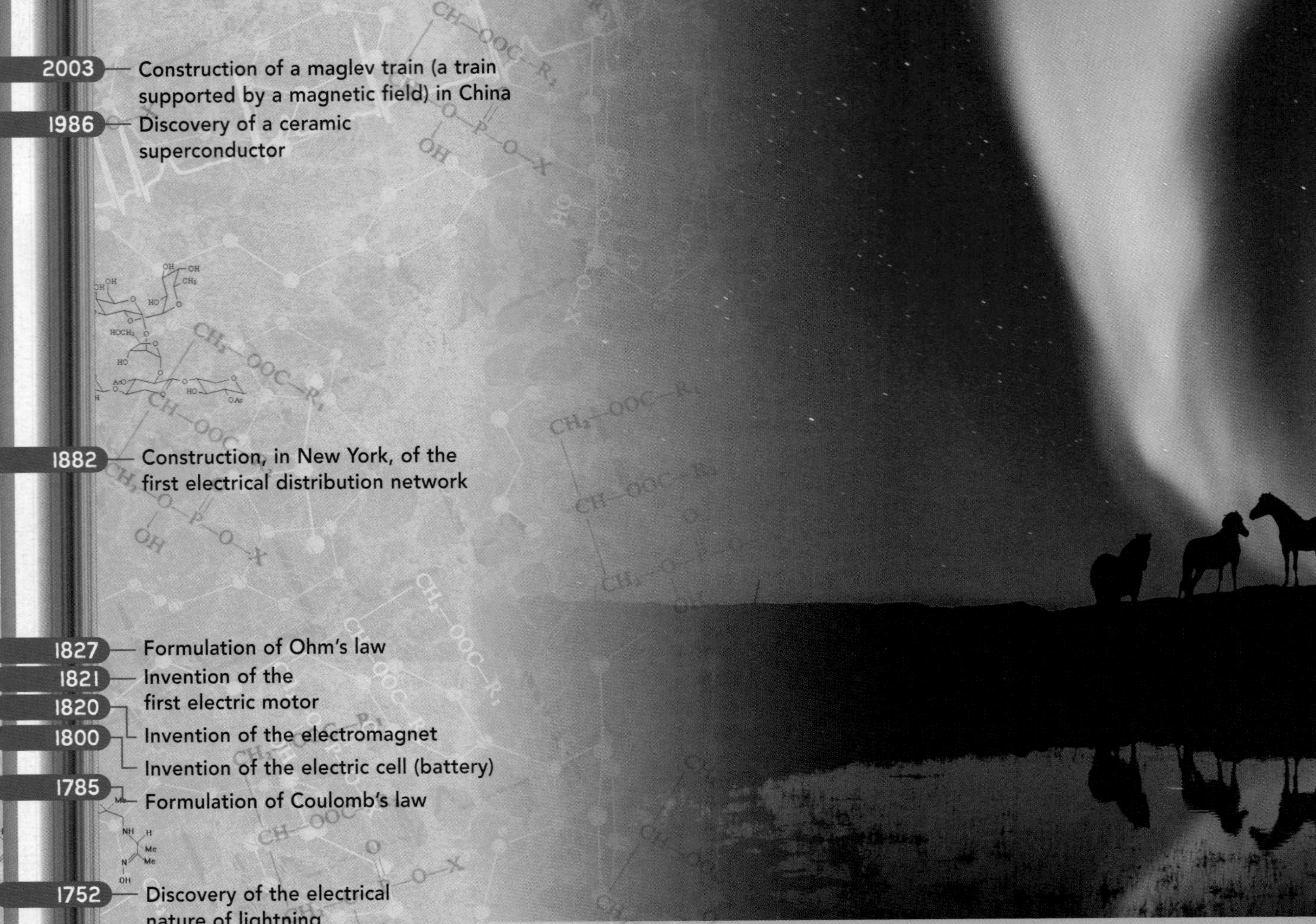

Polar auroras are the result of a spectacular interaction between electrical charges from the Sun and from the Earth's magnetic field. The glow of polar lights is therefore related to both electricity and magnetism, two phenomena that play important roles in our daily lives through their application in a wide variety of technologies. Where and how do electrical and magnetic phenomena originate? Under what conditions is an electric current or a magnetic field produced? Is there a connection between electricity and magnetism? In this chapter, we will try to answer these and other questions.

THE MATERIAL WORLD

5

Electricity and magnetism

CONTENTS

ST EST AST 1 What is electricity?

CONCEPT REVIEW
- Atom
- Energy transformations

Many natural phenomena are electrical in nature. Examples include the transmission of nerve impulses in cells, bolts of lightning and chemical reactions between atoms and molecules. The technological applications that depend on electrical phenomena are also many and varied. Electricity is one of the main forms of energy that power the machines we use every day.

Electrical phenomena were discovered a long time ago. In approximately 600 BCE, the Greek philosopher Thales of Miletus (circa 625–546 BCE) noticed that when a piece of yellow amber was rubbed against wool, the amber acquired the ability to attract small objects, such as pieces of straw. This property of amber was named the *electrical effect*.

Electrical comes from the Greek *ēlektron*, meaning "amber."

In the 16th century, William Gilbert (1540–1603), an English doctor and physicist, observed that other substances, such as glass, resin and sulphur, had similar properties to those of yellow amber. Since that time, any material that can attract small objects after being rubbed is said to be *electrically charged* (or *electrified*).

It was also noted that electrically charged objects could either attract or repel one another, depending on their constituent material.

5.1 Yellow amber is a hard, translucent fossil of resin from conifers.

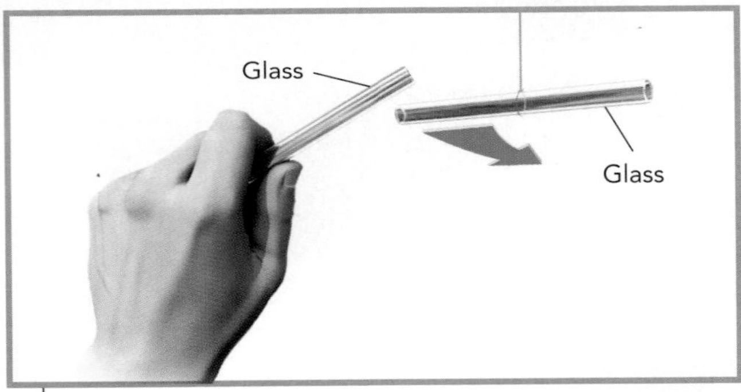

5.2 Two electrically charged glass rods repel each other.

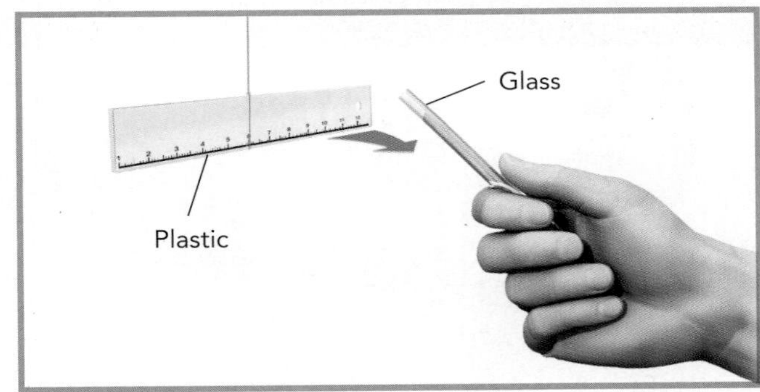

5.3 An electrically charged glass rod and an electrically charged plastic ruler attract each other.

Based on observations similar to those in Figures 5.2 and 5.3, the American physicist, philosopher and politician Benjamin Franklin (1706–1790) identified two types of electricity. He determined that any material that behaved like rubbed glass was charged with *positive electricity*. Conversely, any material that behaved like rubbed plastic (in Franklin's time, the effect was observed in sealing wax and resin) was charged with *negative electricity*.

Franklin thus believed that electrical charges could be either positive or negative and that they could be transferred from one object to another.

ELECTRICITY describes all the phenomena caused by positive and negative charges.

ST EST AST 1.1 ELECTRICAL CHARGES

Where do the charges causing electrical phenomena come from? A satisfactory answer to this question was not found until the 19th century, when electrons and protons were discovered (Figure 5.4).

Each proton carries a positive charge, and each electron carries a negative charge. Protons are tightly contained in the nucleus of an atom, but the electrons in the outermost shell (the **VALENCE ELECTRONS**) can be transferred from one atom to another. Negatively charged bodies are therefore those with surplus negative charges (more electrons than protons), while positively charged bodies are those with a deficiency of negative charges (fewer electrons than protons).

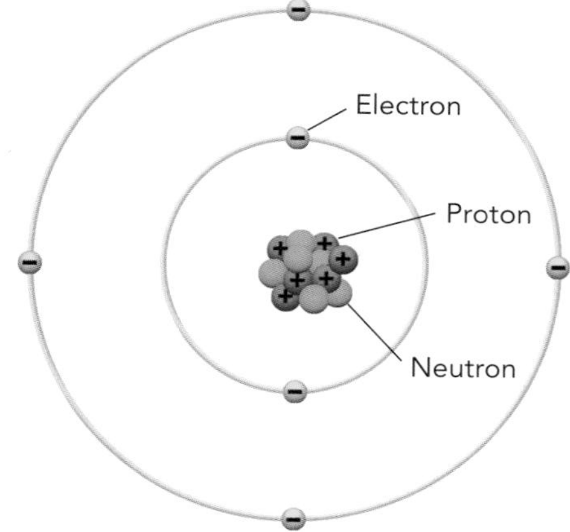

5.4 Atoms, the building blocks of matter, contain a nucleus made up of protons (positively charged particles) and neutrons (particles with no charge). Electrons (negatively charged particles) revolve around the nucleus.

- **ELECTRICAL CHARGE is a property of protons and electrons. A proton carries a positive charge, while an electron carries a negative charge.**

- **A NEGATIVELY CHARGED BODY contains more electrons than protons.**

- **A POSITIVELY CHARGED BODY contains fewer electrons than protons.**

The unit of measurement for electrical charge is the coulomb (C). In equations, electrical charge is often symbolized by the variable q. (Some references prefer the symbol Q instead.)

A coulomb is a multiple of the elementary charge, which is the charge carried by an electron or a proton. Through his experiments, the American physicist Robert Andrews Millikan (1868–1953) discovered that the charge of an electron is 1.602×10^{-19} C.

- **The ELEMENTARY CHARGE is the charge carried by a single electron or proton. It has a value of 1.602×10^{-19} C.**

- **The COULOMB is the unit of measurement for electrical charge. One coulomb is equal to the charge of 6.25×10^{18} electrons or protons.**

ST EST AST ELECTRICAL FORCES OF ATTRACTION AND REPULSION

Studies of the behaviour of electrically charged matter have revealed the following facts:

- Electrical charges of like signs (two positive or two negative charges) repel each other.
- Electrical charges of opposite signs (one positive and one negative charge) attract each other.

- The force at work in the attraction or repulsion between charges is called the *electrical force*.
- Electrical charges can be neither created nor destroyed; they can only be transferred from one body to another. This is called the *law of conservation of charge*.

ST EST AST 1.2 CONDUCTORS AND INSULATORS

Most objects are electrically neutral, which means that they carry an equal number of positive charges (protons) and negative charges (electrons). However, by transferring electrons from one atom to another, some objects can acquire a charge. This process is known as *charging* an object.

CHARGING an object consists in creating an imbalance in the electrical charge of that object.

In accordance with the law of conservation of charge, the total number of positive charges is always equal to the number of negative charges, so that the overall charge remains neutral.

Depending on how objects react on receiving electrical charges, they can be classified into three categories: conductors, semiconductors and insulators.

When an insulated metallic conductor is charged, the electrons in it move rapidly, distancing themselves from one another as much as possible. A new balance is quickly re-established, in which the charges spread out uniformly over the surface of the conductor (Figure 5.5), while the inside of the conductor remains neutral.

Insulated metallic conductor

5.5 When an insulated metallic conductor is charged, the charges spread out uniformly over the surface of the object.

Charging a metallic conductor in a circuit forces the electrons to move in one general direction. One electron "pushes" another, causing the charge to move along the length of the circuit.

At the atomic level of the metallic conductor, the attraction between the nuclei of the metal atoms and their valence electrons is weak. The valence electrons can therefore easily pass from one atom to another.

Another type of substance also conducts electrical charges: **ELECTROLYTIC SOLUTIONS**. These substances contain **IONS**, which are electrically charged particles. When electrodes are placed in an electrolytic solution, the positive ions move toward the negative terminal, while the negative ions move toward the positive terminal (Figure 5.6).

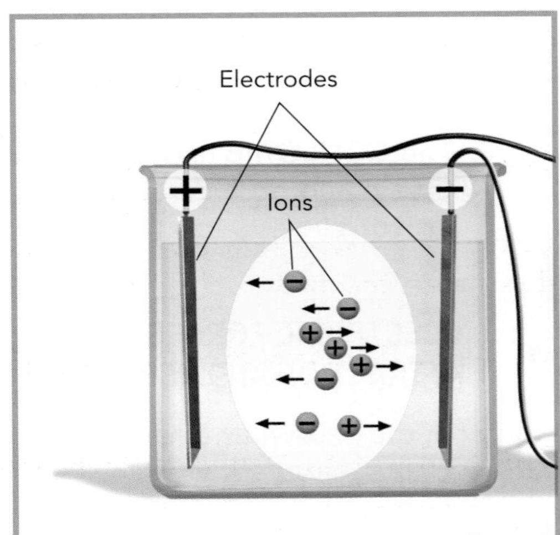

5.6 When an electrolytic solution is charged, the positive ions move toward the negative electrode, while the negative ions move toward the positive electrode.

Metals and electrolytic solutions are therefore usually conductors.

A CONDUCTOR is a substance that permits the free flow of electrical charges.

5.7 The human body conducts electricity. In this photo, charges are acquired through contact with a Van de Graaff generator. The charges then spread uniformly across the entire surface of the body. Charged hairs seek to move as far away from one another as possible.

1901
1967

Robert Van de Graaff

In 1929, this American physicist invented a machine that could produce large amounts of static electricity by friction. The machine is called a *Van de Graaff generator.*

An insulator is a substance that impedes the free flow of charges. When an insulator is charged, the charges do not move (Figure 5.8). At the atomic level, insulators hold on tightly to their valence electrons, making it difficult for the electrons to leave the atom. **NONMETALS** are usually insulators, as are many other widely different substances, such as wood, plastic, glass, paper, ceramics, rubber, silk and air.

An INSULATOR is a substance that impedes the free flow of electrical charges.

Other substances exhibit variable conductivity, depending on different factors. These substances are called *semiconductors* and are widely used in electronics, particularly in the manufacture of transistors. **METALLOIDS** and carbon are examples of semiconductors.

5.8 When an insulator is charged, the charges do not move.

EST 1.3 ELECTRICAL FIELDS

Electrical charges interact with one another. Any electrically charged body placed near another charged body is subjected to an electrical force. This force is capable of what physicists call *action at a distance*, which means that charged objects are affected by the force without actually coming in contact with one another.

The concept of a "field" is often used to explain how a force can act over a distance. Imagine that a charged object produces an electrical field and that this field acts as an intermediary, transmitting an electrical force to any charged object that crosses the field.

An ELECTRICAL FIELD is the area of space in which the electrical force of a charged body can act on another charged body.

Electrical fields are invisible. However, they can be represented by electrical field lines, which are lines showing the direction of the force that would be exerted on a positive charge placed in the field.

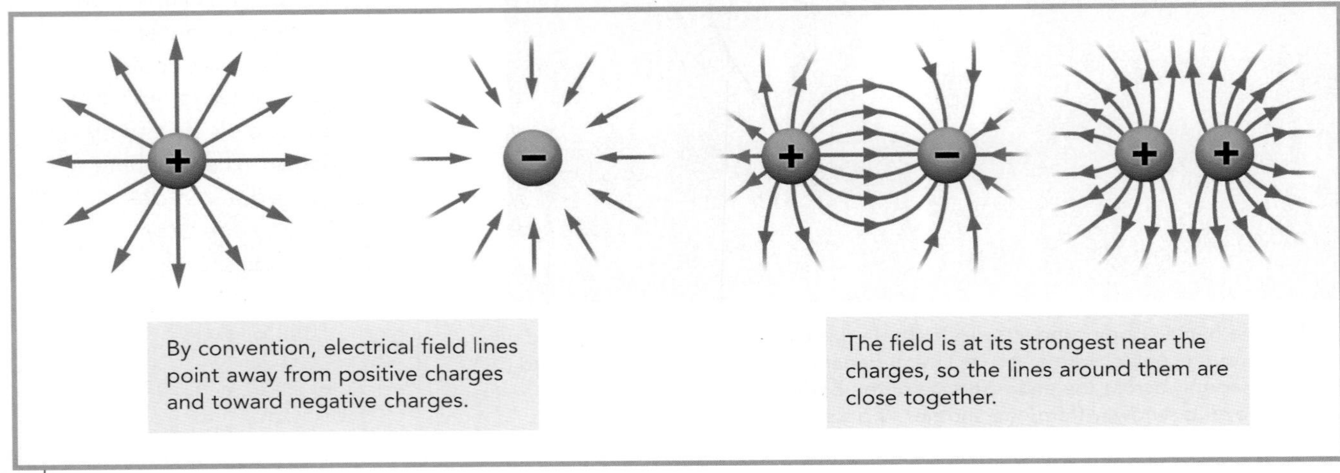

5.9 Electrical fields can be represented graphically with electrical field lines.

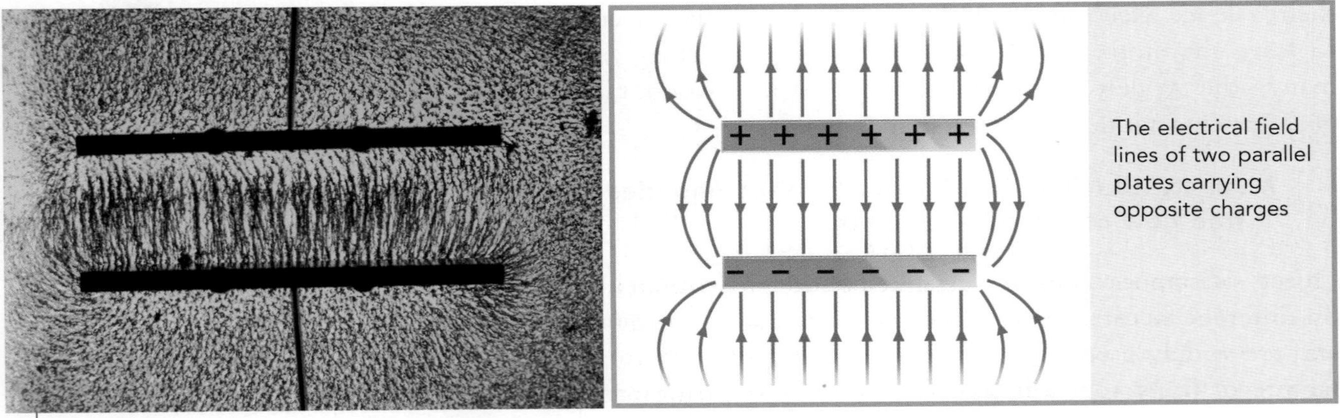

5.10 Exposure to an electrical field makes grass seeds on a film of oil place themselves spontaneously along the electrical field lines.

2 Static electricity

In the course of their research and through their discoveries, scientists eventually realized that the properties and behaviour of insulated charges are different from those of charges in circuits. They thus distinguished two fields of study: static electricity (also called *electrostatic electricity*) and dynamic electricity.

Static electricity deals with electrical phenomena related to insulated charges, which are usually immobile.

Static comes from the Greek *statikos*, meaning "causing to stand."

STATIC ELECTRICITY describes all the phenomena related to electrical charges at rest.

A metal-leaf electroscope is an apparatus used to detect the presence of static electricity in an object. Figure 5.11 explains how an electroscope works.

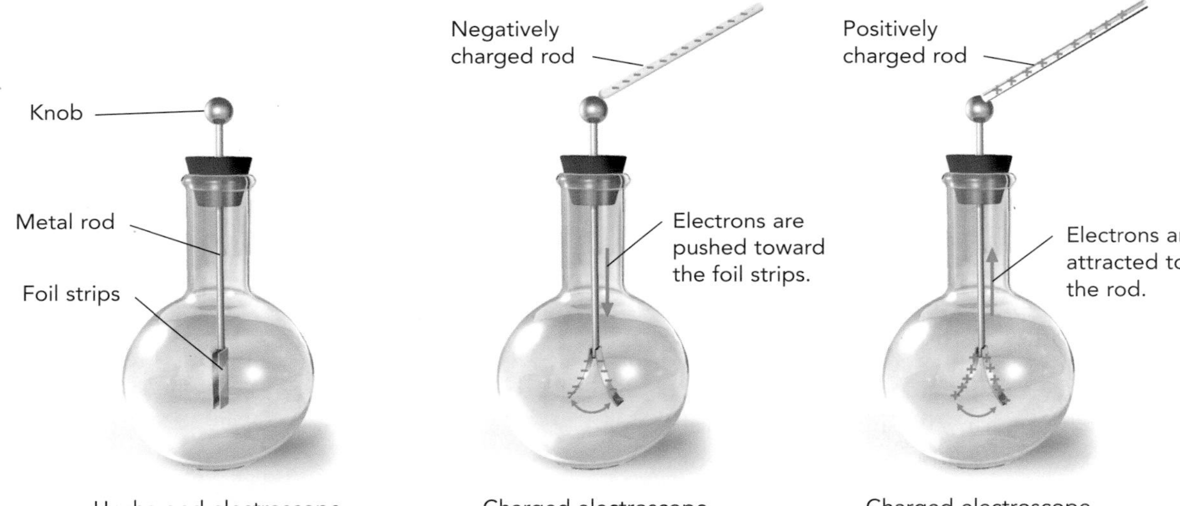

5.11 When the knob of the electroscope is touched with a charged object, the charge is transmitted to the metal rod. Since the two foil strips at the end of the rod acquire the same charge, they repel each other.

Electrically charged objects do not remain permanently charged. Sometimes they gradually lose their charge, for example, by combining with water molecules in the surrounding air. This loss explains why the effects of static electricity are less frequent during humid weather. In other cases, however, charged objects recover their neutral state very quickly. This happens when two objects of opposite charges come close to each other or touch. The result is referred to as an *electrostatic discharge*. The discharge is sometimes accompanied by a spark, which shows that electrons have passed through the air and heated it, making it light up (Figure 5.13, page 146).

AN ALTERNATE ROUTE FOR LIGHTNING

A lightning rod is an instrument that protects us from lightning, a phenomenon involving strong electrostatic discharges. The rod offers lightning bolts a direct path to the ground, keeping them away from people, animals or buildings. 

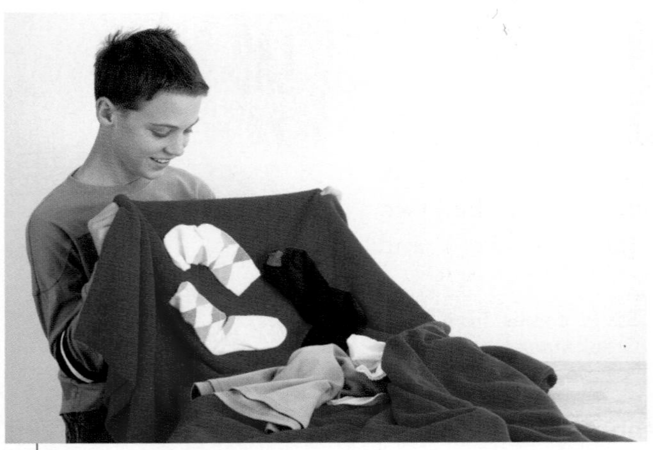

5.12 The drier the clothes as they come out of the dryer, the greater their tendency to stick together because of static electricity.

5.13 A lightning bolt is a spectacular example of an electrostatic discharge, which involves the rapid neutralization of two charged objects (for example, a cloud and the ground).

2.1 CHARGING AN OBJECT

An object can be charged in various ways: by friction, by conduction or by induction.

CHARGING BY FRICTION

When two neutral bodies are rubbed against each other, some atoms in one of the bodies may pull electrons away from the atoms of the other body. The result is two bodies with opposite charges.

The direction of this transfer depends on the tendency of the materials to capture or give up electrons. Table 5.14 provides some examples. A substance at the top of the list, called the *triboelectric series,* is more likely to acquire a negative charge than a substance at the bottom.

5.14 SUBSTANCES IN THE TRIBOELECTRIC SERIES

Tendency	Substance
High affinity for capturing electrons (tendency to acquire a negative charge)	Plastic
	Sulphur
	Gold
	Nickel, copper
	Hard rubber (ebonite)
	Wood, yellow amber, resin
	Cotton
	Paper
	Silk
	Lead
	Wool
Strong tendency to give up electrons (tendency to acquire a positive charge)	Glass

5.15 When a glass rod is rubbed against silk, the silk atoms pull some electrons away from the glass atoms. The silk temporarily acquires a negative charge, and the glass, a positive charge.

ST EST AST

CHARGING BY CONDUCTION

An object can be electrically charged by putting it in contact with another object that is already charged. The two objects then share the charge between them. The result is two similarly charged bodies, but with charges that are weaker than that of the original object.

When the knob of a metal-leaf electroscope is touched with a charged object, the electroscope is charged by conduction, as shown in Figure 5.11 (page 145).

ST EST AST

CHARGING BY INDUCTION

In science, the term *induction* refers to an action that occurs without direct contact between objects. When an electrically charged object (A in Figure 5.17 below) approaches a neutral object (B), without actually touching it, opposite charges will gradually accumulate on the side of B that is facing A. If B is a conductor, an equal number of charges like those of A will gather on the other side, in accordance with the law of conservation of charge (Figure 5.17, illustration on the left).

If B is insulated, however, the opposite charges will neutralize each other as soon as A is withdrawn. To give B a more sustainable charge, its other side must be in contact with a conductor (Figure 5.17, illustration on the right).

5.16 Through induction, a charged object (the comb) can attract small neutral objects (the pieces of paper).

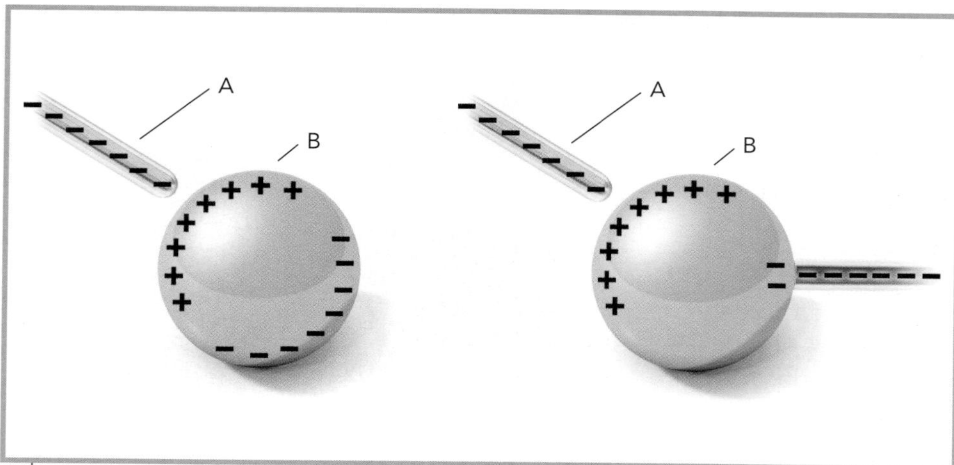

5.17 Charging by induction causes the charges in a previously neutral conductor to separate. In the illustration on the left, if object B is insulated, it will return to its neutral state as soon as the charged object A is removed, since the opposite charges in B neutralize each other. In the illustration on the right, B is in contact with a conductor, so some of the charges accumulating on the side touching the conductor will be transferred to it by conduction. When A is withdrawn, B will carry a charge opposite to that of A.

5.18 THREE METHODS OF CHARGING AN OBJECT

Method	Before	During	After
Friction	Two neutral objects	Friction pulls electrons away from one of the objects and transfers them to the other.	Two objects with opposite charges + −
Conduction	One charged object and one neutral object ++	The charge of one object is shared between two objects when they come into contact.	Two objects with like charges + +
Induction	One charged object and one neutral object +	The proximity of the charged object causes the charges in the neutral object to separate.	One charged object and one object carrying a partial positive charge on one side and a partial negative charge on the other side +

ENVIRONMENT EXTRA

Filtering pollution at the source

One of the best ways to fight atmospheric pollution is to eliminate it at the source. Through the installation of filters in factory chimneys, many dust particles and suspended droplets can be captured, thus reducing the amount of contaminants in the air.

Different types of filters are available on the market, including electrostatic precipitators. These collectors are more expensive than the mechanical ones, but they are also more effective at retaining very fine particles. High-voltage electrodes (from 30 000 V to 75 000 V) ionize the impurities in the air. The charged particles are then attracted to, and captured by, plates of the opposite charge. All that remains to be done is to clean the plates from time to time.

The first electrostatic filters were developed around 1906. They helped reduce air pollution not only in big cities but also in certain homes, thanks to residential models that can be connected to a forced-air heating system.

Installing electrostatic precipitators reduces polluting emissions from factory chimneys.

EST 2.2 COULOMB'S LAW

In 1785, the French physicist Charles Augustin de Coulomb (1736–1806) measured the forces of attraction and repulsion between two immobile and electrically charged particles. He demonstrated that the magnitude of the force of one particle over the other depends on their charges and the distance separating them. The greater the charges on the particles, the greater the electrical force. Conversely, the greater the distance between the particles, the weaker the electrical force.

COULOMB'S LAW states that the magnitude of the force between two immobile and electrically charged particles is directly proportional to the product of their charges and inversely proportional to the square of the distance between them.

Coulomb's law can be expressed by the following equation:

$$F_e = \frac{kq_1q_2}{r^2}$$

where F_e is the electrical force (in N)
k is Coulomb's constant, which is $9 \times 10^9 \frac{\text{Nm}^2}{\text{C}^2}$
q_1 is the charge of the first particle (in C)
q_2 is the charge of the second particle (in C)
r is the distance between the two particles (in m)

Let's take an example of two positively charged bodies, each with a charge of 5×10^{-8} C and placed 1 cm (0.01 m) apart. The electrical force between the two bodies is calculated as follows:

$$F_e = \frac{kq_1q_2}{r^2}$$

$$= \frac{9 \times 10^9 \text{ N}\cancel{\text{m}^2}/\cancel{\text{C}^2} \times 5 \times 10^{-8} \cancel{\text{C}} \times 5 \times 10^{-8} \cancel{\text{C}}}{(0.01 \cancel{\text{m}})^2}$$

$$= 0.225 \text{ N}$$

The electrical force acting on each of the bodies is 0.225 N.

1736
1806

Charles Augustin de Coulomb

A highly methodical researcher, Charles Augustin de Coulomb designed and conducted many experiments on matter, friction, electricity and magnetism. At a time when there was no reliable method of measuring charges, Coulomb invented the torsion balance, which he then used to discover the law that bears his name.

Coulomb's law is valid only for charges at rest. When charges are in motion, other forces must also be taken into account.

ST EST AST 3 Dynamic electricity

When electrical charges are not insulated but are placed instead in a circuit, meaning that they can flow in a loop, the flow is referred to as *dynamic electricity*.

DYNAMIC ELECTRICITY describes all the phenomena related to electrical charges in motion.

Electricity has changed our way of life, and this "revolution" is due to dynamic electricity. It is a form of energy with endless possibilities of application.

ST EST AST 3.1 ELECTRIC CURRENT

Owing to the force of repulsion between like charges, the electrons of conductors in a circuit are constantly "pushed" from one atom to the next. This force explains the rapid action of electric current. As soon as current is generated at one point in a circuit, all the electrons in the loop are set in motion. The effect can be felt almost simultaneously in every part of the circuit.

ELECTRIC CURRENT is the orderly flow of negative charges carried by electrons.

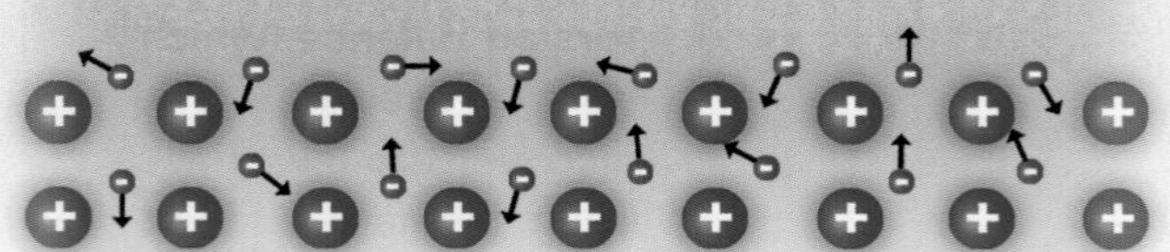

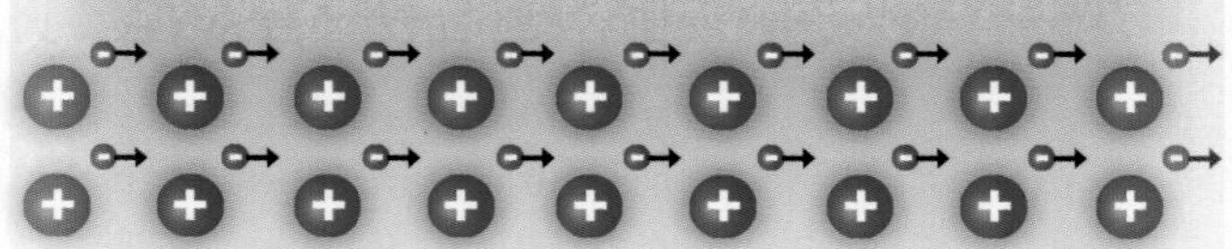

5.19 When electrons move in a disorderly fashion, as on the left, there is no electric current. When electrons flow in an orderly fashion, as on the right, an electric current is generated.

Current direction is, by convention, the path that a positive particle would take when flowing in a circuit. This rule was determined before scientists really understood the nature of electric current. Today, we know that the moving particles are generally electrons, which are negative particles. The real direction of the current is therefore the opposite of the direction identified by convention.

The CONVENTIONAL CURRENT DIRECTION is the direction in which a positive particle would flow in an electrical circuit. For this reason, the direction goes from the positive terminal of the power supply to its negative terminal.

Now let's look at the various characteristics of current and the forms it may take.

ST
EST
AST

CURRENT INTENSITY

Current intensity refers to the number of charges that pass a given point in an electrical circuit every second. It is symbolized by the letter I and is measured in amperes (A), commonly referred to as *amps*. The unit of measurement was named after the French physicist André-Marie Ampère (1775–1836). In a current of one ampere, a charge of one coulomb flows through the circuit every second. This relationship is expressed mathematically by the following equation:

$$1 \text{ A} = \frac{1 \text{ C}}{1 \text{ s}}$$

CURRENT INTENSITY is the number of charges that flow past a given point in an electrical circuit every second.

The current intensity in a circuit can be determined using the following formula:

$I = \dfrac{q}{\Delta t}$ where I is the current intensity (in A)
q is the charge (in C)
Δt is the time interval (in s)

For example, the data sheet for a car headlight indicates that the light requires a current of 15 A. The charge needed for one minute of operation can be calculated as follows:

$$I = \frac{q}{\Delta t}$$
$$q = I \times \Delta t$$
$$= 15 \text{ A} \times 60 \text{ s}$$
$$= 900 \text{ C}$$

It takes a charge of 900 C to make the headlight work for one minute.

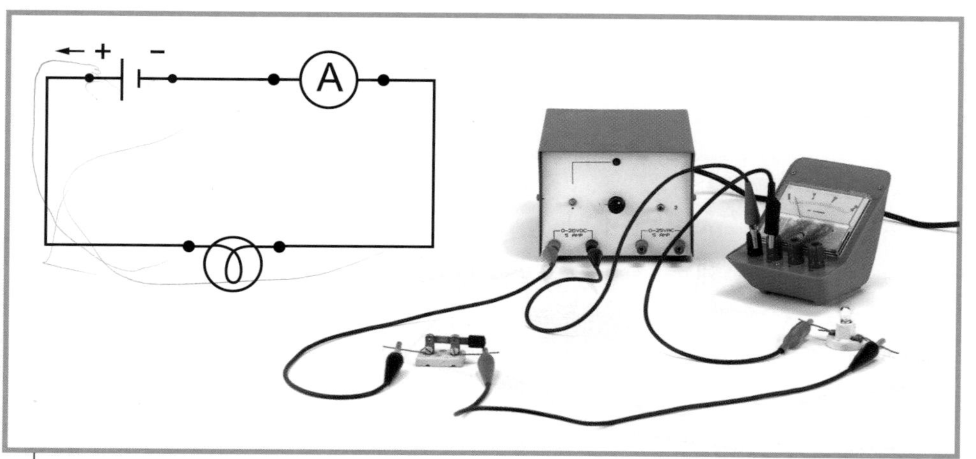

5.20 An ammeter is an instrument for measuring current intensity. It acts like a checkpoint, counting the number of charges that flow past a given point in a circuit in one second. For this reason, ammeters must be installed in the path a charge will take.

HOW TO DETERMINE THE CHARACTERISTICS OF AN ELECTRIC CURRENT

ST
EST
AST

POTENTIAL DIFFERENCE

Electrical potential is the energy that can be supplied by each of the charges in an electric current. By flowing from one point to the next in a circuit, the charges transfer their energy to other components for a variety of purposes. To measure the potential difference (symbolized by the letter V) between two points in a circuit is to evaluate the amount of energy transferred between those two points. The greater the potential difference between two points, the larger the amount of energy transferred. The unit of measurement for potential difference is the volt (V), named after the Italian physicist Alessandro Volta (1745–1827). One volt is equal to the energy of one joule per coulomb of charge. This relationship is expressed mathematically by the following equation:

$$1\,\text{V} = \frac{1\,\text{J}}{1\,\text{C}}$$

The POTENTIAL DIFFERENCE is the amount of energy transferred between two points in an electrical circuit.

The potential difference between two points in a circuit can be determined using the following formula:

$V = \frac{E}{q}$ where V is the potential difference (in V)
E is the energy transferred (in J)
q is the charge (in C)

The electrical circuits in our homes usually supply a potential difference of 120 V. The amount of energy provided by a charge of 200 C is calculated as follows:

$$V = \frac{E}{q}$$
$$E = V \times q$$
$$= 120\text{ V} \times 200\text{ C}$$
$$= 240\,000\text{ J}$$

A 200-C charge providing a potential difference of 120 V can transfer 240 000 J (or 240 kJ) of energy.

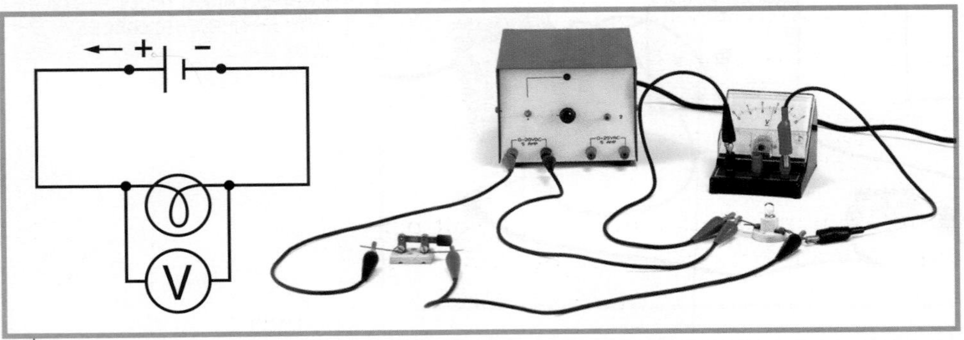

5.21 A voltmeter is an instrument for measuring potential difference. It acts like a checkpoint, calculating the amount of energy each of the charges transfers to a circuit element (such as a light bulb or a motor). For this reason, voltmeters must be installed at the points where the circuit enters and exits this element.

In an electrical circuit, the energy of the charges comes from a power supply, a device capable of generating electrical energy. Batteries and generators are examples of power supplies. A battery is a device that can transform chemical energy into electrical energy, while a generator transforms **MECHANICAL ENERGY** into electricity.

A voltmeter measures both the energy transferred from the power supply to the charges and the energy transferred from the charges to the circuit elements.

1942
–

Monique Frize

This electrical engineer, who was born in Montréal, is currently a professor in the engineering departments of both Carleton University and the University of Ottawa. She actively encourages women to pursue careers in fields of science and technology, giving frequent talks and maintaining websites on the subject.

RESISTANCE

Each component in a circuit has a specific function. The role of some components, called *resistors*, is to transform electrical energy into another form of energy. There are different types of resistors. For example, the heating elements in a toaster transform electrical energy into **THERMAL ENERGY**, and the blades of a fan turn because mechanical energy is produced by an electric motor. Heating elements and motors thus transform electrical energy into other forms of energy, which results in a drop in the amount of energy carried by the charges.

In an electrical circuit, resistance can be described as a force that hinders the flow of the current. The higher the resistance of a material, the more energy it takes for the current to flow.

ELECTRICAL RESISTANCE is the ability of a material to hinder the flow of electric current.

5.22 FACTORS AFFECTING THE RESISTANCE OF A SUBSTANCE TO CURRENT FLOW

Factor	Description
Nature of the substance	Poor conductors resist current flow more than good conductors.
Length	The longer an element or a wire, the greater its resistance to current flow.
Diameter	An element with a very small diameter (such as the filament of a light bulb) resists current flow more than an element with a larger diameter.
Temperature	A warm element usually resists current flow more than a cold element.

Resistance (R) is measured in ohms. Ohms are symbolized by the Greek letter omega (Ω). Resistance produces the opposite effect on charges from the effect of the power supply: resistance lowers their energy levels instead of increasing them.

By definition, an ohm is equal to a potential difference of one volt per ampere. This relationship is expressed mathematically by the following equation:

$$1\ \Omega = \frac{1\ \text{V}}{1\ \text{A}}$$

ST EST AST

OHM'S LAW

LAB 40

The German physicist Georg Simon Ohm (1789–1854) established a mathematical relationship between current intensity, potential difference and resistance. Through his experiments, he discovered that, for a given resistance, the potential difference is directly proportional to the current intensity.

OHM'S LAW states that, for a given resistance, the potential difference in an electrical circuit is directly proportional to the current intensity.

The mathematical formula for Ohm's law is:

$V = RI$ where V is the potential difference (in V)
R is the resistance (in Ω)
I is the current intensity (in A)

This law can also be expressed in other ways:

$R = \frac{V}{I}$ (definition of resistance)

or

$I = \frac{V}{R}$ (another definition of current intensity)

SOLVING THE SUPERCONDUCTOR MYSTERY

A team headed by Louis Taillefer, physicist and professor at Université de Sherbrooke, has made a discovery that could lead to a technological revolution. The team has solved a 20-year-old mystery about the nature of high-temperature superconductors. "Superconductors are the most remarkable materials on Earth. They can transmit electricity without resistance and without any energy loss," explained Dr. Taillefer.

"For the past 20 years, we have been stumped as to why these particular materials are the best superconductors." The reason finally became clear when the team, on observing electron behaviour in a phenomenon called *quantum oscillations*, proved beyond doubt that the materials are metals.

Superconductors are already used in magnetic resonance imaging scanners, and plans are under way to use them to transport electricity. Until now, however, scientists have not been able to take full advantage of their potential because too many questions remained unanswered.

Source: Adapted from Isabelle Pion, "L'équipe de Louis Taillefer perce le mystère des supraconducteurs," *La Tribune*, June 1, 2007, p. 9. *[Translation]*

Louis Taillefer is a physicist and professor at Université de Sherbrooke.

The following are examples of applications of Ohm's law:

- If the current intensity in a circuit is doubled, without changing the resistance, then the potential difference will also be doubled.
- If, for a given resistance, the potential difference is halved, then the current intensity will also be halved.
- If an element is replaced by another with higher resistance but a constant potential difference is maintained, the current intensity will drop.

It is important to note that Ohm's law applies only to conductors and not to insulators or semiconductors.

3.2 ELECTRICAL POWER

The electrical power of a device indicates the amount of work it can do, or, in other words, the amount of energy it can transform in a certain period of time. The more powerful the device, the faster it works. Consequently, the more work a device does in a given time interval, the more powerful it is. Electrical power is therefore a measure of the rate of transformation of electrical energy. The unit of measurement for electrical power is the watt (W). A device with an electrical power of one watt works at one joule per second. This relationship is expressed by the following equation:

$$1\ \text{W} = \frac{1\ \text{J}}{1\ \text{s}}$$

ELECTRICAL POWER is the amount of work an electrical device can perform per second.

The formula for electrical power is:

$$P_e = \frac{W}{\Delta t}$$ where P_e is the electrical power (in W)
W is the work (in J)
Δt is the time interval (in s)

1736
1819

James Watt

This Scottish mathematician and engineer developed a number of devices that improved the performance of steam engines, opening the way for more powerful and efficient machines. For this reason, the unit of measurement for power was named after him.

The electrical power of a device can also be expressed as a function of the potential difference at its terminals and of the intensity of the current flowing through it.

$P_e = VI$ where P_e is the electrical power (in W)
V is the potential difference (in V)
I is the current intensity (in A)

In other terms: $1\ \text{W} = 1\ \text{V} \times 1\ \text{A}$

$$= 1\ \frac{\text{J}}{\text{C}} \times 1\ \frac{\text{C}}{\text{s}} = 1\ \frac{\text{J}}{\text{s}}$$

ST
EST
AST

THE RELATIONSHIP BETWEEN POWER AND ELECTRICAL ENERGY

The amount of electrical energy used by a device can be determined by multiplying its electrical power by the time:

$$1\ \text{W} \times 1\ \text{s} = 1\ \frac{\text{J}}{\cancel{\text{s}}} \times 1\ \cancel{\text{s}}$$
$$= 1\ \text{J}$$

Electrical energy can therefore be measured in joules, but it can also be expressed in kilowatt hours (kWh), as shown by the following equation:

$1\ \text{kWh} = 1000\ \text{W} \times 3600\ \text{s} = 3\,600\,000\ \text{J}$

The kilowatt hour is the unit used to calculate consumption for electricity bills.

The following mathematical formula describes the relationship between electrical power and electrical energy:

$E = P_e \Delta t$ where E is the electrical energy used (in J or kWh)
P_e is the electrical power (in W or kW)
Δt is the time interval (in s or h)

For example, if a 1000-W microwave oven operates for six minutes, the amount of energy it will use is calculated as follows:

- $E = P_e \Delta t$
  $= 1000\ \text{W} \times 360\ \text{s}$
  $= 360\,000\ \text{J}$
- $E = P_e \Delta t$
  $= 1\ \text{kW} \times 0.1\ \text{h}$
  $= 0.1\ \text{kWh}$

After six minutes of use, the microwave oven will have consumed 360 000 J or 0.1 kWh of energy.

In Québec, homeowners pay roughly eight cents per kilowatt hour for electricity. Using the microwave oven in the example above for one hour would therefore add eight cents to the owner's monthly electricity bill.

ST
EST
AST

3.3 ELECTRICAL CIRCUITS

For charges to flow, they must be able to move in a loop, continually returning to their starting point. The loop thus formed is called a *closed circuit*. (See also Chapter 14, page 469.)

▶ **An ELECTRICAL CIRCUIT is a network in which electrical charges can flow continuously in a loop.**

AN END IN SIGHT FOR MINIATURIZATION?

In the world of microelectronics, small means powerful. Manufacturers are engaged in a fierce competition to miniaturize transistors, the building blocks of microprocessors. In 2001, a transistor measured 0.25 microns (micrometres, or 10^{-6} m), which was already tiny. In 2007, transistor size was down to only 0.065 microns, or 65 nanometres. Soon the figure will be 45 nanometres, and then 32. The principle is simple: the more transistors a manufacturer manages to install on a microchip, the lighter and more powerful the product.

Miniaturization has its limits, however. The technology behind transistor manufacture is highly complex; the transistors are engraved directly onto the silicon chip. At such small scales, it becomes increasingly difficult to etch perfect transistors without damaging those on either side.

Scientists now foresee the day when production techniques will become too complex and expensive to be worth the effort. Will transistors become as small as 12, 10 or even 6 nanometres? Scientists have their doubts.

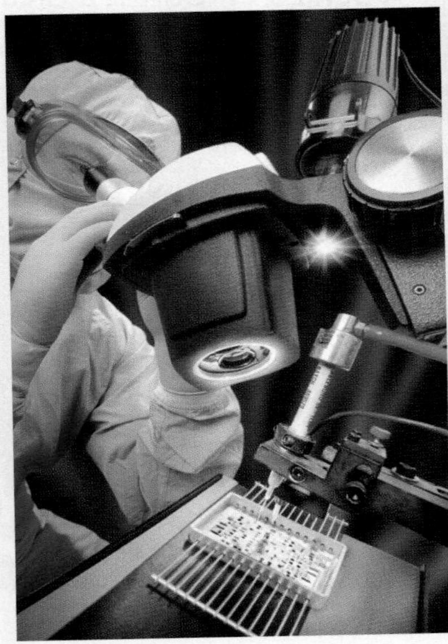

The technical difficulties involved in manufacturing microchips increase as the chips become ever smaller.

All electrical devices contain an electrical circuit. Some circuits are very simple, while others are highly complex. However, they all contain at least the following three components:

- a power supply to create a potential difference (measured in volts)
- one or more elements that use electrical energy, such as a light bulb or a heating element (their resistance is measured in ohms)
- wires that carry the charges from the power supply to the elements and then from the elements back to the source (the current intensity in these wires is measured in amperes)

HOW TO DRAW A DIAGRAM - SYMBOLS

HOW TO DRAW A DIAGRAM - CIRCUIT DIAGRAM

Diagrams and symbols are often used to represent electrical circuits. The current direction shown in a diagram usually corresponds to the conventional current direction.

When a circuit contains two or more elements, the components can be connected in different ways. Series circuits and parallel circuits are two types of connections.

ST EST AST

SERIES CIRCUITS

In a series circuit, components are connected end to end. Since the circuit does not branch out at any point, the current can follow only one path.

A SERIES CIRCUIT is a circuit in which the elements are connected end to end.

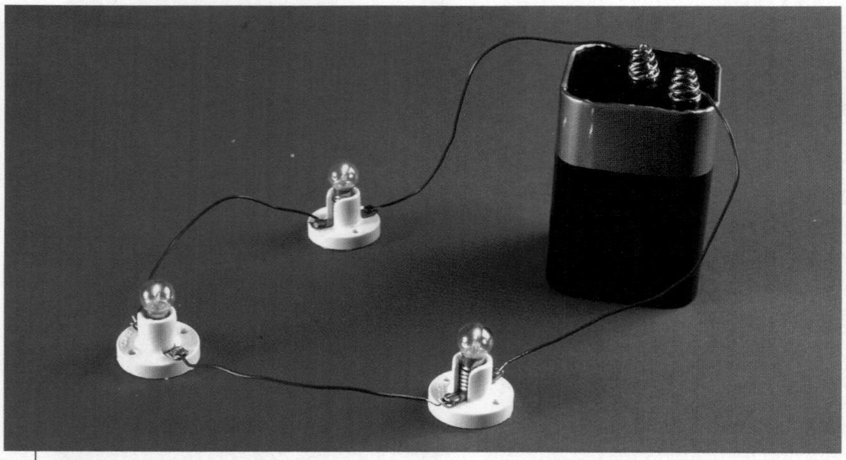

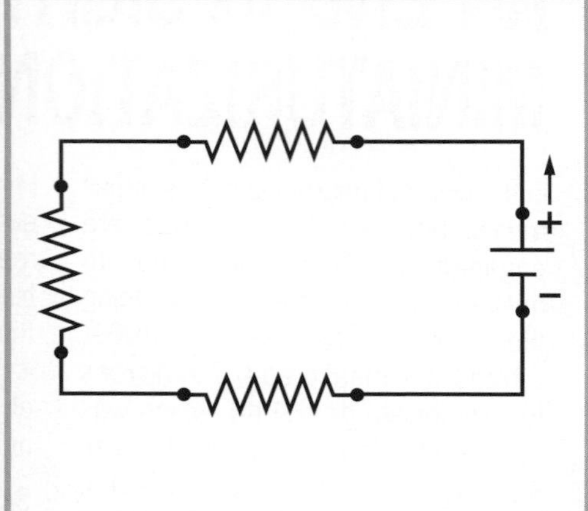

5.23 All the elements in this circuit are connected end to end. They are therefore connected "in series."

This type of circuit features the following characteristics:

- If one of the circuit components is defective, the entire circuit stops working because the charges can no longer flow through it.
- The energy used by the resistors adds up so that with each new resistor, the amount of energy available is reduced. (This explains why, in Figure 5.23, the light from the bulbs is dim.)

FUSES and **CIRCUIT BREAKERS** provide protection in electrical circuits, but they must be installed in series so that the current will be cut off in the event of an overload.

5.24 Christmas tree lights are sometimes connected in series.

ST EST AST

PARALLEL CIRCUITS

When a circuit branches out at least once, the elements are said to be connected *in parallel*. The current may then follow different paths. The point at which a circuit separates into two or more paths and the point at which two or more branches merge into one are called *nodes*.

A PARALLEL CIRCUIT is a circuit that contains at least one branch.

This type of circuit features the following characteristics:

- If an element of the circuit is defective, the elements in the other branches can continue functioning because the current still flows through them.

- The effect of each resistor is shared among the various pathways. The total resistance therefore drops instead of increasing as resistors are added.
- Current intensity is shared among the various resistors, with the result that every time a resistor is added, the demand for current increases, as does the risk of an overload. It is therefore useful to install protective devices, such as fuses or circuit breakers, in this type of circuit.

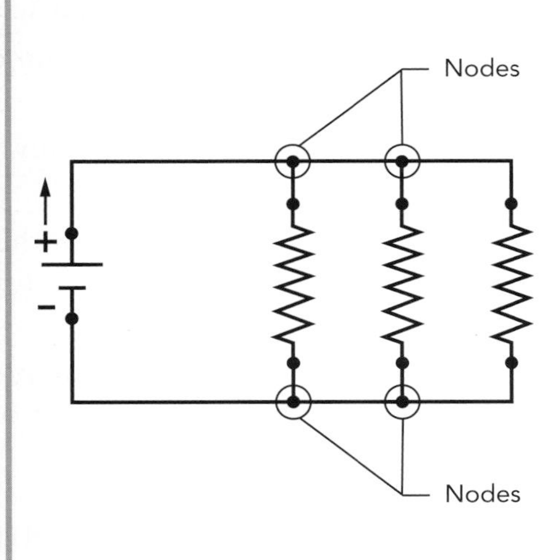

5.25 In a parallel circuit, the current may flow along different pathways.

EST 3.4 KIRCHHOFF'S LAWS

A German physicist by the name of Gustav Robert Kirchhoff (1824–1887) studied the relationship between current intensity, potential difference and resistance in series and parallel circuits. The two laws he derived from his experiments are based on the law of conservation of charge and the law of conservation of energy.

The first law concerns current intensity. It states that when charges arrive at a branch in an electrical circuit, they separate, following one of the possible pathways. However, the number of charges flowing into a node or a circuit element always remains equal to the number of charges flowing out of the node or element. This law derives from the law of conservation of charge.

> **KIRCHHOFF'S FIRST LAW states that the intensity of a current that flows into an element or a node of an electrical circuit is always equal to the intensity of the current that flows out of the element or node.**

Kirchhoff's second law concerns potential difference. Kirchhoff demonstrated that charges in an electrical circuit acquire a certain amount of energy when they flow through a power supply. Whatever pathway they follow, the charges will transmit all of the energy they have acquired before returning to the power supply. This law derives from the law of conservation of energy.

KIRCHHOFF'S SECOND LAW states that in an electrical circuit, the total energy acquired by the charges from the power supply is always equal to the total energy transferred by these charges, whatever pathway they may take in the circuit.

Now let's look at how these two laws apply to different electrical circuits, by using an analogy. Let's compare the electric current in a circuit to a fleet of trucks delivering goods along a particular route:

- The current intensity (I) corresponds to the number of trucks that pass a given point per minute.
- The electrical potential corresponds to the number of boxes a truck is transporting (its energy level).
- The potential difference (V) is the difference between the number of boxes a truck is transporting before and after a delivery or a stop at the factory.
- The resistance (R) is a measurement specific to each customer, who decides how many boxes to take from each truck.

THE CASE OF SERIES CIRCUITS

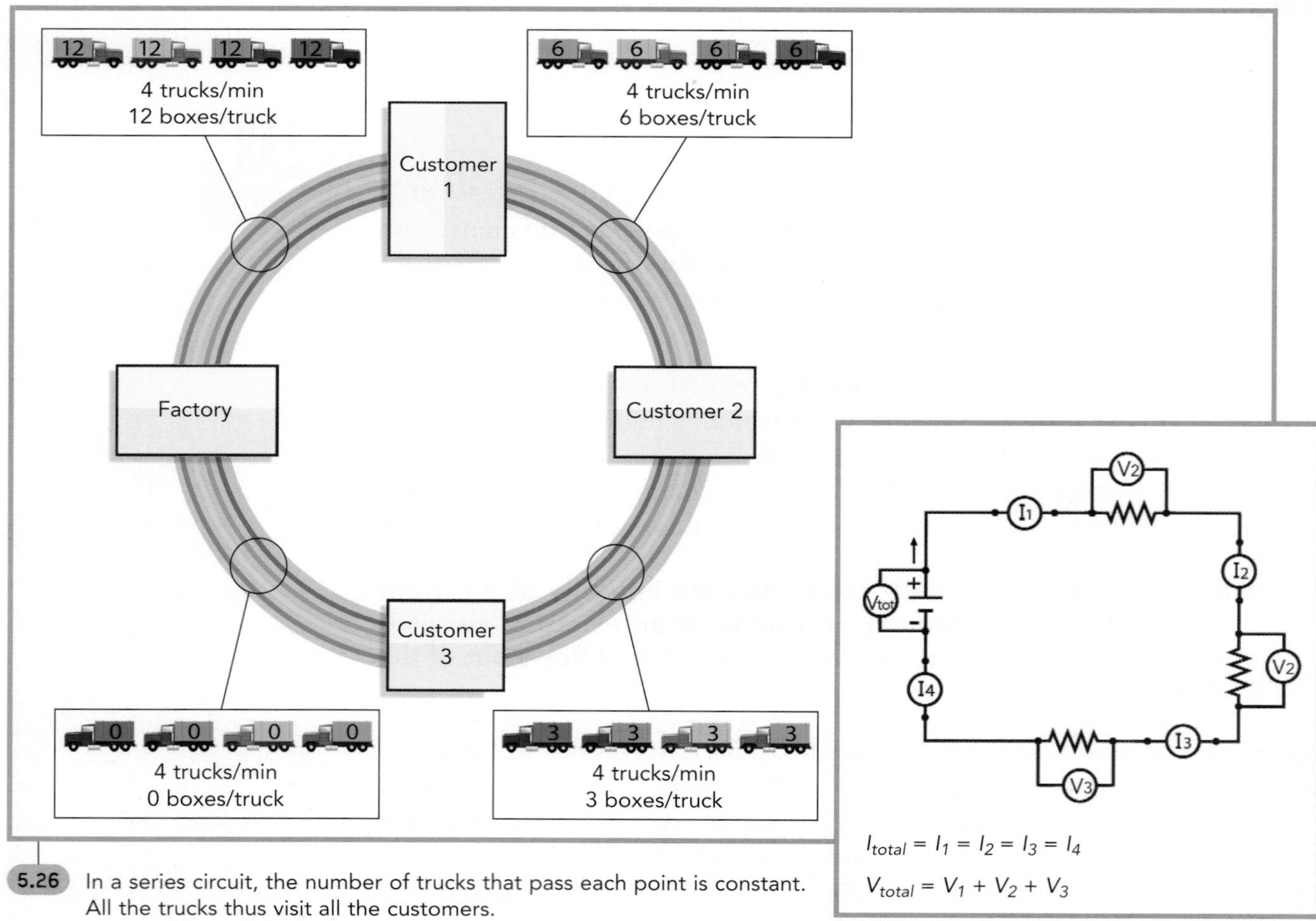

5.26 In a series circuit, the number of trucks that pass each point is constant. All the trucks thus visit all the customers.

In a series circuit, only one path is possible. The number of trucks remains the same at any point in the circuit. In other words:

$$I_{total} = I_1 = I_2 = I_3 = I_4, \qquad \text{(Kirchhoff's first law)}$$

which is four trucks per minute, or four amperes.

Every time a truck stops at a customer's place of business, a certain number of boxes are delivered (part of the truck's energy is transferred). The number of boxes delivered corresponds to the potential difference at the terminals of each resistor. In the example of Figure 5.26 (page 160), the first customer receives six boxes from each truck (or six volts), the second receives three, and the third receives the remaining three. In other words:

$$\begin{aligned} V_{total} &= V_1 + V_2 + V_3 \qquad \text{(Kirchhoff's second law)} \\ &= 6 + 3 + 3 \\ &= 12, \end{aligned}$$

which is 12 boxes per truck, or 12 volts.

EST THE CASE OF PARALLEL CIRCUITS

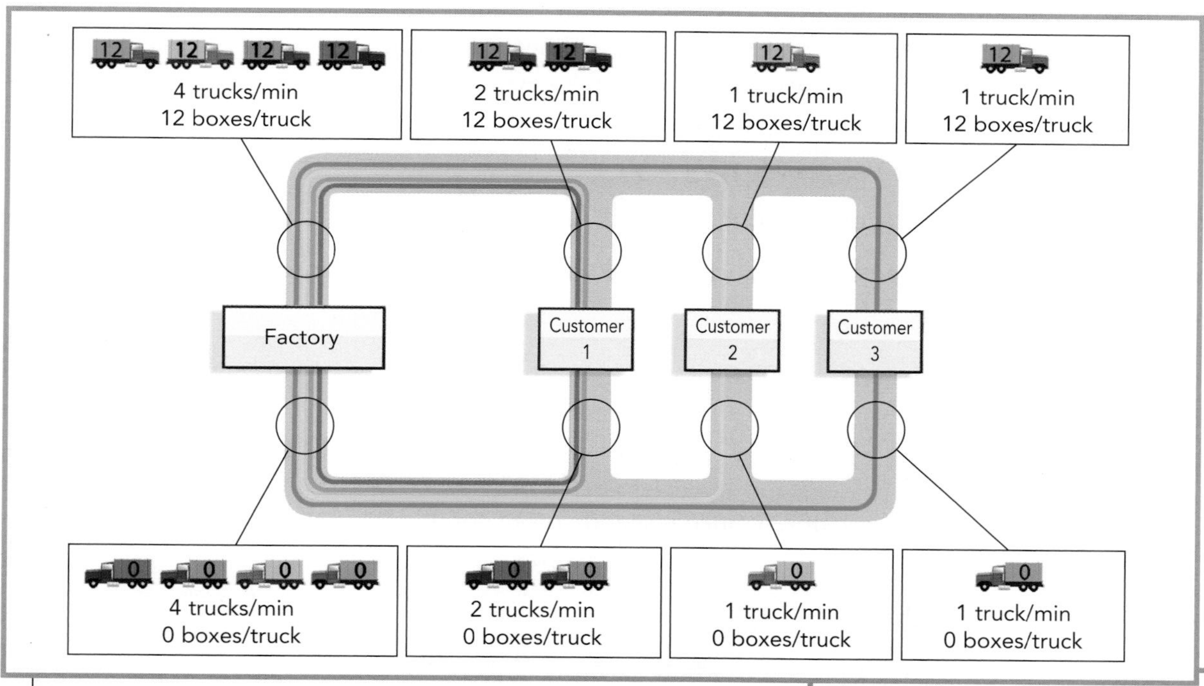

5.27 In a parallel circuit, the number of trucks is not the same everywhere because each one follows a particular pathway. Each truck thus serves only one customer.

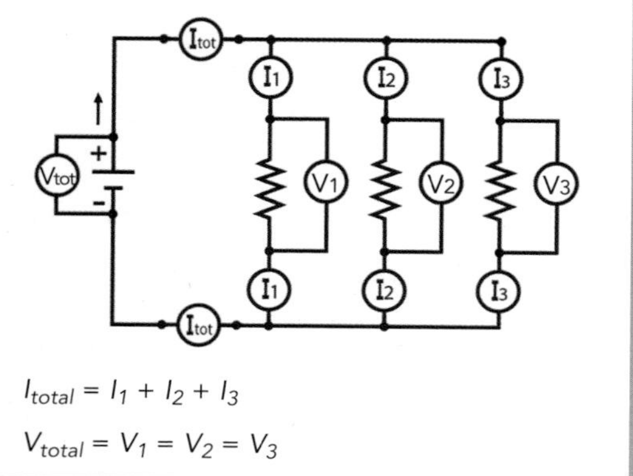

$I_{total} = I_1 + I_2 + I_3$

$V_{total} = V_1 = V_2 = V_3$

The trucks must make a choice when they come to a branch in a parallel circuit. Since they do not all follow the same path, they necessarily split up. However, when the number of trucks arriving at a branch (a node) and the number of trucks driving away from it are compared, the two numbers are always the same. Furthermore, the sum of the numbers of trucks in each of the branches corresponds to the total number of trucks in circulation. In other words:

$$I_{total} = I_1 + I_2 + I_3 \quad \text{(Kirchhoff's first law)}$$
$$= 2 + 1 + 1$$
$$= 4,$$

which is four trucks per minute, or four amperes.

In a parallel circuit, the potential difference in each of the possible pathways must match the potential difference acquired from the power supply. In Figure 5.27 (page 161), each truck must deliver all the boxes it received at the outset to its customer before returning to the factory, regardless of the path it takes. In other words:

$$V_{total} = V_1 = V_2 = V_3 \quad \text{(Kirchhoff's second law)}$$
$$= 12 = 12 = 12,$$

which is 12 boxes per truck, or 12 volts.

EST EQUIVALENT RESISTANCE

In certain situations, it may be useful to know a value called the *equivalent resistance* (R_{eq}). It represents the amount of resistance needed in a single resistor to replace the entire collection of resistors in a circuit. The equivalent resistance can be calculated using Ohm's law and Kirchhoff's laws.

In a series circuit, we know that $V_{total} = V_1 + V_2 + V_3 + \ldots$

Using Ohm's law, V can be replaced by RI: $R_{eq} I_{tot} = R_1 I_1 + R_2 I_2 + R_3 I_3 + \ldots$

Since the current intensity is the same throughout, all values in the equation can be divided by I. We thus obtain:

$R_{eq} = R_1 + R_2 + R_3 + \ldots$

The equivalent resistance of a series circuit is therefore equal to the sum of all the individual resistance values.

In a parallel circuit, calculating the equivalent resistance is slightly more complex.

In a parallel circuit, we know that $I_{total} = I_1 + I_2 + I_3 + \ldots$

Using Ohm's law, I can be replaced by $\frac{V}{R}$: $\frac{V_{tot}}{R_{eq}} = \frac{V_1}{R_1} + \frac{V_2}{R_2} + \frac{V_3}{R_3} + \ldots$

Since the potential difference is the same throughout, all values in the equation can be divided by V. We thus obtain:

$$\frac{1}{R_{eq}} = \frac{1}{R_1} + \frac{1}{R_2} + \frac{1}{R_3} + \ldots$$

By isolating the equivalent resistance, we obtain the following formula:

$$R_{eq} = \frac{1}{\frac{1}{R_1} + \frac{1}{R_2} + \frac{1}{R_3} + \ldots}$$

In a parallel circuit, the value of the equivalent resistance is always lower than the value of the smallest resistance in the circuit.

Let's look again at the examples in Figures 5.26 and 5.27 (pages 160 and 161). Since we know the current intensity and the potential difference, we can find the value of the resistance of each of the elements (customers) in the circuit, using Ohm's law ($R = V/I$).

- In the example of a series circuit, in Figure 5.26, we obtain:

$$R_1 = \frac{V_1}{I_1} = \frac{6\ \text{V}}{4\ \text{A}} = 1.5\ \Omega$$

$$R_2 = \frac{V_2}{I_2} = \frac{3\ \text{V}}{4\ \text{A}} = 0.75\ \Omega$$

$$R_3 = \frac{V_3}{I_3} = \frac{3\ \text{V}}{4\ \text{A}} = 0.75\ \Omega$$

The equivalent resistance can then be calculated as follows:

$$\begin{aligned} R_{eq} &= R_1 + R_2 + R_3 \\ &= 1.5\ \Omega + 0.75\ \Omega + 0.75\ \Omega \\ &= 3\ \Omega \end{aligned}$$

- In the example of a parallel circuit, in Figure 5.27, we obtain:

$$R_1 = \frac{V_1}{I_1} = \frac{12\ \text{V}}{2\ \text{A}} = 6\ \Omega$$

$$R_2 = \frac{V_2}{I_2} = \frac{12\ \text{V}}{1\ \text{A}} = 12\ \Omega$$

$$R_3 = \frac{V_3}{I_3} = \frac{12\ \text{V}}{1\ \text{A}} = 12\ \Omega$$

The equivalent resistance can then be calculated as follows:

$$\begin{aligned} R_{eq} &= \frac{1}{\frac{1}{6\ \Omega} + \frac{1}{12\ \Omega} + \frac{1}{12\ \Omega}} \\ &= 3\ \Omega \end{aligned}$$

5.28 APPLYING OHM'S LAW AND KIRCHHOFF'S LAWS TO SERIES AND PARALLEL CIRCUITS

	Series circuit	Parallel circuit
Current intensity	$I_{total} = I_1 = I_2 = I_3 = \ldots$	$I_{total} = I_1 + I_2 + I_3 + \ldots$
Potential difference	$V_{total} = V_1 + V_2 + V_3 + \ldots$	$V_{total} = V_1 = V_2 = V_3 = \ldots$
Equivalent resistance	$R_{eq} = R_1 + R_2 + R_3 + \ldots$	$R_{eq} = \frac{1}{\frac{1}{R_1} + \frac{1}{R_2} + \frac{1}{R_3} + \ldots}$

ST EST AST

4 What is magnetism?

Around 600 BCE, near a region named Magnesia, the Greeks discovered an ore with the ability to attract small iron objects. This ore, which the Greeks named *magnetite,* is itself composed primarily of iron.

We know today that iron is not the only element with properties similar to those of magnetite. Cobalt and nickel can also act like magnets or be attracted by magnets.

- **A MAGNET is an object that can attract other objects containing iron, cobalt or nickel.**

- **MAGNETISM describes all the phenomena caused by magnets.**

ST EST AST 4.1 MAGNETS

Certain substances may sometimes act like magnets (and sometimes not), while other substances never acquire any magnetic properties. How can this phenomenon be explained?

Examining an iron sample under a microscope reveals that the iron is made up of a set of regions called *domains*. Each of these domains acts like a tiny magnet, with its own north and south poles.

When iron is not magnetized, its domains are not aligned. When the iron is magnetized, however, its domains fall into alignment. The greater the number of aligned domains, the more powerful the magnet.

Nonmagnetized iron

Magnetized iron

5.29 When iron is not magnetized, its domains are not aligned. When it is magnetized, many of its domains are aligned.

ENVIRONMENT EXTRA

The Earth's magnetic field

The Earth behaves like a huge magnet. One of its magnetic poles is in Canada, about 1000 km from the geographic North Pole. The magnetic poles form an angle of approximately 11.5° with the Earth's axis of rotation. The movement of molten metallic substances in the planet's core is believed to be the source of the Earth's magnetic field.

The Earth's magnetic field, which is also called the *magnetosphere*, resembles the magnetic field of a bar magnet. However, the field is compressed on the side facing the Sun and elongated on the other side of the planet. This deformation is caused by the solar wind, made up of a constant flow of proton and electron emissions from the Sun. The magnetosphere stretches between 200 km and 5000 km beyond the Earth's surface.

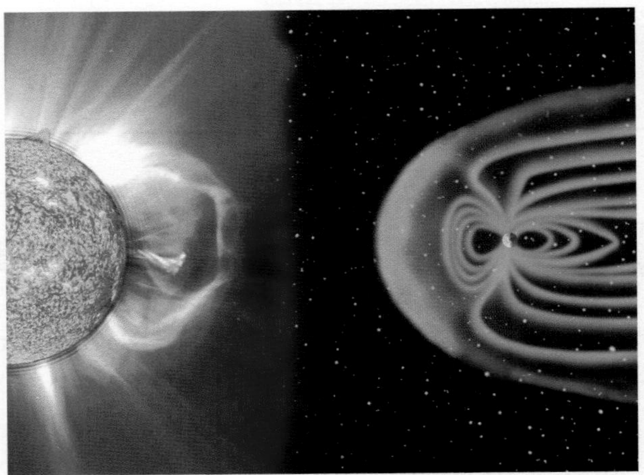

The Earth's magnetic field is deformed by the solar wind. The field shields us from space particles.

The Earth's magnetic field plays an important role as a shield, redirecting the majority of space particles toward the poles.

JAPAN TO HAVE ITS FIRST MAGLEV TRAIN IN 2025

The electromagnetic levitation train, often simply referred to as the *maglev*, has been in and out of the news for the past 30 years. Now it is making headlines again, as the world's only operating maglev, in China, is soon to have a Japanese counterpart. A second maglev line is planned to connect Tokyo and Nagoya by 2025. This passenger train could reach speeds of more than 500 km/h.

The existing high-speed train Tokaido Shinkansen, which crosses Japan from east to west at 300 km/h, could eventually be replaced by a maglev. The 550-km trip between Tokyo and Osaka would then take no more than an hour.

The maglev is a train that uses magnetic force to levitate above the rails and move forward. Unlike conventional trains, the maglev does not touch the rails, which minimizes friction and makes it possible to travel at very high speeds. During a test run in 2003, the maglev achieved a speed of 583 km/h.

Source: Adapted from Fabrice Amedo, "Le Japon aura son premier train à lévitation en 2025," *Le Figaro*, December 27, 2007, p. 17. *[Translation]*

For the moment, the only maglev train in the world runs in China, where it connects Shanghai to the city airport.

ST
EST
AST

MAGNETIC FORCES OF ATTRACTION AND REPULSION

All magnets have a north-seeking and a south-seeking pole. By convention, the north pole of a magnet corresponds to the end that naturally turns toward the Earth's magnetic pole that is located closest to the geographic North Pole. The other extremity of the magnet is its south pole. This means that the Earth's magnetic pole is, in fact, a south pole since opposite poles attract (page 166).

5.30 If a magnet is broken into pieces, each piece has its own north pole and south pole; in other words, each piece constitutes a new magnet. It is theoretically impossible to isolate either a north pole or a south pole and so create a "monopole"—a magnet with only one pole.

5.31 A compass is equipped with a freely moving magnetized needle, which rapidly locates the magnetic North Pole and, consequently, the four cardinal points.

The NORTH POLE of a magnet is the end that naturally seeks the Earth's magnetic pole near the geographic North Pole. The other end of the magnet is its SOUTH POLE.

Magnets interact with one another through forces of attraction and repulsion. The south pole of one magnet will be attracted to the north pole of another, but it will be repelled by another south pole. In general, the following is true of magnetic poles:

- Opposite magnetic poles attract each other.
- Like magnetic poles repel each other.

ST EST AST 4.2 MAGNETIC FIELDS

The force of attraction or repulsion between magnets is called the *magnetic force*. It can act over a distance through a magnetic field, generated by all magnetized objects.

A MAGNETIC FIELD is the area of space in which the magnetic force of a magnet can act on another magnet.

A magnetic field can be represented by magnetic field lines, as shown in Figure 5.33. By convention, the direction of the lines corresponds to the direction the north pole of a magnet would take along each line. For this reason, magnetic field lines are drawn coming out of a north pole and entering into a south pole.

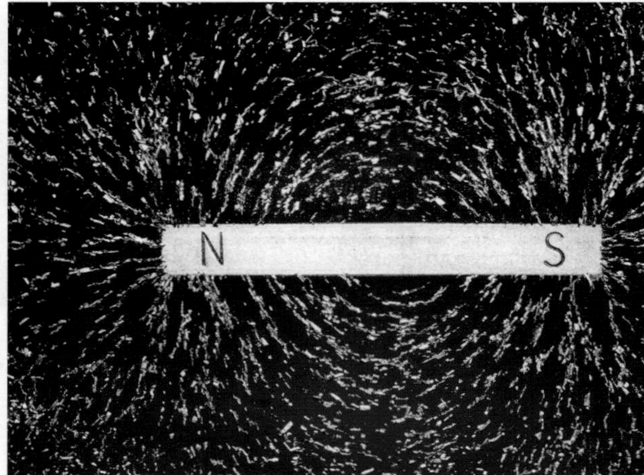

5.32 Iron filings align themselves with magnetic field lines because each particle of iron behaves like a minuscule magnet.

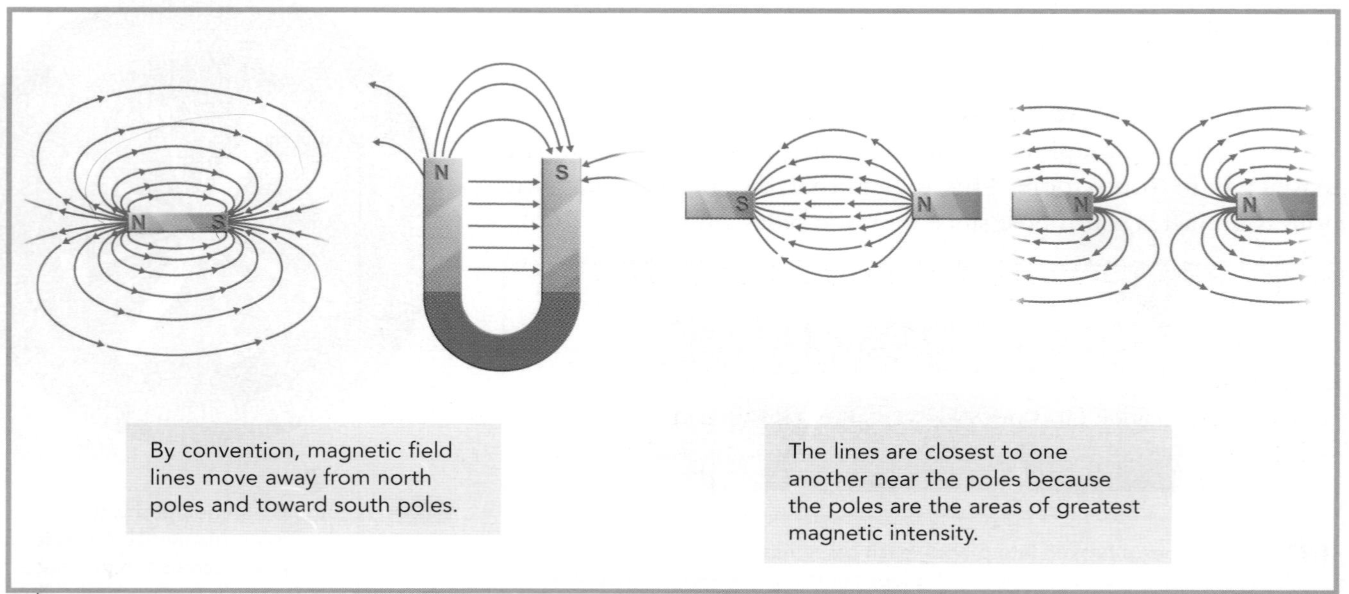

5.33 The shape of a magnetic field depends on the shape of the magnet or magnets.

EST 4.3 MAGNETIZING OBJECTS

Magnetite is a natural magnet, but it is also possible to make artificial magnets with objects containing iron, cobalt or nickel. To do this, the objects are exposed to the magnetic field of another magnet. Substances with the ability to become magnets are said to be *ferromagnetic*.

A FERROMAGNETIC SUBSTANCE is a substance with the ability to acquire magnetic properties.

A magnet can be demagnetized by a strong, sharp blow, for example, if it is dropped. It can also be demagnetized if heated or placed in a magnetic field of opposite polarity.

Two types of magnets can be distinguished depending on their ability to conserve their magnetic properties. Magnets that acquire and lose these properties easily—in other words, those whose domains are easily aligned or misaligned—are called *temporary magnets*. They are said to have a *low magnetic remanence*. Iron containing few impurities, which is also called *soft iron*, is an example of a temporary magnet. Permanent magnets, on the other hand, have a high magnetic remanence. They are difficult to both magnetize and demagnetize (it is difficult to align or misalign their domains). Steel is often used to make permanent magnets.

MAGNETIC REMANENCE describes the ability of a material to acquire and conserve magnetic properties.

REVERSING THE EARTH'S MAGNETIC POLES

The Earth's crust was formed when molten rock from the depths of the planet cooled and solidified on the surface. When this type of rock contains iron, the iron solidifies in alignment with the Earth's magnetic field lines. Studies of the Earth's crust have revealed that the magnetic poles of our planet have reversed themselves many times over the centuries.

ST EST AST 5 Electromagnetism

Electricity and magnetism are connected. Under certain circumstances, an electric current can generate a magnetic field. The opposite is also true: a magnetic field can, in some cases, generate an electric current.

ELECTROMAGNETISM describes all the phenomena resulting from the interaction between electricity and magnetism.

ST EST AST 5.1 MAGNETIZATION BY ELECTRICITY

To generate a magnetic field using electricity, the electrical charges must be in motion. This means that a magnetic field can be generated only by dynamic electricity (and not by static electricity) and that the magnetic field will last only as long as the current flows. As soon as the current ceases, the magnetic field disappears.

5.34 On the left, the current is disconnected, so the compasses point north. On the right, the current is flowing, so the compasses follow the directions of the magnetic field lines generated by the electric current.

ST EST AST

THE MAGNETIC FIELD OF A LIVE WIRE

In 1819, a Danish scientist named Hans Christian Oersted (1777–1851) noticed that the needle of a compass was deflected when it came close to a live wire (a wire carrying an electric current). Before that time, no connection had been established between electrical and magnetic phenomena.

Oersted discovered that magnetic field lines formed circles around the wire and that their direction depended on the current direction. To picture the direction of the magnetic field lines generated by a live wire, we can use the "right-hand rule," illustrated in Figure 5.35.

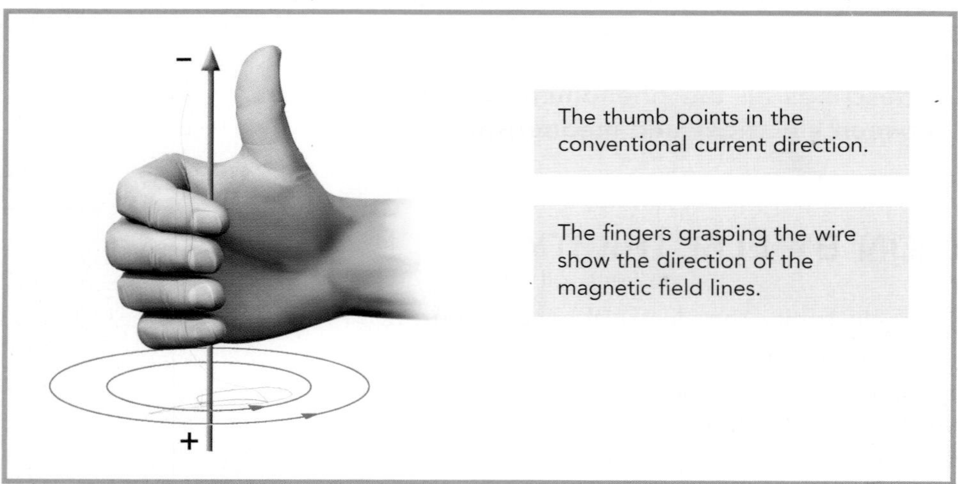

5.35 The right-hand rule can be used to determine the direction of the magnetic field lines generated by a live wire.

EST AST

THE MAGNETIC FIELD OF A SOLENOID

The magnetic field of a straight live wire can be intensified if the wire is rolled into a coil of regularly shaped loops. This formation is called a *solenoid*.

A SOLENOID is a cylindrical coil of live wire.

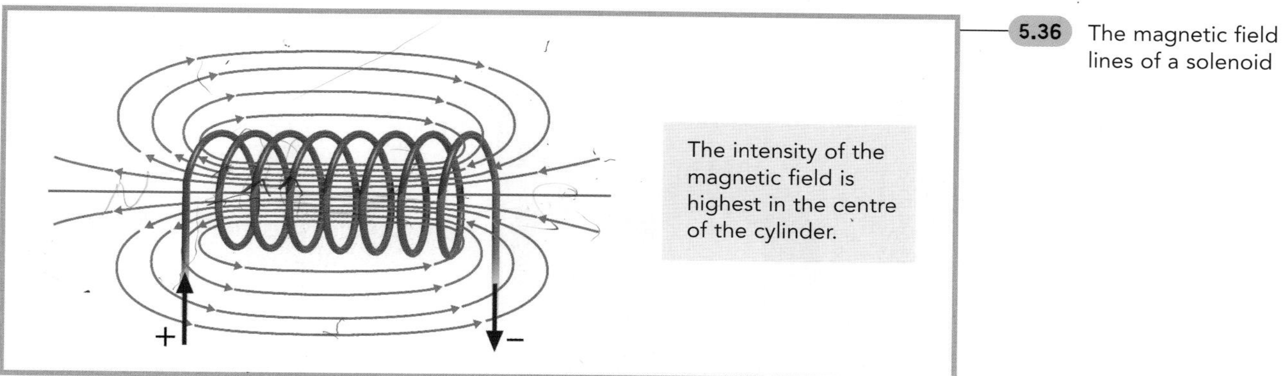

5.36 The magnetic field lines of a solenoid

To determine the direction of the magnetic field lines of a solenoid, another right-hand rule can be applied (Figure 5.37).

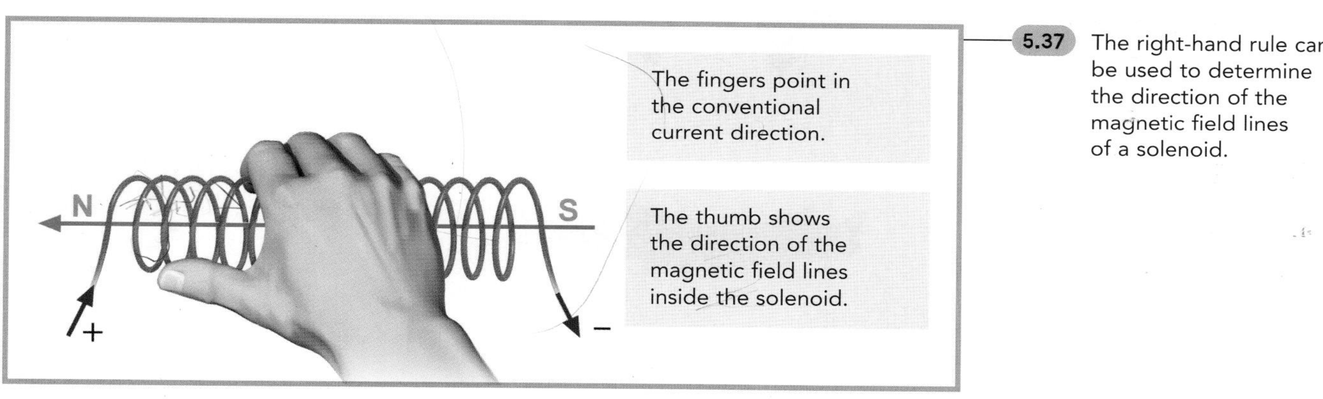

5.37 The right-hand rule can be used to determine the direction of the magnetic field lines of a solenoid.

Figure 5.36 shows that the magnetic field of a solenoid is very similar to that of a bar magnet. However, three differences distinguish the two:

- The magnetic field of a solenoid can be "switched on" or "switched off" at will, but the magnetic field of a magnet cannot.
- The direction of the magnetic field lines of a solenoid can be altered by reversing the current direction, while the magnetic field lines of a magnet cannot be reversed because the poles of the magnet cannot be reversed (unless the polarity of the entire magnet is reversed).
- The intensity of the magnetic field of a solenoid can be modified, but the same is not true for a magnet.

These characteristics of solenoids explain why they are widely used in technological applications, especially since they can be easily transformed into electromagnets, as we will see in the following section.

EST AST ELECTROMAGNETS

To transform a solenoid into an electromagnet, a ferromagnetic substance is inserted inside the solenoid, creating a core. The magnetic field of the electromagnet comes from both the electric current of the solenoid and the magnetization of the core. The result is a very powerful magnet, which can be turned on or off at will.

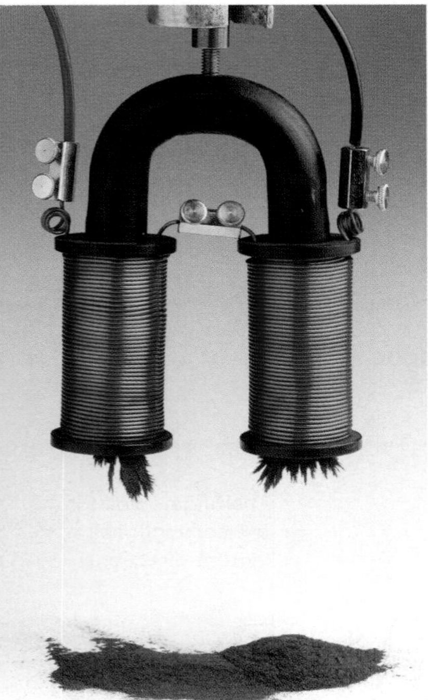

5.38 On the left, an electromagnet when switched on, and on the right, an electromagnet when switched off

1775
1836

André-Marie Ampère

This French physicist studied many electromagnetic phenomena. In 1820, he invented the electromagnet by inserting a cylinder of soft iron inside a solenoid. The invention led to the development of many applications, including the electric motor, the speaker and the telephone.

The power of an electromagnet can be increased in three ways:

- by increasing the intensity of the electric current flowing through the solenoid
- by adding more loops to the solenoid
- by using a core with a lower magnetic remanence (whose domains can be aligned more quickly and easily)

Electromagnets are widely used in the field of electricity, notably to transform electrical energy into mechanical energy.

AST 5.2 CHARGING BY MAGNETISM

With the discovery of the relationship between electricity and magnetism, scientists were encouraged to experiment. They wanted to see if they could achieve the reverse process of magnetizing by electricity: generating an electric current from a magnetic field. In 1831, Michael Faraday (1791–1867), a British physicist and chemist, proved that this could be done. He thus demonstrated the principles of what is known today as *electromagnetic induction*.

AST ELECTROMAGNETIC INDUCTION

To generate an electrical field, a magnetic field must be in motion relative to a charge or a conductor. This can be achieved in one of two ways:

- by moving a conductor inside a magnetic field
- by moving a magnet around a conductor

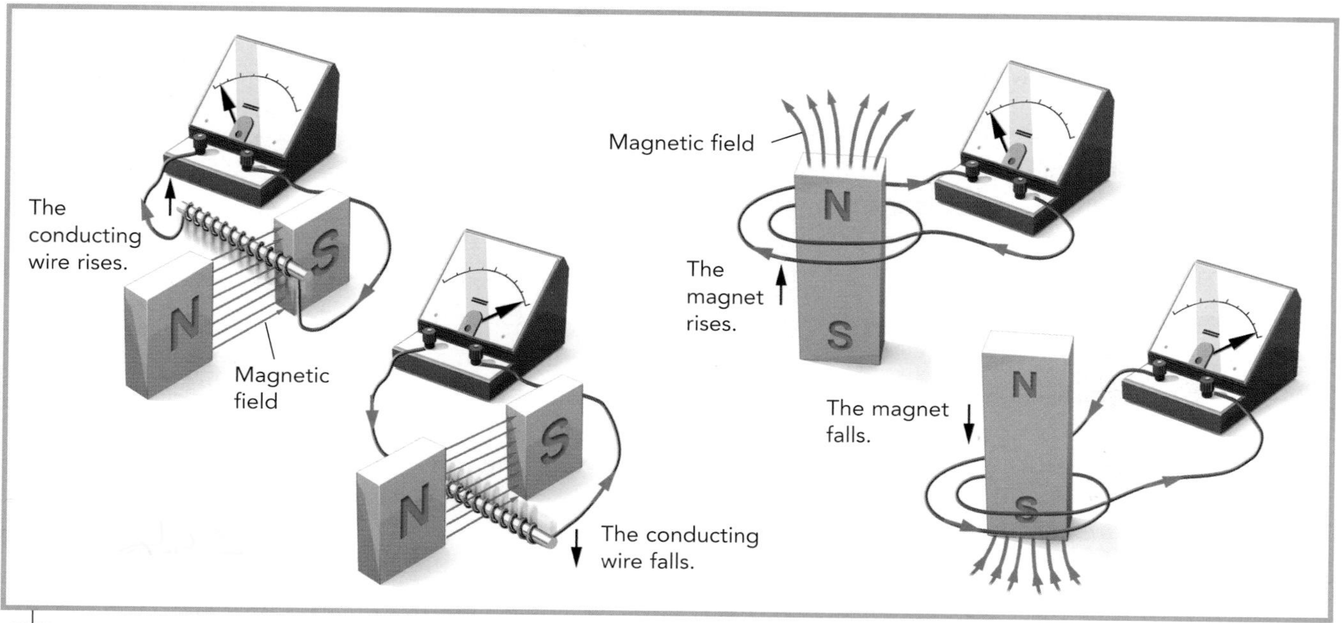

5.39 Two methods of producing electromagnetic induction. On the left, a conductor is moved. On the right, a magnet is moved.

Both the intensity of the magnetic field and the speed at which it moves in relation to the conductor are important factors in electromagnetic induction.

ELECTROMAGNETIC INDUCTION consists in generating an electric current in a conductor by varying a magnetic field around that conductor.

Electromagnetic induction is widely used to transform mechanical energy into electrical energy. It is the principle at work in most electric generators.

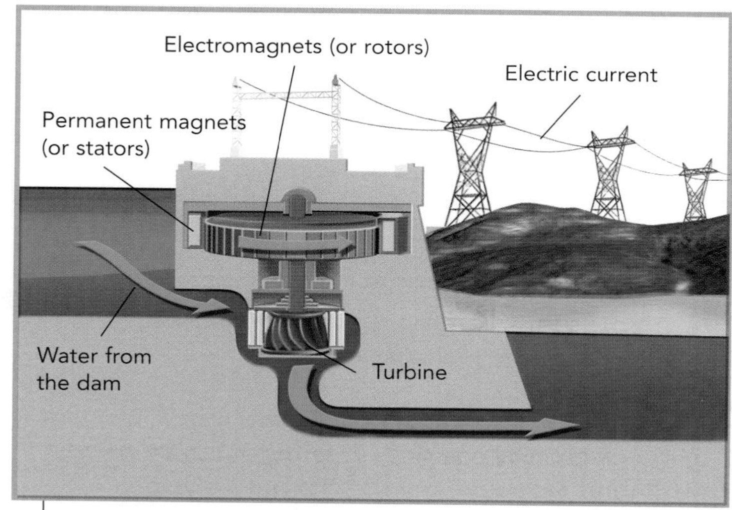

5.40 An electric generator is an important part of a hydroelectric power plant. Water flowing through the dam spins a turbine, causing the electromagnets to rotate and generate an electric current.

CHECKUP

ST 1–5, 7–8, 10–18, 21–23, 25, A and D.

AST 1–5, 7–8, 10–18, 21–23, 25–27, A and D.

EST 1–26 and A–D.

SE None.

1 What is electricity? (pp. 140–144)

1. Vanessa observes that an object is positively charged. Has it gained or lost electrons? Explain your answer.

2. The five spheres below, identified A to E, carry an electrical charge. If sphere A carries a positive charge, what is the sign of the charges on each of the other spheres? Explain your answer.

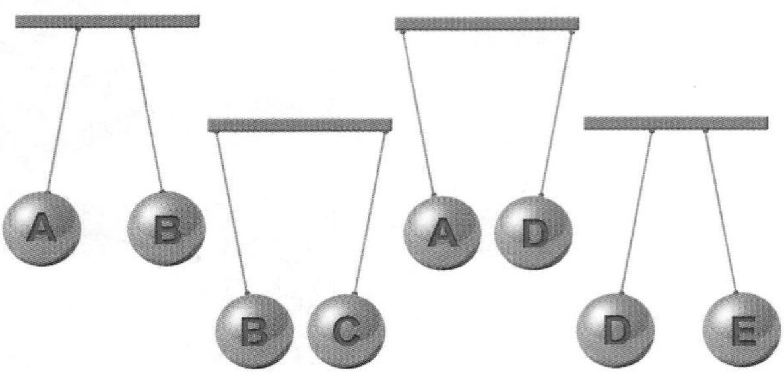

3. During a storm, impressive bolts of lightning form jagged lines across the sky. The lightning is caused by a brief but powerful electrical discharge. If the electrical discharge of a lightning bolt is equal to 20 C, how many electrons were involved in the neutralization process?

4. After charging a piece of fabric, Jonathan calculates that it has lost 2×10^{15} electrons.

a) What is its charge in coulombs?

b) Is this charge positive or negative? Explain your answer.

5. A copper rod and a plastic rod are electrically charged. In terms of attraction and repulsion, will the charges behave in the same way in the two rods? Explain your answer.

6. Look at the illustration below.

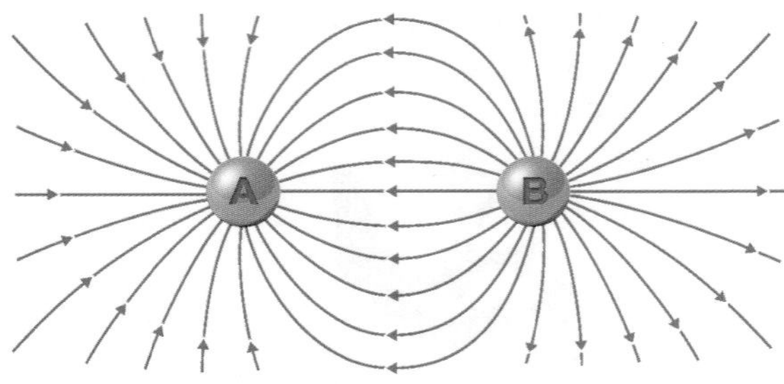

a) What is the charge of particle A? Explain your answer.

b) What is the charge of particle B? Explain your answer.

c) Is the force exerted by each particle on the other attraction or repulsion? Explain your answer.

2 Static electricity (pp. 145–149)

7. Are the following objects charged by friction, conduction or induction?

a) Carl brings a charged comb close to his hair without touching it, and his hair stands on end.

b) A certain number of charges are transferred from one body to another, resulting in two bodies carrying like charges.

c) When we walk about, our bodies may accumulate an electrical charge.

8. To clean his copper trophy, Brad rubs it with a woollen cloth. What will be the charge on each of these objects? Explain your answer.

9. Two positively charged particles with respective charges of 0.02 C and 0.05 C are placed 2 cm apart. What is the intensity of the electrical force each particle exerts on the other?

3 Dynamic electricity (pp. 150–163)

10. Do the following situations describe an example of static electricity or dynamic electricity? Explain your answer.

a) an engine belt charging by friction

b) an MP3 playing your favourite music

11. In which of the circuits below is the ammeter correctly connected? Explain your answer.

a)

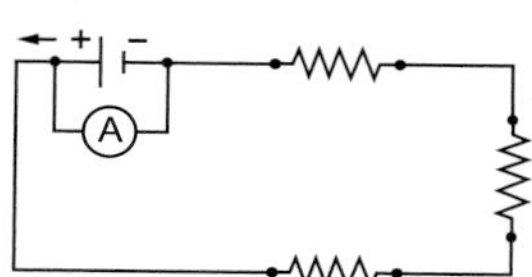

b)

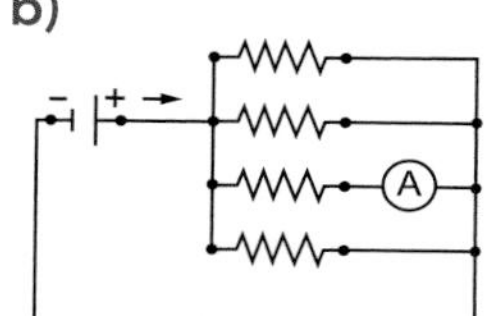

12. A hair dryer runs on an eight-ampere current. After five minutes' use, what charge will have been transferred to this appliance?

13. A charge of 5400 C flows through a circuit element in one hour. What is the intensity of the electric current?

14. In which of the circuits below is the voltmeter correctly connected? Explain your answer.

a)

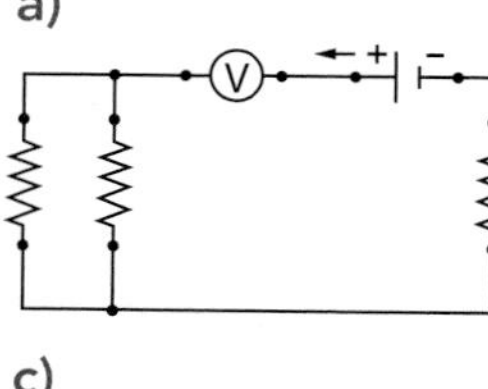

b)

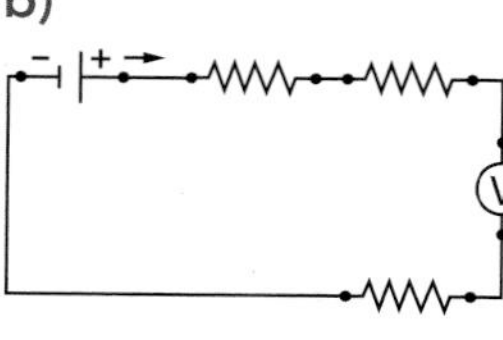

c)

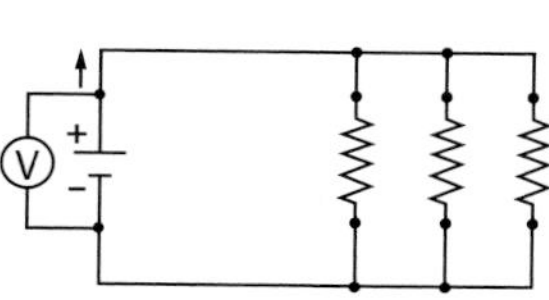

d)

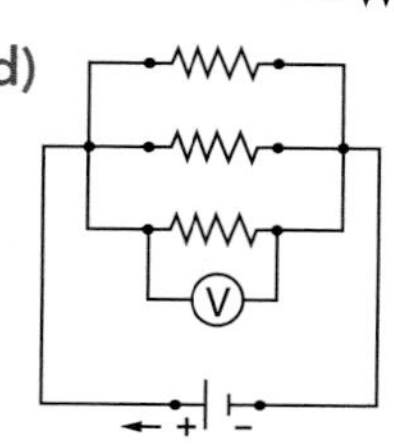

15. A wide variety of batteries are available on the market. What is the energy supplied by a 1.5-V battery if 200 C of charge flow through an electrical appliance in 20 minutes?

16. To find the resistance of a heating element, Maria conducts an experiment. She discovers that when the current intensity is 3.5 A, the potential difference at the terminals of the element is 10 V. What is the resistance of the heating element?

17. How much energy will an electrical appliance have consumed after 15 minutes' use if the current flowing through it has an intensity of 15 A and the potential difference is 120 V?

18. Which of the circuits below are connected in series, and which are connected in parallel?

a)

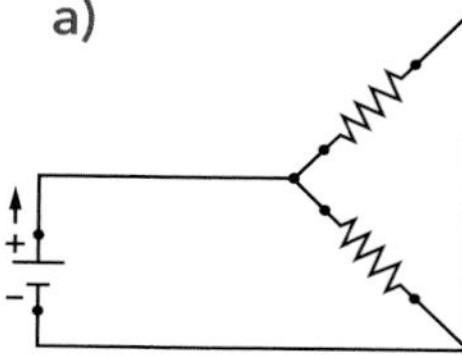

b)

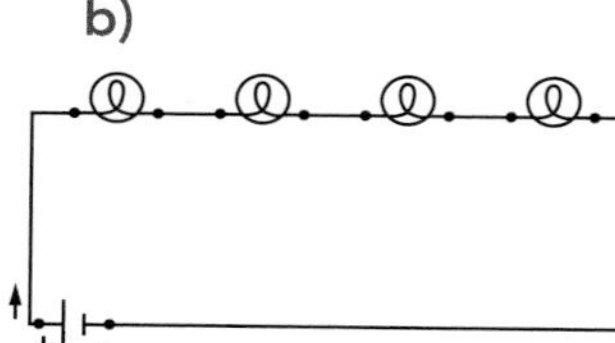

c)

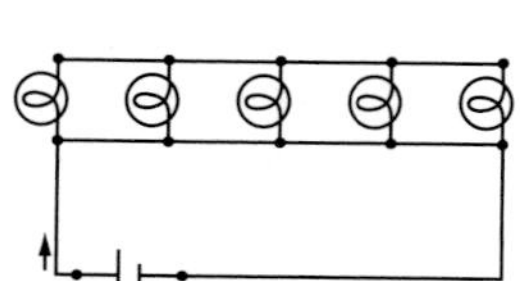

d)

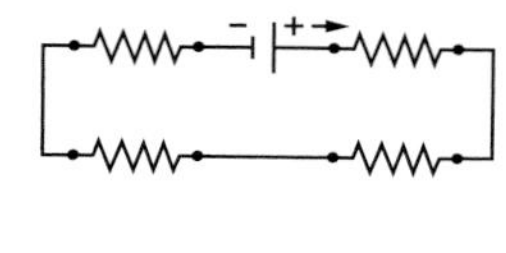

19. In each of the following circuits, calculate the equivalent resistance.

a)

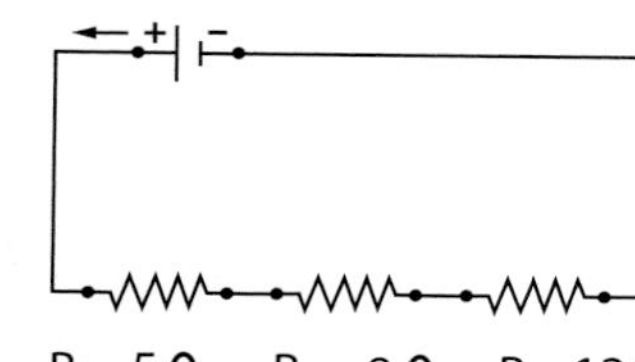

b)

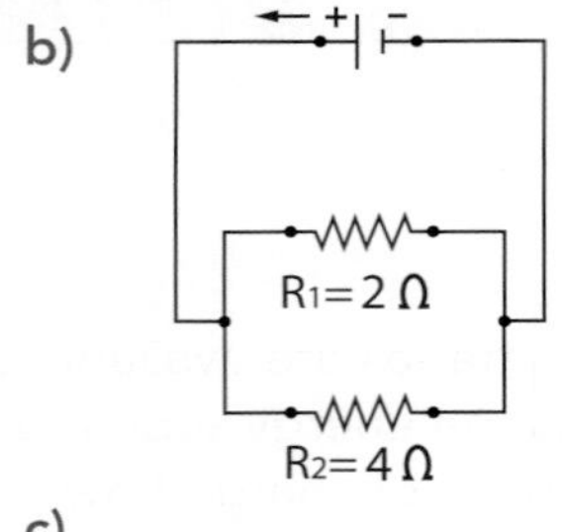

c)

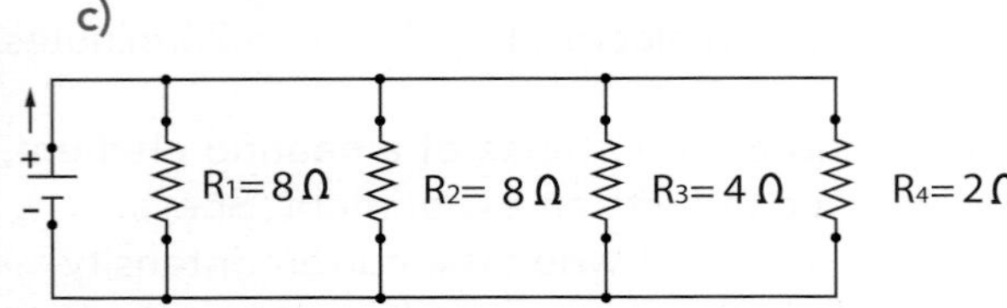

20. Find the missing value in each of the circuits below.

a)

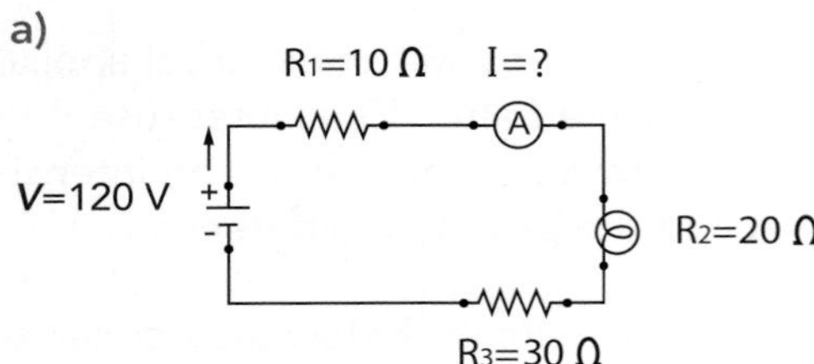

b)

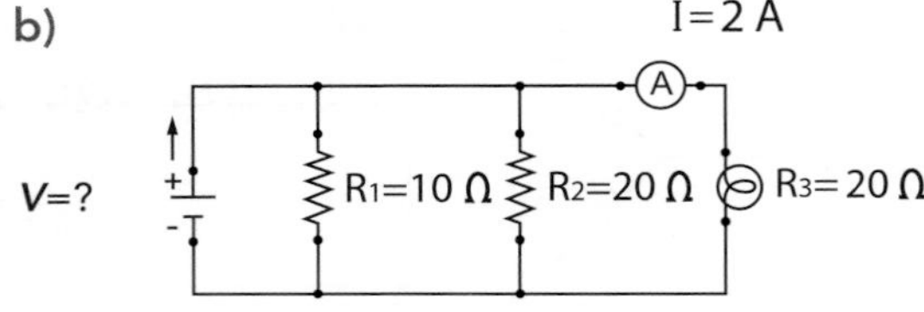

4 What is magnetism? (pp. 163–167)

21. If the north pole of a magnet is moved toward the south pole of another magnet, will the north pole be subjected to an attractive or a repulsive force? Explain your answer.

22. Which of the illustrations below is an accurate representation of the magnetic field of a bar magnet? Explain your answer.

a)

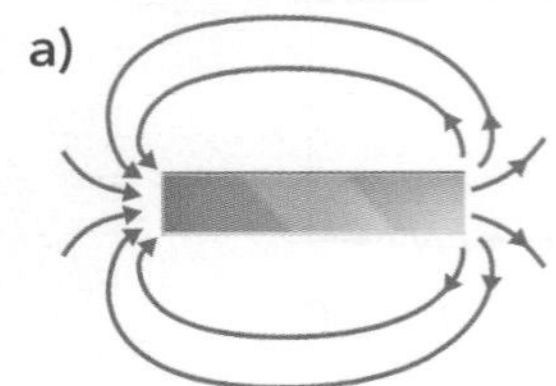

b)

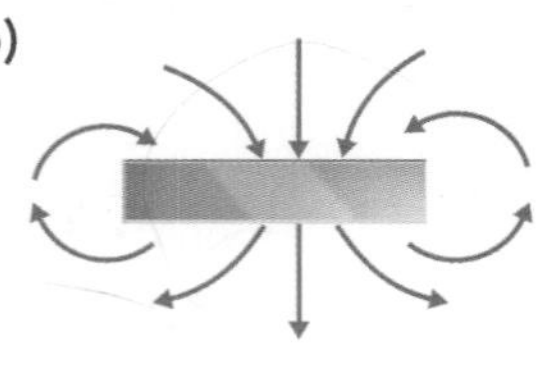

23. Is a ferromagnetic substance necessarily a magnet? Explain your answer.

5 Electromagnetism (pp. 167–171)

24. Which of the illustrations below is an accurate representation of the magnetic field of a live wire? Explain your answer.

a) b)

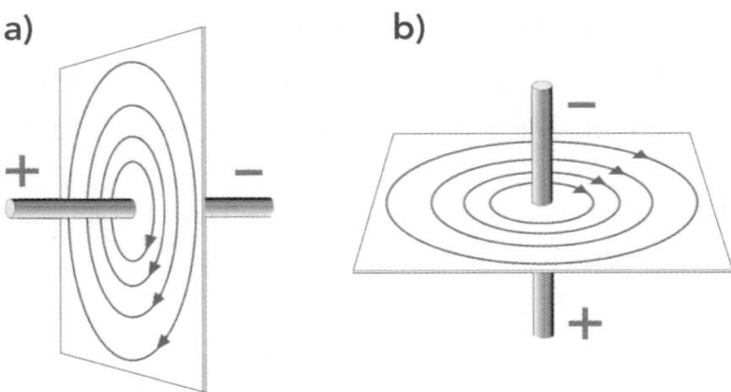

25. Which of the illustrations below is an accurate representation of the magnetic field of a solenoid? Explain your answer.

a)

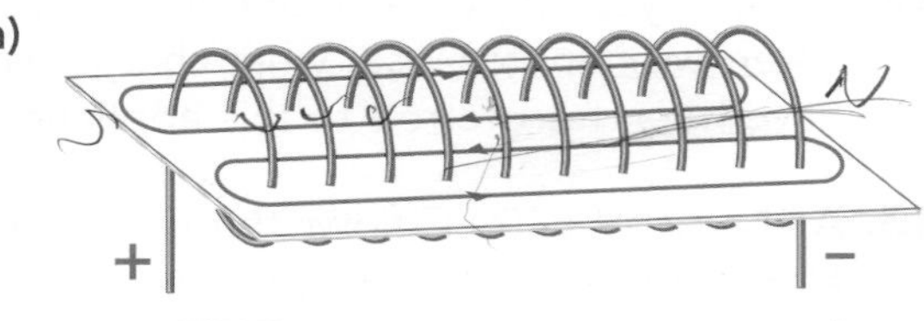

b)

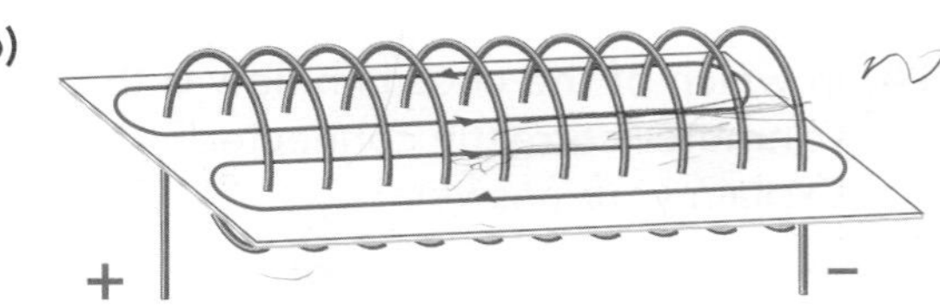

26. Max wants to buy an electric generator to have a backup power supply at his cottage. He asks the salesperson to briefly explain the principles at work in the generator. If you were the salesperson, how would you answer Max?

review questions

A. Valerie charges an ebonite comb by rubbing it on her pants. She thus gives it a charge of 5×10^{-8} C. She then tries to lift up small pieces of paper with the charged comb.

a) If Valerie's pants are made of wool, will the electrical charge of the comb be positive or negative? Explain your answer.

b) How will the charges on the comb be distributed? Explain your answer.

c) When Valerie moves the comb close to the pieces of paper, they become charged. Will the electrical charges accumulating on the side of the paper closest to the comb be positive or negative? Explain your answer.

d) When she moves the comb close to a metal ruler, Valerie sees a spark. She concludes that the two objects have cancelled each other's charge. If 5×10^{-8} C have been transferred from one object to the other in 0.001 s, what was the intensity of the electrical discharge?

e) Air is an insulator with a resistance of $2 \times 10^{10}\ \Omega$. What is the potential difference of the electrical discharge between the comb and the metal ruler?

B. To lift a piece of paper weighing 0.01 N, how close will Valerie have to move her charged comb, bearing in mind that the piece of paper acquires a charge equivalent to that of the comb?

C. Below are diagrams of two different electrical circuits. If the power supply provides a potential difference of 60 V, and if the resistance of each light bulb is 120 Ω, what current intensity will be measured by each of the ammeters? Show your calculations.

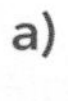

a)

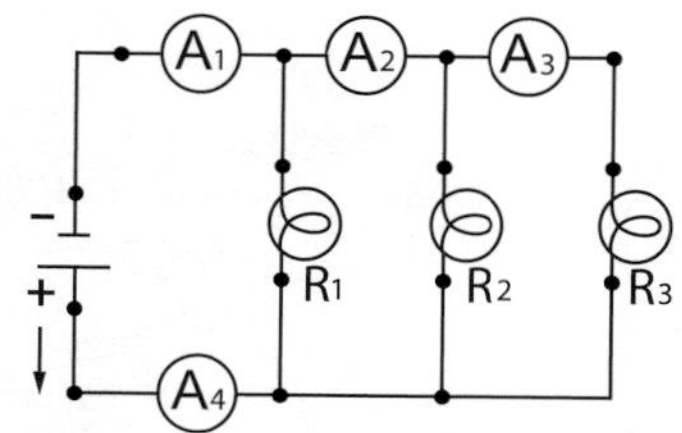

b)

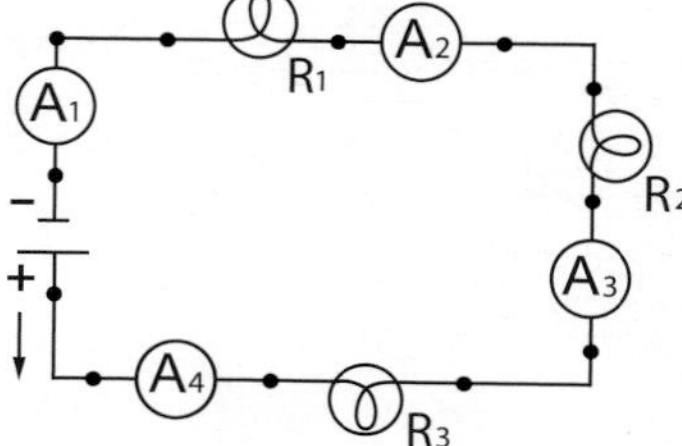

D. Prepare your own summary of Chapter 5 by building a concept map.

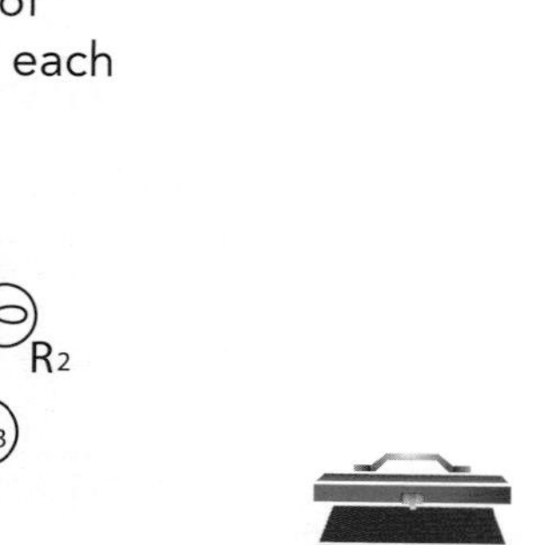

THE SHIFT TOWARD WIND POWER IN QUÉBEC

Between 1985 and 2005, global demand for energy increased by 50 percent. Conventional energy sources—coal, oil, natural gas, hydroelectricity and nuclear power—have all been affected. In Canada, demand rose by 18 percent between 1982 and 2002, and another increase of almost 12 percent is expected between 2005 and 2014. How can we meet this demand? In Québec, part of the answer lies in the development of wind power.

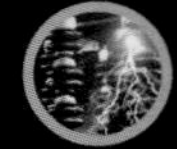

INSTALLING WIND TURBINES IN THE FOUR CORNERS OF QUÉBEC: FIRST IN GASPÉSIE, THEN ALL OVER THE PROVINCE

In its energy strategy for 2006–2015, the Québec government set out several ways to meet the expected increase in energy demand. For example, the strategy includes the construction launch of large-scale hydroelectric dams. This type of project takes a long time to complete, however, and requires huge investments. The government therefore also decided to gradually add almost 4000 MW (megawatts) of wind power to the Hydro-Québec network by 2015. The wind farms should meet 10 percent of our electricity demand during peak periods.

In April 2007, Québec had 272 wind turbines, supplying a total of 322 MW of electricity. By 2011, about 660 new turbines will be installed in the Gaspésie countryside, boosting wind power production to almost 1500 MW. Many other projects will follow throughout the province.

Wind power offers many advantages. It has experienced spectacular growth in Europe, so the production costs are falling. Québec is thought to have exceptional potential for developing wind energy. In addition, it takes only two to three years to build a wind farm, and farming on the site can continue. Wind power creates little waste and does not add to greenhouse gas emissions. Finally, the technology has greatly improved in recent years, so much so that new wind turbines provide four times as much energy as older models.

The main difficulty for Hydro-Québec will be to integrate wind power into its existing network. The corporation will also have to learn how to use wind power as an effective complement to hydropower. Wind power can provide only a supplementary energy source because wind is not available on demand and because wind turbines, unlike dam reservoirs, cannot store energy.

WILL CALLING THE WIND BRING ON A STORM?

Nothing is perfect: wind power also has its disadvantages. Wind turbines, whose towers can reach up to 100 m—the equivalent of a 20-storey building—are sometimes accused of spoiling the landscape. Some people are worried that wind farms will turn tourists off or that they will lead to a drop in the value of surrounding properties. Other concerned citizens want the possible impacts on birds to be studied, especially along migratory bird flight paths. The most severe criticism, however, comes from economic quarters, where it is feared that foreign interests may take control of a booming sector. In fact, wind farms are currently in the hands of private enterprise. The power produced is then bought by Hydro-Québec, which distributes the electricity through its network.

The government must consider the best way to oversee the development of this new form of energy. Among the solutions proposed are a fixed rate for the purchase of wind-generated electricity and the nationalization of the wind power sector.

QUÉBEC WIND FARMS IN 2007

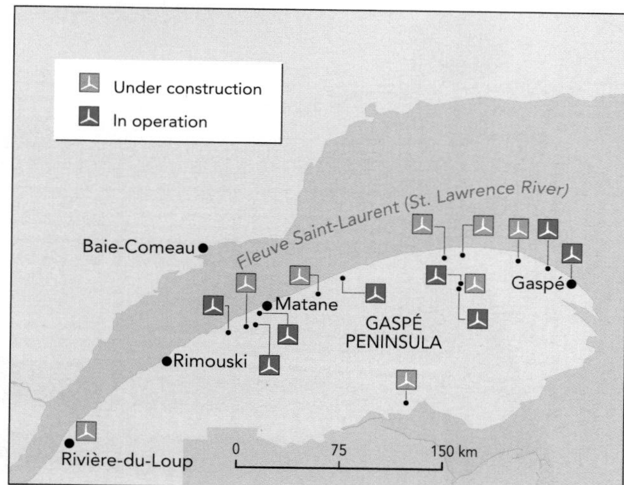

1. Briefly explain how a wind turbine can generate electricity using wind energy.
2. Do you think it would be a good idea to build wind turbines in your region? Explain your answer, suggesting at least one advantage and one disadvantage.

Science at work IN...

A WATER TREATMENT PLANT

Nothing beats thirst like a nice glass of cold, clean water. However, clean water is a commodity that is becoming increasingly rare. In Québec, many towns have built water treatment plants to ensure that the drinking water distributed in their water supply systems meets quality standards. Even if specific procedures differ from place to place, treatment plants generally filter surface water from nearby lakes and rivers and treat it chemically. The water is then tested several times a day before it makes its way to our taps, providing us with a constant supply of safe drinking water.

Let's meet a few people who work in water treatment plants.

Occupation	Education	Length of study	Main tasks
Water treatment plant supervisor	*DEC en assainissement de l'eau* (program available in French only)	3 years	• Oversees purification procedures • Manages workers
Plant mechanic	DVS in industrial construction and maintenance mechanics	1800 hours	• Installs, maintains and repairs mechanical, hydraulic and other systems
Chemist	Master's degree in chemistry	5 years	• Conducts tests to evaluate the quality of products or procedures • Analyzes test results
Laboratory technician	DCS in laboratory technology	3 years	• Conducts analyses • Compiles and processes data
Water treatment plant operator	*DEP en conduite de procédés de traitement de l'eau* (program available in French only)	1800 hours	• Operates water treatment plant equipment • Conducts analyses of drinking water • Ensures health and safety in the workplace

Claude Durivage, water treatment plant supervisor

Danielle Spinelli, water treatment plant operator and purchasing officer

Michel Gobeil, plant mechanic

Daniel Duchesne, chemist

Martine Picard, laboratory technician

André L'Archevêque, water treatment plant operator and plant foreman

THE EARTH

AND SPACE

FROM THE DROP OF WATER FALLING ONTO DRY EARTH TO THE MOON CALLING THE RHYTHM OF THE TIDES,

many phenomena maintain the balance of life on our planet. In this unique environment, humanity has been able to develop and prosper.

We have learned to extract resources from the Earth to make materials. To satisfy our energy needs, we have harnessed river waters, captured heat from within the Earth and burned fossil fuels. We have bent the sun's rays, the winds and the tides to our purposes.

With a global population nearing seven billion, we must rethink how we use our planet's resources. We know now that the Earth has its limits.

CONTENTS

2001 Discovery of diamonds in Québec

1972 Report by the Club of Rome, demonstrating that global resources are limited

1959 Signing of the Antarctic Treaty prohibiting all development of natural resources on that continent

1915 Invention of sonar, making it possible to detect the submerged part of icebergs

1857 First oil well in Canada

1848 Earliest maps of ocean currents

1774 First mineral classification system

1681 First suggestion that the Earth consists of a solid crust floating on a liquid interior

CIRCA -85 First map of part of the Mediterranean sea floor

CIRCA -3000 Early metal mines (silver, lead, tin, iron)

CIRCA -5000 First use of copper

CIRCA -10 000 First coal mines in China

The Earth's crust and its oceans are rich in natural resources, which have given civilizations on our planet the means to survive and prosper. Thanks to these resources (minerals, rocks, arable land, fresh water, etc.), we have built skyscrapers, manufactured computers, fuelled jet engines, heated our homes and grown our food.

How are these resources extracted from beneath the Earth's surface? Are their quantities unlimited? Why are some resources more costly than others? This chapter presents the principal natural resources found in the lithosphere and the hydrosphere—two components of the Earth's outer shell.

THE EARTH AND SPACE

6

The lithosphere and the hydrosphere

CONTENTS

ST EST AST SE

1 The lithosphere

CONCEPT REVIEW
- Lithosphere
- Internal structure of the Earth
- Types of rocks (basic minerals)

Measuring the distance from the centre of the Earth to its surface—with an extraordinarily long tape measure!—would reveal a distance of more than 6300 km. However, the hard shell covering our planet is only about a hundred kilometres thick on average. This outer shell is called the *lithosphere*. It consists of the Earth's crust and the topmost part of the upper mantle, two layers forming the external structure of our planet.

Lithosphere comes from the Greek words *lithos*, meaning "stone," and *sphaira*, meaning a "spherical object."

The LITHOSPHERE is the hard shell of the Earth, consisting of the crust and the topmost part of the upper mantle.

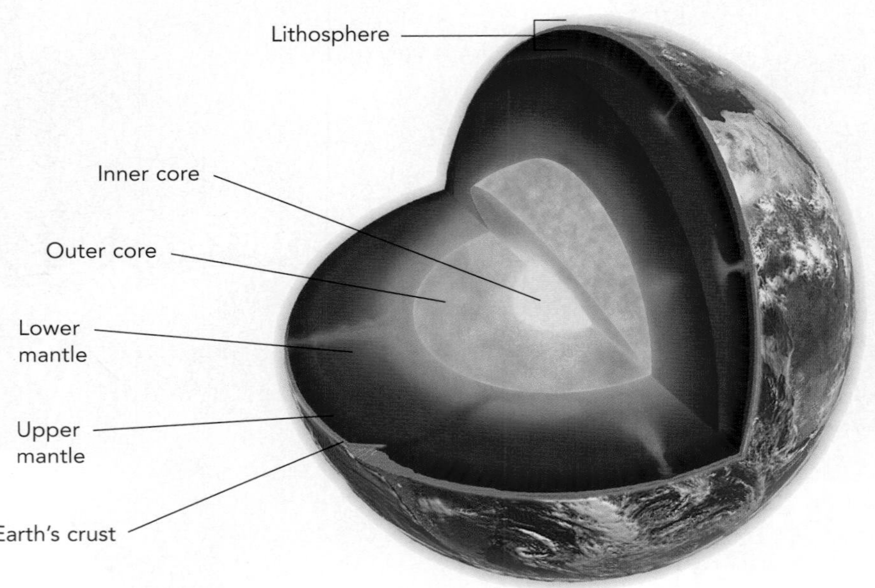

6.1 The internal structure of the Earth

The lithosphere contains minerals and rocks that have been essential to the development of human civilization. It is the source of building materials, metals of all kinds and even precious stones for jewellery.

ST EST AST

1.1 MINERALS

Minerals are inorganic substances, which means that they derive from neither animals nor plants. For substances to be considered minerals, they must have certain characteristics. For example, they must exist naturally on Earth; they cannot be manufactured.

Most minerals have an ordered atomic structure: their atoms are organized in the form of identically shaped crystals. For example, Figure 6.2 (page 185) shows salt crystals, which are always cubic in shape.

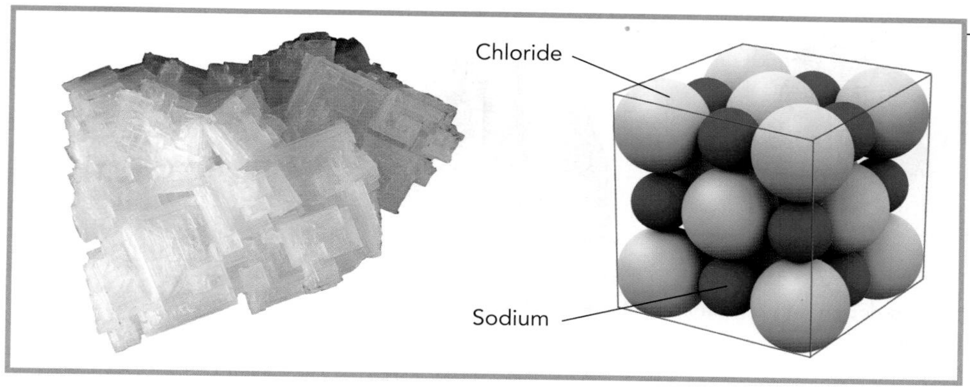

6.2 Chloride and sodium ions are arranged in cubic form, creating clearly visible salt crystals.

Each mineral is also distinct in its chemical composition. Some minerals are made up of a single chemical element, such as gold (Au), copper (Cu) or iron (Fe). Others contain several elements that are chemically bonded. Quartz (SiO_2), for example, contains silicon (Si) and oxygen (O) atoms. Copper sulphate ($CuSO_4$) is composed of copper (Cu), sulphur (S) and oxygen (O) atoms.

Because they are consistently made up of the same elements, forming crystals of a specific shape, minerals exhibit certain well-defined properties, such as hardness, transparency, colour and streak. Some of these properties will be discussed in greater detail in the next section.

6.3 Small gold crystals in quartz

MINERALS are solid inorganic substances with clearly defined composition and properties.

More than 4000 different minerals are known to exist on Earth. Some are very common, such as feldspar, quartz and mica. Others, such as diamonds, rubies, sapphires and emeralds, are extremely rare and therefore precious.

Ruby comes from the Latin *rubeus*, meaning "red."

ST EST AST MINERAL CLASSIFICATION

Geologists classify minerals according to their properties, such as those described in the following paragraphs.

Colour

Many minerals have a characteristic colour: blue for azurite, green for malachite, red for rhodochrosite, etc. The element that gives them their colour is part of their chemical composition. They are called *idiochromatic* minerals. Other minerals may vary in colour, so they are described as *allochromatic*. If they were chemically pure, allochromatic minerals would be colourless, but minute quantities of impurities give them different colourings.

Idiochromatic comes from the Greek words *idios*, meaning "own," and *khrōma*, meaning "colour."

Allochromatic comes from the Greek words *allos*, meaning "other," and *khrōma*, meaning "colour."

NOT FOOLS AFTER ALL!

Pyrite was nicknamed *fool's gold* because it is similar in colour to real gold. Its metallic shine deceived many prospectors, who thought they had struck gold. Their hopes were not entirely misplaced, however, because gold is sometimes found alongside pyrite. 

6.4 Quartz can take on different colours depending on the impurities it contains. It is therefore an allochromatic mineral.

Transparency

Transparency is the property by which a substance allows light to pass through it. Some minerals let light pass straight through them; they are *transparent*. Others let light through, but it is impossible to distinguish an object through them; they are *translucent*. Still others let no rays through at all; they are *opaque*.

6.5 Rock crystal is transparent, olivine is translucent, and pyrite is opaque.

Hardness

Hardness depends on the strength of the bonds uniting the atoms in a mineral. The Mohs scale assigns a value from 1 to 10 to a mineral to indicate its hardness, measured by its resistance to scratching. The softest minerals, such as talc, can be easily scratched and are placed at the bottom of the scale. The hardest minerals, such as diamonds, are at the top of the scale. A mineral can scratch all softer minerals—those with a lower number on the Mohs scale. Hardness is of the utmost importance to jewellers: they would not be so successful in cutting and polishing diamonds, for example, if the mineral were not so hard.

6.6 The Mohs scale of hardness

Streak

When a mineral is rubbed on a surface of unglazed porcelain, it leaves a powder trace. The colour of the powder may be different from that of the mineral itself, but it is always the same for that mineral. This trace is called *streak* and is considered one of the mineral's characteristics. Idiochromatic minerals leave a brightly coloured powder. Allochromatic minerals leave a white or pale powder.

6.7 Amethyst is a purple variety of quartz. It leaves a white powder when rubbed.

MINING

To mine minerals and transform them into all kinds of useful objects, geologists must first locate them and then extract them from the lithosphere. The extracted material is called *ore;* it is rock containing the mineral. When the amount and concentration of a mineral in a particular site are high enough for mining, the mineral layer is then referred to as a *deposit.*

Québec is known for its deposits of gold, copper, zinc, nickel and iron. The Abitibi-Témiscamingue region is particularly famous for its mineral deposits, some of which are among the largest in the world (Map 6.8). Table 6.9 (page 188) shows possible uses for some of the minerals mined in Québec.

6.8 MINES AND MAIN MINERAL DEPOSITS IN PARTS OF QUÉBEC

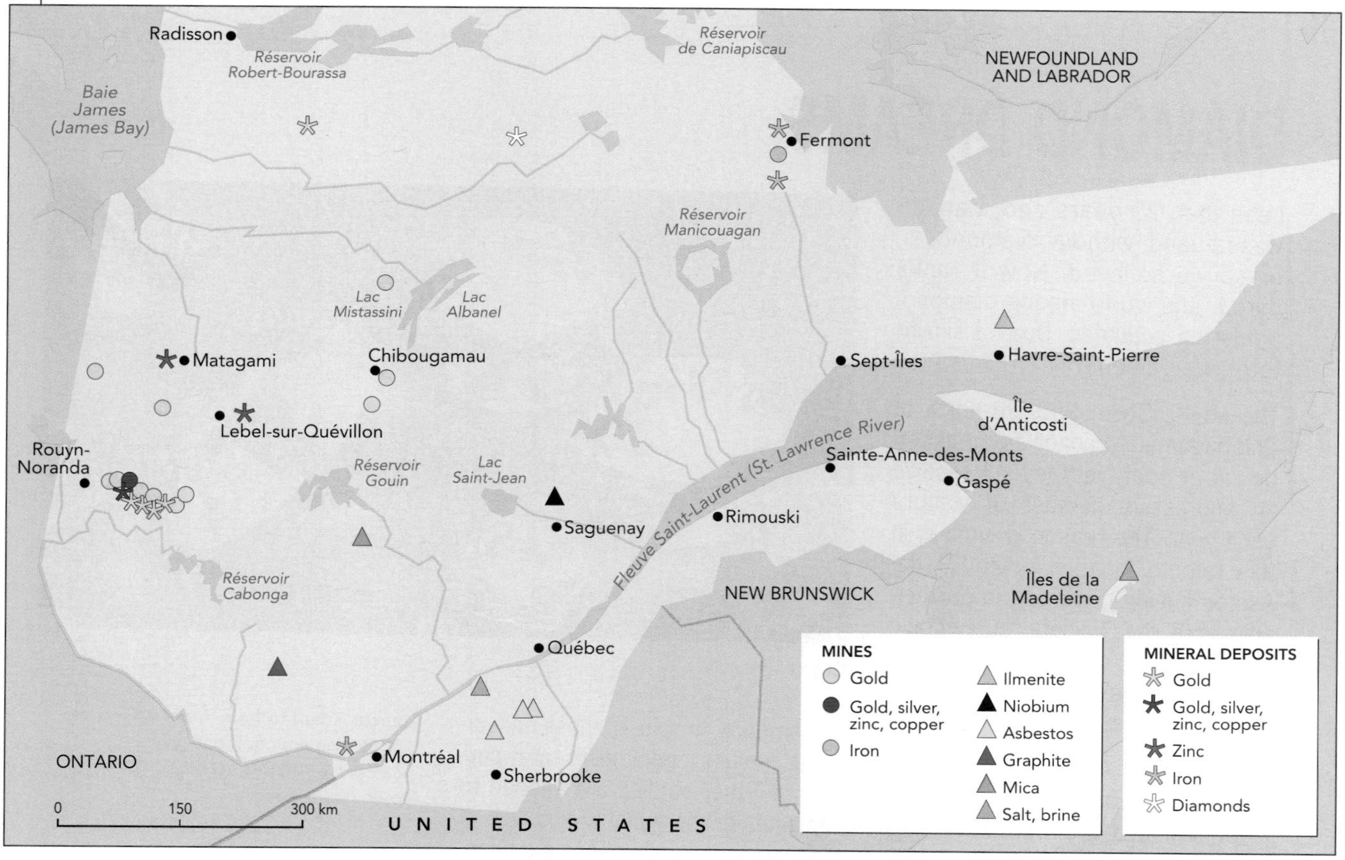

MINES: Gold; Gold, silver, zinc, copper; Iron; Ilmenite; Niobium; Asbestos; Graphite; Mica; Salt, brine

MINERAL DEPOSITS: Gold; Gold, silver, zinc, copper; Zinc; Iron; Diamonds

6.9 POSSIBLE USES OF SOME MINERALS MINED IN QUÉBEC

Mineral	Possible uses
Gold	Jewellery Trade Electronic equipment
Copper	Pipes for plumbing Electrical wire Electronic equipment Construction (roofing)
Zinc	Galvanized steel (to prevent corrosion) Automotive parts
Nickel	Stainless steel manufacture Coins Magnets
Iron	Steel manufacture

6.10 An open-pit gold mine

Mining involves complex and costly procedures. If the deposit is near the surface, an open-pit mine is dug. The upper layers of earth are removed, one by one, and the ore is extracted with drilling machines, excavators and enormous dump trucks.

DIAMOND DREAMS

Less than 20 years ago, Canada was a land without diamonds—or so we believed. Now it ranks third in the world among diamond-producing countries. Does a similar fate await Québec?

The Monts Otish, 250 km north of Chibougamau, cannot be reached by car or boat, yet they still receive an impressive number of visitors each year. The reason is simple: in this remote location in 2001, the Ashton mining company, in partnership with the Société québécoise d'exploration minière (SOQUEM), discovered the province's first diamond deposits.

In 2006, the Ashton-SOQUEM duo invested 29 million dollars to remove 6000 tonnes of ore, from which they extracted almost 6000 carats (1.2 kg) of diamonds. In spite of these encouraging results, geologists are cautious. Further studies are needed to see whether the quantity and size of the diamonds justify opening a mine.

Cut diamonds

Source: Adapted from Thomas Gervais, "Ces diamants qui font rêver," *La Presse Affaires*, April 26, 2007, p. 9. *[Translation]*

If the deposit is too far down, underground passages must be dug. First, a huge vertical shaft is built, with an elevator for transporting material and personnel. Then, horizontal passages, or *drifts*, are dug, radiating out from the shaft along the veins of the deposit. The drifts are fitted with air ducts and water supply lines.

6.11 A mine drift

Once the ore has been extracted, the mineral is separated from the rock in several stages. Each type of ore is processed differently. For example, gold ore is crushed and then treated with chemicals such as cyanide to isolate the precious metal. The gold is then melted and poured into moulds to form ingots.

SO MUCH FOR SO LITTLE

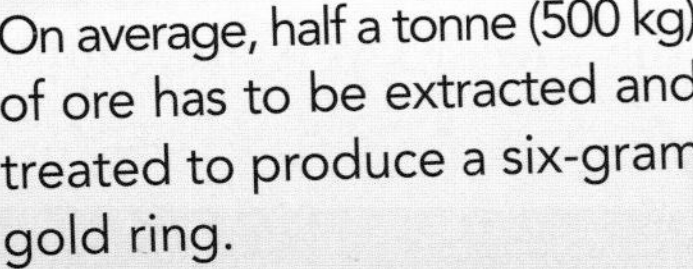

On average, half a tonne (500 kg) of ore has to be extracted and treated to produce a six-gram gold ring.

1.2 ROCKS

In the lithosphere, minerals are rarely found in isolation. They cluster together in heterogeneous masses, namely, rocks. Unlike minerals, the physical and chemical properties of rocks are not strictly defined.

ROCKS are heterogeneous solids composed of many minerals.

For a long time, the question of how rocks were formed was the subject of debate. In the late 18th century, the German geologist Abraham Werner (1750–1817) put forward the "Neptunism" theory (after Neptune, the god of the sea), which stated that all the compounds that make up rocks once lay under a huge ocean. Rocks were created by the pressure of the water. A few years later, the British geologist James Hutton (1726–1797) suggested a different theory: "Plutonism" (after Pluto, the god of the underworld). According to this theory, rocks were volcanic in origin.

In fact, both men were right. Today, we know that rocks are formed through both of these processes. Rocks that are formed by water pressure are called *sedimentary* rocks, while those that result from volcanic activity are called *igneous* rocks. There is also a third type of rock, referred to as *metamorphic*.

TYPES OF ROCK

ST EST AST

The lithosphere is composed of three main families of rock, defined by their formation processes.

Igneous rocks

The magma bubbling at the centre of the Earth is under heavy pressure and sometimes makes its way up to the surface of the lithosphere, creating volcanoes. On contact with the air, the lava cools very rapidly and solidifies, creating *extrusive* igneous rocks.

Igneous comes from the Latin *ignis*, meaning "fire."

Sometimes, magma solidifies before reaching the surface. It then forms *intrusive* igneous rocks.

IGNEOUS ROCKS are formed when magma cools and solidifies.

6.12 Granite is an intrusive igneous rock. It contains a variety of minerals: quartz, feldspar and mica. Rhyolite is an extrusive igneous rock. It is essentially made up of the same minerals as granite, but it forms on contact with the air.

Sedimentary rocks

Over time, rocks crumble on contact with the air and water, a process called *erosion*. Rock fragments combine with plant and animal remains, fall to the bottom of bodies of water and accumulate in successive layers. Under pressure, the lowest layers are compacted, forming sedimentary rock.

6.13 This photo shows the layers of rock formed by successive deposits of various sediments.

SEDIMENTARY ROCKS are formed by the accumulation and compaction of debris.

Metamorphic rocks

In the depths of the Earth, igneous or sedimentary rocks are often subjected to high temperatures or pressure—for example, when two tectonic plates are pushed together. The rock is then transformed, changing in both appearance and properties. The rocks resulting from this transformation are said to be *metamorphic*. For example, limestone, a sedimentary rock, can turn into marble, a metamorphic rock. Similarly, granite, an igneous rock, can become gneiss. The transformation process can take millions of years.

Metamorphic comes from the Greek words *meta*, meaning "after," and *morphē*, meaning "form."

METAMORPHIC ROCKS are former igneous or sedimentary rocks that have been transformed by heat or pressure.

6.14 Gneiss is formed by the metamorphosis of rocks such as granite, while slate results from the transformation of shale.

USES OF ROCK

Like minerals, certain rocks are extracted from the ground to meet human needs. Table 6.15 presents some examples of possible uses of rocks.

6.15 POSSIBLE USES OF SOME ROCKS

Rock	Type	Possible uses
Granite	Intrusive igneous	Ornamental stone
Diorite	Intrusive igneous	Ornamental stone
Pumice	Extrusive igneous	Light building materials, cosmetic industry
Basalt	Extrusive igneous	Insulation, floor tiles, road construction
Sandstone	Sedimentary	Building materials
Limestone	Sedimentary	Cement, building materials
Gneiss	Metamorphic	Building materials
Marble	Metamorphic	Interior design, decorative objects

ST EST SE 1.3 SOIL

CONCEPT REVIEW
Types of soil

Soil comes from **PARENT ROCK**, which makes up the solid part of the Earth's crust. Over time, frost, wind and rain wear down the rock on the surface of the lithosphere. This disintegration leads to the formation of lithosol, a soil consisting mainly of large rock fragments. The fragments mix with organic matter from decomposing plant and animal residues. The mixture sets off a series of complex physical and chemical reactions that eventually produces soil. On average, it takes 200 years to form a layer of soil only one centimetre thick!

SOIL HORIZONS

As soil develops, it thickens and forms distinct layers. Each layer, called a *horizon*, can be distinguished by its colour, texture and composition. Horizons are identified by letters, as shown in Figure 6.16.

> **SOIL HORIZONS are differentiated layers running roughly parallel to the surface of the ground.**

Soil absorbs, filters and stores water. It also contains all kinds of different matter as well as air, small living organisms, and microorganisms that decompose organic matter, creating nutrients for plant life.

Figure 6.16 clearly shows the differences between soil horizons. In general, fine dark particles—associated with a high concentration of organic matter—are in the upper layers, especially in the A horizon. It is the horizon where plants put down their roots to absorb water and nutrients. Deeper underground, the particles become coarser and paler.

Three conditions must be met for soil to be fertile enough to support plant life:

- a sufficient amount of minerals (water-soluble nutrients)

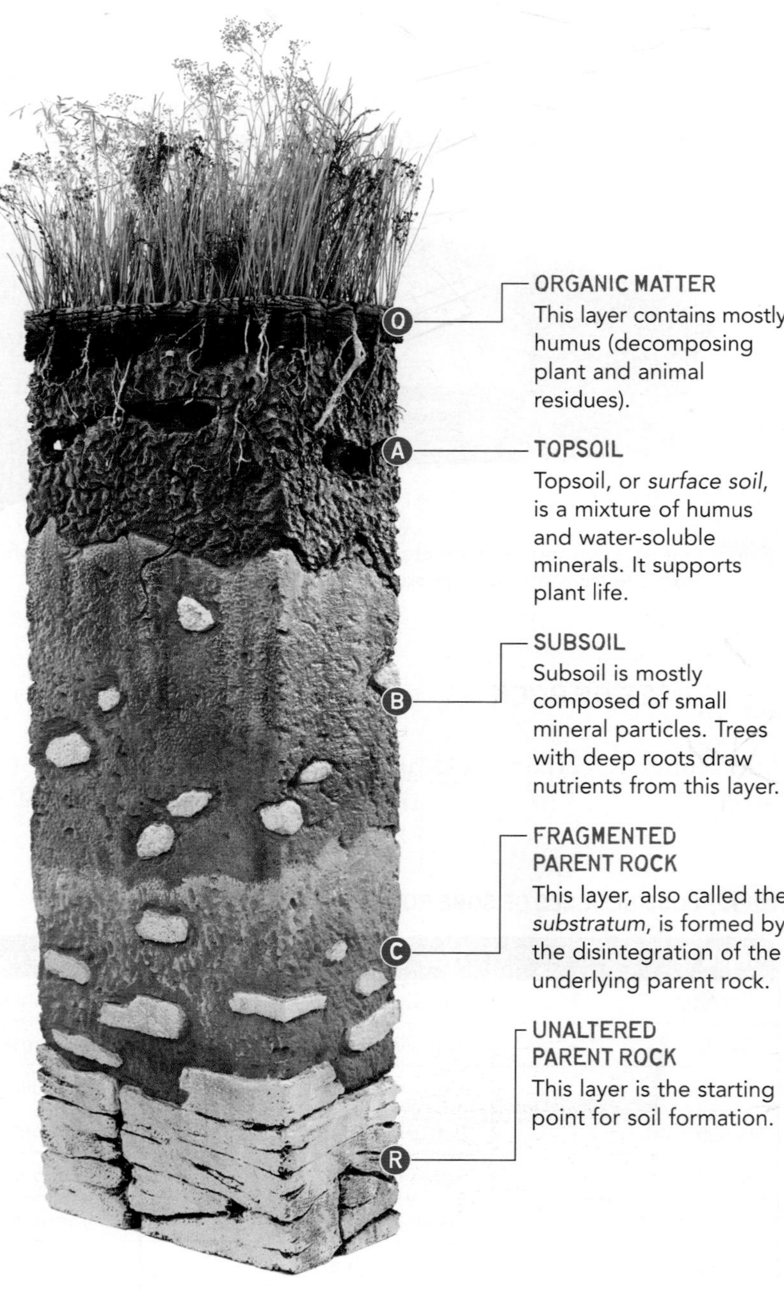

ORGANIC MATTER
This layer contains mostly humus (decomposing plant and animal residues).

TOPSOIL
Topsoil, or *surface soil*, is a mixture of humus and water-soluble minerals. It supports plant life.

SUBSOIL
Subsoil is mostly composed of small mineral particles. Trees with deep roots draw nutrients from this layer.

FRAGMENTED PARENT ROCK
This layer, also called the *substratum*, is formed by the disintegration of the underlying parent rock.

UNALTERED PARENT ROCK
This layer is the starting point for soil formation.

6.16 The above cross section shows the various soil horizons.

6.17 Parent rock can be identified in places where there is little or no vegetation.

- adequate moisture
- an appropriate soil pH. Soil that is too acidic or too alkaline jeopardizes the transfer of mineral nutrients to the roots.

EST SE

BUFFERING CAPACITY

Soil acidity, or its *pH*, is measured on a scale of 0 (very acidic) to 14 (very alkaline). Soil that is too acidic or too alkaline hinders plant growth because the roots cannot absorb nutrients properly. Plants generally adapt to soil with a pH between 6 and 7. However, some species, such as conifers, prefer more acidic soil.

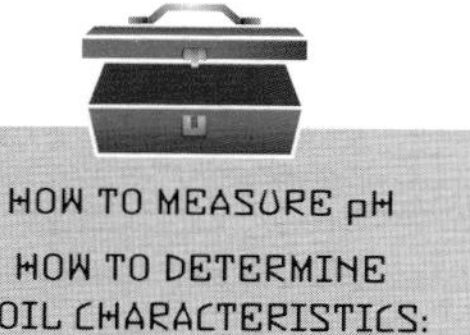

HOW TO MEASURE pH
HOW TO DETERMINE SOIL CHARACTERISTICS: TEXTURE

Soil has the ability to neutralize a certain amount of acidic or alkaline substances without affecting its pH. This ability is called the soil's *buffering capacity*. It allows soil to compensate, to a certain extent, for variations in pH.

A soil's BUFFERING CAPACITY is its ability to resist changes in its pH when acidic or alkaline compounds are added to it.

6.18 The texture of a soil can suggest its buffering capacity. The finer the texture, the better the buffering capacity. Organic matter and grains of clay, which are both very fine, help counter variations in pH.

1638
1686

Niels Stensen

In 1669, the Danish anatomist and geologist Niels Stensen discovered that the layers in geological formations are arranged in chronological order. Older layers lie deeper underground, while the more recent layers are found near the surface.

ST EST 1.4 PERMAFROST

In northern regions, large expanses of soil are permanently frozen. This type of ground is called *permafrost*.

PERMAFROST is ground whose temperature has been 0°C or lower for at least two years.

Almost 50 percent of the land in Canada is covered in permafrost. In some areas, this frozen layer can go as deep as 500 m. Permafrost is not limited to polar regions; it can also be found at high altitude—for example, on mountain peaks in western Canada.

A TICKING TIME BOMB?

If permafrost were to disappear one day because of global warming, the microorganisms trapped inside would also thaw, emitting an enormous amount of methane, a powerful greenhouse gas. 8

6.19 AREA COVERED BY PERMAFROST IN CANADA

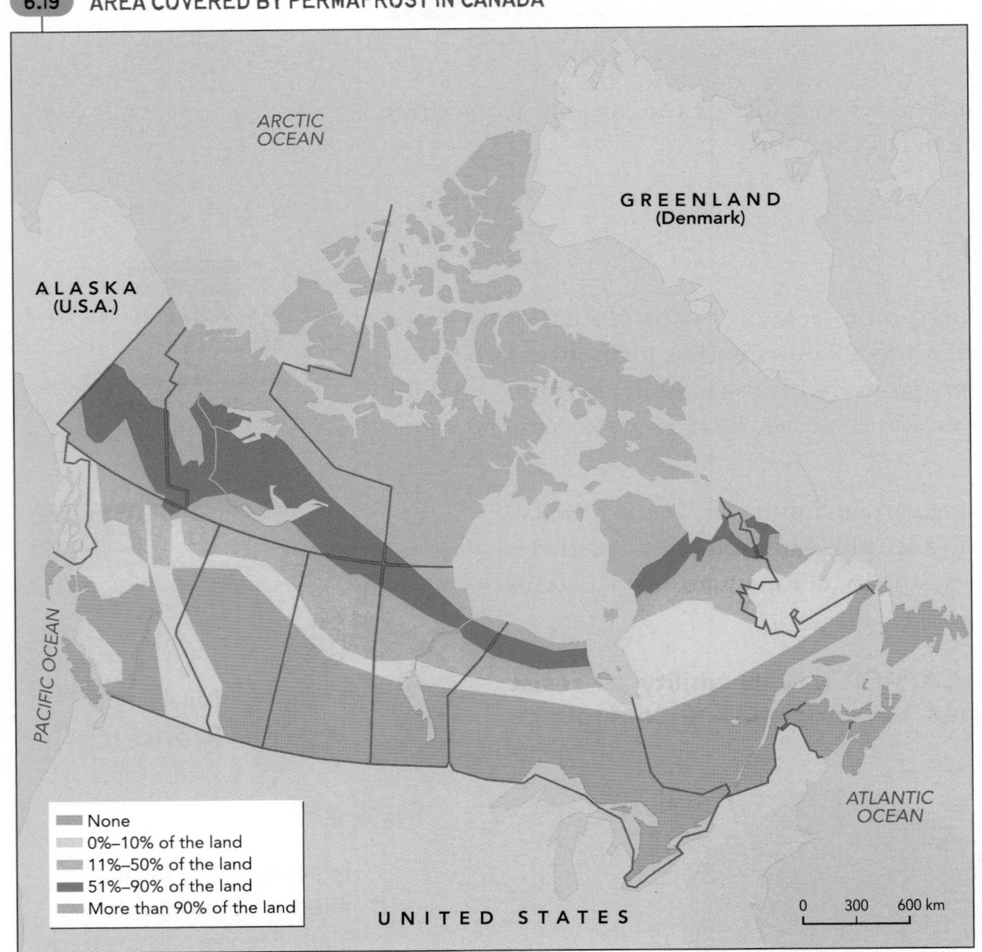

In certain regions, the upper layer of permafrost thaws in summer, and certain plants and other organisms can enjoy a brief growing season. When winter returns, the ground freezes again. This top layer is called the *active layer*.

Permafrost makes agriculture impossible, and construction, difficult. Arctic peoples have nonetheless found ingenious ways to build homes on the frozen ground. Their houses are built on piles that pass through the active layer and sit directly on the permafrost.

6.20 In Yukon Territory, global warming is threatening building stability.

Even if the frozen ground of permafrost is as hard as rock, it remains extremely sensitive to external influences. A rise in temperature of only a few degrees can sometimes cause the ground to soften, compromising the stability of all the buildings on it.

ST EST AST 1.5 ENERGY RESOURCES

The wealth contained in the lithosphere is not limited to minerals. In its depths lie rich reserves of energy resources—oil, natural gas and coal—which humans extract in great quantities. Thanks to these resources, we can heat buildings, power factories and fuel truck and car engines.

CONCEPT REVIEW

- Natural energy sources
- Renewable and nonrenewable energy resources
- Forms of energy (chemical, thermal, mechanical, radiation)
- Energy transformations

6.21 An oil drilling platform. Opinions differ as to the amounts of natural gas, oil and coal still available, but all those concerned agree that reserves of these fuels are limited and could be depleted within the next few decades.

ST
EST
AST

FOSSIL FUELS

Almost two thirds of the world's electricity is produced from fossil fuels, which consist of coal, natural gas and oil. The energy that comes from these fuels is called **FOSSIL ENERGY**.

One of these fuels, oil, comes from small marine animals and algae that lived in the seas a very long time ago. When they died, these organisms sank to the sea floor, where they were gradually covered in sand, silt and other rocks and minerals. Under pressure from the layers of sediment above them, they very slowly turned into oil. Natural gas is produced in the same way and from the same source as oil.

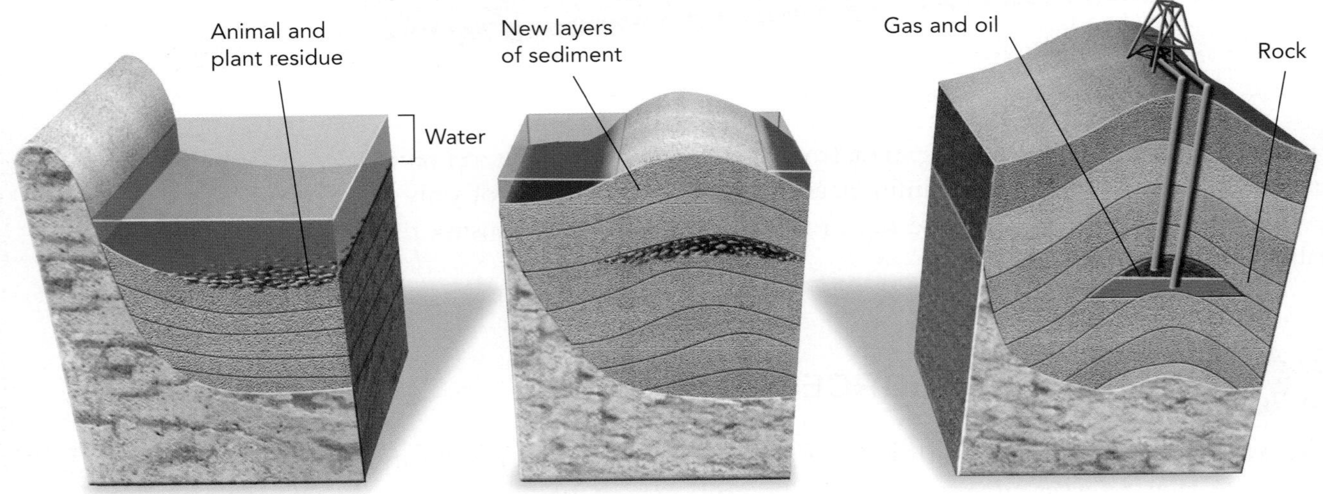

6.22 Formation of oil and natural gas

Coal does not come from marine organisms but from terrestrial plants and trees that once grew in swamps. Over time, these swamps were buried under sand and silt. The organic residue was compressed, and it turned into coal. Unlike oil, which is a liquid, and natural gas—obviously a gas—coal is a solid.

FOSSIL FUELS result from the transformation of organic residue. These energy sources consist of oil, natural gas and coal.

6.23 Formation of coal

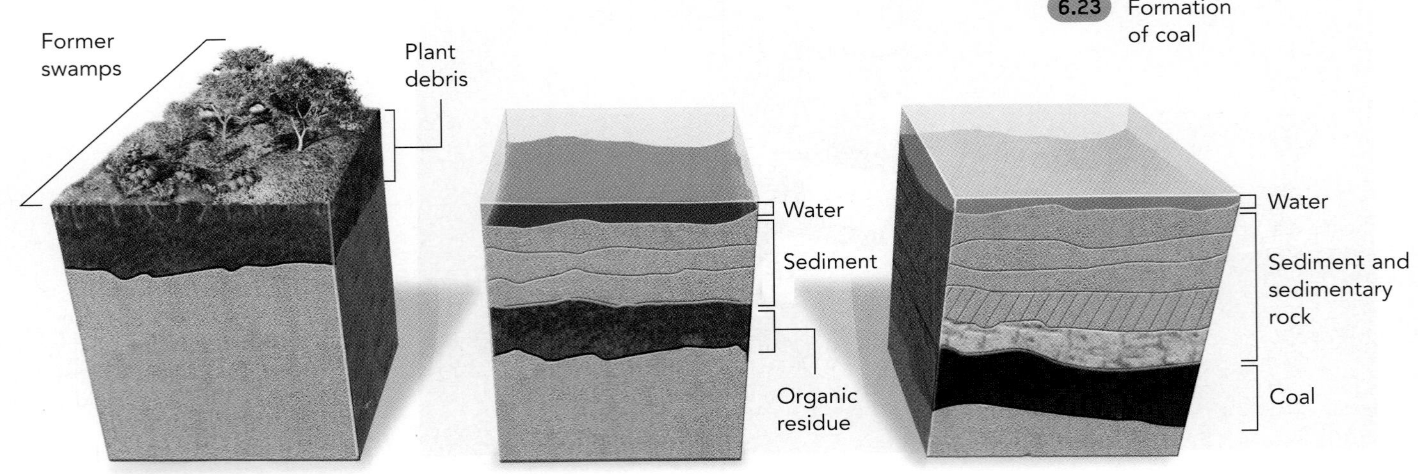

ENVIRONMENT EXTRA

The long life of plastics

Oil and natural gas do not only fuel engines; they also provide the raw materials for manufacturing plastics. They are found in soft-drink bottles, grocery bags, computer screens—and, eventually, in landfills. Plastics can take hundreds of years to decompose.

To reduce our use of precious natural resources and ease the pressure on our overflowing landfills, governments have been promoting recycling. Plastics are recovered—along with metals, glass and paper—and sent to sorting centres. Although some computerized systems can distinguish different plastics, most of the sorting is done by hand. Thermoplastics (plastics that soften easily when heated) are melted down and made into new products. Thermosetting plastics (which harden permanently once moulded) are ground into powder and mixed with thermoplastics.

Mechanical sorting

Alternatives to recycling also exist: reducing our consumption of new products, reusing products instead of throwing them away, making repairs when necessary, and recovering products for new uses, such as using thermoplastic waste in road resurfacing. Efforts can also be made to educate the population about the consequences of waste disposal.

When fossil fuels burn, they emit **THERMAL ENERGY**, which can be converted into electrical energy or **MECHANICAL ENERGY**—to make an engine work, for example. Combustion also gives off by-products, especially carbon dioxide (CO_2), the principal **GREENHOUSE GAS** behind global warming. Other pollutants produced by combustion include sulphur dioxide (SO_2) and nitrogen oxides (NO_x), responsible for **ACID RAIN**. Note that natural gas is mainly composed of methane (CH_4), a greenhouse gas 21 times more powerful than CO_2.

ST
EST
AST

URANIUM

Uranium is a radioactive element that occurs naturally in the Earth's crust. Splitting the nucleus of uranium atoms produces a large amount of energy, called *nuclear energy*, that can be converted into electricity. A handful of uranium can produce as much electrical power as approximately 70 tonnes (70 000 kg) of coal. Fission, the splitting of atoms that creates nuclear energy, does not release greenhouse gases into the environment. However, it does cause other problems.

NUCLEAR ENERGY is the energy stored in the bonds between the particles in the nucleus of an atom.

FROM ENERGY TO MEDICINE

Canada is a major producer of radioactive isotopes. They are used in nuclear medicine, especially for radiotherapy.

The heat emitted by nuclear fission is accompanied by radioactivity. The reactors where the nuclear fission occurs are therefore enclosed in thick containment buildings made of reinforced concrete. The buildings are also earthquake-resistant. Nevertheless, the risk of an accident remains a constant concern.

Another problem associated with nuclear energy is waste. The material and equipment that come in contact with radiation continue to be radioactive for hundreds of years. The waste is therefore cooled in huge pools and then buried either in former mines or in custom-built concrete pits. No method currently exists to neutralize radioactivity. In Québec, there is only one nuclear plant, the Gentilly-2 Nuclear Generating Station.

GEOTHERMICS

Beneath the Earth's crust lies molten rock containing enormous amounts of energy. This type of energy is called *geothermal energy*.

Geothermal comes from the Greek words *gē*, meaning "Earth," and *thermos*, meaning "hot."

GEOTHERMAL ENERGY is the energy that comes from the internal heat of the Earth.

To make use of geothermal energy, a fluid is circulated deep underground. It is heated by the molten rock and rises to the surface. It is now charged with energy, which can then be converted into electricity or used directly to heat buildings.

Geothermal energy is used mainly in parts of the world where hot rock is located near the surface—for example, in volcanic regions. In these areas,

6.24 Iceland alone is home to nearly 200 geothermal power plants. The lagoon shown opposite is fed by surplus water from the Svartsengi power plant and is used for bathing.

the hot water from underground rises to the surface by itself. No other fluid is necessary to capture the heat.

In North America, a few geothermal systems for heating houses have appeared (Figure 6.25). These systems reduce heating costs and CO_2 emissions, and they use renewable energy. For the moment, however, installing geothermal systems is much more expensive than using conventional heating methods.

6.25 Example of a residential geothermal heating system

ST EST AST

THE ENERGY OF TOMORROW?

Fossil fuels are in danger of running out within the next few decades, nuclear power raises concerns among the population, and geothermal energy is expensive. Consequently, engineers are increasing their efforts to discover new sources of energy that are both renewable and "clean."

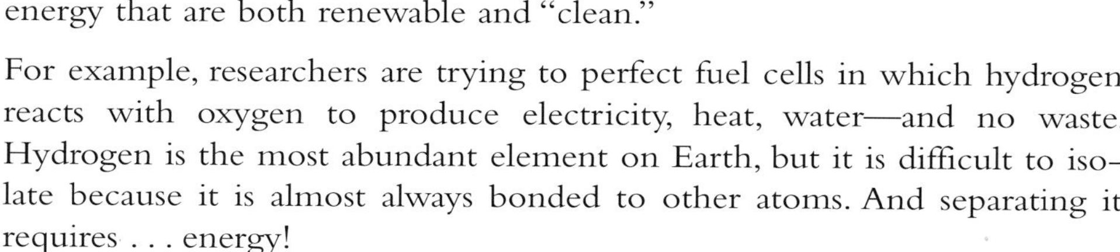

For example, researchers are trying to perfect fuel cells in which hydrogen reacts with oxygen to produce electricity, heat, water—and no waste. Hydrogen is the most abundant element on Earth, but it is difficult to isolate because it is almost always bonded to other atoms. And separating it requires . . . energy!

EST SE

1.6 POLLUTION AND DEGRADATION

We drink water and breathe air directly, but the earth feeds us in a more indirect way. Perhaps that is why soil is a subject that receives less attention in environmental circles than water and air pollution. Human activities are nonetheless modifying the soil, too.

EST

SOIL DEPLETION

To meet the food needs of an ever-growing global population, farming practices have changed over the last few decades. For example, widespread use of heavy machinery has made harvesting easier, but it also compacts the soil, depriving it of precious oxygen.

Compaction also prevents rain from penetrating the earth. Instead, rainwater runs off the surface into lakes and rivers, carrying with it organic matter, microorganisms and essential nutrients for plant life. Plants no longer receive the water and nutrients they need to grow, and the soil becomes less fertile.

SOIL DEPLETION is the loss of soil fertility.

Rather than letting the land rest periodically, some farmers accelerate crop rotation, preventing the soil from regenerating naturally. To compensate, they apply increasing amounts of fertilizer. Any excess may flow into lakes and promote the growth of algae (such as cyanobacteria, also called *blue-green algae*).

Excessive use of pesticides is another cause of farmland degradation. The pesticides remain in the environment and accumulate in the tissues of living organisms. They kill many microorganisms, insects and small animals that help maintain soil balance, and they threaten **BIODIVERSITY**.

SIDE EFFECTS

In certain South American countries, gas at the pump may contain up to 80 percent ethanol, which is used to make gas less polluting. However, when ethanol is produced from cereal crops, notably corn, it encourages intensive farming, takes up large areas of farmland, reduces wooded areas and increases soil degradation.

EST SE

CONTAMINATION

In addition to fertilizers and pesticides, various other contaminants undermine soil quality. Some gas-station tanks leak hydrocarbons, landfills sometimes leak water containing heavy metals, and mining waste spreads acid residue.

CONTAMINATION is the abnormal presence of a harmful substance in an environment.

Precipitation that falls to the ground also carries all kinds of chemicals. For example, sulphur dioxide (SO_2) and nitrogen oxide (NO_x) emissions, which are released into the atmosphere by industrial processes and fossil fuel combustion, become mixed with rainwater. They form sulphuric acid (H_2SO_4) and nitric acid (HNO_3), and the rain becomes acid rain.

Acid rain has a disastrous effect on **ECOSYSTEMS**. Acidified soil can no longer retain the nutrients essential to plant life. Acid rain also kills microorganisms that are beneficial to plants. Trees and plants grow more slowly and may even stop growing altogether. Soils with a low buffering capacity are particularly vulnerable to acid rain.

ST EST AST SE

2 The hydrosphere

CONCEPT REVIEW
- Hydrosphere
- Water (distribution)

More than two thirds of the Earth's surface is covered in water, filling oceans, seas, lakes and rivers. Water is also found underground, in the atmosphere (in the form of a vapour) and in glaciers (in the form of snow and ice). No wonder the Earth is nicknamed the "Blue Planet"! The layer of water enveloping the Earth—on, in and above it—is called the *hydrosphere*.

Hydrosphere comes from the Greek words *hudōr*, meaning "water," and *sphaira*, meaning a "spherical object."

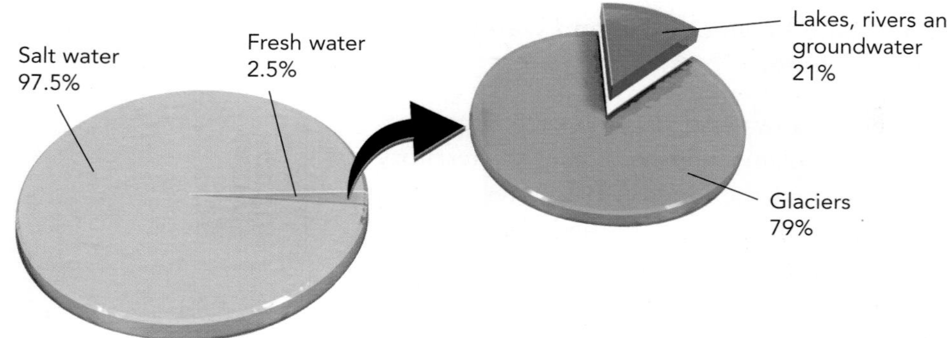

6.26 The distribution of water on Earth

- **The HYDROSPHERE is the Earth's outer layer of water, uniting water in all its states: liquid, solid and gas.**

Water is a precious resource. This is especially true of fresh water because it represents only 2.5 percent of the water on Earth and is often difficult to reach: 79 percent of its volume is frozen in glaciers. On land, fresh water flows in lakes and rivers as well as underground.

ST EST AST 2.1 INLAND WATERS

Inland waters consist in water found on the continents, as opposed to water found in the oceans. This water falls to earth as rain or snow, runs into streams, infiltrates the ground, seeps into natural cracks in rocks and minerals, flows into lakes and rivers, etc.

- **INLAND WATERS are all the freshwater bodies found on continents, uniting rivers, lakes and groundwater.**

On land, the path water takes may be full of twists and turns. A drop of water can fall to the ground, seep into a crevice, travel underground and emerge in a river 100 km away.

ST EST AST WATERSHEDS

To manage and preserve inland waters, hydrologists (water specialists) divide a territory into watersheds (also called *catchment areas* or *drainage basins*). A watershed is an area of land whose lakes and rivers all empty into the same larger body of water. The limits of a watershed are determined by natural boundaries, formed by virtual lines along the crest of nearby mountains, hills or other high ground. These boundaries are called *watershed divides* (often shortened to simply *watersheds*; the term may thus designate both the area and the divide). The natural slope of the land causes the waters to flow in the same direction.

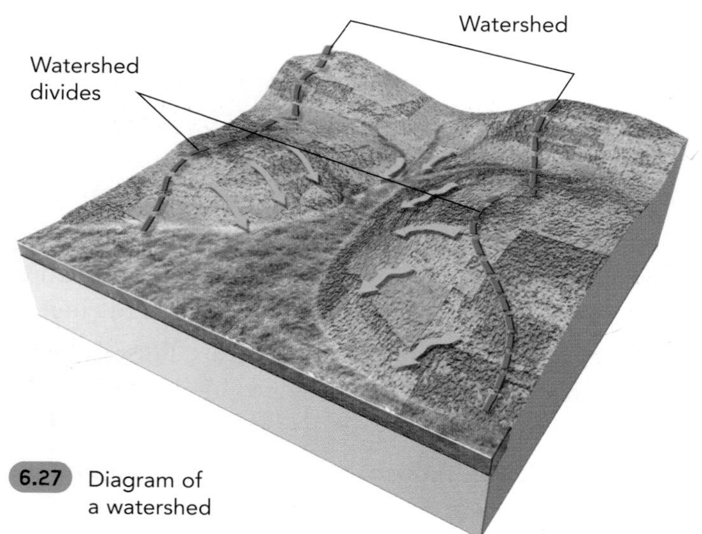

6.27 Diagram of a watershed

A WATERSHED is an area of land in which all inland waters drain into the same larger body of water.

A watershed encompasses any number of subwatersheds, with each larger area containing many smaller watersheds. Three main watersheds drain the territory of Québec: the St. Lawrence River watershed, the Hudson Bay watershed and the Ungava Bay watershed. Each contains many subwatersheds. The Rivière Chaudière watershed, for example, is part of the St. Lawrence River watershed.

6.28 THE THREE MAJOR WATERSHEDS OF QUÉBEC

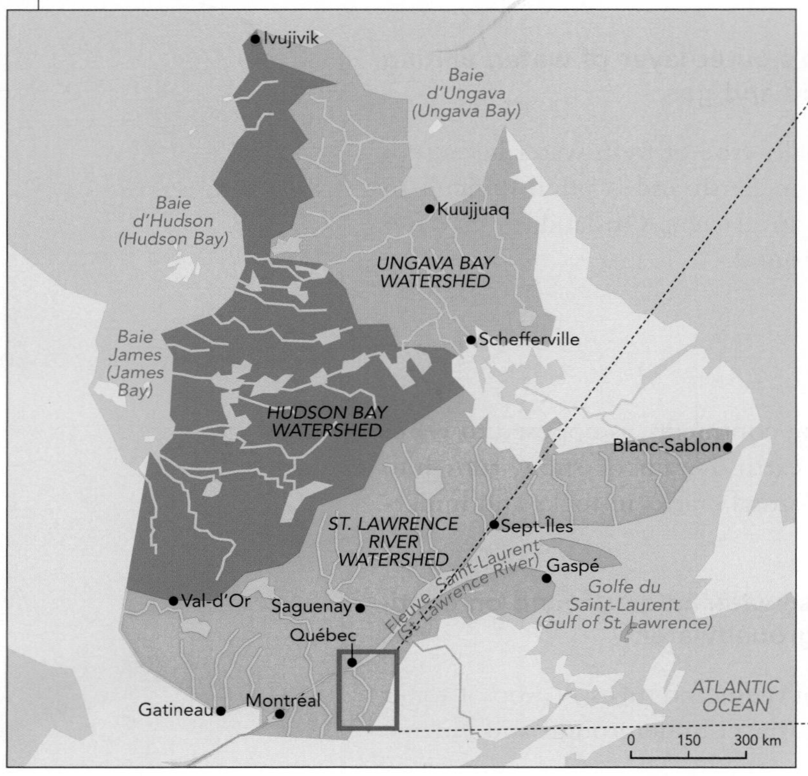

THE RIVIÈRE CHAUDIÈRE WATERSHED

Many aspects of the surrounding land and climate can affect how water flows within a watershed, either slowing down the flow by placing obstacles in the water's path or accelerating its course. The following are a few examples of these factors:

- topography: the shape, slope and terrain of the area. For example, steeply sloped land drains easily.
- geology: the type, depth and structure of the rock. For example, water flows more easily through the holes and gaps in crushed rock than through compact clay.
- climate: rain or snowfall, winds and temperature. For example, water flows more quickly after a rain shower than during a drought.
- vegetation: its density and diversity. For example, when it rains, the surface-water runoff is slowed by wooded areas on riverbanks. Rainwater flows into streams and rivers less rapidly.
- agricultural, industrial and urban development. For example, a dam can prevent water from flowing freely.

2.2 THE OCEANS

ST
EST

The continents divide the ocean waters covering the Earth into five main areas: the Pacific Ocean, the Atlantic Ocean, the Indian Ocean, the Arctic Ocean and the Southern Ocean (officially recognized in 2000). Along the edges of these oceans, closer to the coastlines, lie smaller and shallower seas.

Ocean waters are moved by currents that carry them all around the world. Before discussing these movements, however, we will explain two important parameters in the study of oceans: water temperature and salinity.

Many factors can influence water temperature, including the following:

- **Depth.** Sunlight penetrates the upper layers of the oceans and warms the water. The first layer, called the *mixed layer*, varies in depth depending on wind, tides and the extent of the turbulence caused by waves. Since solar energy does not reach very far, water temperature falls rapidly below the 200-m mark. This transition zone is called the *thermocline*. Beneath it, the water becomes very cold. The depths of the ocean are dark, and the water temperature drops to as low as 4°C.

ASSISTANT OCEANOGRAPHERS

To obtain data on the temperature, pressure and salinity of the Southern Ocean, elephant seals were equipped with locating and data collection devices. These animals travel thousands of kilometres each year and can dive several hundred metres for periods of almost 20 minutes.

6.29 OCEAN TEMPERATURE ZONES

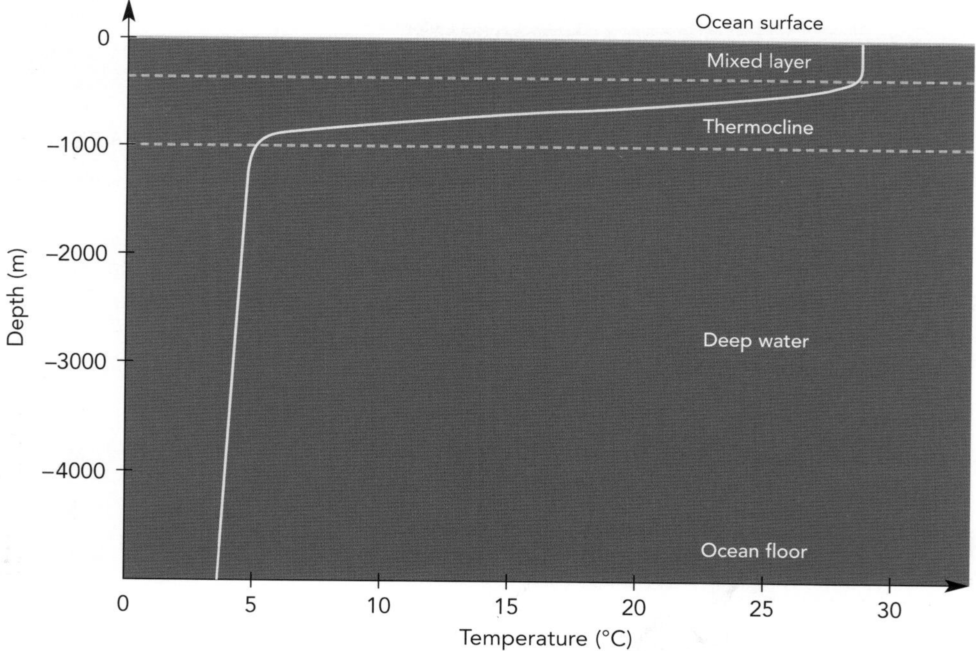

- **The seasons.** The seasons also cause variations in water temperature. In the winter, the ocean loses some of the heat it stored during the summer. Land masses lose heat, too, but since water loses heat more slowly than the ground, the differences in seasonal temperatures are less pronounced at sea than on land.

THE OCEANS AND MAIN SURFACE CURRENTS

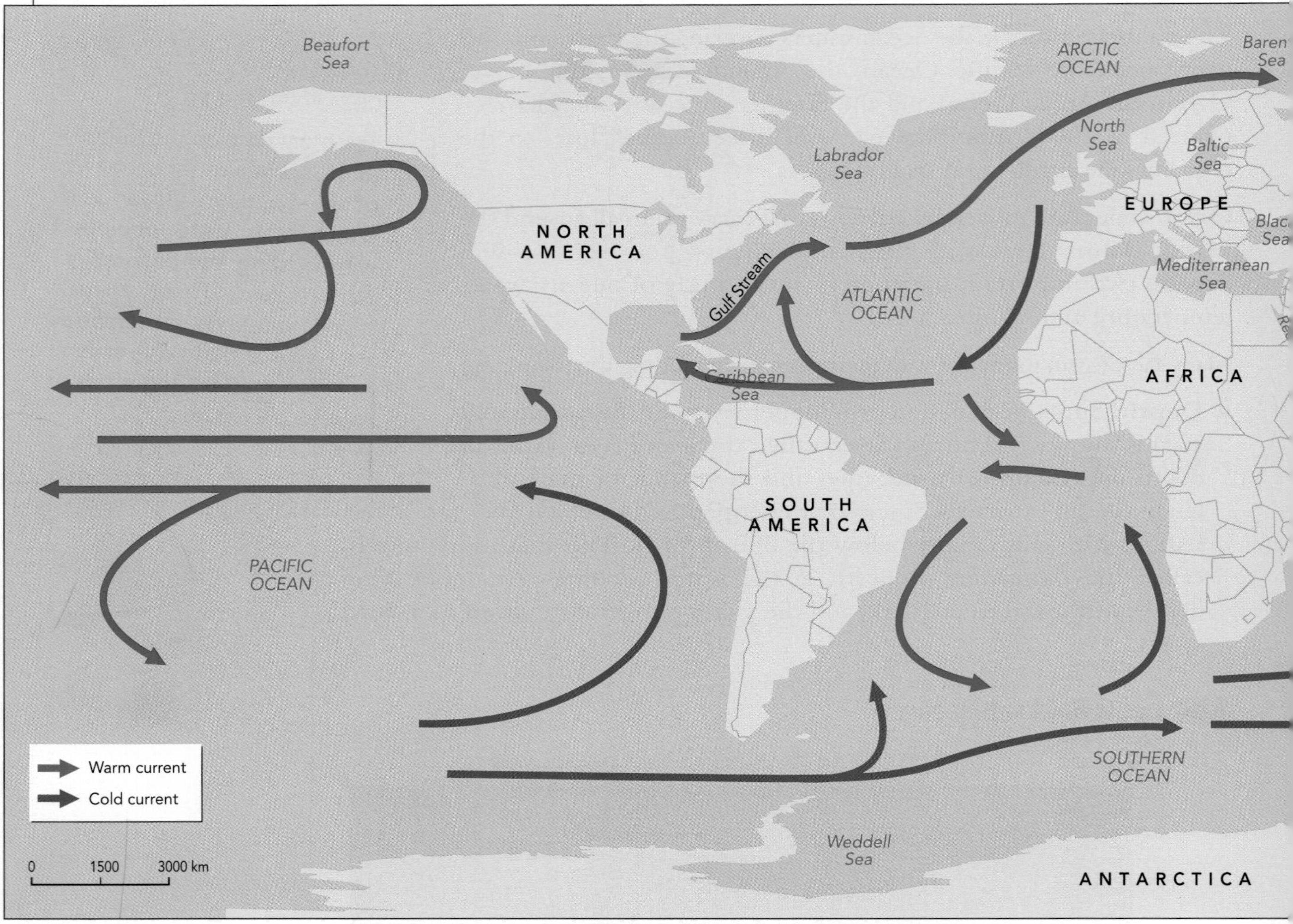

Beaufort Sea
ARCTIC OCEAN
Barents Sea
North Sea
Baltic Sea
Labrador Sea
EUROPE
Black Sea
NORTH AMERICA
Mediterranean Sea
Gulf Stream
ATLANTIC OCEAN
Caribbean Sea
AFRICA
SOUTH AMERICA
PACIFIC OCEAN
SOUTHERN OCEAN
Warm current
Cold current
0 1500 3000 km
Weddell Sea
ANTARCTICA

- **Latitude.** Latitude also greatly influences water temperature. Surface waters reach mean temperatures between 25°C and 28°C at the equator and between 12°C and 17°C in temperate zones.

Salinity is another important parameter in ocean studies. Seawater continually pounds against the rocks of the lithosphere, dissolving the salts in them. The rivers and groundwater that flow over rock also accumulate salts and carry them to the oceans. Since these salts do not evaporate, they become concentrated in the water, giving it a salty taste. The average salinity of most of the oceans is between 3.4 and 3.7 percent.

SALINITY is a measure of the amount of salt dissolved in a liquid.

Near the poles, melting pack ice and glaciers dilute the seawater and reduce its salt content (salinity) to nearly three percent. Meanwhile, in the Red Sea, heat and drought accelerate water evaporation and concentrate the salts, raising the salinity to four percent.

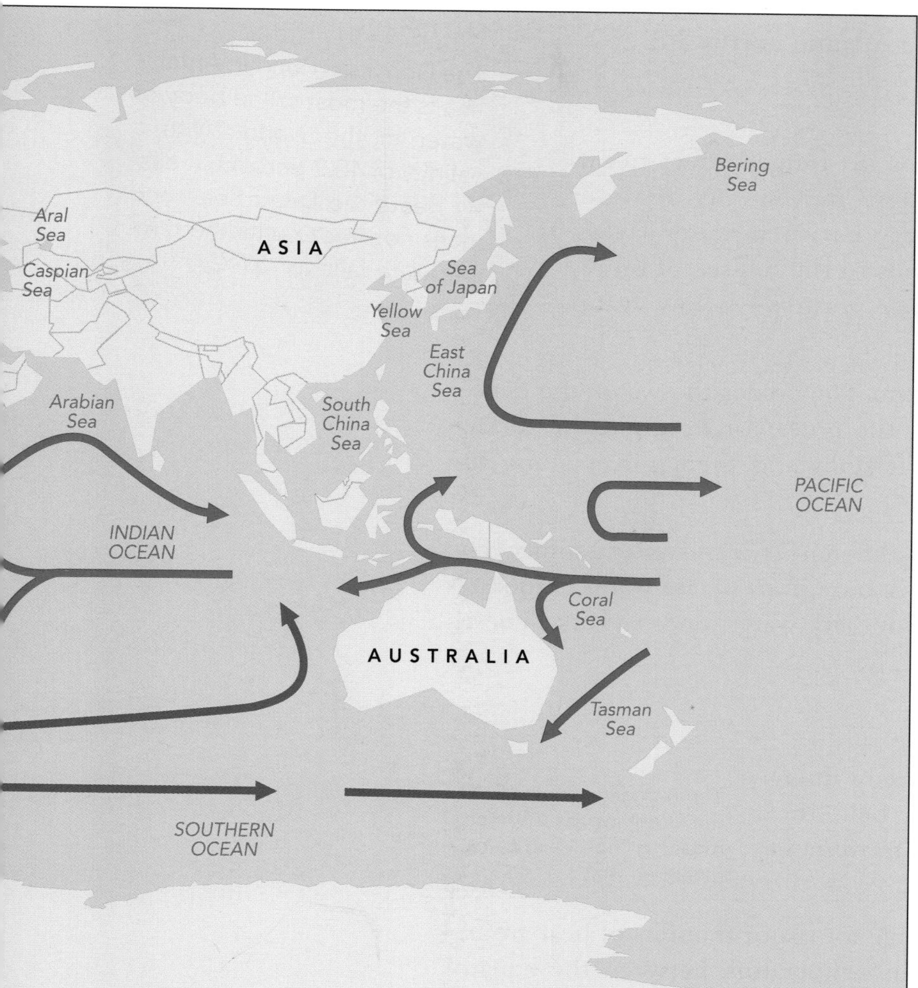

1806
1873

Matthew Fontaine Maury

In 1848, the American oceanographer Matthew Fontaine Maury drew the first maps of ocean currents. A few years later, he formulated the hypothesis that the Gulf Stream plays a major role in regulating temperatures in Europe.

ST
EST

OCEAN CIRCULATION

The water in the oceans is in constant motion. This movement is not only a question of waves and tides but also the result of the continual circulation of ocean currents, both on the surface of the water and in its depths.

An OCEAN CURRENT is the movement of seawater in a certain direction.

There are two main types of ocean currents: surface currents and subsurface currents. The two types are closely connected and together form the patterns of movement that make up ocean circulation.

OCEAN CIRCULATION is the combined effect of all the currents that move across the oceans.

Surface currents

Surface currents are mostly wind-driven. These currents move horizontally, usually in the first 400 m of water below the surface (Map 6.30).

The Gulf Stream is undoubtedly the surface current Quebeckers know best. It originates near the equator and, driven by the wind, carries the warm and salty waters of the Atlantic northward.

EXTRA-SALTY BUT COLD!

The Don Juan Pond in Antarctica is the most saline body of water in the world. With a salinity of 40.2 percent, it easily beats the Dead Sea—and does not freeze until the temperature falls to –57°C.

Subsurface currents

At depths of more than 800 m, winds no longer affect ocean circulation. Deep currents prevail. These movements of water are mostly due to variations in density between water layers. Among these layers, density corresponds to the degree of buoyancy: the denser the water, the deeper it sinks—below water that is less dense.

Water density varies with the temperature. The colder the water, the denser it is, so cold water tends to sink. Near the poles, for example, the surface water cools on contact with the air. It sinks and then moves along the ocean floor.

Subsurface currents are also caused by differences in seawater salinity. The higher the salinity, the denser the water is. In regions where water evaporates quickly, the salt content increases, and the salty water tends to sink beneath the less saline water.

Thermohaline circulation

Surface and subsurface currents are closely interconnected and form a huge "conveyor belt" that moves water all around the world. This movement is referred to as *thermohaline circulation*.

Thermohaline comes from the Greek words *thermos*, meaning "hot," and *halos*, meaning "salt."

THERMOHALINE CIRCULATION is responsible for major transfers of heat around the world. Without it, the differences in temperature between the equator and the poles would be much more dramatic. In fact, the ocean is as essential as the atmosphere in regulating the Earth's climate.

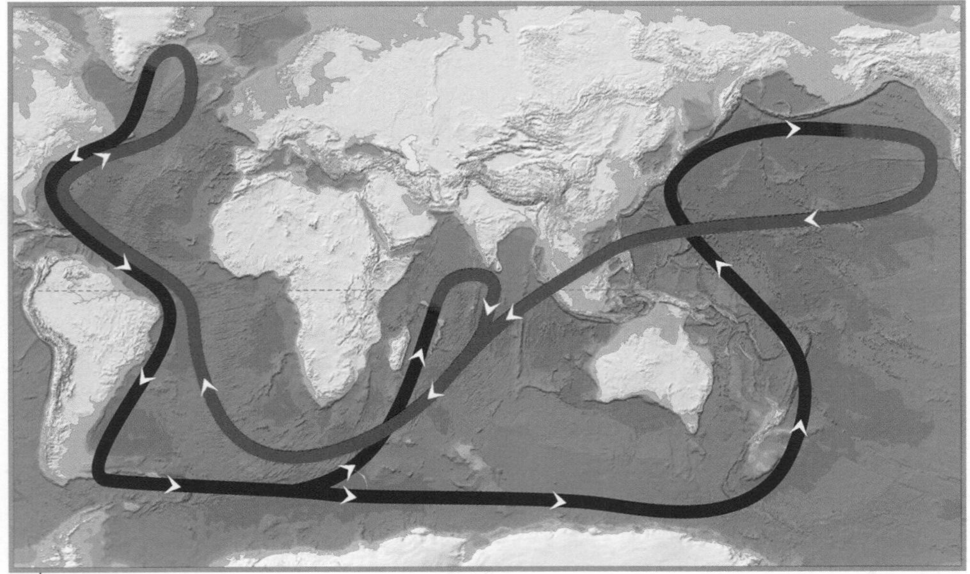

6.31 Thermohaline circulation

ST EST 2.3 THE CRYOSPHERE

The cryosphere is the portion of the Earth's surface where water is found in solid form. It consists of pack ice, glaciers, frozen lakes and rivers, vast expanses of snow, and the ice in permafrost.

Cryosphere comes from the Greek words *kruos*, meaning "icy cold," and *sphaira*, meaning a "spherical object."

The CRYOSPHERE consists of all the frozen water on the Earth's surface.

ST EST PACK ICE

In the Arctic Ocean and around the continent of Antarctica, the upper layer of water freezes on contact with the cold air. This creates huge slabs of ice that crowd together, shattering one another and disintegrating. Altogether, they form pack ice. Smaller, free-floating sheets of ice are called *ice floes*.

PACK ICE is composed of the ice floating on the oceans near the North and South poles.

In the Arctic, pack ice usually forms near Russia. The prevailing winds then drive it out to open sea, and the sheets accumulate on the surface of the Arctic Ocean. Pack ice expands and contracts with the seasons. In the winter, it stretches over 12 million square kilometres on average; at the end of the summer, its area is considerably reduced.

Under the effect of global warming, the polar ice packs are showing signs of weakening. Since the 1970s, the area of pack ice during summer has shrunk by several million square kilometres.

6.32 From 1979 to 2005, the Arctic ice pack lost more than two million square kilometres in area during the summer. Over the two years that followed, it shrank by more than one million square kilometres.

6.33 Melting pack ice threatens the survival of species that depend on the ice, such as polar bears or ringed seals.

ST EST

GLACIERS

Unlike pack ice, glaciers do not float on water; they lie on land. Some can be found at mountain peaks, but the most imposing ones are at the poles, in Greenland and Antarctica. Altogether, glaciers contain 79 percent of the world's freshwater reserves. Large glaciers are called *ice caps* or *ice sheets*.

A GLACIER is a mass of ice on land, formed by compressed snow.

Snow accumulates on the surface of glaciers, compressing the lower layers, which turn into ice. The pressure causes surplus ice to leak out around the edges of the glacier. Ice that is no longer supported by rock breaks off and falls into the sea, creating icebergs.

Climate change is threatening the stability of the Greenland and Antarctic ice sheets. Global warming is making the surface ice on glaciers melt. The water seeps to the base of the sheet, making the rock underneath slippery, so the glacier slides more quickly.

The ice that falls into the ocean raises the sea level, like an ice cube falling into a glass of water. This phenomenon could become a cause of concern among populations in many countries where the land is barely above sea level.

6.34 Approximately 90 percent of the volume of an iceberg lies below the water surface.

6.35 A flood in Bangladesh. In this country, 17 million people live less than one metre above sea level.

Melting ice sheets in Greenland and Antarctica could cause other environmental problems. The thaw releases abnormally high amounts of fresh water (glacier water is not saline) into the Norwegian Sea, where they mix with the Gulf Stream. The seawater becomes less dense and does not sink as easily, which could slow the ocean currents and affect the climate in many regions. Even so, scientists do not consider it likely that thermohaline circulation will stop altogether.

ST EST AST 2.4 ENERGY RESOURCES

The force of moving water represents a tremendous source of energy: hydraulic energy. Transforming it into electricity is a huge challenge, however, since enormous facilities are required to generate and distribute the electricity.

> **HYDRAULIC ENERGY is the energy that can be derived from moving water.**

ST EST AST WATER FROM RIVERS AND WATERFALLS

Thanks to the impressive discharge (rate of flow) of its rivers, Québec generates almost all of its electricity in hydroelectric power plants. How do these plants work? First, a dam is built across a river to hold back its waters. The water level rises, filling huge artificial reservoirs, which put pressure on the dam.

To produce electricity, the dam gates are opened, and the water rushes through large pipes that lead to turbines. The force of the water spins the turbines, which are connected to alternators that convert the mechanical energy into an electric current. The current is then distributed to homes and factories.

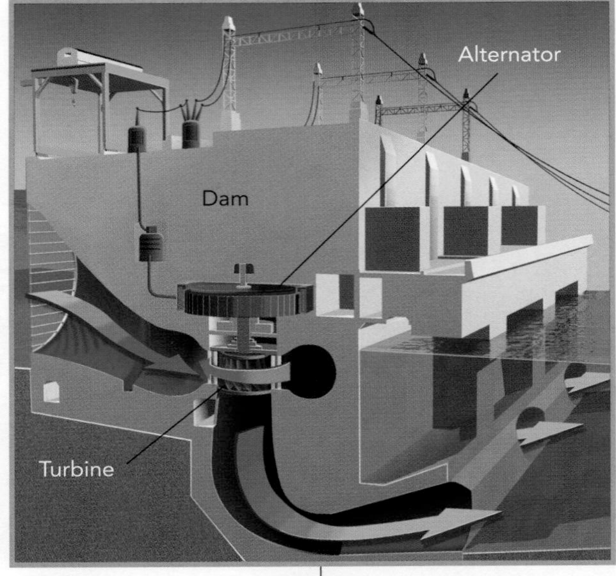

6.36 How water passes through a hydroelectric power plant

A HYDROELECTRIC DAM converts a river's hydraulic energy into electrical power.

In contrast to fossil and nuclear energies, hydroelectric power depends on a renewable resource. It also generates very little greenhouse gas. It does have considerable impact on the environment, however, because flooding hundreds of square kilometres of forest to create reservoirs swallows up entire ecosystems.

Scientists have also discovered that mercury from industrial activities, which has accumulated in the soil, is released into the water of reservoirs. Bacteria convert it into methylmercury, a toxic compound that is stored in the bodies of fish and thus introduced into the food chain. When humans eat the fish, they, too, absorb the toxic substance.

ST
EST
AST

WAVES AND OCEAN CURRENTS

Waves and ocean currents also contain large amounts of energy. Engineers are developing systems to transform this energy into electrical power. For example, some have designed buoys that rise and fall with the waves, creating movement that then activates turbines. Another innovative idea involves underwater turbines that look like wind turbines but whose blades are turned by ocean currents. For the moment, however, these systems are too expensive for widespread application, and the few existing projects are still at the prototype stage.

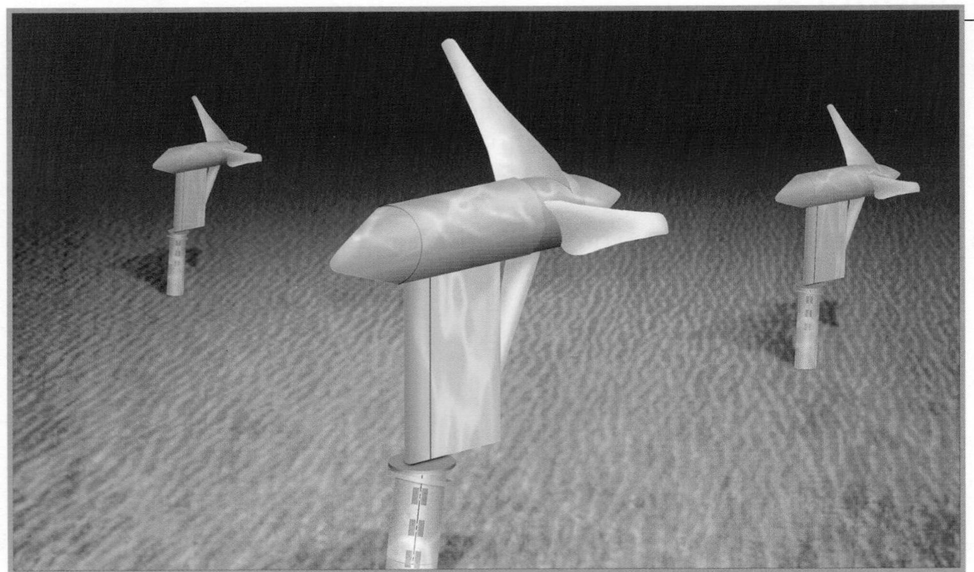

6.37 This illustration shows what underwater turbines could look like.

EST SE 2.5 POLLUTION AND DEGRADATION

Human activities—whether domestic, industrial, agricultural or navigational—can affect natural waters and endanger not only the quality of drinking water sources but also the health of surrounding ecosystems and the beauty of their landscapes.

Chemicals are not the only threats to ecosystems. Certain factories discharge warm water into rivers, which also causes pollution. Warm water alters the natural environment by raising the temperature and reducing the concentration of oxygen in the water, which can be harmful to aquatic animals. This alteration is called *thermal pollution*. As you can see in Figure 6.38, oxygen solubility drops as the water temperature rises.

6.38 THE SOLUBILITY OF OXYGEN IN WATER AS A FUNCTION OF TEMPERATURE

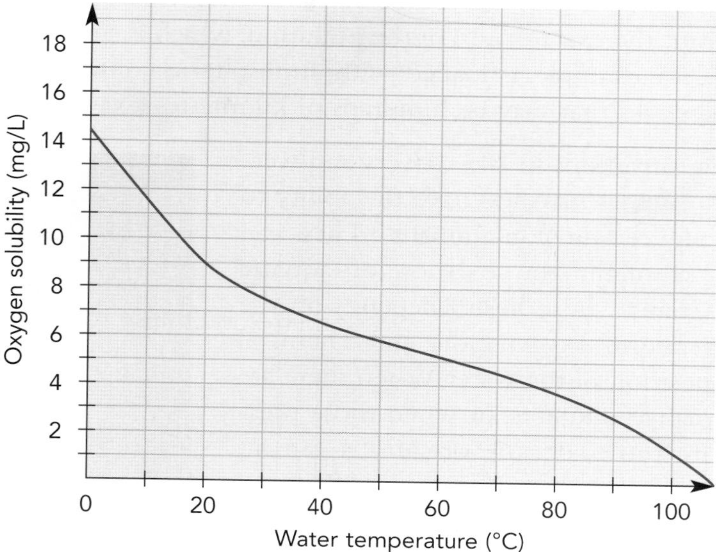

ENVIRONMENT EXTRA

Drinking water: vulnerable sources

In Québec, 75 percent of the population draws its water supply from surface waters—mainly the St. Lawrence (Fleuve Saint-Laurent) and other rivers. The rest of the population uses groundwater wells. When water is drawn from the natural environment, it is usually treated in a plant. First, it is filtered through screens to remove larger objects like branches or floating debris. It then passes through various other filters or treatment units, which remove waterborne particles and contaminants.

Treatment plants cannot remove all the contaminants from the water. Certain viruses, bacteria and chemicals may still make their way to household taps; however, the risk to human health is minimal. It is nonetheless important to protect drinking water sources to preserve water quality. Drinking water intakes, for example, would never be placed downstream from a factory that discharges its waste into the river.

Water quality in the natural environment must be preserved to ensure a safe supply of drinking water.

Some small towns do not have a treatment plant because the quality of the water is considered good enough for it to be delivered directly to homes. In cases like these, it is especially crucial to protect the sources of supply.

EST SE THE CONTAMINATION AND EUTROPHICATION OF NATURAL WATERS

LAB 56

The pollution in lakes and rivers comes from many different sources. They can be *point sources*, in cases where the pollution can be traced to a well-defined site, or they can be *non-point sources*, which means it is difficult to pinpoint the exact origin of the pollution, which is spread over a broad area. Rain, for example, is loaded with atmospheric contaminants from factory smokestacks that may be hundreds of kilometres away in any direction.

Living organisms in lakes, rivers and wetlands (such as marshes) have the ability to degrade certain contaminants. They can thus maintain the balance of aquatic ecosystems whose health depends on the temperature, oxygenation and chemical composition of the water. When there are too many pollutants, or when those present are too toxic, the organisms can no longer compensate for their effect. In addition, some contaminants, such as plastics, metals and certain pesticides, are not at all biodegradable.

6.39 An example of the effects of eutrophication

An aquatic environment becomes polluted when its ecosystem becomes unbalanced, and the effects are long-lasting. When this happens, contaminants accumulate in the environment, endangering the more fragile species and jeopardizing the quality of drinking water sources. The effects of pollutants on aquatic ecosystems depend on the nature and concentration of the contaminants. The more toxic and concentrated they are, the greater their harmful impact. Their effect also depends on certain characteristics of the ecosystem. In an environment where water moves sluggishly—a marsh, for example—contaminants tend to stagnate and concentrate in one place.

Farming activities are another cause of non-point source pollution. Pesticides and excess fertilizers make their way into rivers and lakes. Biologists are particularly concerned about phosphorus. It promotes algae growth and leads to the eutrophication of lakes, a phenomenon of reduced oxygen concentration in the water.

EUTROPHICATION is the process by which natural waters lose their oxygen because of an excessive accumulation of organic matter and nutrients.

Eutrophication occurs when dead algae sink to the bottom of a lake and are decomposed by bacteria. The bacteria consume large amounts of oxygen during the decomposition process, so the concentration of oxygen in the water starts to fall. Fish and other living organisms suffer from the lack of oxygen, and the lake slowly dies.

EST SE

THREATS AT SEA

Since 1972, the London Convention has banned the dumping of waste into the sea. Nevertheless, the oceans are still awash with all kinds of pollutants.

For example, approximately six million tonnes of petroleum are discharged into the oceans every year. Accidental oil spills are responsible for only a small proportion of this dumping. As offshore drilling platforms pump oil from under the ocean floor, some of it leaks into the surrounding waters. And once unloaded, some oil tankers clean out their reservoirs on the open sea.

Hydrocarbons float on the water's surface and pollute the coastlines. They coat the bodies of marine animals and poison them. It may take years for the pollutants to decompose through bacterial action.

6.40 Cleanup after an oil spill

THE RIVIÈRE YAMASKA POLLUTES REGIONAL WATERS

The flooding of the Rivière Yamaska has major repercussions on the level of pollution in other rivers of the Montérégie region. "There will be serious consequences," said Martine Ruel, the director of the local watershed management committee (Conseil de gestion du bassin versant de la Yamaska). "Over the last two weeks, farmers have applied a lot of manure to their crops. Now, with the flooding, all that natural fertilizer is going directly into the river." Phosphorus and nitrogen figure prominently among the contaminants affecting the Yamaska.

Environmentalists currently see few viable solutions to the pollution problem in the river. Planting trees to act as a buffer against the transportation of soil particles into the river waters is the only useful suggestion for the moment, and even that could take decades.

The pollution carried by the Rivière Yamaska into the St. Lawrence River (Fleuve Saint-Laurent) is clearly visible from the air.

Source: Adapted from Canadian Press, "Le débordement de la Yamaska contribue à polluer les cours d'eau de la région," *Les Affaires*, May 22, 2006. *[Translation]*

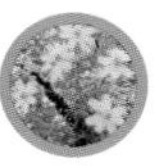

CHECKUP

ST 1–10, 12–16, 20–33, A, C and D.
EST 1–36 and A–D.
AST 1–9, 15–16, 20–23, 33, A and D.
SE 1, 10–11, 19–21, 34–36 and B.

1 The lithosphere (pp. 184–200)

1. Look at the illustration below.

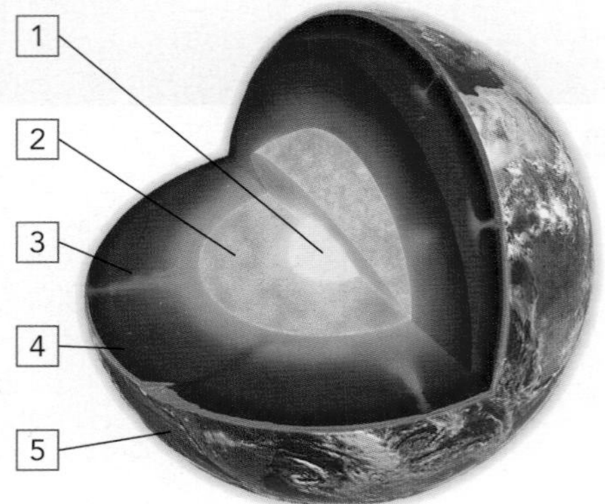

a) Name the different layers of the Earth's structure.
b) Which layers form the lithosphere?

2. What distinguishes a mineral from a rock?

3. What am I? A rock, a mineral or both?

a) I am crystalline in nature.
b) I am neither animal nor vegetable in origin.
c) I am a solid substance.
d) I am a mixture.
e) I am found in the lithosphere.
f) I always have the same chemical composition.
g) I am a product of cooled lava.

4. True or false? Explain your answer.

a) Light passes straight through crystal. It is a translucent mineral.
b) Gold is always yellow. It is an idiochromatic mineral.
c) Amethyst has a hardness of seven on the Mohs scale. It is harder than topaz.

5. At first glance, pyrite looks very much like gold. What tests could you conduct to try and distinguish one mineral from the other?

6. What can be compared using the Mohs scale?

7. A teacher takes an enormous rock from her garden and shatters it into small pieces. She gives each of her students a piece, and they must analyze its hardness, colour and streak. The students all obtain different results. Why?

8. Which type of rock is it (igneous, sedimentary or metamorphic)?

a) Sandstone is formed by the accumulation and compaction of layers of sand.
b) Slate is formed from sedimentary rock subjected to heavy pressure.
c) Granite results from the cooling of magma.

9. The Raglan Mine in northern Québec produces nickel. What can this mineral be used for?

10. A building contractor wants to build a high-rise apartment building with a five-level underground parking lot. Before beginning construction, he must remove the layers of soil covering the rock. Name the layers of soil (in order) that the contractor must remove.

11. Matthew buys a hydrangea at the nursery. He also wants to buy a bag of soil so he can plant the shrub in his garden. Knowing that Matthew lives near a highway and that rain in his region is more acidic than average, what type of soil would you recommend?

12. In the Canadian Arctic, houses are sinking into the ground, and runways are cracking. Explain why.

13. Is there any vegetation in the Far North of Québec? Explain why or why not.

14. Vicky, who lives in the village of Kuujjuaq in northern Québec, wants to build a house on piles.

    a) Given that the active layer in her region is 1.5 m thick, how long should the piles be? Why?

    b) Can Vicky be sure of the long-term stability of her house?

15. Name three fuels that come directly from the lithosphere.

16. Name the form of energy described in each statement.

    a) It is produced by atomic fission.

    b) It is the result of the decomposition of prehistoric plants and animals.

    c) It is derived from the internal heat of the Earth.

    d) It emits more greenhouse gases than any other form of energy.

    e) It leaves behind radioactive waste.

    f) It is in danger of running out within the next few decades.

17. Name three farming practices that lead to soil depletion.

18. Name one advantage and one disadvantage of using heavy machinery on farmland.

19. Nitrogen oxides (NO_x) and sulphur dioxide (SO_2) are emitted by car engines and industrial processes.

    a) What happens when they come into contact with rainwater?

    b) How does this rain affect the soil?

2 The hydrosphere (pp. 200–213)

20. What am I? I represent 2.5 percent of the hydrosphere, and 79 percent of my total volume is contained in glaciers.

21. Name five forms of water in the hydrosphere.

22. Environmental experts divide inland waters among watersheds. How do they define the boundaries of watersheds?

23. Name four factors that affect the flow of water within a watershed.

24. The differences in seasonal temperatures are not as great in the ocean as on land.
   a) Explain why.
   b) Name three factors that affect the temperature of ocean waters.

25. Is seawater more saline at the poles or in the tropics? Explain your answer.

26. What am I?
   a) I am a wind-driven ocean current.
   b) I am an ocean current caused by differences in water density.
   c) I form a huge "conveyor belt" that transports ocean waters around the world.

27. Name three factors that affect ocean circulation.

28. Which water is denser?
   a) water with three-percent salinity or water with four-percent salinity?
   b) water at 12°C or water at 18°C?

29. What is the cryosphere?

30. Below are two photos taken during a trip to the Arctic.

   a) Which photo features pack ice?
   b) What distinguishes the glacier from the pack ice?

31. What impact can melting pack ice have on the environment?

32. Name two consequences of melting ice in the Greenland and Antarctic ice sheets.

33. Name one advantage of hydroelectric power.

34. Look at the graph below. What does it demonstrate?

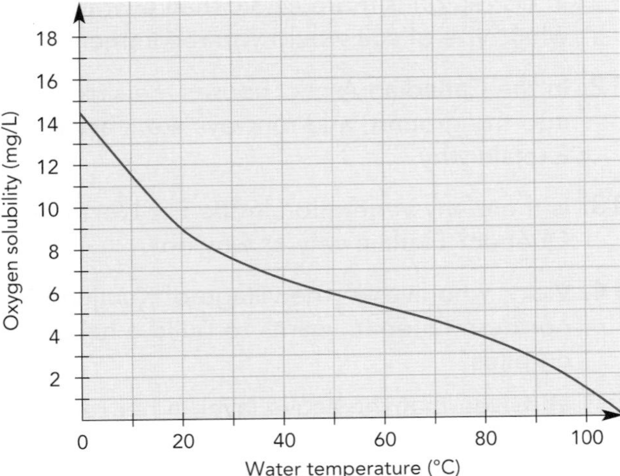

35. A gold mine on the banks of a river discharges water that was used to cool the ingots. The wastewater has a temperature of 22°C, while the river water is at 14°C. How will the wastewater discharge affect the river?

36. Place the stages of eutrophication in the correct order.
   A. drop in the oxygen concentration of the water
   B. growth of algae
   C. increase in the phosphorus concentration of the water
   D. decomposition of algae

review questions

A. A prospecting company has discovered a new gold deposit in Québec, in a belt of volcanic rock. The company must extract the volcanic rock from the ground to recover the gold fragments and shape them into ingots.

a) What is the rock containing the gold fragments called?

b) This rock is the result of volcanic activity. What type of rock is it?

c) To confirm that the prospectors have really found gold, geologists perform various tests. Name three of them.

d) The gold lies deep underground. What type of mine should be built?

B. To mine the deposit described in question A, the company must set up a camp.

a) The camp is not connected to a power grid, so the geologists install gas-powered generators. Which polluting gases will be emitted by the camp?

b) One of the geologists, who must spend the summer at this remote camp, decides to grow a vegetable garden. Given that the deposit is in the Canadian Shield—known for its low buffering capacity—which environmental problem could affect the geologist's gardening plans?

C. Cruise ships regularly offer tours along the shores of Greenland. Tourists can observe the spectacular blocks of ice that break off from the coast and fall into the sea.

a) What are these blocks of ice called?

b) A few fragments of ice melt in the seawater. This water does not stay near the coast; it moves about. What factors will affect its movement?

c) The meltwater will eventually arrive at the equator. Why?

d) In certain places, the Greenland glaciers are melting at twice their previous rate. Which climatic phenomenon explains this acceleration?

D. Prepare your own summary of Chapter 6 by building a concept map.

THAWING GROUND IN THE NORTH

Since the beginning of the 20th century, the Earth's climate has warmed by an average of 0.74°C, but in northern Québec, the temperature has risen 2.2°C—three to four times more than elsewhere. Large areas of permafrost are melting as a result, causing major, and even dramatic, changes to the lifestyle of Aboriginal communities. Landslides are damaging access roads and houses, forcing populations to move. Traditional ice roads are altered or disappear, making hunting and fishing grounds hard to reach. Drownings have increased, as have boating and snow-mobile accidents caused by breaking ice. The thaw damages runways, complicating the delivery of supplies, which depends heavily on air transport.

IN SEARCH OF SOLUTIONS

In the north of Québec lies a region called Nunavik, home to approximately 10 000 Inuit. They live in 16 scattered villages, the largest of which is Kuujjuaq, with a population of 1600. While the Inuit population of Nunavik is rapidly increasing, the people are facing many threats to their traditional lifestyle. Inuit representatives defend their "right to a cold land" to governments and even to the United Nations. The most effective solution would be to significantly reduce the world's greenhouse gas emissions, but present efforts in this direction are insufficient. In the short term, other solutions are needed to help Inuit adapt to climate change.

An effective solution depends on a proper understanding of the problem. Some Canadian and Québec research teams have taken a particular interest in climate conditions in the North. For the past 30 years or so, they have been digging holes in the villages there and measuring the temperature at different depths every day, using thermistor cables.

Other researchers are trying to combine scientific data with Inuit knowledge. For example, satellite observations of the ice confirm what hunters have been saying: Year after year, the ice forms later in Hudson Bay (Baie d'Hudson) and Ungava Bay (Baie d'Ungava).

Scientists are developing climate models to explain the roles of snow, wind and water flow. Engineers from the transport ministry can then use these results to design new technologies, better adapted to the changing climate. For example, to slow the permafrost thaw rate and prevent the ground from buckling and sinking, scientists decided to improve ventilation in runway embankments and access roads. Vents were installed to evacuate the heat under the runways, and surfaces that block the sun's rays are preferred.

Still other researchers are drawing maps of the terrain in the Inuit villages, indicating soil types, slope and the state of the permafrost. This enables scientists to locate ground at risk of deformation and ensure better town development planning.

The terrible Ouranos (Uranus) of Greek mythology, god of the sky and son of Gaia (the Earth), inspired the name of an important group of Québec and Canadian specialists in the field of climate change. The Ouranos Consortium provides decision makers with information on the evolution of the climate and advises them on suitable adaptation strategies, especially with respect to the permafrost in Nunavik.

NORTHERN CHALLENGES

Despite all efforts, many challenges remain. Research is still at the stage of observing and testing phenomena to understand them. Preventive measures are very expensive and not always effective. In the Yukon, for example, traditional dwellings were moved away from the coast to prevent them from collapsing, but their new site is also at risk; other solutions must be found. Population growth is rapid, and it is increasingly difficult for young people to find stable land where they can build homes.

A runway in northern Québec

1. The Inuit diet consists mainly of food that the people have hunted or fished and food that has been brought in from southern regions. How does climate change interfere with their diet?
2. Although Inuit are responsible for a tiny fraction of global greenhouse gas emissions, they are more profoundly affected by climate change than any other population. How can people living farther south demonstrate solidarity with their northern neighbours?

1997 — Signing of the Kyoto Protocol, for the reduction of greenhouse gas emissions

1987 — Signing of the Montréal Protocol, for the reduction of CFC emissions

1913 — Demonstration of the existence of the ozone layer

1863 — Proposal of the concept of the greenhouse effect

1839 — Discovery of the photovoltaic effect

1835 — Demonstration of the Coriolis effect

1783 — Earliest analysis of the composition of air

1687 — Explanation of the tides by Newton's theory of gravitation

1686 — Demonstration that winds are caused by differences in atmospheric pressure

1450 — Invention of the anemometer, to measure wind speed

CIRCA -79 — Attribution of tidal movements to the influence of the Moon

CIRCA -250 — First estimate of the distances between the Earth and the Moon, and the Earth and the Sun

CIRCA -334 — Publication of Aristotle's treatise *Meteorology*

At first glance, the Earth seems well-endowed with all the resources we need for our survival and comfort. Without the atmosphere and the Sun, however, life on Earth would be impossible. The Sun provides our planet with an enormous amount of energy, vital to both animal and plant species. The atmosphere retains some of this energy, and the winds send it in every direction. How does this energy travel around the Earth? What forms does it take in the atmosphere? How can humans harness it for their needs without harming the environment? These are a few of the questions that we will answer in this chapter.

THE EARTH AND SPACE

7

The atmosphere and space

CONTENTS

ST
EST
AST
SE

1 The atmosphere

The atmosphere is the layer of air that envelopes the Earth. It is made up of gases that are essential to life on our planet for the following reasons:

- They act as a screen, blocking out dangerous rays from the sun, such as ultraviolet rays.
- They ensure a relatively stable climate on Earth by retaining heat.
- They include oxygen (O_2), which is essential for **CELLULAR RESPIRATION**, and carbon dioxide (CO_2), necessary for **PHOTOSYNTHESIS** in plants.

CONCEPT REVIEW
- Atmosphere
- Atom
- Molecule
- Physical changes
- Chemical changes

The ATMOSPHERE is the layer of air surrounding the Earth.

The Earth's gravitational force pulls the particles in the atmosphere toward the planet. For this reason, air particles are closer to one another near the Earth's surface than they are at high altitude. In fact, 99 percent of the mass of the atmosphere is concentrated within the first 30 km above the surface.

From space, the atmosphere looks like a fine halo of blue light embracing the Earth. The atmosphere is not a thin layer, however; it is considered to extend more than 10 000 km above the Earth's surface.

7.1 Satellites are sent into orbit around the Earth in the upper atmosphere, usually at an altitude of more than 500 km.

ST
EST
AST
SE

1.1 THE COMPOSITION OF THE ATMOSPHERE

The atmosphere is made up of 21 percent oxygen (O_2) and 78 percent nitrogen (N_2). Other gases are also present but in very small quantities. This gaseous mixture is what we call *air*. Figure 7.2 (page 223) shows the proportions of the gases in the air. These proportions change only at very high altitude (approximately 100 km above the Earth's surface).

CONCEPT REVIEW
- Air (composition)
- Atmospheric layers

AIR is the mixture of gases, especially nitrogen and oxygen, that makes up the atmosphere.

Water vapour (H_2O) is also an important component of air, particularly in meteorology because it is responsible for cloud formation and precipitation. Its measure is referred to as *relative humidity*. Depending on the region and the day, water vapour can represent up to four percent of the air volume.

Meteorology comes from the Greek words *meteōros*, meaning "high in the air," and *logia*, meaning "theory."

7.2 The composition of the atmosphere at low altitude

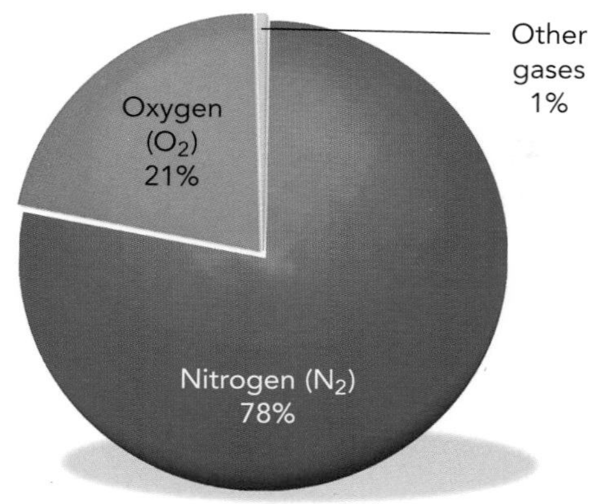

OTHER COMPONENTS OF AIR

Gas	Symbol	Volume (%)
Water vapour	H_2O	0 to 4
Argon	Ar	0.93
Carbon dioxide	CO_2	0.038 (variable)
Neon	Ne	0.001 8
Helium	He	0.000 52
Methane	CH_4	0.000 17 (variable)
Krypton	Kr	0.000 11
Hydrogen	H_2	0.000 05
Nitrous oxide	N_2O	0.000 027 (variable)
Xenon	Xe	0.000 008 7
Ozone	O_3	0.000 001 (variable)
CFCs (chlorofluorocarbons)	$C_nF_nCl_n$	0.000 000 1 (variable)

The air also contains suspended solid and liquid particulate matter. It comes from the Earth's surface (dust, pollen, soot, smoke, droplets, etc.) and mixes with the gases in the air.

ENVIRONMENT EXTRA

Cosmic pollution

The area of space around the Earth is polluted. Ever since the beginning of space exploration, in the 1950s, waste has gradually accumulated in the exosphere (the layer of the atmosphere farthest from the Earth). Debris from rockets used to launch spaceships on their travels, obsolete satellites and old batteries are among the waste, as well as tools lost by astronauts, such as screwdrivers and bolts.

According to estimates by NASA specialists, "space waste" includes approximately 9000 large objects (like old rocket parts), 110 000 pieces of smaller debris (1–10 cm) and 35 million fragments (about 1 mm), such as flakes of paint.

In the exosphere, a single bolt can travel at a speed of 8 km/s—10 times faster than a bullet! The impact from a projectile like this would be enough to shatter the porthole of a space shuttle or seriously damage a satellite, and even make it explode. It is not surprising, then, that NASA specialists closely monitor the trajectory of space debris.

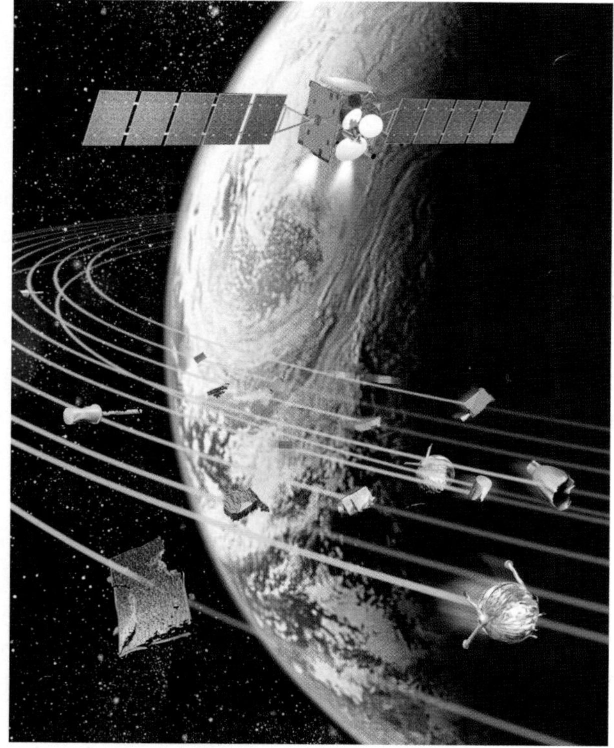
The exosphere contains a lot of debris from space exploration (simulated image).

The Earth's atmosphere is divided into five main layers, illustrated in Figure 7.4 (page 225). This chart also describes two important characteristics of air—pressure and temperature—which vary with altitude. It is important to remember that the higher the altitude, the fewer the air particles in the atmosphere.

The following section deals with atmospheric pressure, one of the essential aspects of the study of the atmosphere.

ST
EST
AST
SE

ATMOSPHERIC PRESSURE

CONCEPT REVIEW
- Pressure
- Compressible fluid
- Relationship between pressure and volume
- Density
- Winds

Air is a gaseous mixture, and therefore a **COMPRESSIBLE FLUID**, so it exerts pressure because it contains particles that are constantly colliding with one another. These collisions determine the air pressure, or *atmospheric pressure*.

ATMOSPHERIC PRESSURE is the pressure of the air in the atmosphere.

The more collisions that occur in a given area, the higher its atmospheric pressure (Figure 7.3). At sea level, the average atmospheric pressure is 101.3 kilopascals (kPa). One kilopascal equals the pressure of a 100-kg mass on an area of one square metre.

Two main factors affect atmospheric pressure:

- When the number of particles increases, they collide more frequently, and the pressure rises. When the number of particles drops, however, the pressure falls. That is why pressure falls with increasing altitude (Figure 7.4, page 225).
- When the air warms, its particles move more rapidly and therefore collide more frequently. In a bell jar, where volume is constant, the pressure thus increases with temperature. In the atmosphere, however, air pressure approaches a state of equilibrium; when the temperature rises, the particles move away from one another, restoring the pressure to a value closer to normal. As a result, the air **DENSITY** drops. Warm air is thus lighter than cold air and tends to rise.

Atmospheric pressure varies with time and place. These variations explain many atmospheric phenomena since air particles move away from high-pressure areas (where particles are numerous) to low-pressure areas (where particles are fewer). This movement gives rise to winds.

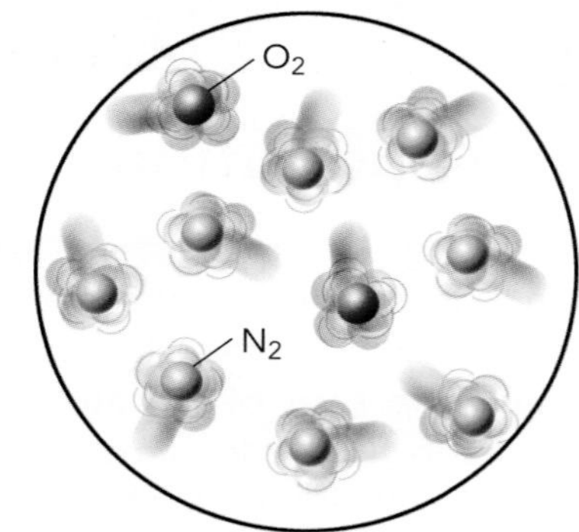

High pressure

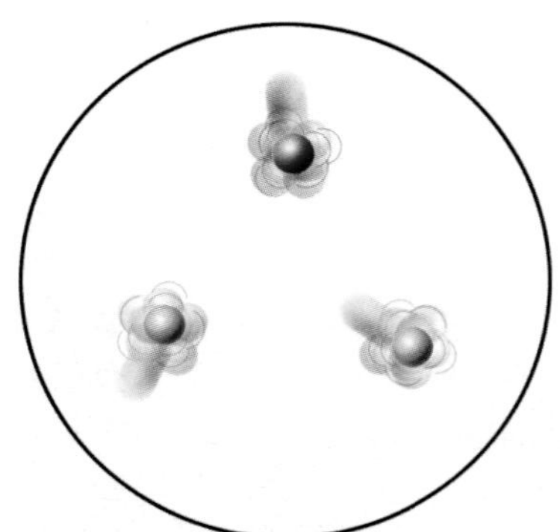

Low pressure

7.3 The greater the number of air particles, the higher the pressure because the particles collide more frequently.

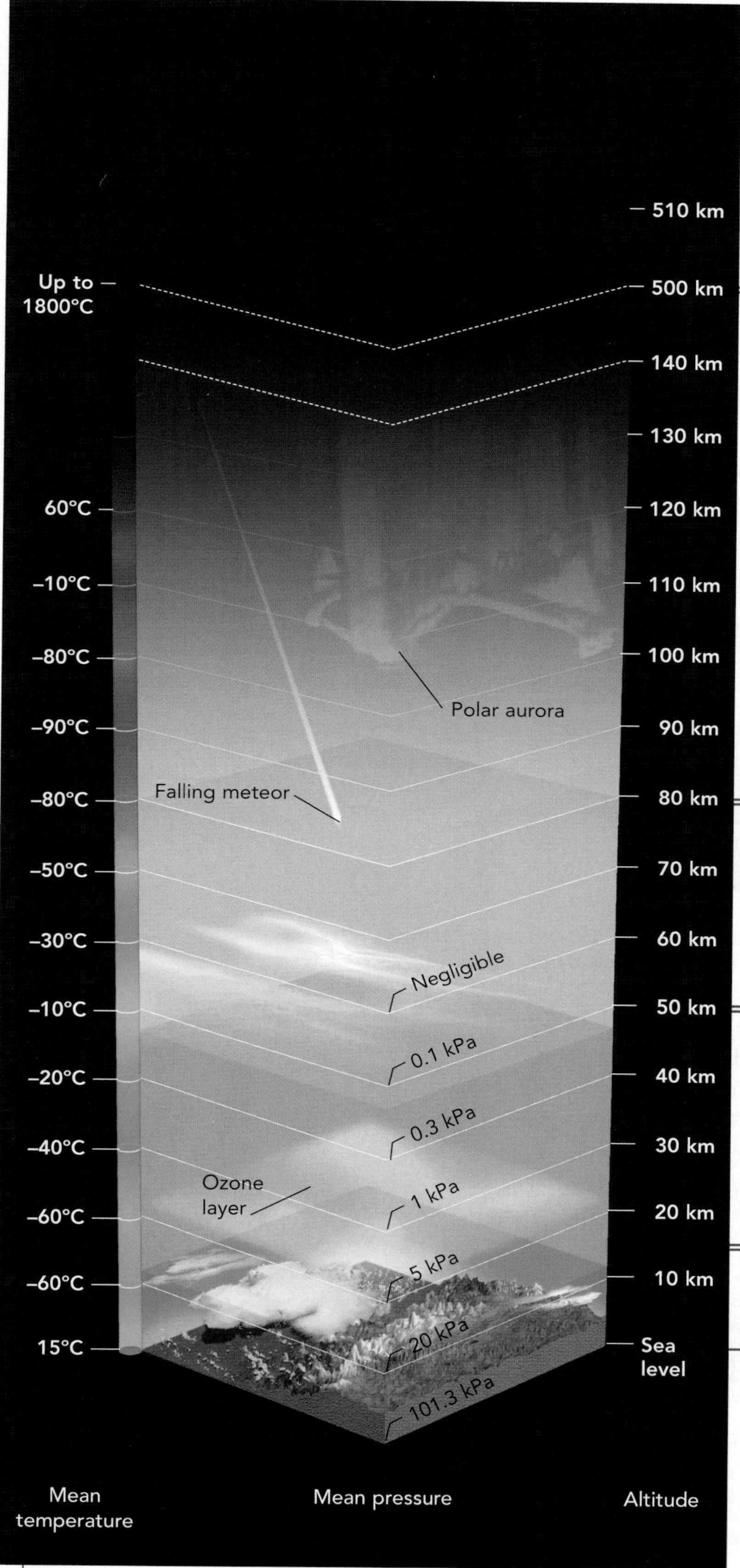

7.4 The five layers of the Earth's atmosphere

EXOSPHERE (500 km and more)

- This layer of the atmosphere is practically empty. The few air particles present can travel thousands of kilometres without colliding.
- The air is so rare that it is impossible to gauge its temperature (with a thermometer).
- Most Earth observation and telecommunications satellites sent into space travel in this layer.

THERMOSPHERE (80–500 km)

- This layer absorbs most of the sun's rays. It is the hottest layer of the atmosphere, with temperatures as high as 1800°C at upper altitudes.
- Celestial bodies that come into contact with the thermosphere (meteors) burn up rapidly, leaving visible trails better known as *shooting stars*.
- Polar auroras usually form in this layer.

MESOSPHERE (50–80 km)

- This is the coldest layer of the atmosphere. As altitude increases, temperature decreases, plummeting below –80°C in the upper reaches of the mesosphere.
- The mesosphere contains very few air particles. A human being would suffocate there in only a few minutes.

STRATOSPHERE (15–50 km)

- The stratosphere is where the sun's ultraviolet rays are absorbed. This occurs in the ozone layer due to the presence of ozone gas.
- Temperatures increase with altitude in the stratosphere because of the ozone layer.
- Air particles become increasingly rare at higher altitudes.

TROPOSPHERE (0–15 km)

- Most meteorological phenomena, such as cloud formation and storms, occur in the troposphere.
- The higher the altitude in the troposphere, the lower the temperature. With every 1000 m of altitude, the temperature drops approximately 6.5°C.

ST EST AST SE

1.2 ATMOSPHERIC CIRCULATION

LAB 57

The air surrounding the Earth is in constant motion. It rises in the atmosphere above the warm, humid regions at the equator (low-pressure zones), heads toward the poles and then descends over cold, dry regions (high-pressure zones). At the same time, the cold polar air makes its way to the equator. This phenomenon of **CONVECTION** helps distribute the solar energy the Earth receives. Without atmospheric circulation, the differences in temperature between the equator and the poles would be much greater.

ATMOSPHERIC CIRCULATION is the global-scale movement of the layer of air surrounding the Earth.

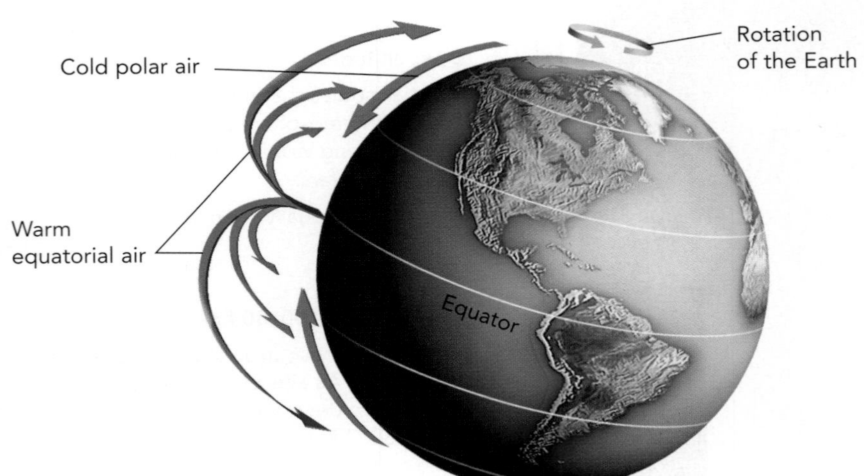

7.5 Air that has been warmed at the equator becomes lighter and less dense; it moves toward the poles. It is replaced by the heavier cold air coming from the poles.

THE DOLDRUMS

The doldrums is a name for an equatorial region of light or no winds. In the past, sailing ships were sometimes becalmed there for weeks on end. To conserve their freshwater supplies, sailors would throw their horses overboard. 9

Theoretically, air masses should move in a straight line from north to south or from south to north. However, the rotation of the Earth changes their trajectories through what is called the **CORIOLIS EFFECT**. Discovered by the French engineer and mathematician Gaspard-Gustave Coriolis in 1835, this effect operates when a body moves in an environment that is itself in rotation, directing the body in a course perpendicular to its original movement. The Coriolis effect causes winds to deviate to the right in the Northern Hemisphere and to the left in the Southern Hemisphere, thus affecting the trajectories of air masses.

Hemisphere comes from the Greek words *hēmi*, meaning "half," and *sphaira*, meaning a "spherical object."

These movements of air occur in the troposphere and play an important role in meteorological phenomena. For example, they are responsible for the formation of cold fronts, warm fronts and the subsequent clouds, which occurs when air masses of different properties come into contact.

7.6 Due to the rotation of the Earth, the Coriolis effect causes a deviation in wind direction.

EST SE

PREVAILING WINDS

The atmospheric circulation between the equator and the poles is more complex than the previous section suggests. In fact, winds form great loops called *circulation* cells. The movement of air within these cells is very regular.

Cell comes from the Latin *cellula*, meaning "small room."

As Figure 7.7 shows, each hemisphere contains three circulation cells: the Hadley cell, from the equator to the 30th parallel; the Ferrel cell, from the 30th to the 60th parallel; and the Polar cell, which circulates over the pole.

- In the Hadley cell, warm air over the equator rises into the atmosphere. It then gradually cools as it travels north or south toward the 30th parallel. There it runs into winds from the Ferrel cell, which force it to descend and return to the equator.
- In the Ferrel cell, part of the falling air over the 30th parallel surges toward the pole. Near the 60th parallel, this air collides with winds from the Polar cell, which make it rise and return toward the 30th parallel.
- The temperature of the air in the Polar cell drops to its lowest over the pole. The air sinks to the Earth and then turns toward the 60th parallel, where it collides with the Ferrel cell. The air is forced to rise and return to the pole.

7.7 Circulation cells and prevailing winds

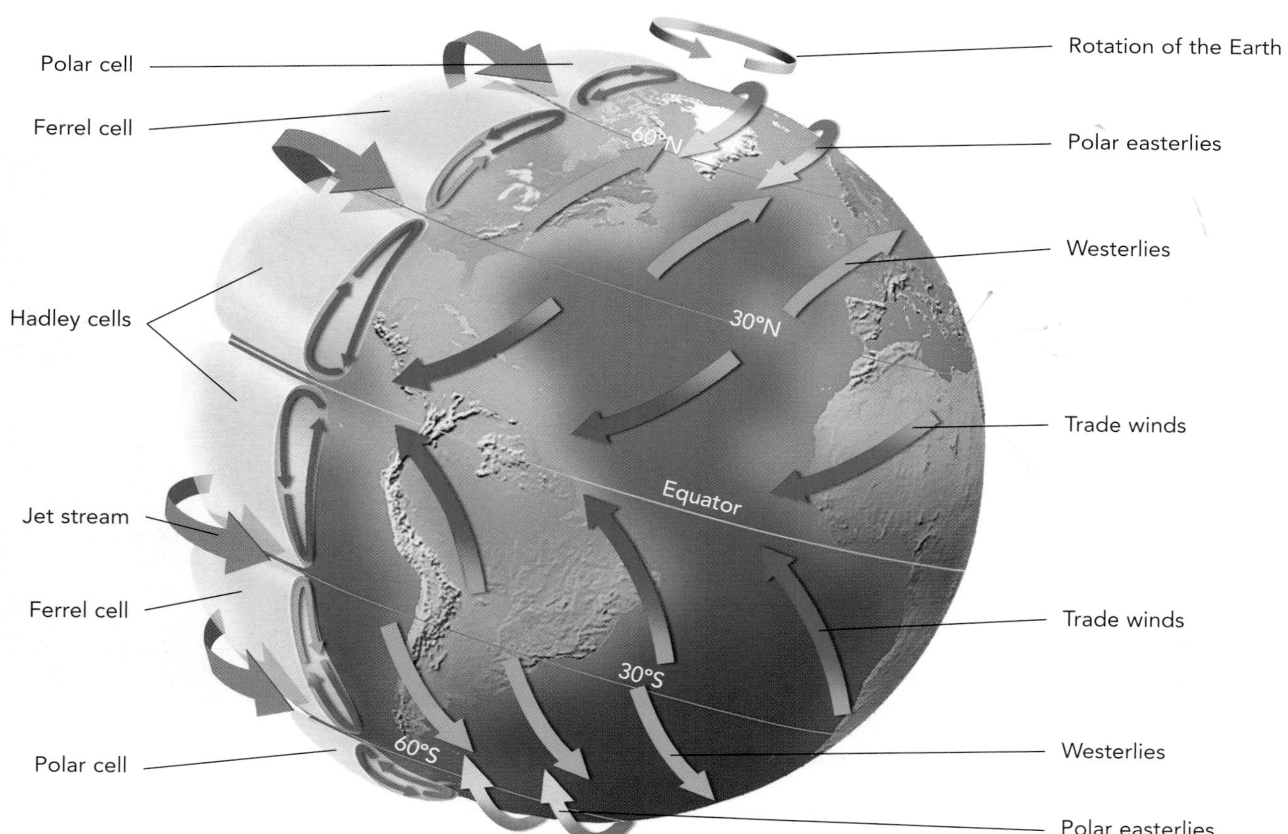

Near the surface, the atmospheric circulation cells create prevailing winds, which are winds that blow in characteristic directions on a global scale. Their course is determined by the Coriolis effect.

> *Prevailing* comes from the Latin *praevalēre*, which means "to be stronger."

PREVAILING WINDS are major atmospheric currents that blow in a given direction according to global patterns of movement.

Prevailing winds are illustrated in Figure 7.7 (page 227). They consist of:

- polar easterlies, moving between the pole and the 60th parallel
- westerlies, which blow in the middle latitudes, between the 60th and 30th parallels
- trade winds, which are easterly winds moving between the 30th parallel and the equator

Prevailing winds play an important role in meteorological phenomena. For example, in Québec, prevailing winds are westerlies, which explains why most weather systems move from west to east across the province.

On the regional level, however, winds do not always blow in the same direction as the prevailing winds. They are influenced by local high-pressure and low-pressure systems.

7.8 This tree has grown in the direction of a prevailing wind.

At very high altitude, powerful winds called *jet streams* blow from west to east around the Earth, between the circulation cells (Figure 7.7, page 227). They are particularly strong in winter.

Each hemisphere has two jet streams: a subtropical jet stream and a polar jet stream. The subtropical jet stream blows around the 30th parallel at an altitude of between 11 000 and 14 000 m and can reach speeds of 400 km/h in winter. The polar jet stream travels at a height of 9000 to 10 000 m near the 60th parallel and can blow as fast as 300 km/h in winter.

Airplane pilots know these currents well since they have to avoid the jet streams when they are travelling from east to west, against the wind. When they fly eastward, however, they use the jet streams to their advantage, allowing their aircraft to be carried by the wind and thus saving fuel.

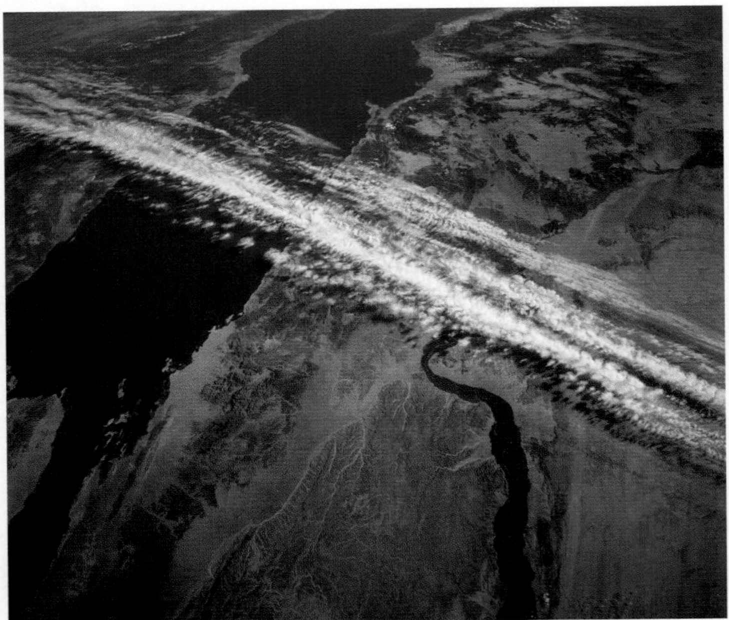

7.9 This satellite image shows a cloud-bearing subtropical jet stream travelling at a speed of 160 km/h above Egypt and the Red Sea.

ST
EST
AST

AIR MASSES

LAB 58

Air masses are large expanses of the atmosphere which have stayed in a region long enough to acquire a specific temperature and humidity. Driven by the winds, air masses bring a change of weather to an area. Meteorologists therefore watch them closely.

An AIR MASS is a large expanse of the atmosphere with relatively uniform temperature and humidity.

The climate in Québec is subject to the effect of warm air masses from tropical regions and cold air masses from polar regions (Figure 7.10).

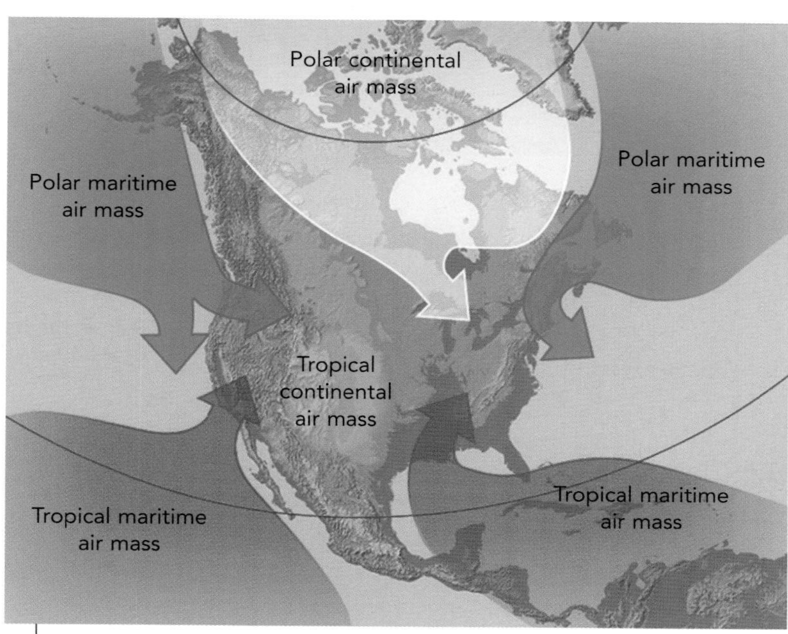

7.10 Air masses over North America affect the climate in Québec.

When two air masses meet, they do not combine. The denser cold air slides beneath the lighter warm air. The line where the two masses meet is called a *front*. It is a transition zone where wind direction, temperature and relative humidity change rapidly. There are warm fronts and cold fronts, and both types can reach lengths of several thousand kilometres.

A cold front occurs when a mass of cold air meets a mass of warm air (Figure 7.11). The warm air rises rapidly, in a sharp ascent, and then cools. The resulting condensation forms puffy clouds, called *cumulus*, which often produce wind and heavy rain.

Cumulus comes from Latin and means "heap."

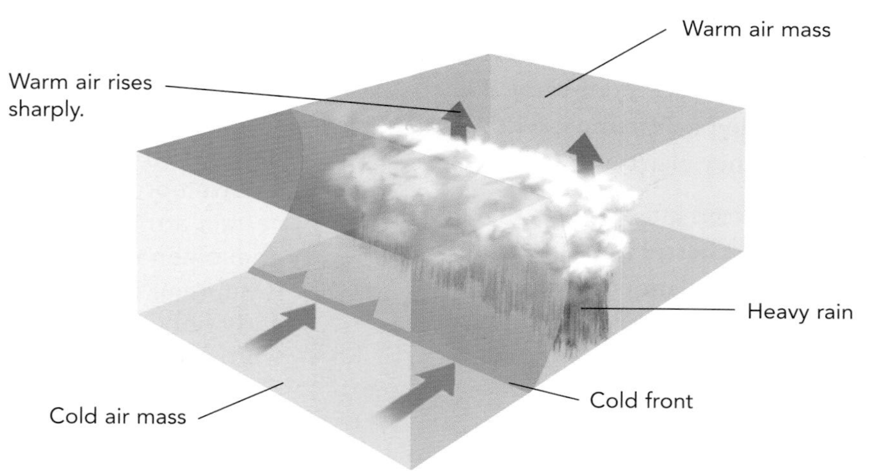

7.11 On weather maps, cold fronts are symbolized by a line, usually blue, with a row of triangles.

A warm front forms when a mass of warm air moves toward a mass of cold air (Figure 7.12), rising gently above the cold air and creating light clouds of many stratified layers, called *nimbostratus*. Warm fronts often bring cloudy weather and showers that are slow to disperse because warm fronts do not travel as fast as cold fronts.

Nimbostratus comes from the Latin words *nimbus*, meaning "cloud," and *stratus*, meaning "spread out."

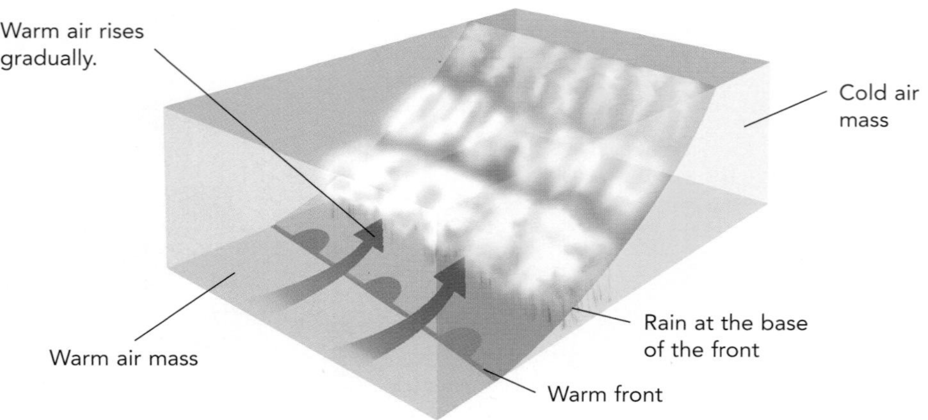

7.12 On weather maps, warm fronts are symbolized by a line, usually red, with a row of semicircles.

ST EST AST

ANTICYCLONES AND DEPRESSIONS

Most air masses move horizontally, parallel to the Earth's surface. However, vertical movement also occurs.

When air cools, its particles do not collide as frequently, and the pressure tends to fall. To compensate, the particles move closer together, and the air density increases. The air mass thus becomes heavier and sinks toward the ground, compressing the particles beneath it and creating an area of high pressure. This area is called an *anticyclone*, symbolized by an *H* (for "high pressure") on weather charts.

Conversely, when air warms, its density decreases. The air mass becomes lighter and rises, leaving an empty space beneath it. The space becomes an area of low pressure called a *depression*, symbolized by an *L* (for "low pressure") on weather charts.

Near anticyclones and depressions, the Coriolis effect causes the air to start turning as it rises or falls. In the Northern Hemisphere, the wind spirals in a clockwise direction around an anticyclone, and in a counterclockwise direction around a depression. In the Southern Hemisphere, the directions are reversed.

–384
–322

Aristotle

This famous Greek philosopher wrote many treatises, covering every aspect of knowledge in his day. In *Meteorology*, he attempted to explain certain atmospheric phenomena, such as wind, rain, dew and rainbows. The word *meteorology* comes from the title of this work.

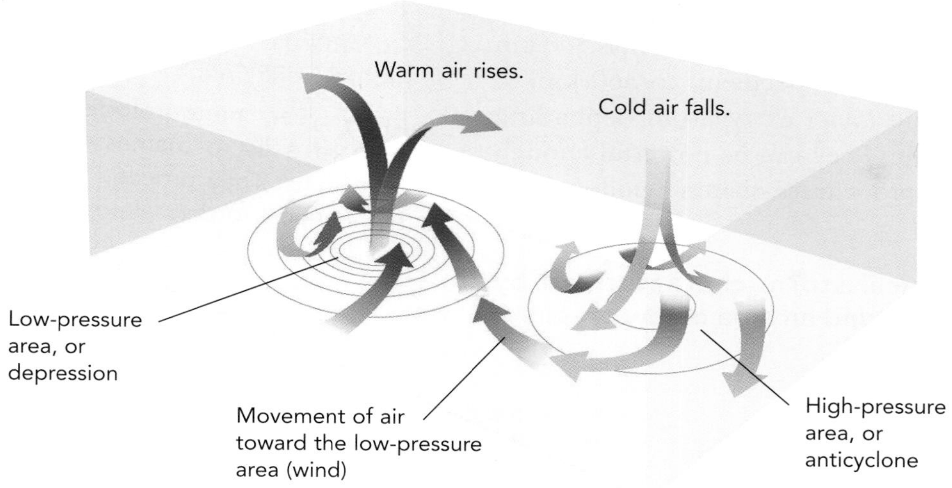

7.13 A depression and an anticyclone in the Northern Hemisphere

- **An ANTICYCLONE is an area of atmospheric circulation surrounding a high-pressure centre. The air turns clockwise in the Northern Hemisphere and counterclockwise in the Southern Hemisphere.**

- **A DEPRESSION is an area of atmospheric circulation surrounding a low-pressure centre. The air turns counterclockwise in the Northern Hemisphere and clockwise in the Southern Hemisphere.**

Anticyclones and depressions are closely related to the weather. In an anticyclone, falling air particles prevent cloud-forming movements. The sky is clear, and the weather, stable: dry and sunny in summer and cold in winter.

When a depression forms, however, rising air encourages cloud formation, which results in precipitation.

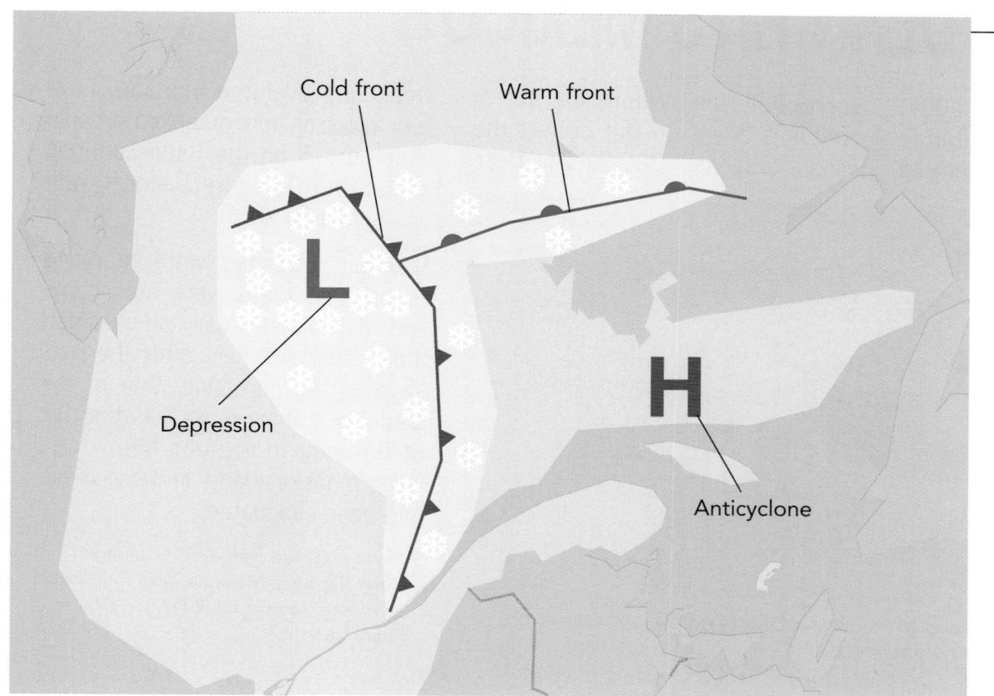

7.14 This map shows the symbols used in meteorology to represent fronts, anticyclones and depressions. The information on such weather maps is used to forecast precipitation and temperature.

Strong depressions sometimes develop over the warm waters of tropical oceans. A huge spiral then forms, stretching as far as 800 km in diameter. Inside, the wind blows at speeds up to 360 km/h. These storms, called *cyclones*, *hurricanes* or *typhoons* depending on the region, bring torrential rain. They can be powerful enough to cause floods and landslides, uproot trees, shatter windows and rip the roofs off buildings.

A CYCLONE is a tropical storm characterized by violent winds revolving around an area of low pressure.

THE ABCs OF NAMING HURRICANES

Every year, meteorologists prepare a list of names for hurricanes. They proceed by alphabetical order, alternating between girls' and boys' first names.

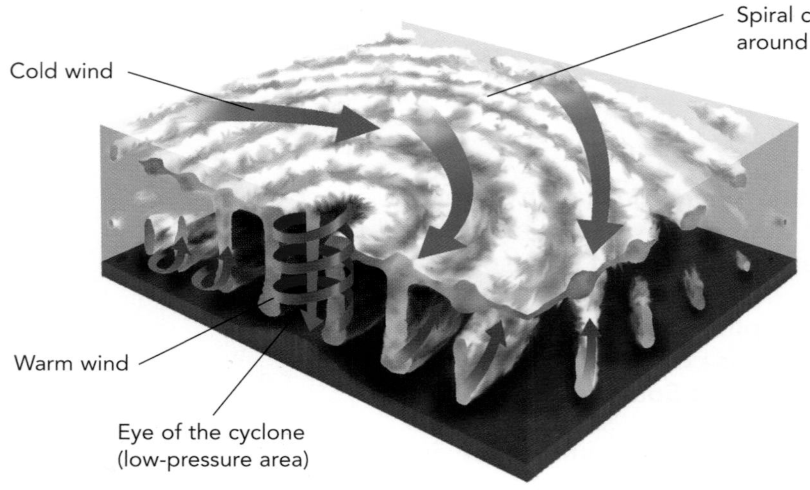

7.15 Cross section of a cyclone

HURRICANE DEAN HITS MEXICO

On the morning of August 21, 2007, Hurricane Dean hit the Yucatán Peninsula in eastern Mexico, bringing torrential rain. When the storm touched down on the coast, the winds exceeded 300 km/h. Dean weakened over the morning, however, dropping from maximum strength (Category 5 on the Saffir-Simpson scale) to a Category 1 storm, with winds of 140 km/h.

This satellite image shows the eye of Hurricane Dean and the surrounding spiral of clouds caused by the violent winds.

Mexican authorities were happy to report that there were no victims and that tourist areas had resumed their usual activities after the passage of the hurricane. One of the authorities' main fears was the risk of flooding in regions below sea level; most residents in these areas had been evacuated.

Source: Adapted from AFP, "L'ouragan Dean frappe le Mexique, puis s'affaiblit," *La Presse*, August 22, 2007, p. A18. *[Translation]*

ST EST SE

1.3 THE GREENHOUSE EFFECT

LAB 59

GREENHOUSE GASES—mainly water vapour (H_2O), carbon dioxide (CO_2), methane (CH_4) and nitrous oxide (N_2O)—have always existed around our planet. Suspended in the atmosphere, they act somewhat like a greenhouse roof by keeping in some of the energy the Earth receives from the Sun. This phenomenon is called the *greenhouse effect*. We are fortunate that it exists because without it, the mean temperature on Earth would be −18°C!

The GREENHOUSE EFFECT is a natural process that allows the Earth to retain some of the heat it receives from the Sun.

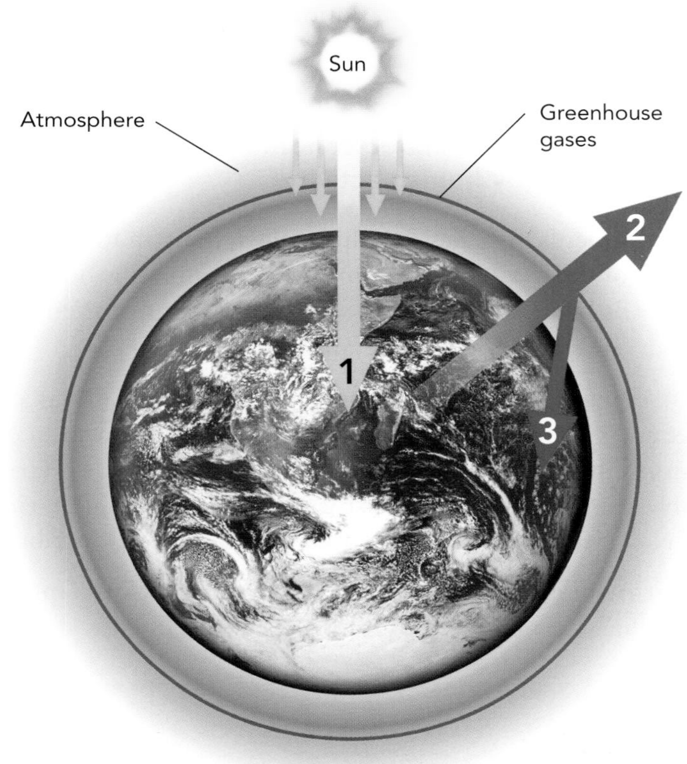

7.16 The greenhouse effect

Figure 7.16 explains how the greenhouse effect works:

1. Most of the sun's rays that reach the Earth's surface are absorbed by the ground.
2. Once heated, the ground emits **INFRARED** rays into the atmosphere. Some infrared rays pass through the atmosphere and are lost in space.
3. Greenhouse gases trap some of the infrared rays and send them back to Earth, further heating its surface.

ST EST SE

THE INTENSIFICATION OF THE GREENHOUSE EFFECT

For thousands of years, the concentration of greenhouse gases in the atmosphere remained relatively constant. Emissions of CO_2, for example, came mainly from forest fires, volcanic eruptions and cellular respiration. These emissions were offset by the absorption of CO_2 by growing plants, through photosynthesis, and by the oceans' ability to capture large amounts of this gas. This balance kept temperatures on Earth relatively stable.

Over the last century, however, the balance has been disrupted. CO_2 is the main product of the **COMBUSTION** of oil, natural gas and coal, so our increased consumption of these fossil fuels (in cars and factories, for example) has caused enormous amounts of the gas to be released into the atmosphere. CO_2 is not dangerous in itself: we expel some every time we breathe out! When human activities discharge it by the billions of tonnes, however, it has a profound effect on the climate.

Clearing land for farming also contributes to increased levels of CO_2 in the atmosphere. When forests are burned or when felled trees and plants decompose, the carbon stored in them returns to the atmosphere in the form of CO_2.

Surplus CO_2 accumulates in the atmosphere, trapping an increasingly large proportion of the infrared rays emitted by the Earth. This phenomenon is the cause of global warming and of changes in patterns of precipitation, wind and other aspects of climate.

CLIMATE CHANGE is the abnormal modification of climatic conditions on Earth, caused by human activity.

7.17 The increased use of cars causes more CO_2 to be released into the atmosphere, contributing to a stronger greenhouse effect.

Other greenhouse gas surpluses also contribute to climate change. The impact of these other gases on the environment is not as great as that of CO_2 emissions because we release smaller amounts of them into the atmosphere. This is the case for methane and nitrous oxide.

- In equal concentrations, however, methane (CH_4) causes a greenhouse effect 21 times greater than that of CO_2. Main sources of methane emissions from human activity include digestion in farm animals (such as sheep and cattle), manure storage and management, rice farming in paddy fields, decomposing household waste and the distribution of natural gas.
- Nitrous oxide (N_2O) comes primarily from applying nitrogen-rich fertilizer to farm crops and from certain chemical processes.

7.18 Decomposing household waste is one of the sources of methane in the atmosphere.

WARMING RIVER WATERS

The waters of the St. Lawrence River (Fleuve Saint-Laurent) are warming up, and present increases in temperature are only the beginning. Researchers believe that before the end of the century, the province of Québec could see temperature increases of between 2°C and 5°C, depending on the season and the region.

From one year to the next, the river waters are navigable for increasingly longer periods. Ice forms later and melts earlier because of the warming water. One day, it might be possible to travel on the river all year round without using icebreakers.

Many species of fish could disappear, however, if the water temperature rises further. Warm-water species, such as sunfish and bass, would prosper, while cold-water species, like walleye and sturgeon, would suffer.

The St. Lawrence River (Fleuve Saint-Laurent) could become navigable all year round because the water temperature is rising so dramatically.

Source: Adapted from "Le fleuve a chaud," *Le Journal de Québec*, October 9, 2007. *[Translation]*

According to a report submitted in 2007 by the Intergovernmental Panel on Climate Change (IPCC), the mean temperature on Earth rose by 0.76°C between 1850 and 2005. Scientists estimate that an increase of two degrees Celsius is a critical point beyond which serious climate disruption would be inevitable. Changes would include an increase in the occurrence of droughts, heat waves and floods and a rise in sea levels.

EST SE 1.4 THE CONTAMINATION OF THE ATMOSPHERE

The composition of the atmosphere has been upset by human presence on Earth. The increase in greenhouse gas emissions described in the previous section is an example of the imbalance we have created.

Besides greenhouse gases, other substances are considered atmospheric **CONTAMINANTS**. The following are a few examples:

- sulphur dioxide (SO_2) and nitrogen oxides (NO_x), which are factors in the formation of **ACID RAIN** (see page 200). They are also sources of smog, to be discussed in a later section (page 237).

- metals such as mercury (Hg), arsenic (As) and lead (Pb), which come mainly from oil and coal combustion, waste incineration and glass-making. Even if they are present in small amounts, these metals are toxic to human health because they accumulate in living organisms.
- chlorofluorocarbons (CFCs), which are chemical compounds that destroy ozone molecules (See the next section on the ozone layer.)
- dust and airborne particles, discharged from factory chimneys and automobile exhaust pipes

These different forms of atmospheric pollution have a contaminating effect because they occur in too great a quantity and because they react with other components of the atmosphere. Once in the air, the wind can carry them over thousands of kilometres. The **CONTAMINATION** of the atmosphere can therefore occur far from the point of emission. A substance discharged in a populated area may thus end up contaminating the air of a relatively uninhabited region such as the Arctic.

7.19 Some factories discharge toxic substances into the atmosphere.

Two specific phenomena of atmospheric contamination will be examined in greater detail in the next sections: the thinning of the ozone layer and smog formation.

EST SE

THE THINNING OF THE OZONE LAYER

Ozone (O_3) is a molecule composed of three oxygen atoms, which exists as a gas in the atmosphere. It is more highly concentrated in the stratosphere, at an altitude of 20 to 30 km. Ozone forms a protective covering called the *ozone layer*. This layer absorbs some of the harmful ultraviolet rays from the sun, which are responsible for skin cancer in particular. Unlike sunglasses, which act as a physical screen by blocking rays, the ozone layer is a chemical filter that absorbs ultraviolet rays.

The OZONE LAYER is a part of the atmosphere with a high concentration of ozone molecules, which absorb some of the ultraviolet rays from the sun.

In the late 1970s, satellite images showed that the ozone layer above the South Pole was considerably thinner than before. Scientific studies revealed that chlorofluorocarbons (CFCs),

DWINDLING AWAY

In southern Canada, the ozone layer has thinned by an average of six percent since the late 1970s. The situation is more serious in the spring, when the thinning reaches an average of 8 to 10 percent and can even climb to 20 percent for short periods. 

chemical compounds used in refrigeration systems and aerosol cans, were responsible for destroying ozone molecules in the stratosphere. When an ultraviolet ray is absorbed by a CFC molecule, the CFC releases a chlorine (Cl) atom. The chlorine atom bonds with an ozone molecule and destroys it.

In 1987, environmentalists and diplomats met in Montréal to discuss the threat to the ozone layer. As a result, 190 countries signed the Montréal Protocol to gradually phase out the use of CFCs until 2010, by which time all CFC production will have ceased. According to predictions, the ozone layer should recover its thickness of 1980 sometime between 2055 and 2065.

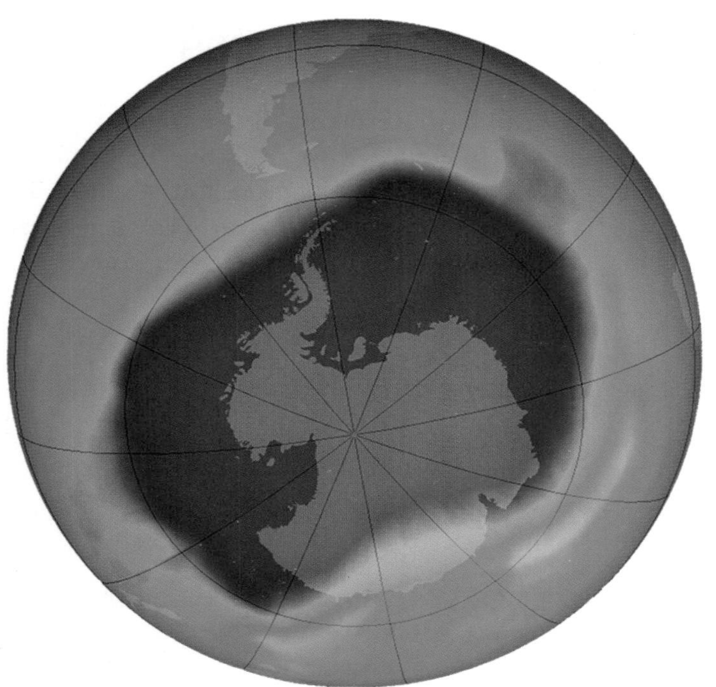

7.20 This photo was taken on September 24, 2006. The area over the South Pole where the ozone layer is the thinnest is shown in purple. The continent in mauve is Antarctica.

SMOG

While the ozone molecules in the stratosphere play a beneficial role by protecting us from ultraviolet rays, the ozone found at low altitude, in the troposphere, enters our lungs and is harmful to our health.

Tropospheric ozone molecules (O_3) are formed when the sun's rays hit nitrogen oxide molecules (NO_x), which come mainly from car exhaust or factories.

Tropospheric ozone can cause serious respiratory problems. It combines with other atmospheric pollutants, such as nitrogen dioxide (NO_2) or sulphur dioxide (SO_2), to form smog. Smog is a thick fog of pollution that hangs over urban areas when a high-pressure system prevents it from rising into the atmosphere.

Smog is a blend of the words *smoke* and *fog*.

7.21 Smog over Montréal

SMOG is a thick mixture of fog, smoke and atmospheric pollutants.

The intensity of smog depends on weather conditions, and its composition varies with the time of the year.

ST EST AST 1.5 ENERGY RESOURCES

For centuries, humans have taken advantage of wind energy. Windmills, whose turning sails would drive a millstone to grind grain, were used to convert the wind's energy into **MECHANICAL ENERGY**. Today, engineers are going even farther: they are using huge turbines to convert wind energy into electricity and thus supply entire regions with power.

CONCEPT REVIEW

- Natural energy sources
- Renewable and nonrenewable energy sources
- Forms of energy (chemical, thermal, mechanical, radiation)
- Energy transformations

ST EST AST WIND ENERGY

Wind energy is a renewable resource, which means that it regenerates naturally, and in sufficient quantities, even as it is used.

WIND ENERGY is the energy that can be drawn from the wind.

Today's wind turbines are huge machines reaching up to 120 m in height and equipped with gigantic blades. When the wind hits these blades, they turn, activating an electric generator hidden in the nacelle (Figure 7.23). The power is then distributed to consumers. A one-megawatt (1-MW) wind turbine can produce enough electricity to supply 150 to 300 households.

7.22 A wind farm in Gaspésie

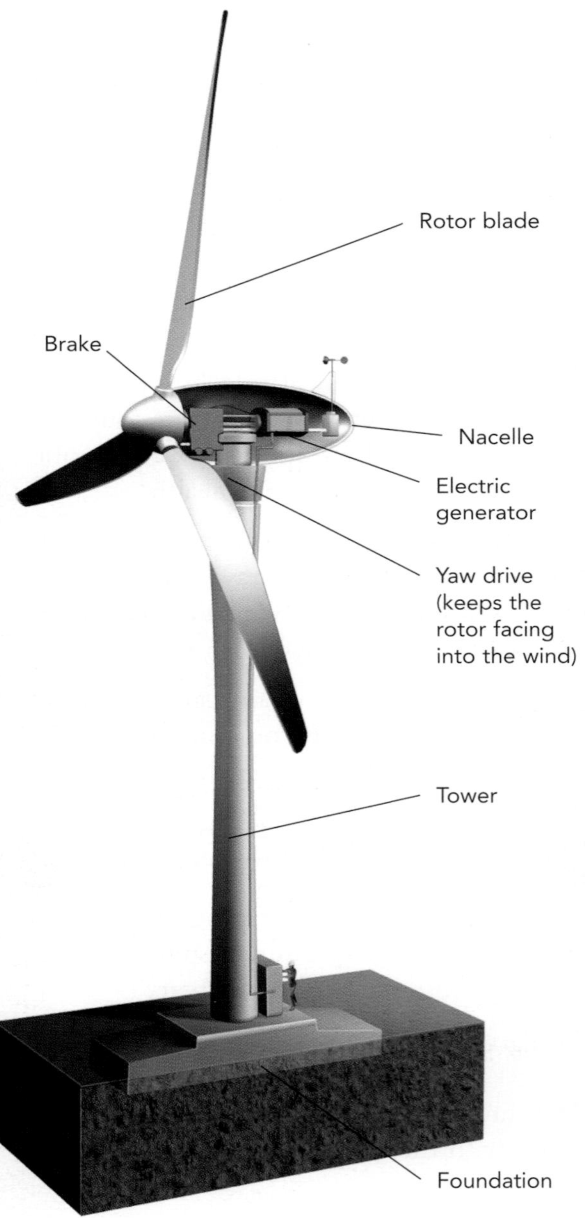

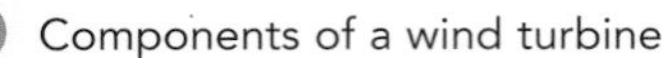

7.23 Components of a wind turbine

Since wind is a renewable resource, wind turbines are often perceived as an environmentally friendly way to meet energy needs. In addition, they do not produce any greenhouse gases during operation.

Nevertheless, developing wind power has certain disadvantages. First, some people think that the towers ruin the beauty of the landscape, especially when they are concentrated within a small area. Second, it is impossible to predict when or how fast the wind will blow. Finally, wind energy cannot be stored. For this reason, wind turbines are usually used in combination with another power-generating system, such as a hydroelectric dam. The dam can then take over from the wind turbines and keep producing power when the wind drops.

URBAN WIND TURBINES

Can wind turbines be installed in urban areas to generate electricity? Designers have tested some prototypes of smaller wind turbines, which they installed on the roofs of tall buildings. Although still in the research-and-development stage, the concept looks promising.

ST EST AST 2 The effect of the Sun and the Moon on the Earth

The Sun and the Moon are the two bodies in the solar system that most affect the Earth. The Sun is vitally important because its energy emissions provide us with light and heat. The Moon, through its proximity to Earth, exerts a **GRAVITATIONAL FORCE** that explains the movement of the tides.

CONCEPT REVIEW
- Solar system
- Electromagnetic spectrum

ST EST AST 2.1 SOLAR RADIATION

The Sun is a star composed of 75 percent hydrogen (H) and 25 percent helium (He). The extremely high temperature of its core—15 million degrees Celsius—causes **NUCLEAR REACTIONS** that transform the hydrogen into helium. This solar activity produces energy, which is dispersed throughout space in the form of radiation. It also explains why the Sun shines. Solar energy, carried by electromagnetic waves, takes only eight minutes to travel the 150 million kilometres separating the Sun from the Earth.

7.24 Solar radiation is the result of nuclear reactions.

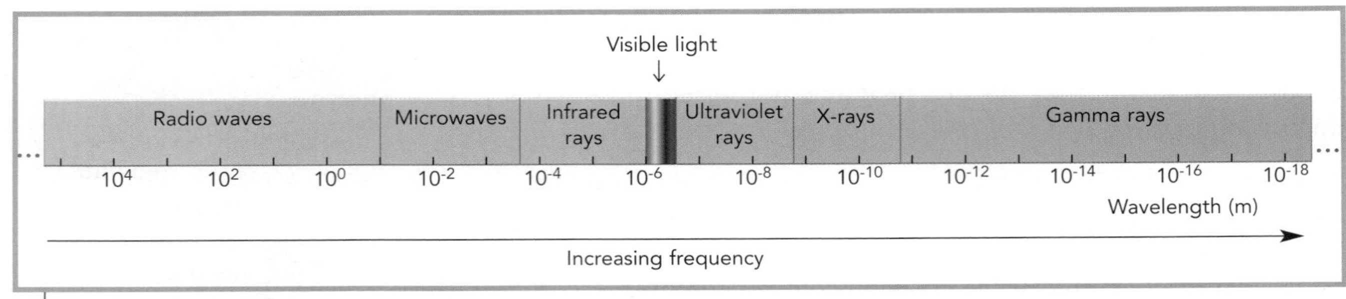

7.25 The electromagnetic spectrum

Solar radiation contains all the waves in the electromagnetic spectrum, but only some of these waves reach the Earth. Only visible light, some infrared rays and a tiny proportion of the ultraviolet rays make their way to the Earth's surface.

Infrared contains the Latin word *infra*, meaning "below," to indicate that the frequency of these waves is lower than that of red light in the visible spectrum.

Ultraviolet contains the Latin word *ultra*, meaning "above," to indicate that the frequency of these waves is higher than that of violet light in the visible spectrum.

These rays heat the atmosphere, the oceans and the land. Because of the curvature of the Earth, the tropical regions receive more solar energy than the polar regions, which explains the marked difference in temperature between the equator and the poles. These temperature disparities create atmospheric movements (winds) and ocean currents, which carry heat from the equator to the poles. The uneven distribution of warmth and cold around the globe is at the root of many natural phenomena.

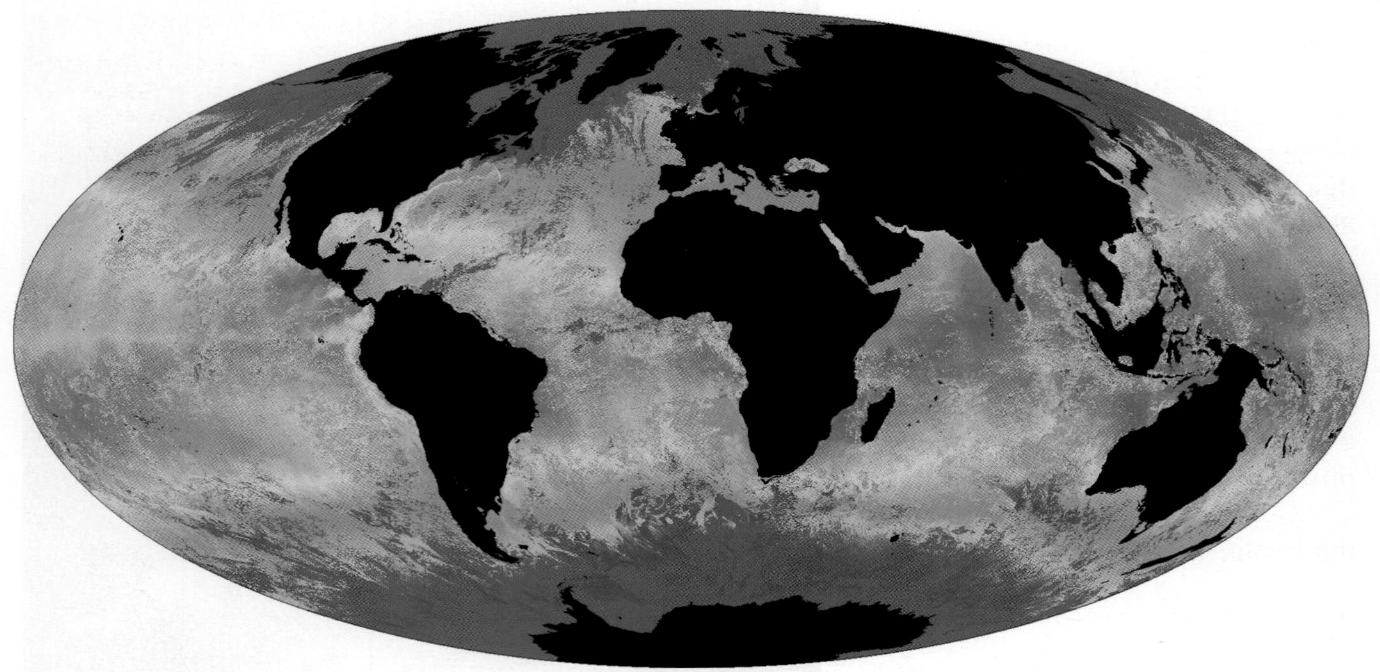

7.26 Ocean temperatures as measured by satellite. The areas in red receive the most solar energy, and the areas in mauve receive the least.

ST EST AST

SOLAR ENERGY

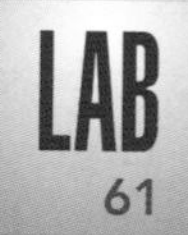

LAB 61

In just one hour, the Earth receives enough solar energy, in the form of heat and light, to satisfy the world's energy requirements for a year. Harnessing and transforming this energy to meet our needs is, however, a huge challenge.

SOLAR ENERGY is the energy that comes from the sun in the form of radiation through the atmosphere.

Various technologies have been developed to put solar energy to use:

- **Passive heating systems.** These systems involve positioning houses, at the design phase, so that they make the most of heat and light from the sun. The sun shines through large, mostly south-facing windows, heating the air. Inside the house, materials like concrete absorb the surplus energy and release it later, when the sun sets.
- **Photovoltaic cells.** They are used to supply various appliances or entire homes with electricity. When the material that makes up these cells (often silicon) is hit by light, **ELECTRONS** are set in motion. This movement of electrons creates an electric current. Usually, photovoltaic cells are assembled into large panels, which can be found on some houses or on satellites in space.

Photovoltaic comes from the Greek word *photo*, meaning "light," and *Volta*, the name of the inventor of the electric cell (battery).

1564
1642

Galileo Galilei

This Italian scientist built a telescope powerful enough to observe sunspots (on the Sun) as well as mountains and craters on the Moon. His various observations showed that it was impossible for the Earth to be the centre of the universe—a revolutionary idea in his day.

7.27 The International Space Station is equipped with immense solar panels to meet its electrical needs.

- **Solar collectors.** They are primarily used to heat air in buildings, and water in homes or swimming pools. They are large glass panels that capture the heat of the sun's rays. Below the panels are copper pipes filled with moving water. The heat stored in the panels warms the water in the pipes, which then moves on to radiators or other types of heating unit.

Large-scale use of solar power is not widespread for several reasons. First, the costs of building systems to collect and transform solar energy are very high. Second, the amount of energy available varies constantly with the sun's position in the sky and cloudy conditions.

Solar power does offer several advantages, however, particularly its dependence on a renewable source of energy that does not emit greenhouse gases. Solar power also provides an option for facilities in isolated areas such as the Far North, or even space, where there is no electrical distribution network.

7.28 This house was designed to take advantage of solar energy.

ENVIRONMENT EXTRA

Eco-construction

In recent years, growing awareness of environmental problems has encouraged the development of "green" building practices. The objective of eco-construction is to build or renovate buildings without harming the environment but still offering residents all the usual home comforts.

First, the energy efficiency of the building is maximized. Examples of energy-efficient choices include installing adequate insulation and using renewable-energy technologies, such as solar panels or wind turbines.

Next, the health and comfort of the residents must be taken into consideration. Materials must be non-toxic. Proper ventilation and the use of wood, ceramic tiles and natural finishes prevent health problems caused by humidity and dust.

Finally, building materials must not be wasted. The use of new materials should be kept to a minimum by reusing old ones and preferring recycled products.

Using natural materials like wood is one of the basic principles of eco-construction.

These steps cover only a few of the recommended green building practices in the increasingly popular field of eco-construction.

ST EST AST 2.2 THE EARTH-MOON SYSTEM

The Moon has been revolving around the Earth for billions of years. Its average diameter is 3476 km, which is a little more than one quarter of the Earth's diameter.

CONCEPT REVIEW
- Universal gravitation

From their analysis of lunar rock samples collected during space expeditions, scientists have put forward a theory on the origins of the Moon. About 4.6 billion years ago, the Earth is thought to have been struck by a meteorite as big as the planet Mars, causing part of the Earth to explode. The pieces scattered in space and then reunited to form the Moon.

The Moon not only circles around the Earth; it also rotates on its own axis. These two movements are synchronized. A complete rotation of the Moon takes 27.3 days, which is exactly the same time it takes to travel around the Earth.

ST EST AST TIDES

Since the Earth spins like a top, the side facing the Moon changes throughout the day. The water masses on the side closest to the Moon are then attracted to it. As a result, they swell, forming a slight bulge in the Moon's direction (Figure 7.29). Like the Earth, the Moon exerts a force of attraction, a gravitational force, on the bodies around it.

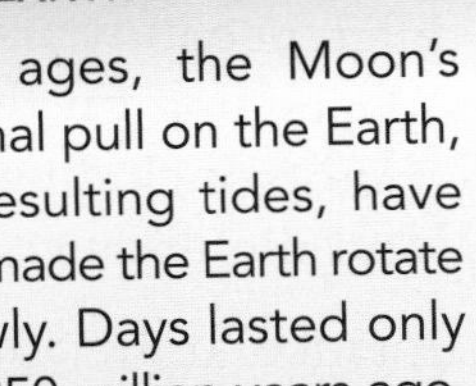

A SLOWER EARTH

Over the ages, the Moon's gravitational pull on the Earth, and the resulting tides, have gradually made the Earth rotate more slowly. Days lasted only 22 hours 350 million years ago, and a year lasted 400 days.

At the same time, the waters on the opposite side of the Earth (farthest from the Moon) also swell. The waters here are less attracted to the Moon than the Earth itself is, so the Earth is drawn away from them, toward the Moon.

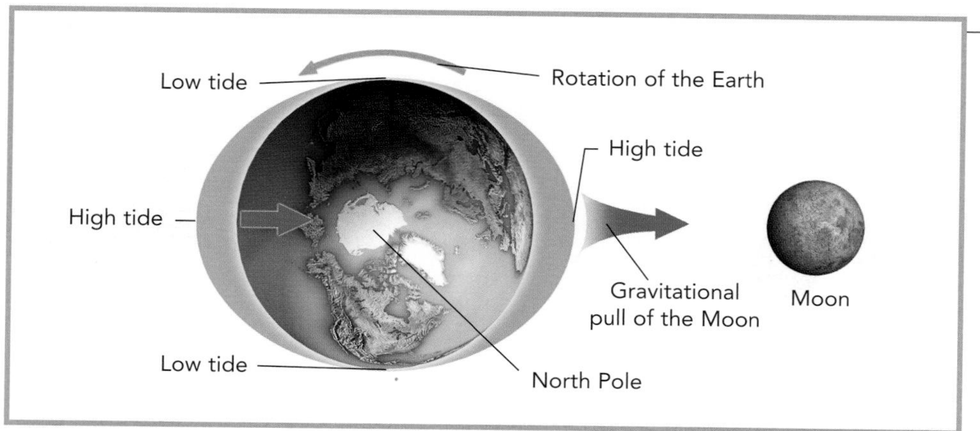

7.29 Two high tides and two low tides occur every day because of the rotation of the Earth.

Gravitational force is responsible for the tides. The parts of the world where the water swells experience high tides because the water level is high. The parts of the world where no swelling occurs are at low tide because the water level is low.

7.30 The Bay of Fundy at low tide

Since the Earth takes 24 hours to rotate and the Moon's position in relation to the Earth hardly changes during that time, the oceans swell twice a day: first when they are on the side of the Earth facing the Moon and then when they are on the opposite side. Consequently, there are two high tides and two low tides every day.

The difference in water levels at low and high tide is called the *tidal range*. It varies depending on the place and the season. Tidal range is influenced by many factors, including the shape and slope of the coastline, the depth of the water and the distance of the Moon or Sun from the Earth.

The distance to the Sun is important because the Sun, like the Moon, exerts a gravitational force on the Earth. The Sun's pull is weaker than the Moon's, however, because the Sun is much farther away (about 150 000 000 km from the Earth). When the Sun and the Moon are aligned with the Earth, the tidal range is at its maximum, as shown in Figure 7.31. The extremely high and low tides at these times are called *spring tides*.

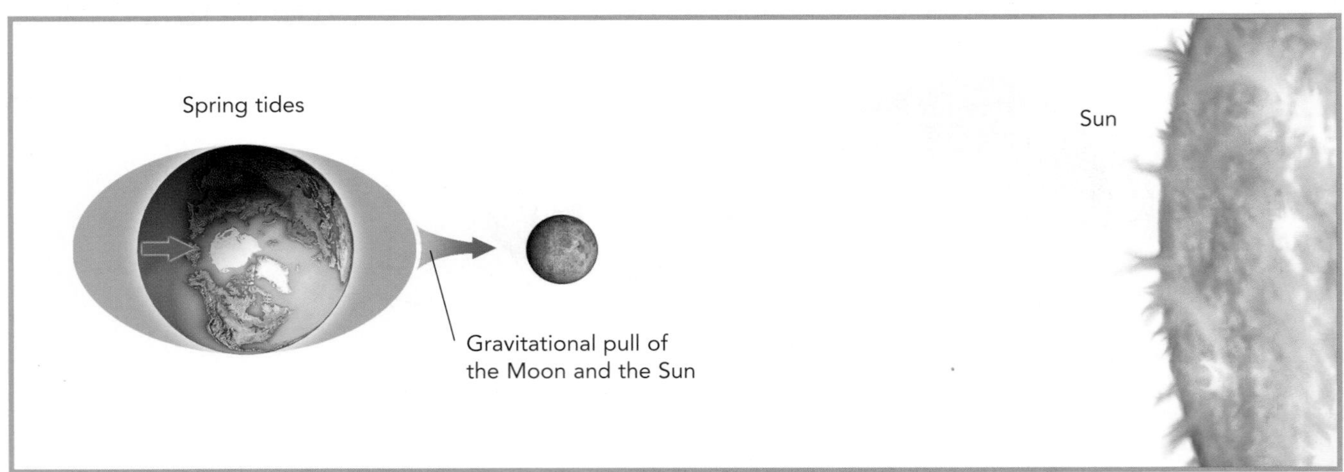

7.31 The gravitational pull of the Sun on the Earth's water masses affects the tidal range.

A TIDE is the rise and fall of water in the seas and oceans. It is caused by the gravitational force of the Moon and, to a lesser extent, of the Sun.

7.32 The Bay of Fundy at high tide

The Bay of Fundy, which lies between Maine, New Brunswick and Nova Scotia, has tides with a range of up to 17 m. They are the highest tides in the world. Meanwhile, small tides can be observed in the Great Lakes and the estuary of the St. Lawrence River (Fleuve Saint-Laurent).

ST EST AST

TIDAL ENERGY

The ebb and flow of tides represent a powerful energy potential that humans have learned to harness and convert into electricity in tidal power plants.

TIDAL ENERGY is the energy obtained from the ebb and flow of tides.

Tidal power plants work a little like hydroelectric plants (see Figure 6.36, page 210). When the tide comes in, the water gradually fills a huge basin. The water remains there while the tide goes out again, creating a difference in water level between the basin and the sea. A gate is opened, releasing the basin water to flow through a turbine. The turbine is set in motion, which generates an electric current.

UNIQUE IN NORTH AMERICA

The Annapolis plant in Nova Scotia is the only tidal power plant in North America. Located between the Annapolis River and the Bay of Fundy, it has been harnessing the energy from the high Fundy tides since 1984.

Tidal power provides numerous advantages. It depends on an entirely renewable source of energy, whose use produces no greenhouse gas emissions. Unlike wind power, it is perfectly reliable since meteorologists can pinpoint exactly when the tide will ebb and flow by studying the positions of the Moon and the Sun.

In spite of these advantages, generating electricity from tidal energy has met with several obstacles. Building plants is complex and costly because installations have to stand up to harsh ocean conditions. There are also few suitable sites in the world for building this type of power plant. To be effective, the plant must be able to draw on a large tidal range of at least five metres.

CHECKUP

ST 1–9, 12–17, 21–32, A, C and D.
AST 1–9, 12–14, 21–32, A, C and D.
EST 1–32 and A–D.
SE 1–11, 15–20, B, C and D.

1 The atmosphere (pp. 222–239)

1. True or false? Explain your answers.
   a) The atmosphere is the 30-km-thick layer of air surrounding the Earth.
   b) The atmosphere is composed mainly of oxygen.
   c) The atmosphere protects us from the sun's harmful rays.

2. Which layer of the atmosphere matches each of the following descriptions?
   a) It is the coldest layer of the atmosphere.
   b) Meteorological phenomena occur in this layer.
   c) It contains the ozone layer.
   d) It is the warmest layer of the atmosphere.
   e) Most satellites travel in this layer.

3. On October 23, 2007, the space shuttle *Discovery* blasted off from the Kennedy Space Center, in Florida, to deliver equipment to the International Space Station. Name, in order, the layers of the atmosphere the shuttle passed through.

4. Name three characteristics of air that are important to meteorology.

5. To measure atmospheric conditions at high altitude, meteorologists use weather balloons that can rise up to 30 km in the air. These balloons are equipped with measuring instruments and radars that send the data back down to Earth. As they rise, the air-filled balloons expand. Explain why.

6. Do air particles exert more or less pressure as the temperature rises? Explain your answer.

7. What causes winds to blow?

8. A highly trained cyclist leaves Montréal for Québec. At the same time, another cyclist, of equal ability, makes the trip in the opposite direction. If a high-pressure system is hanging over Montréal, and a low-pressure system, over Québec, which cyclist will be the first to arrive at destination? Explain your answer.

9. How is heat from the sun distributed between the equator and the poles?

10. The Earth's atmosphere contains large circulation cells with belts of prevailing winds. How many circulation cells are there in all? What are they called?

11. A flight from Montréal to Paris lasted 6 hours 25 minutes. The return trip took 7 hours 35 minutes. Why?

12. What does each of the following definitions describe?
    a) a large expanse of the atmosphere where temperature and humidity are relatively uniform
    b) the leading edge of a cold air mass where it meets a warm air mass, causing puffy clouds, or cumulus, to form
    c) the leading edge of a warm air mass where it meets a cold air mass, causing long layered clouds to form

13. Look closely at the photo below.

    a) Was the photo taken in an area of high or low atmospheric pressure?
    b) What is such an area called?
    c) If this area is in the Northern Hemisphere, in which direction do the winds turn?
    d) What is the opposite phenomenon called?

14. Do winds generally blow in a straight line from a high-pressure area to a low-pressure area? Why or why not?

15. True or false? Explain your answers.
    a) The greenhouse effect is a recent phenomenon, caused by human activity on Earth.
    b) By accumulating in the atmosphere, greenhouse gases trap increasing amounts of ultraviolet radiation.
    c) Clearing land intensifies the greenhouse effect because carbon dioxide is released as felled trees decompose.
    d) Photosynthesis in plants plays a major role in stabilizing temperatures on Earth.

16. For each of the following greenhouse gases, name a human-caused source of emissions.
    a) carbon dioxide (CO_2)
    b) methane (CH_4)
    c) nitrous oxide (N_2O)

17. Decomposing waste in landfills produces methane (CH_4). In some sites, this gas is collected and burned to transform it into carbon dioxide (CO_2). Does this practice have a positive or negative impact on the environment? Explain your answer.

18. Explain the difference between tropospheric and stratospheric ozone.

19. Which molecules are mainly responsible for the thinning of the ozone layer? What were, or are, these molecules used for?

20. Look closely at the photo below.

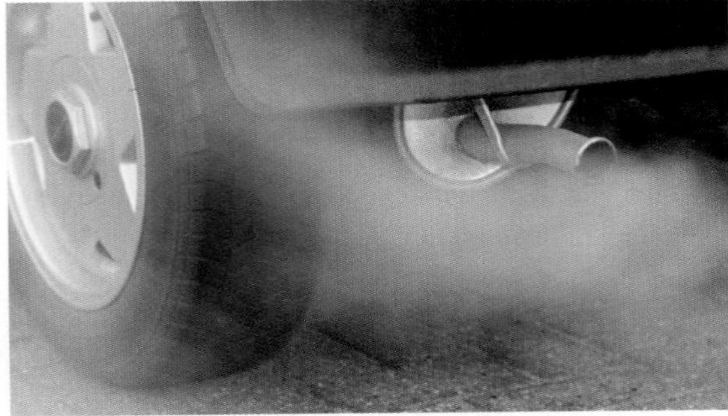

a) Which gases emitted by cars form tropospheric ozone?

b) What is the name of the thick fog of pollution formed by ozone and other atmospheric pollutants under certain conditions?

c) Does this fog always have the same composition? Explain your answer.

21. Name two advantages and two disadvantages of wind power.

2 The effect of the Sun and the Moon on the Earth (pp. 239–245)

22. What kind of reactions transform hydrogen into helium in the Sun's core?

23. In what form does solar energy reach the Earth?

24. Which electromagnetic waves from the Sun reach the Earth's surface?

25. Explain the meaning of the following statement: The curvature of the Earth is at the origin of many atmospheric phenomena.

26. What does each of the following definitions describe?

a) a large glass panel that captures the sun's heat and transfers it to a liquid running beneath the panel surface

b) a device that converts sunlight into electric current

27. Describe two elements of a passive heating system.

28. Name two advantages and two disadvantages of solar power.

29. At 11 a.m., Jennifer left her towel and book on the beach to go for a walk. When she came back an hour later, her belongings had been swept away by the tide. She was surprised; the day before, the tide had been high around midnight. Why is it already high again?

30. True or false? Explain your answers.

a) Tides are caused by the gravitational force of the Moon only.

b) At any one time, there are two high tides and two low tides on Earth.

c) The Moon's gravitational force is due to its rotation.

31. The following are stages in tidal power generation. Place them in the correct order.

A. The tide goes out.

B. The tide comes in.

C. The water is released, setting a turbine in motion.

D. A gate is opened.

E. The water is held in a basin.

32. Name two advantages and two disadvantages of tidal power.

review questions

A. Out of concern for the environment, Sophie has chosen to leave her car at home two days a week and walk to the office instead of driving. Before leaving home, she listens to the radio. According to the weather report, a high-pressure area has appeared over the city where she lives.

a) What is the name of the weather system affecting the city?

b) Should Sophie think about taking an umbrella to work? Explain your answer.

B. Answer the following questions using the information from question A.

a) With her new routine, which well-known polluting gases does Sophie avoid emitting?

b) Which environmental problems is Sophie helping to prevent?

c) Sophie's fellow citizens are not all as willing as she is to change their habits. Thousands of drivers are stuck in traffic jams on their way downtown. A yellowish cloud of smoke appears over the city. Would you expect this smoke to disappear during the day? Explain your answer.

C. The Smith and Schwartz families each built a hunting cabin in an isolated region of northern Québec. The province's power grid does not reach their cabins. The Smiths decided to install a small wind turbine to meet their electrical needs. The Schwartzes installed solar collectors and photovoltaic panels.

a) In terms of greenhouse gas emissions, which family is the more environmentally friendly? Explain your answer.

b) What problem will each family have to deal with in its choice of power supply?

c) The two families are thinking of combining their generating systems to create a small supply network for the two cabins. What do you think? Is this the answer to their problems?

D. Prepare your own summary of Chapter 7 by building a concept map.

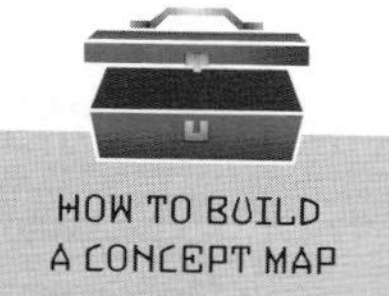

HOW TO BUILD A CONCEPT MAP

Air quality in Canada

FIGHTING SMOG ALL YEAR ROUND

Smog thickens the air, gives it a yellowish tinge and makes it hazardous to human health. Smog hangs over cities, causing respiratory problems such as bronchitis and asthma. It can also cause allergies and cardiac and neurological disorders. In 2006, smog was responsible for nearly 6000 deaths in eight major Canadian cities, including Québec and Montréal. Smog occurs mostly in summer, but winter smog is becoming more frequent. It is time to take action.

IMPROVING HEATING METHODS

Apart from motor vehicle emissions, heating is one of the leading causes of smog formation. During the particularly cold winter of 1952, the residents of London, England experienced an episode of intense smog. Smoke from the chimneys of coal-heated houses remained trapped above the city, tripling the usual number of deaths each day during a one-week period.

Coal burning remains a problem, even today. It produces nitrogen oxides (NO_x), which react with volatile gases to form tropospheric ozone (O_3), the principal component of smog.

Many American industries and Canadian industries outside Québec, especially power plants, use coal. They belch clouds of smoke, which is then carried by the wind to Québec. The volatile ashes they produce also promote smog formation by combining with the tropospheric ozone. One of the solutions to the ash problem is for companies to collect the ashes at the emission source, using electrostatic precipitators (dust-collecting devices). The ashes can then be used to fill abandoned mines or to manufacture cement.

Wood heating must also be closely monitored. In 2005, Montréal endured nine consecutive days of winter smog, a record largely attributed to wood heating. More than three million homes in Canada use wood for heating. In the fall of 2007, the City of Montréal asked its citizens to reduce this type of heating to a strict minimum, to use only dry wood and never to burn plastics, cardboard and painted or treated wood. Fortunately, wood-burning systems are becoming more efficient and less polluting. Some people suggest that tighter controls are necessary, however, such as regulating the sale of wood stoves, as in the United States.

Other efforts to reduce polluting emissions include the Canada–U.S. Air Quality Agreement, which was modified in 2002 to include an annex specifically on tropospheric ozone (the Ozone Annex).

Wood heating is one of the causes of winter smog in southern Québec.

RALLYING LEADERS TO THE CAUSE

In spite of all the efforts, agreements and well-intended government declarations, smog is still increasing. In May 2007, it was announced that Alberta would not be required to reduce its emissions of two smog-causing pollutants (volatile organic compounds and nitrogen oxides). Clearly, this complex problem is a long way from being solved. Nevertheless, as citizens, we must bear in mind the power we have to influence government decisions concerning the environment.

To protect our health as we wait for concrete improvements in this area, prevention is the order of the day. Info-Smog, a service created in Québec in 1994, provides daily information on air quality.

1. In Québec, smog levels have increased by 15 percent on average since the early 1990s, primarily in the south of the province. Explain why.
2. Québec cannot act alone to solve the problem of smog over its territory. It must collaborate with neighbouring provinces and states. Explain why.

1995 International Conference on Biosphere Reserves (in Seville)

1926 Description of biogeochemical cycles

1918 Classification of global climates

1901 Discovery of nitrogen fixation

1876 Publication of works on the geographic distribution of animals

1875 Coining of the term *biosphere*

1805 Publication of an essay on the geography of plants

1772 Discovery of nitrogen

1669 Discovery of phosphorus

1638 Discovery of carbon dioxide

Living beings form different groups on Earth. Their groupings depend on the climate of the areas where they live. For example, palm trees, parrots and monkeys thrive in warm regions, while spruce trees and moose live in cold regions, like Canada. Wherever it is found, life on Earth forms an endless circle, in which matter is recycled through different processes. What exactly are these processes? How do they work? What factors determine the diversity of life forms and habitats on Earth? By studying the biosphere, the subject of this chapter, we will find answers to these questions.

THE EARTH AND SPACE

8

The biosphere

CONTENTS

ST EST

1 What is the biosphere?

The Earth is wrapped in four overlapping layers:

- the **LITHOSPHERE** (a solid layer)
- the **HYDROSPHERE** (a layer of water)
- the **ATMOSPHERE** (a layer of air)
- the biosphere (a layer of life)

Biosphere comes from the Greek words *bios*, meaning "life," and *sphaira*, meaning a "spherical object."

CONCEPT REVIEW
- Atmosphere
- Hydrosphere
- Lithosphere

The biosphere thus corresponds to the entire system of living organisms and their habitats. All forms of life in the other three layers around the Earth are also part of the biosphere. The soil and sediments of the lithosphere, the oceans, glaciers and other water masses of the hydrosphere and the lower regions of the atmosphere are all part of the biosphere insofar as living organisms can make their homes there.

The BIOSPHERE is the layer around the Earth containing all living organisms.

Atmosphere
Lithosphere
Hydrosphere
Biosphere

8.1 The four layers around the Earth are all represented in this photo.

The chemical elements essential to life are constantly circulating within the biosphere. They move in infinite loops of recycling called *biogeochemical cycles*. The next section of this chapter describes these cycles.

ST EST 2 Biogeochemical cycles

To survive and develop, living organisms need to take in relatively large amounts of certain essential elements, especially carbon, hydrogen, oxygen, nitrogen, phosphorus and sulphur. These elements are found in the soil and rocks, in atmospheric gases and in plant and animal tissues.

Elements constantly pass from one environment to the next and from one form to another. This continuous circulation of elements is referred to as a *biogeochemical cycle* because it unites biological processes (such as respiration or digestion), geological processes (such as rock erosion or sedimentation) and chemical processes (such as combustion or synthesis).

A BIOGEOCHEMICAL CYCLE is a set of processes by which an element passes from one environment to the next and eventually returns to its original environment, in an infinite loop of recycling.

The next sections describe three biogeochemical cycles: the carbon cycle, the nitrogen cycle and the phosphorus cycle.

CONCEPT REVIEW

- Conservation of matter
- Atom
- Element
- Molecule
- Chemical changes
- Air (composition)

SOLUTION TO POLLUTION: BURY IT!

A revolutionary technique promises to eliminate some of the carbon dioxide (CO_2) presently discharged into the atmosphere, where this greenhouse gas disrupts the natural carbon cycle. The technique is being tested in Weyburn, in southeast Saskatchewan—an area of oil wells, many of which have almost run dry.

In Weyburn, CO_2 is trapped in an oil field.

Scientists have discovered a way to trap 5500 tonnes of CO_2 a day in this oil field. The gas travels by pipeline from a plant in North Dakota to Saskatchewan. The amount diverted from the atmosphere is the equivalent of the daily emissions of 107 000 Canadians.

If the experiment lives up to its promise, it will prove a double hit for the oil industry. On the one hand, it will reduce CO_2 emissions in the atmosphere; on the other, it will prolong the oil well operations. By injecting CO_2 deep into the ground, companies can extract oil that is inaccessible by traditional methods.

The technique has yet to be proven harmless, however, and its long-term efficiency remains to be established.

Source: Adapted from Valérie Borde, "La pollution? On l'enterre!" *L'Actualité* 31, 14 (September 15, 2006), p. 46. *[Translation]*

ST EST 2.1 THE CARBON CYCLE

Carbon (C) is the basic element in the complex molecules (proteins, lipids and carbohydrates) that make up the tissues of living organisms. Carbon is also a part of molecules such as carbon dioxide (CO_2) and methane (CH_4), two gases that are present in small quantities in the Earth's atmosphere.

CONCEPT REVIEW
- Photosynthesis and respiration
- Tectonic plate
- Volcano

Carbon atoms are constantly being exchanged between living organisms, dead organisms, the atmosphere, oceans, rocks and soil. This exchange is known as the *carbon cycle* (Figure 8.2).

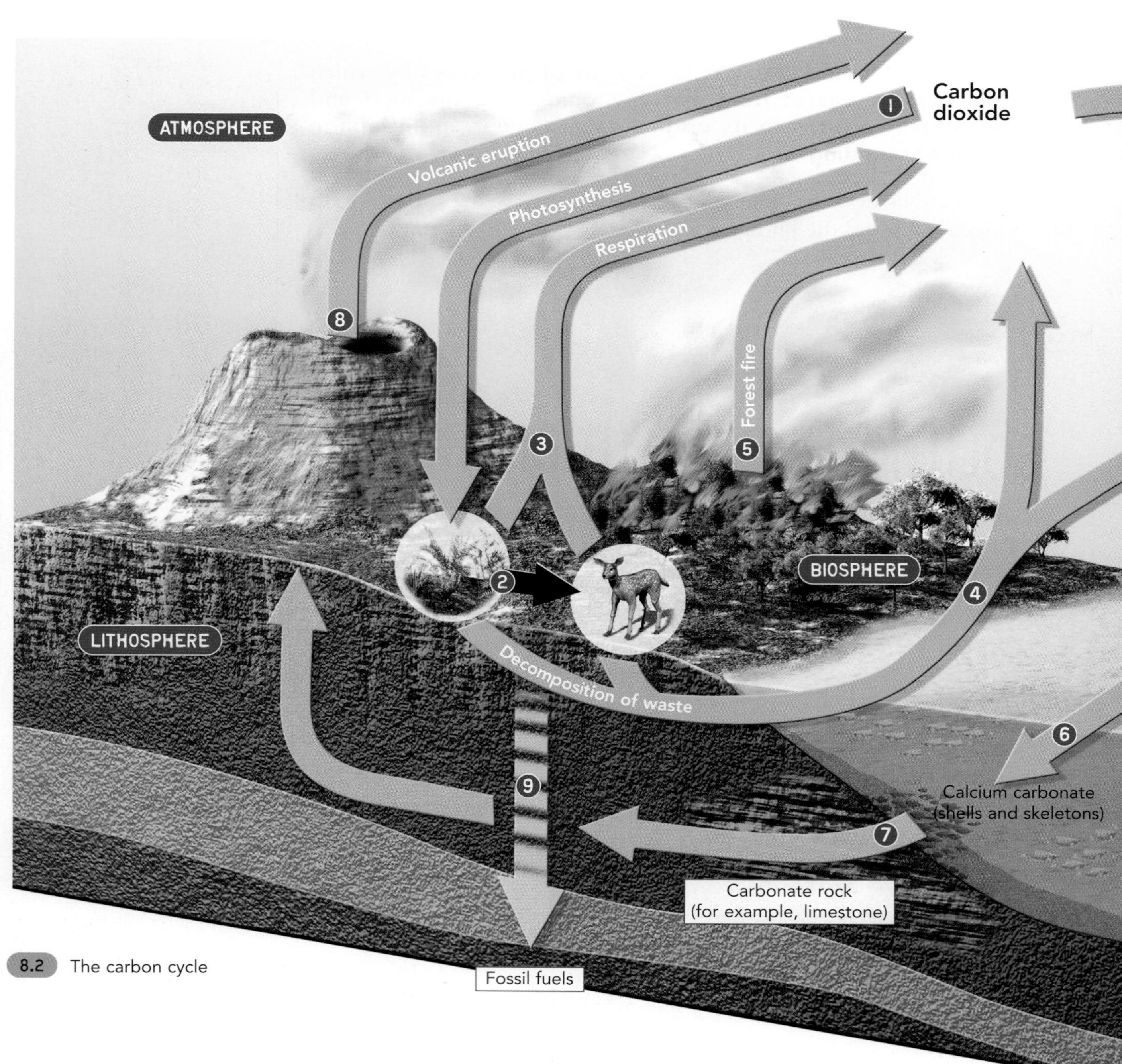

8.2 The carbon cycle

The CARBON CYCLE is a biogeochemical cycle involving all the exchanges of carbon on Earth.

Human activities have upset the natural balance of the carbon cycle, especially since the beginning of the industrial era, around the end of the 19th century. Burning **FOSSIL FUELS** in cars and in many industrial processes has resulted in the transfer of large amounts of carbon dioxide into the atmosphere. Increased methane emissions, mostly from the decomposition of human waste, are also jeopardizing the balance of the cycle.

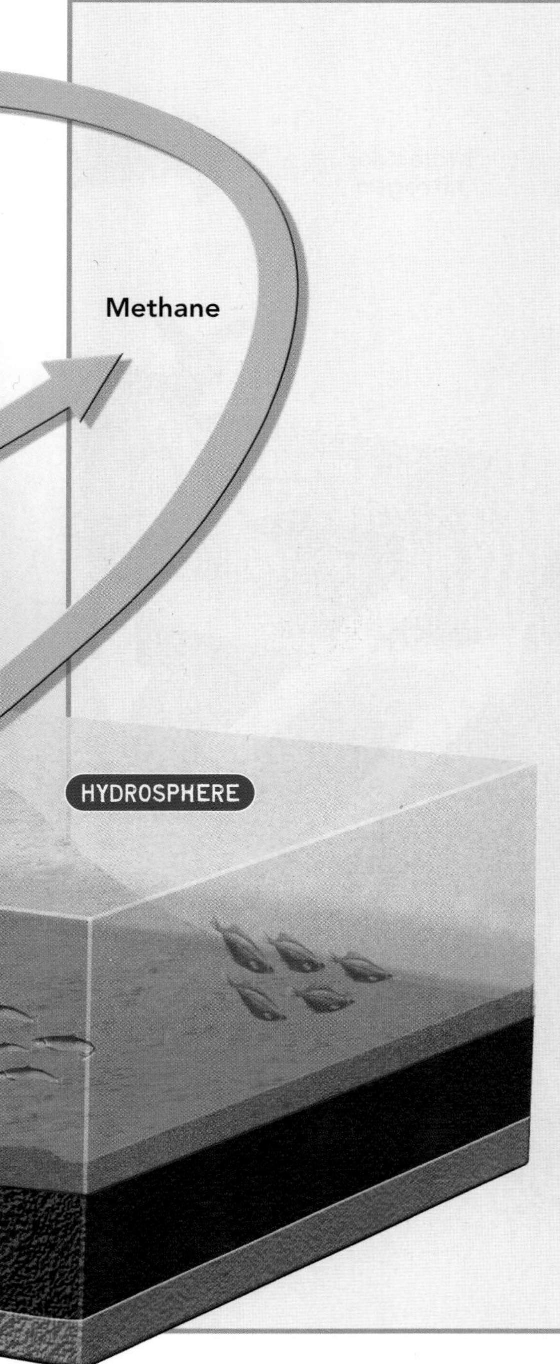

1. **Photosynthesis.** Plants use solar energy to capture the carbon dioxide found in the atmosphere or in water. The carbon dioxide is changed into glucose, a complex molecule that is a source of energy, used especially for plant tissue formation.

2. **Ingestion.** To take in the carbon they need to grow, animals eat plants (if they are herbivores) or other animals (if they are carnivores).

3. **Respiration.** When living organisms breathe, part of the carbon they have ingested returns to the atmosphere as carbon dioxide.

4. **Decomposition of waste.** The portion of carbon that is not released through respiration is eliminated in plant and animal waste (urine, feces, dead organisms, etc.). The waste is decomposed by organisms called *decomposers*, which emit carbon dioxide and methane in the process.

5. **Forest fires.** Forest fires release large amounts of carbon into the atmosphere. Combustion causes the carbon in the trunks and leaves of trees to be converted into carbon dioxide.

6. **Shells and skeletons.** Part of the carbon dioxide dissolved in water reacts with water molecules and then with calcium, to become calcium carbonate. This substance enters into the composition of the shells and skeletons of marine organisms.

7. **Carbonate rock.** The calcium carbonate from shells and skeletons falls to the ocean floor and accumulates in the sediment, where it changes and finally forms carbonate rock. The rock is subject to tectonic movement and can eventually be brought back to the surface.

8. **Volcanic eruptions.** Certain types of carbonate rock can melt on contact with magma. Part of the carbon they contain returns to the atmosphere as carbon dioxide in the event of volcanic eruptions.

9. **Fossil fuels.** When dead organisms fall to the ocean floor, the carbon in them may remain buried in the sediment. The carbon sometimes changes into fossil fuels, such as coal and oil, in a process that takes hundreds of millions of years.

ST EST 2.2 THE NITROGEN CYCLE

Living organisms need nitrogen (N), chiefly for manufacturing proteins and **DNA**. However, most organisms cannot use molecular nitrogen (N_2), the most abundant gas in the Earth's atmosphere (it makes up 78 percent of the air). They need bacteria that can change the nitrogen in the atmosphere into ammonia (NH_3), ammonium (NH_4^+), nitrites (NO_2^-) or nitrates (NO_3^-). Through its biogeochemical cycle, nitrogen can change from one form to another; Figure 8.3 describes this cycle. Note that the same processes occur in the lithosphere and the hydrosphere.

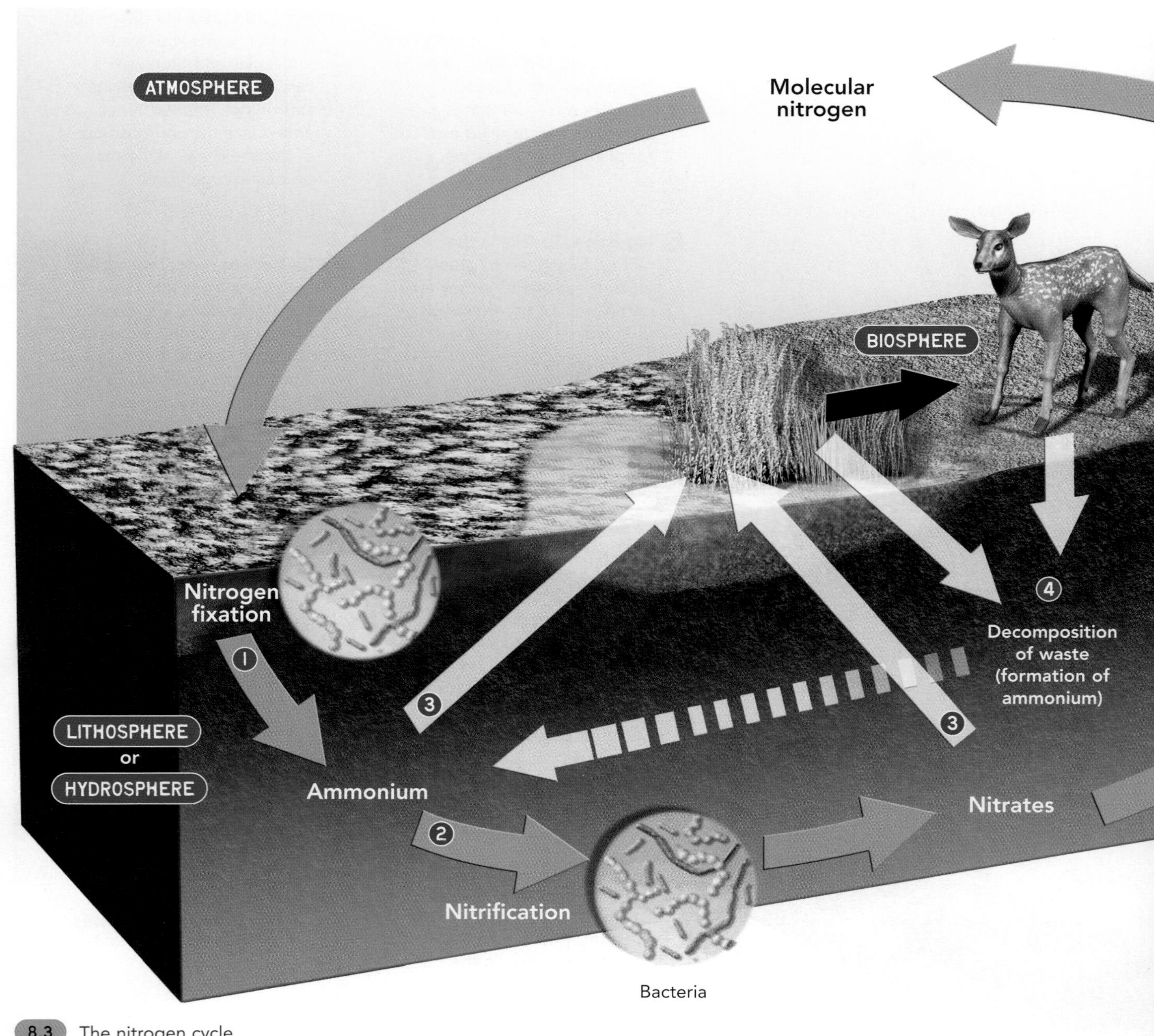

8.3 The nitrogen cycle

The NITROGEN CYCLE is a biogeochemical cycle involving all the exchanges of nitrogen on Earth.

Many natural factors, including temperature, relative humidity and pH, can alter the nitrogen cycle. Human activities, however, have a much greater impact. To improve productivity, farmers apply fertilizers rich in ammonia, ammonium and nitrates to their fields. Nitrogen compounds are also discharged in the wastewater of many factories. Nitrogen surpluses alter the soil balance and, in the long term, interfere with plant growth.

INGENIOUS PLANTS

Carnivorous plants live in nitrogen-poor environments (marshes, peat bogs, rocky ledges, etc.). To obtain the nitrogen they need, they catch insects with traps that are sticky or filled with liquid, or that snap shut. The plants then digest their prey with the help of enzymes.

11

1 **Nitrogen fixation.** Certain bacteria in the soil or water take the nitrogen from the atmosphere and convert it into ammonia. Some of the ammonia reacts with hydrogen to form ammonium.

2 **Nitrification.** Bacteria oxidize ammonium to form nitrites. Other bacteria oxidize nitrites into nitrates.

3 **Nitrogen absorption by plants and animals.** Plants can draw ammonium and nitrates from soil or water. Vegetation represents the only source of nitrogen available to herbivorous animals, which meet their need by eating plants. Meanwhile, carnivores obtain their nitrogen by eating herbivores or other animals.

4 **Decomposition of waste.** Certain bacteria and fungi break down the nitrogen-containing substances in plant and animal waste (urine, feces, dead organisms, etc.). They produce ammonia, which dissolves and forms ammonium.

5 **Denitrification.** Certain bacteria convert nitrates into molecular nitrogen, which returns to the atmosphere.

EST 2.3 THE PHOSPHORUS CYCLE

Like carbon and nitrogen, phosphorus (P) is an element that is essential to life. It is especially important as a basic component of DNA. Many animals also need phosphorus to form their shells, bones and teeth. Phosphorus, in the form of phosphates (PO_4^{3-}), is constantly being exchanged between the lithosphere, the hydrosphere and living organisms. Figure 8.4 describes the phosphorus cycle.

CONCEPT REVIEW
- Erosion

- **The PHOSPHORUS CYCLE is a biogeochemical cycle involving all the exchanges of phosphorus on Earth.**

8.4 The phosphorus cycle

Human activities are destabilizing the natural phosphorus cycle, through the heavy use of phosphate-rich fertilizers on farmland. Similarly, residential and industrial wastewater contains phosphate-laden soap residues, whose discharge causes an imbalance in the biogeochemical cycle. An excess of phosphorus in rivers, lakes and coastal waters accelerates algae growth. Overpopulation of algae in aquatic environments promotes the process of **EUTROPHICATION**, in which the deep-water oxygen concentration falls because of excess nutrients.

WANDERING PARTICLES

Wind erosion can blow away the phosphorus in sandy soil. Phosphorus can thus travel between regions as far away from each other as the Sahara Desert (in northern Africa) and Amazonia (in South America).

1. **Erosion.** Naturally occurring phosphorus is mostly in rocks. The wind and the rain slowly wear away small amounts of phosphorus from the rock, usually in the form of phosphates.
2. **Absorption by living organisms.** Plants can rapidly absorb the phosphates they need for growth. Herbivores ingest phosphates by eating plants, and carnivores, in turn, eat herbivores or other animals.
3. **Decomposition of waste.** Digested phosphates are returned to the soil. All animals eliminate phosphates in their feces and urine. Phosphates are also released when decomposers break down dead plants and animals.
4. **Proliferation of plankton and sedimentation.** Phosphates from rocks or from animal and decomposer excretions make their way into the oceans. Some phosphates promote the growth of plankton—tiny marine organisms that are the food of many larger life forms. Other phosphates sink to the bottom of bodies of water and blend with the sediment. Very slowly, over millions of years, this mixture forms rock, returning phosphorus to its original state.

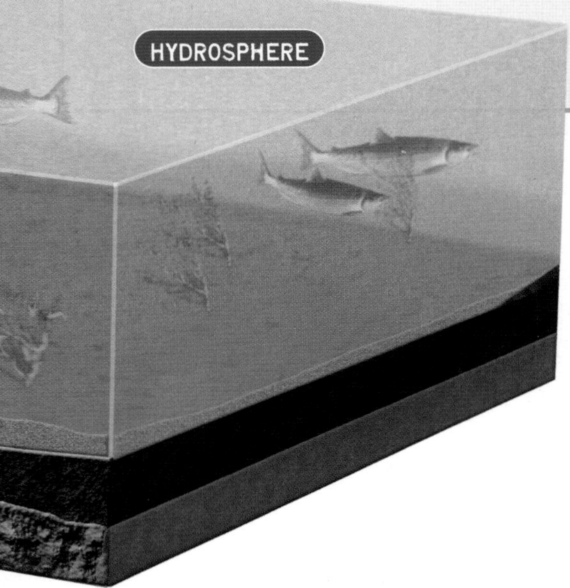

ST EST AST

3 Biomes

The biosphere is not the same everywhere on Earth. It is divided into large climatic regions, each characterized by its own typical fauna and flora. These regions are called *biomes*.

▶ **BIOMES are large regions of the world with distinctive climates, wildlife and vegetation.**

Biomes are generally divided into two main categories: terrestrial biomes and aquatic biomes. The principal biomes in each category will be described in greater detail in Sections 3.2 and 3.3. First, however, we will take a brief look at the factors affecting the distribution of biomes.

CONCEPT REVIEW

- Species
- Habitat
- Physical and behavioural adaptation
- Cycles of day and night
- Relief
- Seasons
- Types of soil
- Water (distribution)
- Water cycle

ST EST AST

3.1 FACTORS DETERMINING BIOME DISTRIBUTION

Many factors play a role in the global distribution of biomes and the species living in them. These factors vary with the type of biome (terrestrial or aquatic), as shown in Table 8.5.

8.5 FACTORS DETERMINING BIOME DISTRIBUTION

Terrestrial biomes	Aquatic biomes
Latitude	Salinity
Altitude	Turbidity (water clarity)
Temperature	Temperature
Precipitation	Direction and strength of the current
Soil type	Presence of oxygen (O_2) and carbon dioxide (CO_2) for respiration and photosynthesis
Solar energy (exposure to sunlight)	Solar energy (exposure to sunlight)
Winds	Nutrients (type, amount, etc.)
Proximity to bodies of water	Water depth

The factors in the table above determine which plant and animal species can live in a biome. For example, some plant species need a lot of water, so they will grow in places with heavy rainfall or near a river. In aquatic biomes, salinity is an important factor: some aquatic species are better suited to life in fresh water, while others thrive in salt water.

8.6 Water lilies, like those in this photo, can grow only in freshwater biomes, in shallow ponds where they can put down roots in the silt. Leopard frogs, too, can live only in freshwater biomes, or in forests or wet meadows.

The following sections will reveal, in greater detail, how these factors vary in different types of biomes.

3.2 TERRESTRIAL BIOMES

Terrestrial biomes are described mainly in terms of temperature and precipitation. These factors determine which plant species can live in an environment. Vegetation then dictates which animal species can share the same habitat.

Map 8.8 (pages 264–265) shows the main terrestrial biomes, which will be the focus of this section.

8.7 Red squirrels make their homes in two types of terrestrial biome: boreal forests and temperate forests. These habitats offer the squirrels the plant species that provide their favourite food (seeds, nuts, cones, bark, samaras, etc.) and the trees they need to make their nests.

8.8 THE MAIN TERRESTRIAL BIOMES

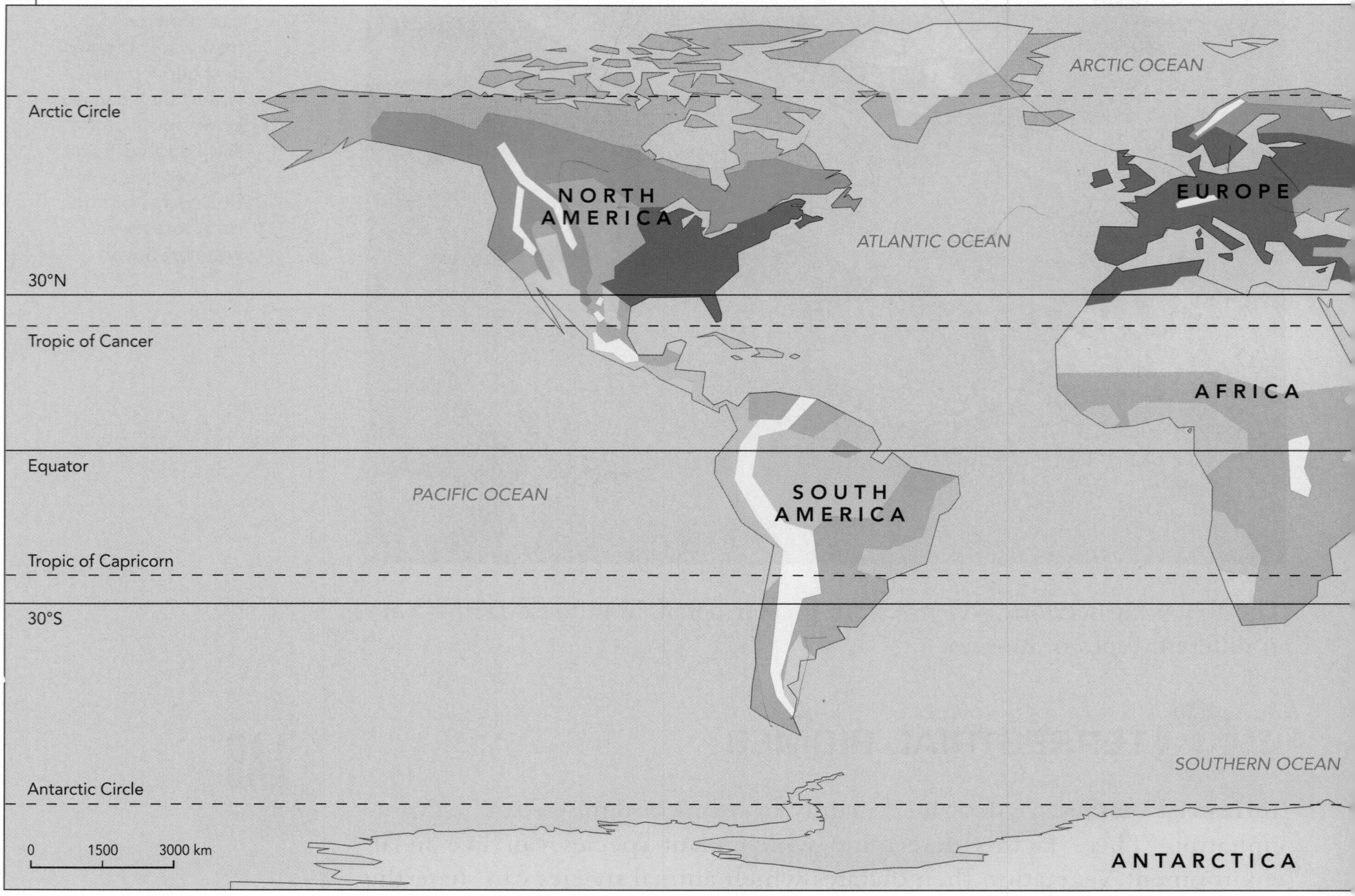

ARCTIC OCEAN
Arctic Circle
NORTH AMERICA
EUROPE
ATLANTIC OCEAN
30°N
Tropic of Cancer
AFRICA
Equator
PACIFIC OCEAN
SOUTH AMERICA
Tropic of Capricorn
30°S
SOUTHERN OCEAN
Antarctic Circle
0 1500 3000 km
ANTARCTICA

TROPICAL FORESTS

ST EST

Tropical forests lie along either side of the equator, mainly between the Tropic of Cancer and the Tropic of Capricorn. At these latitudes, the mean annual temperature varies between 20°C and 34°C.

Depending on the climate and soil type, tropical forests can be seasonal or evergreen. In seasonal forests, dry seasons of varying length occur in alternation with rainy seasons. In evergreen forests (or *rainforests*), there is no dry season, and the rainfall is abundant all year long—up to 10 m of annual rainfall in certain places. Seasonal forests are found mainly in Africa, and evergreen forests, in South America and Asia.

8.9 A tropical rainforest

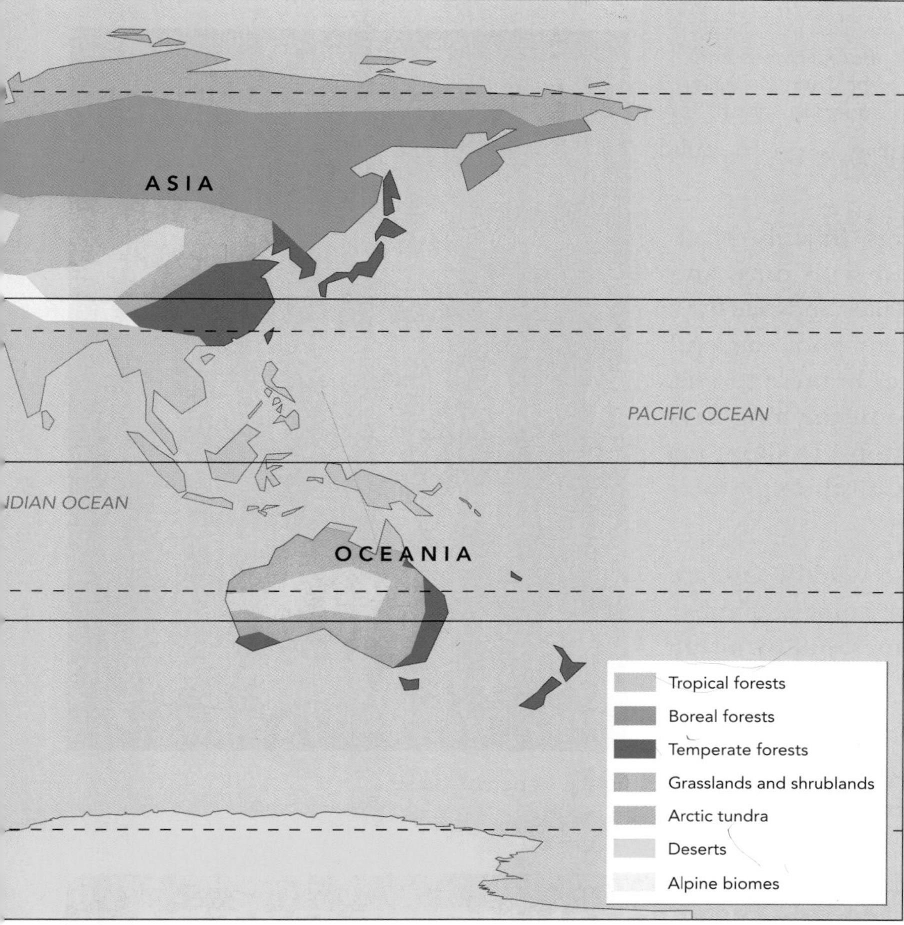

1846
1940

Wladimir Köppen

In 1918, this German climatologist and botanist developed a climate classification system, dividing the world's climates into five groups: tropical, dry, temperate/mesothermal, continental/microthermal and polar climates. These divisions are still used today to define terrestrial biomes.

Although they occupy less than 10 percent of the Earth's land mass, tropical rainforests are home to between 50 and 80 percent of terrestrial plant and animal species.

Unfortunately, tropical forests are at risk. Over the past 30 years, millions of hectares have been destroyed, as forests are burned or cut down to make room for farmland or to sell the timber. Clearing forestland like this has heavy consequences not only for fauna and flora but also for humans. In addition to supporting a rich **BIODIVERSITY**, tropical forests play an essential role in regulating the world's climate.

8.10 Orangutans are a species typical of certain tropical forests.

BOREAL FORESTS

Boreal forests represent slightly more than one quarter of all the forests in the world. They cover the greater part of Canada and northern Russia, forming a green belt below the Arctic Circle.

Boreal comes from the Latin *borealis*, meaning "north."

Boreal forests are composed of conifers (mainly black spruce), and the forest floor is carpeted with moss and lichen. This biome also features many lakes and marshes. In spite of the shallow, acidic and nutrient-poor soil, and the long, cold winters, vegetation thrives in these forests. In the summer, the trees take advantage of the long days (up to 18 hours of daylight in some regions) to shoot up, absorbing water and minerals from the soil through their far-reaching systems of roots.

These dense forests are home to diverse wildlife and are an important source of raw materials for humans. Timber from boreal forests is used to build houses and furniture and to manufacture paper products.

Although natural forces, such as fire, insects and disease, put the balance of boreal forests at risk, disturbances of human origin, such as logging, are much more serious threats.

8.11 A boreal forest

ENVIRONMENT EXTRA

Spruce budworm: a forester's nightmare

The larva of the spruce budworm might be only a few millimetres long, but it is one of the most formidable enemies of the forest. During the 1970s, in Québec alone, it devastated 235 million cubic metres of wood—the equivalent of 10 years' harvesting for the forest industry.

Spruce budworm can be found in all of Canada's coniferous forests. Normally, it causes minimal damage. Every 30 years or so, however, the population increases dramatically, triggering an epidemic. In its larval state (before it changes into a caterpillar and then a grey moth with white spots), the budworm devours tree needles and buds. After four or five years of damage, an affected tree usually dies. Although its name suggests the opposite, the budworm actually prefers balsam fir to spruce trees.

Spruce budworm larvae

Forestry experts expect a new epidemic in the next few years, but this time, scientists will be better equipped to fight it, with new methods such as organic pesticides.

ST EST TEMPERATE FORESTS

Temperate forests are found in southern Canada, the United States and Europe. They also cover part of Asia. In the northernmost regions like Québec, temperate forests are composed of a mixture of conifers and deciduous varieties such as maple, beech and birch. Farther south, temperate forests consist primarily of deciduous trees.

Temperate comes from the Latin *temperare*, meaning "mix in due proportion."

8.12 Autumn landscape in a temperate forest

In Canada, temperate forests cover the area around the Great Lakes and the St. Lawrence Valley (Vallée du Saint-Laurent). The mean annual temperature is between 8°C and 10°C, and precipitation is high throughout the year.

Decomposing leaves make the soil rich in nutrients, stimulating rapid plant growth and creating a dense and multi-layered forest. Plants, grass and moss grow at ground level, followed by a middle layer of bushes and then finally trees. The rich vegetation provides the perfect habitat for many mammals, such as black bears, squirrels and raccoons.

8.13 Québec's temperate forests are home to porcupines.

Because of their location, temperate forests have been largely destroyed by human activity. Today, urban centres such as Montréal and Toronto have taken over territory once occupied by temperate forests, and much of the former forestland is now used for farming. Primary forest (forest that has never been harvested) is very rare.

GRASSLANDS AND SHRUBLANDS

ST EST

A large part of central North America is covered in grasslands and shrublands, also called *prairies*. Similar expanses of grasses and shrubs can be found in many other places around the world, wherever there is enough rainfall to avoid desertification but not enough to support tree growth.

One of the distinctive features of this biome lies in its ability to survive fire, drought and mowing. Unlike other plants, grasses spend a lot more energy developing their root systems than their stems. They grow and spread rapidly by drawing on reserves deep in the soil.

8.14 Temperate grassland in Alberta

There are three main types of grasslands and shrublands:

- **Temperate grasslands.** The summers in these regions are often hot, and the winters are long and cold. The largest temperate grasslands are in North America, Asia and South America.

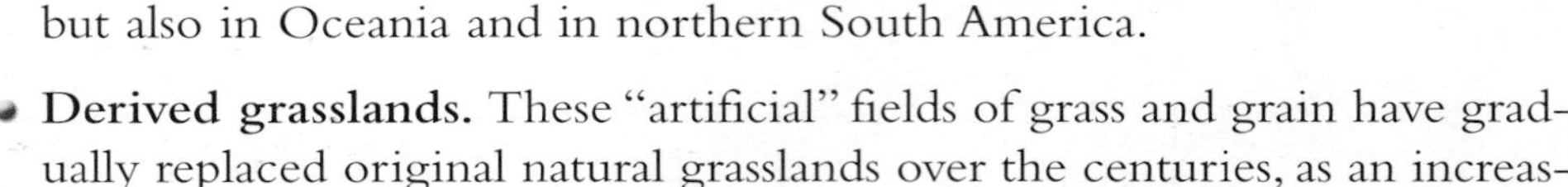

- **Savannas.** These tropical or subtropical grasslands stretch across regions where it is hot all year long, such as in Africa, but also in Oceania and in northern South America.
- **Derived grasslands.** These "artificial" fields of grass and grain have gradually replaced original natural grasslands over the centuries, as an increasing number of farmers worked the land. In North America, more than 90 percent of prairie land has been converted into farmland.

8.15 African savanna

ST EST ARCTIC TUNDRA

To the north of the boreal forest, the Arctic tundra forms a ring of vegetation around the North Pole, covering more than eight million square kilometres, or six percent of the world's land mass. The Canadian Far North is covered in tundra.

Tundra comes from the Finnish *tunturi*, meaning "treeless land."

8.16 Tundra in the Yukon

The Arctic tundra consists mainly of grasses, stunted bushes, moss and lichen. The long, cold winters and very short summers slow plant growth. Even during the summer months, when the average temperature reaches 10°C, the ground does not thaw completely. A thin layer, approximately one metre thick, is warmed by the sunlight, while the deeper layer, the **PERMAFROST**, remains permanently frozen.

In spite of the short period of plant growth, many migratory birds come to spend the summer season on the tundra, where they feed and reproduce. Some animals that have adapted to extreme climate conditions, such as the caribou, the arctic fox and the lemming, live in the Far North all year round. Tundra **ECOSYSTEMS** and their native species are especially at risk from climate change. In fact, the Arctic is warming up twice as fast as the global average.

Arctic comes from the Greek *arktos*, meaning "bear" (in reference to the Great Bear constellation in the northern sky).

8.17 The snowy owl breeds on the Arctic tundra, where it spends the summer. It winters farther south.

ST
EST

DESERTS

Deserts cover approximately one third of the Earth's continental land masses. These regions, little suited to life because of their low precipitation and extreme temperatures, can be found at all latitudes. There are cold deserts, such as the ice deserts of the Arctic, and hot deserts; there are also sand deserts and stone deserts. They all share the following characteristics:

- less than 25 cm of annual precipitation. For example, the Atacama Desert, in South America, receives less than 1.5 cm of rainfall annually.
- very high or very low temperatures. Past records show that temperatures have reached 52.5°C in the Thar Desert, in Asia, and –89°C in Antarctica.
- rare plant life
- only a few animals, which have adapted to desert life

HIGH-PERFORMANCE ROOTS

In the Sonoran Desert, on the border between the United States and Mexico, a cactus called the *saguaro* can grow as tall as 15 m. When it rains, the saguaro can absorb 800 L of water through its roots, and its stems can expand to store the water for its future needs. 12

8.18 The Sahara is the largest desert in the world.

Hot, arid deserts, like the Sahara, in Africa, experience huge differences between daytime and nighttime temperatures. With practically no clouds or air humidity to block them, the sun's rays rapidly heat the earth. As soon as the sun sets, however, the temperature plummets, sometimes falling below 0°C. The variation is also due to the absence of water. Since it retains heat longer than land, water has a moderating effect on temperature swings in the surrounding area.

Sahara comes from the Arabic *Ar-Sahhra*, meaning "desert."

ANTELOPES RETURN TO THE DESERT

The addax and the oryx, two species of antelope typically associated with the Sahelian and Sahara deserts of Africa, are going home. Their populations had been reduced to those animals living in zoos and protected areas, but a Tunisian program promises to reintroduce them to the wild.

The oryx is a desert animal no longer found in the wild.

Tunisian authorities have organized the transfer of 30 antelopes from a park where they have been breeding in semi-captivity to three other national parks. It is the first stage in an ambitious program to reintroduce these animals to the Sahel-Saharan region.

A total of 20 addax and 10 oryx were anesthetized and then transported by truck to their new homes, where they will gradually adapt to the environment before being released in increasingly open spaces. Within a few years, they should have fully adapted to the wilderness.

Source: Adapted from Laure Noualhat, "Antilopes: le retour au désert," *Libération*, March 10, 2007, pp. 37–39. *[Translation]*

ST EST

ALPINE BIOMES

Alpine biomes are defined by altitude rather than latitude. They are found almost everywhere in the world. The Rocky Mountains of North America, the Andes of South America and the Himalayas of Asia are examples of some of the highest mountain chains in the world, and their slopes contain a number of alpine biomes.

The higher the altitude, the lower the mean temperature, which drops by about 0.6°C per 100 m. This temperature change, comparable to the drop associated with latitude, shapes the landscape into vegetation zones. Thus, a deciduous forest at the base of a mountain becomes a coniferous forest, which then changes to tundra and finally to snowy desert at the summit.

- The submontane zone is found below 1300 m altitude. People who live in the mountains usually live in this zone. Deciduous forests may cover these foothills, and grain crops may be grown there.
- The montane zone lies between 1300 and 1800 m. At this altitude, conifers gradually replace deciduous trees, which are less resistant to the cold. The mean annual temperature is between 8°C and 15°C.
- The subalpine zone ranges from 1800 to 2400 m. It is the highest zone with any forest cover: sparse conifers. The mean annual temperature hovers around freezing point, and the ground remains frozen for more than half of the year.

8.19 Alpine biomes feature different vegetation depending on the altitude.

- In the alpine zone, from 2400 m up, only bushes and grasses can survive. The growing season lasts only two to three months, and it is cold almost all year round.
- The nival zone lies above the alpine zone, usually at more than 3000 m altitude. These snowcaps never melt. Vegetation is practically nonexistent, although some plants like lichen have adapted to the climate.

Nival comes from the Latin *nivalis*, meaning "snowy."

ST EST 3.3 AQUATIC BIOMES

Aquatic biomes cover a large part of the Earth's surface—approximately 75 percent. They are divided into freshwater biomes (approximately 2.5 percent) and marine biomes (97.5 percent). In freshwater biomes, the salinity of the water (the amount of salt dissolved in it) is less than 0.05 percent; in marine biomes, it is greater than three percent. This difference may seem minimal, but it is decisive in determining which species can live only in fresh water (a lake, for example) and which can live only in salt water (the ocean).

Unlike terrestrial biomes, the distribution of aquatic biomes is not defined by latitude or altitude. Aquatic biomes can be found almost everywhere on Earth. However, freshwater biomes tend to be more numerous in regions of high precipitation, such as tropical forests, than in arid regions, like deserts.

Map 8.20 illustrates some of Québec's aquatic biomes: lakes, rivers and part of the Atlantic Ocean. The major bays (Ungava, Hudson and James) around the coast of the province and the Gulf of St. Lawrence (Golfe du Saint-Laurent) are considered part of the Atlantic Ocean.

8.20 AQUATIC BIOMES IN QUÉBEC

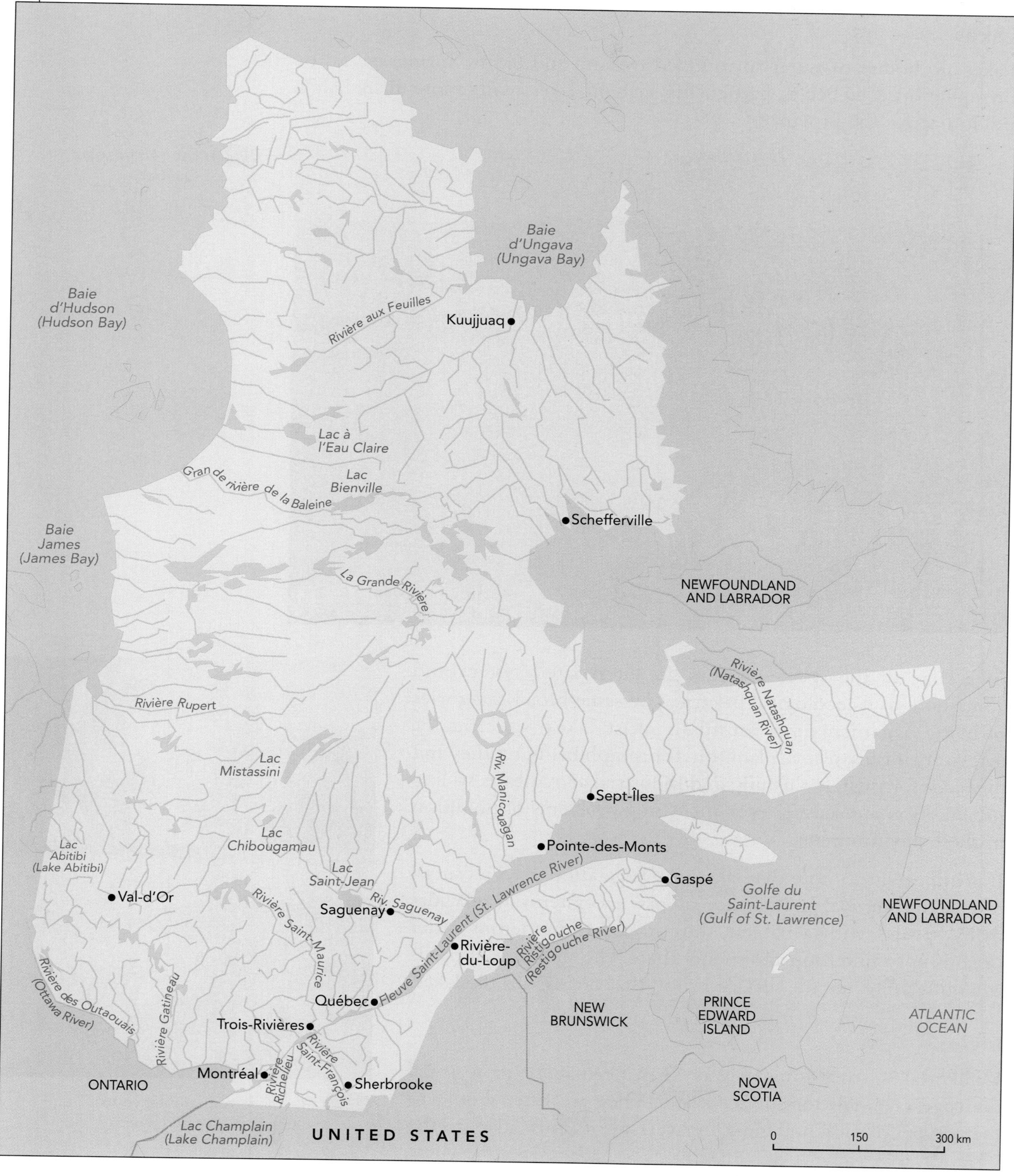

ST EST FRESHWATER BIOMES

Freshwater biomes consist of lakes, rivers and wetlands. They vary in the temperature, chemical composition and depth of the water, its exposure to sunlight and the speed of the current.

Lakes

Lakes are bodies of water surrounded by land and fed by springs, rivers or precipitation. Québec is particularly rich in lakes, with more than half a million across the province.

8.21 Lac Témiscouata, Québec

In a lake, all the species live in an interrelated system and contribute to its ecological balance. The same broad categories of living organisms are found in most lakes, specifically, microorganisms, plants, plankton, fish, amphibians, reptiles and birds. Unfortunately, farming and industrial activities as well as urbanization are causing ever-increasing problems of pollution in these environments.

It is important to note that lakeshore vegetation plays a crucial role in the survival and balance of lake ecosystems. It provides many species with a habitat, thus attracting numerous other organisms to find food and shelter there. The shoreline also acts as a buffer, filtering the surface runoff that drains into the lakes.

8.22 Rainbow trout are native to Québec's lakes and rivers.

Rivers

Unlike lakes, streams and rivers form permanent or seasonal drainage channels for surface water. They are often home to many types of moss and grass. In rivers, plants must adapt to the current and to the highly oxygenated water. River sources are generally at higher altitudes, with the current running down natural slopes into lakes or other rivers and finally flowing into the ocean.

8.23 Plant and animal species that live in rivers must adapt to the strength of the current.

In Québec, water quality in rivers has deteriorated greatly because of agricultural and industrial activities. Many rivers in the St. Lawrence Valley (Vallée du Saint-Laurent) exceed acceptable levels of phosphorus, a **CONTAMINANT** whose main source is farming. In 2002, the Québec Water Policy was introduced by the provincial government to conserve water resources. The goals of the policy are to protect **WATERSHEDS**, reduce contaminant discharge and combat water waste.

Wetlands

Wetlands are areas that are permanently or temporarily covered with water. They are home to plants that grow in water-saturated soil. The areas may be flooded with fresh or salt water. Wetlands are divided into three different types:

- marshes: land covered with stagnant water and without trees
- swamps: land covered with stagnant or slow-moving water in which trees or shrubs grow
- peat bogs: poorly drained soil carpeted with moss

Wetlands cover approximately 9 percent of Québec and 14 percent of Canada. They are found not only near coastlines, lakes and rivers but also in the Prairies, where millions of depressions, called *prairie potholes*, fill up with water as the snow melts. Wetlands are a habitat for many plant and animal species. They also act as huge sponges that absorb rainwater and reduce risks of flooding.

HISTORICAL TREASURE GROUNDS

Peat bogs are water-soaked environments in which plant debris accumulates at a very slow rate, over thousands of years. Thanks to their chemical composition—oxygen-free and acidic—peat bogs provide an ideal environment for preserving fossils, which bear witness to the history of the surrounding area.

8.24 Wetlands are of great ecological value because they absorb large amounts of water.

Until recently, wetlands were considered land of little value. Approximately 90 percent of them have been destroyed in the rural regions of Québec.

ENVIRONMENT EXTRA

Warning: cyanobacteria present

The proliferation of cyanobacteria in Québec lakes is a cause for concern among lakeshore residents. These microorganisms, often called *blue-green algae*, are undermining the quality of the water. Their presence sometimes makes the water unsafe to drink, and it closes the lakes to swimming.

The problem lies in the ability of certain types of cyanobacteria to produce toxins called *cyanotoxins*. When the bacteria are limited in number, the concentration of toxins in the water is insufficient to constitute a human health hazard. However, when lab analyses of the water reveal dangerous levels of toxins, local residents must stop drinking it and avoid swimming in the lake, until further notice.

On the surface of a lake, cyanobacterial contamination resembles a paint spill.

The best way to reduce the amount of cyanobacteria in a lake is to eliminate the nutrients present, especially phosphorus. The phosphorus in lakes comes mainly from fertilizer use in the vicinity, inadequate septic facilities and the use of soaps containing phosphates. Solutions to cyanobacterial contamination therefore begin with attacking these sources.

MARINE BIOMES

Marine biomes, which are saltwater environments, form a category of aquatic biome uniting estuaries, oceans, seas and coral reefs. Like freshwater biomes, they vary in the temperature, chemical composition and depth of the water, its exposure to sunlight and the speed and direction of the current.

Estuaries

The broadening at the mouth of a river that empties into the sea acts as a mixed zone between the maritime and river environments. This area is called an *estuary*. In estuaries, fresh water mixes with salt water, and large deposits of sediment accumulate on the riverbed. The water is therefore rather cloudy (also described as *turbid*). Local wildlife includes certain freshwater marine organisms as well as species typical of estuaries, such as oysters and sponges. The St. Lawrence Estuary, the only one in Québec, stretches from Trois-Rivières to Pointe-des-Monts (refer to Map 8.20, page 273).

Estuary comes from the Latin *aestus*, meaning "tide."

8.25 The St. Lawrence Estuary has been home to an isolated population of belugas for 7000 years.

8.26 The St. Lawrence Estuary, near Québec

Oceans and seas

Oceans and seas provide a wide variety of living conditions. Marine habitats can be subdivided according to the depth of the water, which can reach as much as 3800 m.

At a depth of more than 200 m, sunlight no longer affects the environment; it is completely dark, and average temperatures rarely exceed 4°C. At the surface, on the other hand, phytoplankton—tiny forms of plant life suspended in the seawater—use solar energy to reproduce. Open-water species depend directly or indirectly on plankton for food. This fauna, which consists of crustaceans, fish, jellyfish, mollusks, some bird species (such as penguins) and mammals, has had to adapt to an environment that offers no shelter from predators.

8.27 Some fish live in the open water, far from the ocean floor.

The ocean floor constitutes another type of habitat. Organisms that live in or on the seabed make up a group called the *benthos*. It includes mollusks, crustaceans and certain deepwater fish species, which feed off the dead organisms scattered over the ocean floor. Most of these bottom-dwellers live in coastal areas, between 0 and 350 km from the shore and at a depth of less than 200 m. These areas are greatly affected by human activity because 80 percent of fishing is done near the coasts.

8.28 Sea urchins and starfish are part of the benthos.

Coral reefs

Among the marine biomes, a particular type stands out: coral reefs. These biomes are among the oldest in the world, with histories that date back more than 200 million years. Like tropical forests, the reefs feature an amazingly rich biodiversity, containing between 500 000 and two million plant and animal species. Corals are invertebrates that take a variety of shapes yet all possess a central mouth and tentacles. Although some species live in cold water, most corals are found in tropical seas. Corals usually form colonies, which may contain thousands of individuals and measure several metres in height and diameter.

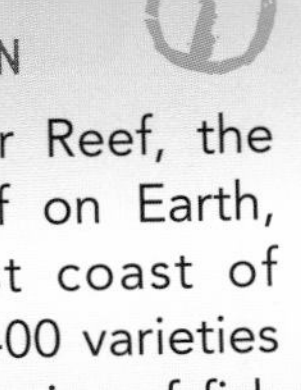

A WORLD OF ITS OWN

The Great Barrier Reef, the largest coral reef on Earth, lies off the east coast of Australia. Some 400 varieties of coral, 1500 species of fish and 4000 species of mollusks live there. The reef is 2000 km long—so long that it can be seen from space.

Reefs are formed out of the calcium carbonate that coral produces. They provide a habitat for thousands of marine species, offering them food and shelter. Coral reefs are also of major economic, social and cultural importance to the more than 30 million people who live nearby. However, pollution, overfishing, global warming and increased sedimentation caused by human activity are all threatening the survival of these extraordinary biomes. At present, 20 percent of the world's reefs have already been destroyed.

8.29 A coral reef can provide a habitat for many plant and animal species.

CHECKUP

ST 1–6, 10–22 and A–C. AST 10.

EST 1–22 and A–C. SE None.

1 What is the biosphere? (p. 254)

1. Can the water in a lake be considered part of the biosphere? If so, explain why.

2 Biogeochemical cycles (pp. 255–261)

2. List the processes of the carbon cycle that are illustrated in the photos below.

3. Carbon dioxide (CO_2) is an important source of carbon for living organisms.
   a) Through which two processes does carbon enter the biosphere?
   b) The carbon absorbed by human beings usually ends up returning to the atmosphere as CO_2. Briefly describe the two processes involved in this transfer.

4. What process matches each of the following descriptions?
   a) the process by which bacteria take atmospheric nitrogen and change it into ammonia
   b) the process by which bacteria change ammonium into nitrites
   c) the process by which bacteria change nitrates into nitrogen

5. Without plants, herbivores would be unable to manufacture the DNA molecules they need to store their genetic information. Explain why.

6. The nitrogen cycle is disrupted by human activity.
   a) Which farming practice is the main source of this imbalance?
   b) What are the consequences of this practice?

7. Look closely at the photo below.

   a) In this scene, where is phosphorus mainly to be found?
   b) Name three sources of phosphorus that are accessible to humans.
   c) The phosphorus absorbed by plants and humans eventually returns to its original state as rock. Explain how.

8. The natural phosphorus cycle is disrupted by human activity.
   a) Which human activities have the greatest impact?
   b) How do these activities affect lakes, rivers and other bodies of water?
   c) What steps can we take in our everyday lives to reduce these effects?

9. Which biogeochemical cycle is related to each of the following phenomena?
   a) Ammonia reacts with hydrogen to form ammonium.
   b) Rocks erode, worn away by rain and wind.
   c) Through photosynthesis, plants manufacture the glucose they need for energy.
   d) Calcium carbonate enters into the composition of the shells and skeletons of certain marine organisms.
   e) Decomposing waste produces methane.
   f) Decomposing waste produces ammonia.

3 Biomes (pp. 262–279)

10. Answer the following questions on the factors that determine biome distribution.
    a) How does latitude affect the distribution of terrestrial biomes?
    b) What factors do you think could determine whether trees grow in a particular environment?
    c) What is the principal factor that differentiates aquatic biomes?

11. Answer the following questions, referring to the photo below.

    a) What type of forest is it?
    b) What are the main differences between tropical forests, boreal forests and temperate forests?

12. The tropical forest is the terrestrial biome with the richest biodiversity, but it is threatened by certain human activities. What are these activities?

13. In Québec and Ontario, a large part of the temperate forest has been cut down. Explain why.

14. Which type of grasslands matches each of the following descriptions?
    a) They are found mainly in Africa and South America, in regions where it is hot all year round.
    b) They cover a large part of Alberta, Saskatchewan and Manitoba, in regions where farming plays an important role.
    c) They are found in certain regions of Asia and North America, where the summers are hot and the winters are cold.

15. Which zone of an alpine biome matches each of the following descriptions?
    a) Only bushes and grasses grow there.
    b) A mixture of conifers and deciduous trees can be found there.
    c) Grain crops and deciduous forests dominate the landscape.
    d) The snow there never melts.
    e) It is the highest zone in which trees can still grow.

16. Look at the two photos below.

    a) Which biome is pictured?
    b) What characteristics are common to these two environments and to all the environments that make up this biome?

17. Is it true that it is hot night and day in sandy deserts? Explain your answer.

18. Name three factors that affect aquatic biomes.

19. Which type of aquatic biome is illustrated in the photo below? Explain your answer.

20. Wetlands help reduce the risks of flooding. Explain how.

21. Which type of aquatic biome matches each of the following descriptions?
    a) They are home to more than 500 000 animal and plant species.
    b) They are the places where rivers and oceans meet.
    c) They are bodies of fresh water surrounded by land.
    d) They contain the greatest part of the water on Earth.

22. Look at the photo below.

    a) Which biome is illustrated in this photo?
    b) Why is this biome at risk?
    c) Why is it important to protect it?

review questions

A. The photo opposite shows a black bear, the most common bear in North America. Black bears usually live in forests and mountains, where they can find food and shelter and easily climb trees when they wish to escape danger. They are omnivores, although their diet consists primarily of plants; they sometimes feed on insects, rodents and fawns. Black bears are good swimmers and can catch fish in rivers to supplement their diet.

a) The forest where this black bear lives contains a mixture of coniferous and deciduous trees. What type of forest is it?

b) How do plants obtain the carbon and nitrogen they need?

c) What are the black bear's sources of nitrogen?

d) The leaves and dead trees on the forest floor will be decomposed by earthworms and microorganisms. Name some products that will be released into the environment as a result of this decomposition.

B. Match each of the species described below with the appropriate biome.

a) The arctic fox lives in an environment with minimal vegetation: a few scrubby bushes, mosses and lichen. To hide from predators, the fox has adapted to its surroundings in a particular way: its fur turns white in winter to help it blend into the snowy landscape.

b) The Fraser fir puts down its roots in acidic soil. It lives in an environment consisting of mosses and lichen.

c) The minnow is a small fish, 10 cm long, which thrives in rapid currents and well-oxygenated water.

d) The Mojave yucca (illustrated opposite) receives an annual average of 13 cm of rain.

e) Alligators live in slow-moving, shallow waters that are rich in vegetation.

C. Prepare your own summary of Chapter 8 by building a concept map.

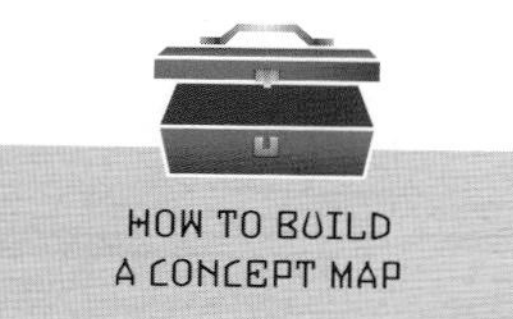

Peat bog degradation
RESTORATION PROJECTS

In Québec, peat moss is often incorrectly associated with grass sod. It actually comes from a specific type of wetland, a *peat bog*, composed of a thick carpet of water-soaked vegetation, which has slowly formed over thousands of years. These ecosystems prevent flooding by holding excess water, they contain many varieties of plants—some unique to peat bogs—and they capture carbon. Industry extracts peat for use as fuel, insulation, absorbent material, etc. Peat bogs are also dried out to make way for farmland, industrial parks and towns. This development of peat bogs, which has accelerated over the past 50 years, is creating environmental concerns.

REPLANTING MOSS IN PEAT BOGS

Peat bogs formed in the beds of ancient lakes, rivers or ponds, dating back to the last ice age. The mosses that make up the bogs, especially sphagnums, have been growing for 10 000 years, building up at a rate of six centimetres per century. The natural regeneration of peat bogs is therefore extremely slow.

In the early 1990s, Line Rochefort, a researcher at Université Laval, decided to come to the rescue of those Québec peat bogs that were being harvested. She wanted to lend nature a hand and help sphagnums grow back.

For three years, Dr. Rochefort tested the effectiveness of about 20 different types of mulch to recreate the necessary humidity for sphagnum growth. She also tried different spraying devices and sun shields. She obtained her best results with straw.

Another of her discoveries had to do with the effect of competition between various moss species on sphagnum growth. The presence of the species *Sphagnum fuscum*—one of the 46 types of Québec sphagnums studied during experiments in Lac-Saint-Jean—was found to be particularly effective in promoting peat bog restoration.

According to the findings of these experiments, it takes 1 m^2 of sphagnum and a great deal of patience to restore 12 m^2 of peat bog. Rehabilitation can take up to 20 years. About a dozen peat bog restoration projects are underway, notably at the Bois-des-Bel research station in the Bas-Saint-Laurent region.

Scientists have not learned all there is to know about peat bogs—far from it. The sphagnums that Dr. Rochefort managed to grow came from existing peat bogs. Her next challenge will be to grow the mosses outside their natural environment and on a wider scale. She is heading such a project at a research station in Shippagan, New Brunswick.

Sphagnums are mosses that form water-soaked carpets in peat bogs.

RENEWING THE RESOURCE

Since experiments have shown that it is possible to restore a bed of sphagnum, researchers are now considering the possibility of farming these mosses. In addition, instead of abandoning peat bogs once the moss has been harvested, companies could eventually harvest one section of a bog at a time, leaving the other sections to regenerate. If sustainable management were applied to peat harvesting, depletion of the resource could be avoided. Québec researchers are recognized as international leaders in this field. Scientists in Indonesia, Chile, the United States (specifically Alaska) and certain European countries wish to apply Québec models.

These carnivorous pitcher plants are typical of Québec peat bogs.

1. What would be the negative consequences of the disappearance of peat bogs?
2. Why is it so difficult to restore a peat bog once it has been destroyed?

Science at work ON...

THE *SEDNA IV*

To study climate change, researchers can adopt no better approach than going directly into the field and observing the impact on one of the world's most fragile ecosystems: Antarctica. From September 2005 to November 2006, a dozen scientists, cinematographers and other adventurers lived on board the *Sedna IV*. Their mission was to measure the impact of the warming and to share their discoveries with the general public all around the world.

Let's meet a few members of the crew.

Jean Lemire, expedition leader, producer and director

Mariano Lopez, mental health worker

Geneviève Lagacée, communications officer

Stevens Pearson, mechanic and diver

Pascale Otis, biologist

Joëlle Proulx, cook

Occupation	Education	Length of study	Main tasks
Film director	Bachelor's degree in cinematography	3 years	• Prepare, organize and coordinate film production • Know and use a variety of film-making techniques and equipment
Mental health worker	Bachelor's degree in psychology	3 years	• Understand human behaviour • Treat and try to prevent problems of adaptation for a person with respect to his or her environment
Communications officer	DCS in media arts and technology	3 years	• Research, process and communicate information • Design and produce messages
Mechanic	DVS in marine mechanics	1350 hours	• Adjust and repair various marine engines • Install or remove injection pumps
Biologist	Bachelor's degree in biology	3 years	• Work to protect the environment • Ensure the conservation of natural resources
Cook	DVS in professional cooking	1350 hours	• Use cooking equipment safely • Prepare well-balanced meals

THE LIVING

WORLD

AT THIS POINT IN HISTORY, THE EARTH IS THE ONLY KNOWN PLACE IN THE UNIVERSE WHERE LIFE AS WE PERCEIVE IT HAS EVOLVED.

Life can be sustained almost anywhere on Earth, even in the harshest conditions: on the glacial expanses of Antarctica, in the depths of an ocean abyss, among the endless dunes of a sandy desert or on the rocky, snow-blown slopes of a mountain.

Of all living species, ours seems to be the one whose actions have the greatest repercussions for other species and for the Earth's resources. To grasp the full extent of the impact of our actions, we need to study how living beings form groups, how they interact with one another and with their environment and how the traits of a living organism are passed on to its descendants.

CONTENTS

1992 — Signing of the Convention on Biological Diversity, in Rio de Janeiro

1973 — Signing of the Convention on International Trade in Endangered Species, in Washington, D.C.

1970 — Creation of the first Canadian national park in Québec (Forillon, in Gaspésie)

1935 — Publication of *La Flore laurentienne*, describing the flora of eastern Canada

1885 — Creation of the first Canadian national park (Banff)

1872 — Creation of the world's first protected area (Yellowstone, United States)

1867 — Discovery of the association between an alga and a fungus (mutualism), forming lichen

CIRCA 1800 — Earliest theories about the biological cycles of Canada's hare and lynx populations

1545 — Creation of the first botanical garden, in Padua, Italy

CIRCA -350 — Publication of treatises on animal and plant species

CIRCA -9500 — Early agriculture in the Middle East

The individuals within a group of living organisms form relationships with varying degrees of closeness to other members of the group. For example, some species, like the snow goose, form colonies; others, like the lynx, live separately. Cohabiting individuals of different species also inevitably form relationships with one another because they have to share the resources of a single environment. What are these relationships among organisms within a group? How do we know whether a species is thriving or endangered? These questions belong to the realm of ecology, which is based primarily on the study of populations and communities of living organisms. In this chapter, we will deal with certain topics from this field of study.

THE LIVING WORLD

9

Populations and communities

CONTENTS

ST EST

1 Studying populations

CONCEPT REVIEW
- Population
- Species
- Habitat

A population, in everyday language, usually refers to a human population. For example, if we talk about "the population of Laval," we mean all the people who live there. In ecology, however, the word *population* is used for all living organisms. Populations can thus refer to the green frogs in a marsh or the balsam fir on a mountainside. Ecological populations like these are the subject of this chapter.

Ecology comes from the Greek words *oikos*, meaning "house," and *logia*, meaning "theory."

A population is a group of individuals of the same **SPECIES**, living in a shared space. Since the individuals in a population share a common environment, they also benefit from the same resources, such as water, food and sunlight. In addition, the probability that these individuals will interact—during the mating season, for example—is very high.

A POPULATION is a group of individuals of the same species, living in a shared space at a specific point in time.

9.1 Caribou that live together and share the same space form a population.

To describe a population, it is usually necessary to specify the area it occupies. For example, several caribou populations, or caribou *herds*, live in Québec, including the Gaspésie caribou herd and the Rivière aux Feuilles herd (Figure 9.2, page 293).

Studying populations reveals how various species evolve. It thus gives ecologists an indication as to whether a species is thriving or in decline. Three main characteristics are used to describe a population: size, density and distribution.

ST EST 1.1 POPULATION SIZE

The size of a population is simply the number of individuals it contains. For example, in 2001, according to the Québec ministry of natural resources and wildlife, the Gaspésie caribou herd had a population of between 200 and 250 individuals. At the same time, the population in the Rivière aux Feuilles region was approximately 628 000. Given the small number of Gaspésie caribou, the herd was designated as vulnerable, and special measures were implemented to try to save it. This example shows how it can be useful to know the size of a population.

POPULATION SIZE refers to the number of individuals in a population.

Over time, the size of a population may increase, decrease or remain stable. Four factors explain these variations: births, deaths, immigration and emigration. They are described in Table 9.3.

9.2 HOMES OF TWO CARIBOU HERDS IN QUÉBEC

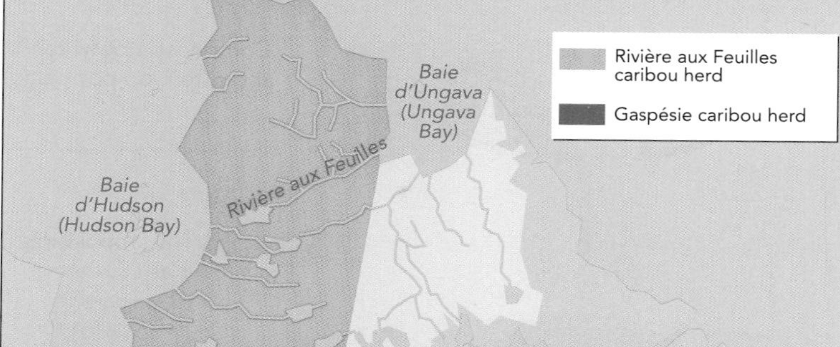
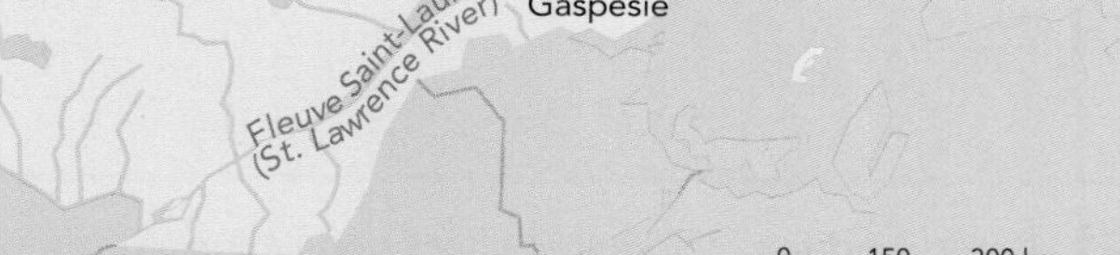

Source: Québec, Ministère des Ressources naturelles et de la Faune, 2002.

9.3 FACTORS AFFECTING POPULATION SIZE

Factor	Description
Births	Births of individuals within a population
Deaths	Deaths of individuals within a population
Immigration	Arrival among the population of individuals from other regions
Emigration	Departure of individuals to other regions

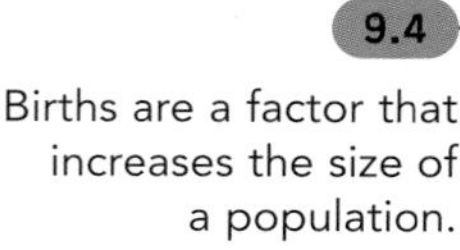

9.4 Births are a factor that increases the size of a population.

To find out whether the size of a population has increased, decreased or remained stable over a certain period of time, the four factors are compared (Figure 9.5). If the birth and immigration rates together are equal to the sum of the death and emigration rates, the population has stayed the same. Otherwise, the population has either increased or decreased in size, depending on the situation.

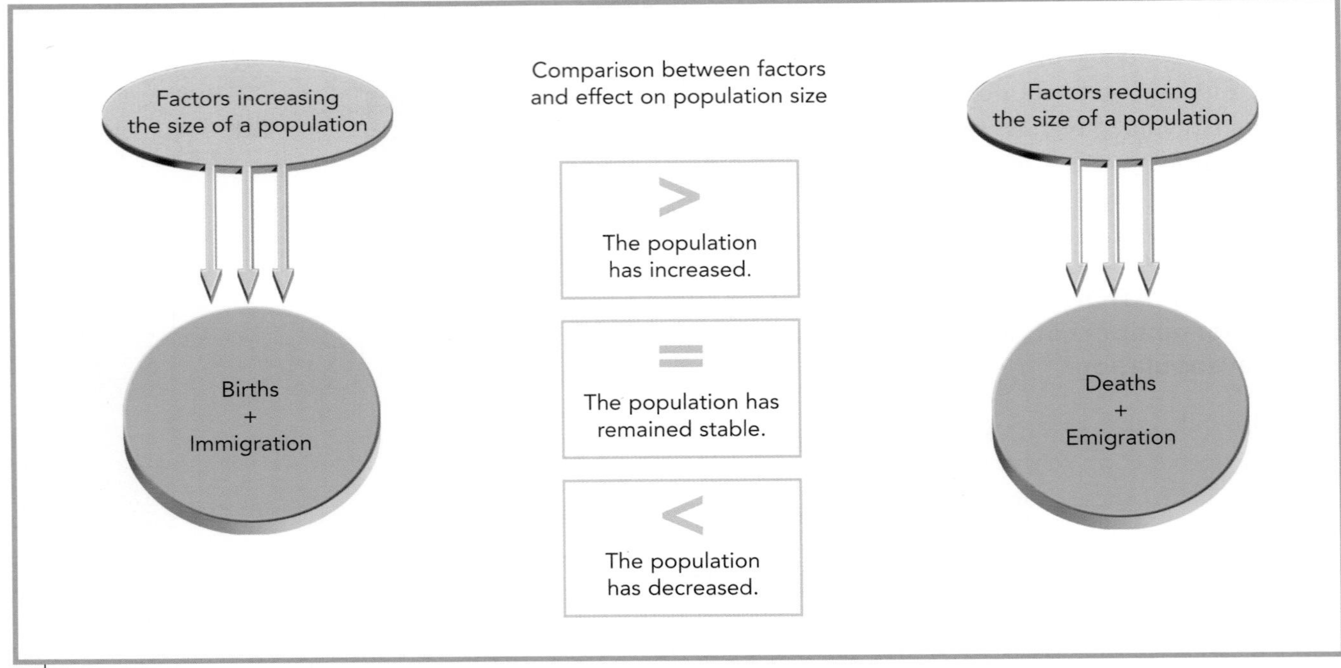

9.5 Comparing the factors that affect population size shows how a population has evolved over a certain period.

ST EST METHODS FOR MEASURING THE SIZE OF A POPULATION

Several methods can be used to measure the size of a population. Among the most commonly used are an individual count, a count by sample area, and the mark-recapture method.

Counting individuals

When possible, the size of a population can be measured by counting all the individuals within the area occupied by that population. For example, a botanist could count all the water lilies in a pond.

Sometimes, scientists calculate the size of a population of large animals living in an open space by using aerial photography. They then study all the photos to count the total number of individuals.

When counting individuals is impossible, the size of a population can be estimated using one of the two sampling methods mentioned above and described in the following pages.

9.6 Aerial photos of zebras can be used to count the total number of animals in a certain region.

Counting by sample area

This method consists in counting the individuals in randomly selected sections of the study area and then estimating the total population size with the following calculation:

$$\frac{\text{Average number of individuals per section}}{\text{Area of a section}} = \frac{\text{Population size}}{\text{Total study area}}$$

Therefore:

$$\text{Population size} = \frac{\text{Average number of individuals per section} \times \text{Total study area}}{\text{Area of a section}}$$

To section off the sample areas, quadrats (rectangular areas marked off with rope or ribbon) are often used. Figure 9.7 illustrates quadrat sampling at work.

9.7 To find out the size of the daisy population in a field of 10 000 m^2, the number of daisies in one-square-metre quadrats is counted. The total size of the population is the average number of flowers in the quadrats, multiplied by 10 000.

Quadrat sampling is useful for estimating the size of a plant population. It can also be used for slow-moving animals or ones that do not run away from humans, such as ants or earthworms.

Mark and recapture

The mark-recapture method is commonly used by scientists to estimate the population size of very mobile animals, such as birds, fish, mammals that are widely scattered within their habitats (hares, for example) or marine mammals (seals, whales, etc.). This method consists of the following stages:

- installing cages or nets in the region inhabited by the population
- counting the captured animals and marking them with tags, rings, collars or dabs of paint
- releasing the marked animals so they mix with unmarked individuals in the population
- reinstalling the cages or nets
- counting captured individuals a second time, with a separate count for marked individuals
- estimating the size of the population, using the following calculation:

9.8 Mark and recapture can be used to study a population of Canada geese.

$$\frac{\text{Number of marked animals recaptured}}{\text{Total number of animals captured the second time}} = \frac{\text{Number of marked animals}}{\text{Population size}}$$

Therefore:

$$\text{Population size} = \frac{\text{Number of marked animals} \times \text{Total number of animals captured the second time}}{\text{Number of marked animals recaptured}}$$

Suppose, for example, that 100 Canada geese have been captured, marked and released. If, on the second capture, 50 out of 200 geese are tagged, then the population size is estimated to be 400 individuals.

$$\text{Population size} = \frac{100 \times 200}{50} = 400 \text{ individuals}$$

ST EST 1.2 POPULATION DENSITY

LAB 65

The size of a population indicates the total number of individuals, while the density of a population indicates the average number of individuals within a given area or volume. For example, in 2006, the Île d'Anticosti was home to an average of 21 white-tailed deer per square kilometre.

POPULATION DENSITY refers to the number of individuals per unit of area or volume.

The following calculation can be used to determine the density of a population:

$$\text{Population density} = \frac{\text{Number of individuals}}{\text{Space (area or volume) occupied}}$$

Suppose that an aquarium contains 100 L of water and five goldfish. The density of the goldfish population in the aquarium would be 0.05 fish per litre of water.

$$\text{Population density} = \frac{\text{5 individuals}}{\text{100 L of water}} = \text{0.05 fish per litre of water}$$

NOW YOU SEE THEM, NOW YOU DON'T

In 1896, 220 white-tailed deer were transported to the Île d'Anticosti. In 2006, their population had climbed to approximately 166 000 (21 deer/km^2). At the same time, the once-numerous black bear population on the island slowly dwindled because the deer were destroying the bears' principal source of food: berries. 13

For any given species (plant or animal), population density can vary depending on the habitat. Access to water and food is an important factor in determining density. If the environment offers a good supply of food and water, the population density will be higher than if these resources were limited. Other factors, such as climate, the presence of predators, parasites or disease, as well as disasters of natural or human origin, can also affect the density of a population.

9.9 The population density of raccoons is often higher in urban areas (up to 100 animals per square kilometre) than in the country (an average of 5 to 10 animals per square kilometre) because food is easier to find than in the wild.

ST EST 1.3 POPULATION DISTRIBUTION

The individuals that make up a population are distributed in different ways within the space they inhabit. There are three main patterns of population distribution, as shown in Figure 9.10.

POPULATION DISTRIBUTION is the way in which individuals are dispersed within their habitat.

9.10 Patterns of distribution of individuals within a population

CLUMPED DISTRIBUTION
Most common pattern of distribution, in which individuals form groups. Often observed when certain areas of the population's habitat offer better living conditions.

Many fish move around their habitat in schools. This reduces the effort involved in swimming, provides some protection from predators and helps the fish feed more efficiently.

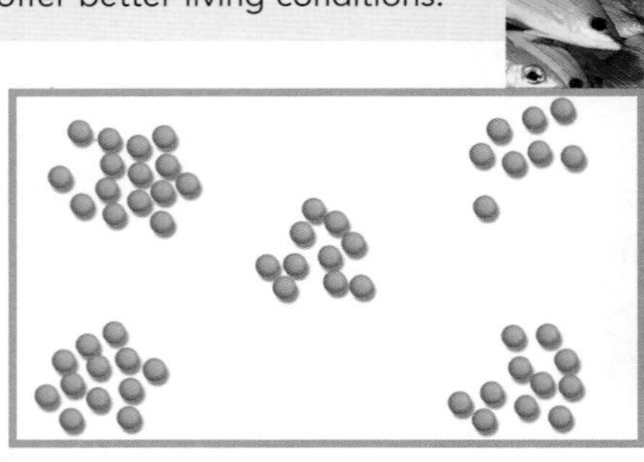

UNIFORM DISTRIBUTION
Pattern of distribution in which individuals are dispersed equally throughout the population's habitat. Often due to competition for natural resources.

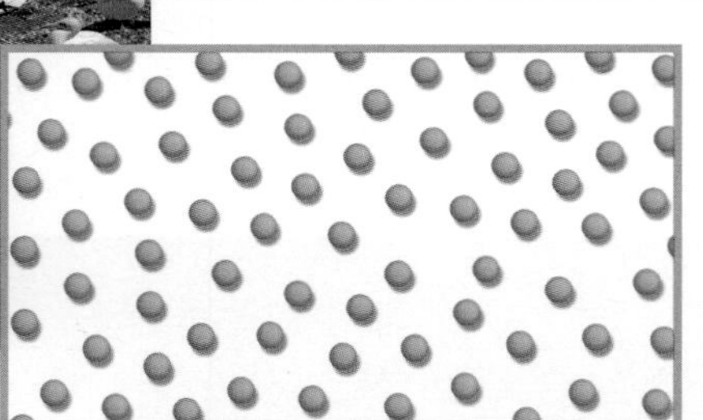

Northern gannets space their nests at regular intervals to allow each bird a certain minimal territory.

RANDOM DISTRIBUTION
Pattern of distribution rarely found in nature, in which individuals are randomly and unpredictably dispersed across the population's habitat.

These bushes are dispersed at random in the field because the individuals in this population cannot clump together or spread out.

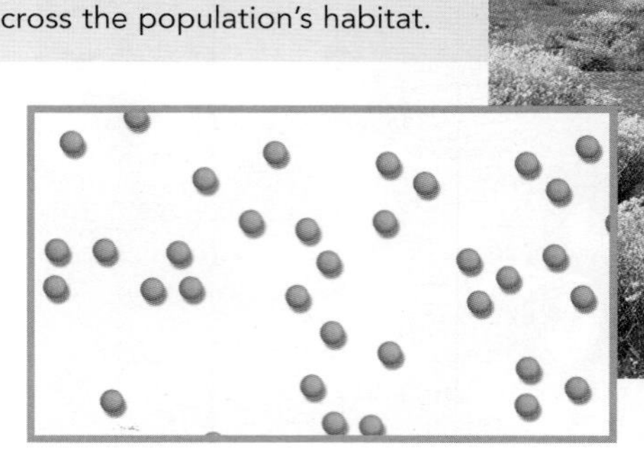

ST EST 1.4 ECOLOGICAL FACTORS

Various aspects of a habitat can affect the individuals of a population and thus the population density. The amount of food available, the number of predators, the temperature and the amount of precipitation are just a few examples. These elements are called *ecological factors*.

An ECOLOGICAL FACTOR is an aspect of a habitat that can affect the organisms living there.

There are two types of ecological factors:

- Abiotic (non-living) factors are physical or chemical aspects of the environment. For example, the pH of the water is an abiotic factor that can affect a population of brook trout in a lake.

Abiotic means the opposite of *biotic* (see below) because it contains the prefix *a-*, meaning "without."

- Biotic (living) factors are related to the actions of living organisms in a habitat. For example, preying by wolves is a biotic factor that can affect a moose herd living on a mountain.

Biotic comes from the Greek *biōtikos,* meaning "concerning life."

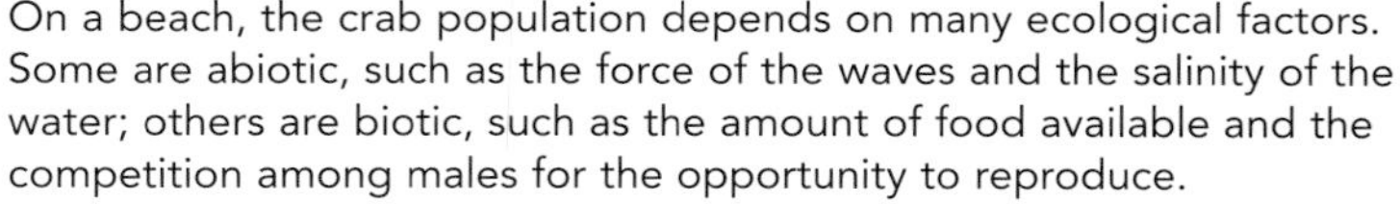

9.11 On a beach, the crab population depends on many ecological factors. Some are abiotic, such as the force of the waves and the salinity of the water; others are biotic, such as the amount of food available and the competition among males for the opportunity to reproduce.

TURTLES LEADING A DANGEROUS RACE

Turtles are pulling ahead of other living organisms, with the highest rate ever recorded in Québec—rate of *decline*, that is. Six of the eight species in the province are at serious risk.

Several factors explain the vulnerability of these animals. First, adults begin breeding very late in life, which limits the number of eggs they may lay in a lifetime. Second, turtles may look like tanks with their tough shells, but they are often preyed on by other animals. Finally, turtle reproduction is highly dependent on the weather: poor conditions can compromise the hatching of the eggs, which are buried in the sand.

This turtle is crossing the road at great risk to its life.

In Québec, the destruction of wetlands, changes to the water regime because of dams, road construction that prevents turtles from moving about freely, and certain forestry practices are all contributing to the decline in the populations of these vulnerable creatures.

Source: Adapted from Louis-Gilles Francoeur, "Les tortues en tête d'une course dangereuse," *Le Devoir*, November 18, 2005, p. B8. *[Translation]*

ABIOTIC FACTORS are ecological factors of physical or chemical origin.

BIOTIC FACTORS are ecological factors related to the actions of living organisms.

Table 9.12 presents a few examples of abiotic and biotic factors.

9.12 EXAMPLES OF ABIOTIC AND BIOTIC FACTORS

Abiotic factors	Biotic factors
Amount of light	Birth rate
Soil or water pH	Disease
Terrain	Amount of food
Depth of snow	Predation
Temperature	Competition
Air humidity	Human activity

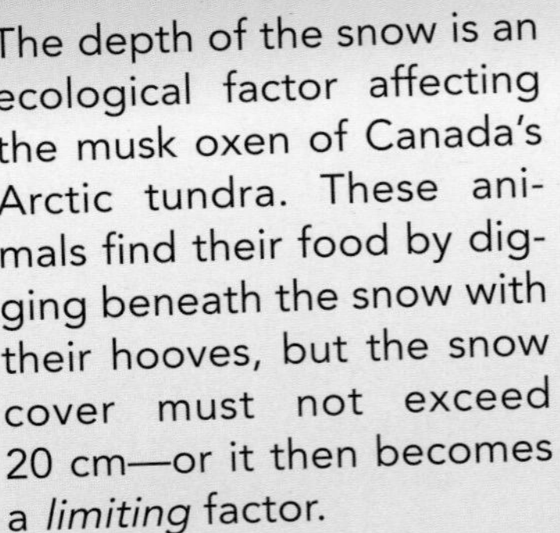

LET IT SNOW— BUT NOT TOO MUCH!

The depth of the snow is an ecological factor affecting the musk oxen of Canada's Arctic tundra. These animals find their food by digging beneath the snow with their hooves, but the snow cover must not exceed 20 cm—or it then becomes a *limiting* factor.

The intensity of an ecological factor determines its effect on the population. In some cases, the factor can be instrumental in reducing the density of a population or in preventing its growth. The ecological factor is then said to be a *limiting factor.*

A LIMITING FACTOR is an ecological factor that causes the density of a population to decrease.

An ecological factor can be limiting if it is absent from a habitat, if it is present but in insufficient quantities, or if it occurs in excess. The following are some examples of limiting factors:

- If direct sunlight is absent or insufficient in an environment, rose bushes cannot produce enough glucose through **PHOTOSYNTHESIS**. Their population density will tend to fall or even disappear. In this case, exposure to direct sunlight is a limiting factor.
- If there is too much water in the ground, cactus roots rot, and the cactus population decreases. In this case, the amount of water is a limiting factor.
- If frogs disappear from a pond after a toxic spill, there is a decline in the populations of their predators, such as water snakes. In this case, the size of the frog population is a limiting factor for the snake population.

Limiting factors explain the presence or absence of individuals in a particular habitat.

1932
1985

Dian Fossey

This American scientist devoted more than 20 years of her life to studying the mountain gorilla population in Rwanda. The thousands of hours she spent observing gorillas provided new knowledge about how they live.

ST EST 1.5 BIOLOGICAL CYCLES IN POPULATIONS

In the wild, some species repeatedly experience periods of growth in their population size, followed by periods of decline. These populations follow patterns called *biological cycles*.

The BIOLOGICAL CYCLE of a population is composed of alternating periods of rise and fall in its size. These periods are of fixed duration and are repeated continually.

Among the biological cycles that have been studied the most extensively in Québec are those of the snowshoe hare and the Canadian lynx. The hare and lynx populations share a regular cycle of approximately 10 years for a simple reason: the lynx is one of the hare's main predators.

9.13 The lynx preys on hares.

As shown in Figure 9.14, a 10-year cycle consists of periods when the hare population is high and others when it is greatly reduced.

- When the hare population rises, the lynx have more food. They eat enough hares to be healthy and to reproduce easily.

  Thus, when the hare population increases, so does the lynx population.
- When the number of lynx increases, they hunt more hares. Over time, the number of hares falls, and the lynx can no longer meet their food needs.

  Thus, when the hare population falls, so does the lynx population.
- When the lynx become fewer, they catch fewer hares.

  Thus, the number of hares increases, and the cycle repeats itself.

9.14 POPULATION CYCLES OF THE LYNX AND HARE

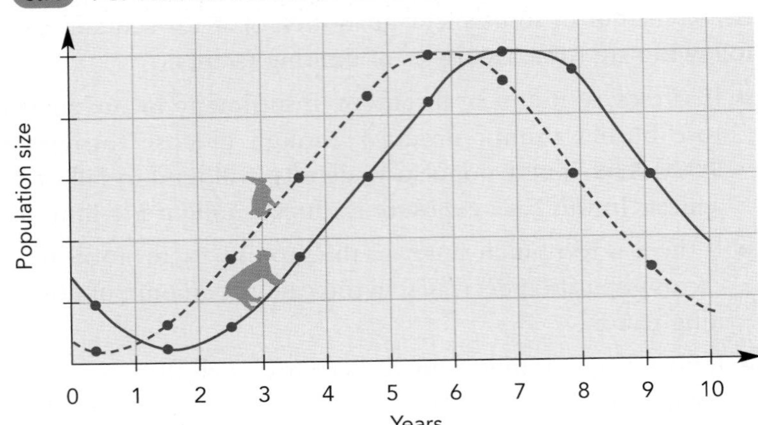

ENVIRONMENT EXTRA

Radio-tracking

To see whether predators really had a major impact on the population cycle of the hare, researchers attached radio collars to individuals of the species. With the help of this technology, ecologists were able to determine the causes of death among the hare population. They found that none of the collared individuals died of hunger, but 90 percent of them had been killed by predators (predators do not eat radio collars). The theory that predators were a main cause of death was thus confirmed.

Collars like those used in this study contain devices that emit radio waves at a set frequency. The radio waves can be captured by receivers, which indicate an animal's location. Ecologists can thus follow the movements of animals in their natural habitat. When no movement is observed for a long time, there is good reason to believe the animal is dead.

Receiving antennae are used to track the movements of animals wearing radio collars.

ST EST 2 Studying communities

If we go for a walk in the forest on a summer day, we can watch squirrels jumping from branch to branch and spot fungus growing on dead tree trunks; and we certainly notice the mosquitoes buzzing around us! When a number of species share the same habitat, the set of populations they form makes up a community. The squirrels, fungi, trees and mosquitoes in the forest are thus part of the same community. Populations living in a lake, on a mountain or in the African savanna, for example, also form communities.

Community comes from the Latin *communitas*, meaning "fellowship."

9.15 In the African savanna, many populations of different species live together, forming a community.

A COMMUNITY is a set of populations of different species sharing the same habitat.

Since populations do not usually live alone in their habitats, studying communities—which implies considering a number of populations within a habitat and the interactions between them—is an indispensable aspect of ecology.

ST EST 2.1 BIODIVERSITY

The number of species varies considerably from one community to another. For example, the variety of life in the Amazon Rainforest differs enormously from life forms in Antarctica. To record the types and numbers of species that coexist in a community is to take an interest in its biodiversity.

BIODIVERSITY describes the variety of species living in a community.

To measure the biodiversity of a community, two components must be considered:

- the number of species in the community, also known as *species richness*
- the relative abundance of each species, meaning the number of individuals of a particular species in relation to the total number of individuals in the community

Let's compare the biodiversity of two imaginary forests, Communities 1 and 2, in Figure 9.16. We can make the following observations with regard to the tree species in these communities:

- Each community contains four varieties of trees. The species richness of the two communities is therefore the same.
- In Community 1, the number of individual trees of each species is roughly the same, so the relative abundance of each species is also equal. In Community 2, species A is predominant, so the relative abundance of the other three species is comparatively low.

Therefore, in terms of tree species, the biodiversity of Community 1 is greater than that of Community 2. To establish the full extent of biodiversity in Communities 1 and 2, however, the variety of all other plant and animal species would also have to be studied.

1885
1944

Brother Marie-Victorin (born Conrad Kirouac)

After founding the Montréal Botanical Garden, this Québec botanist compiled an inventory of the province's flora. In 1935, he published a record of his work under the title *La Flore laurentienne*. The book contained over 900 pages and 2800 illustrations. It has appeared in several editions and is still in use today.

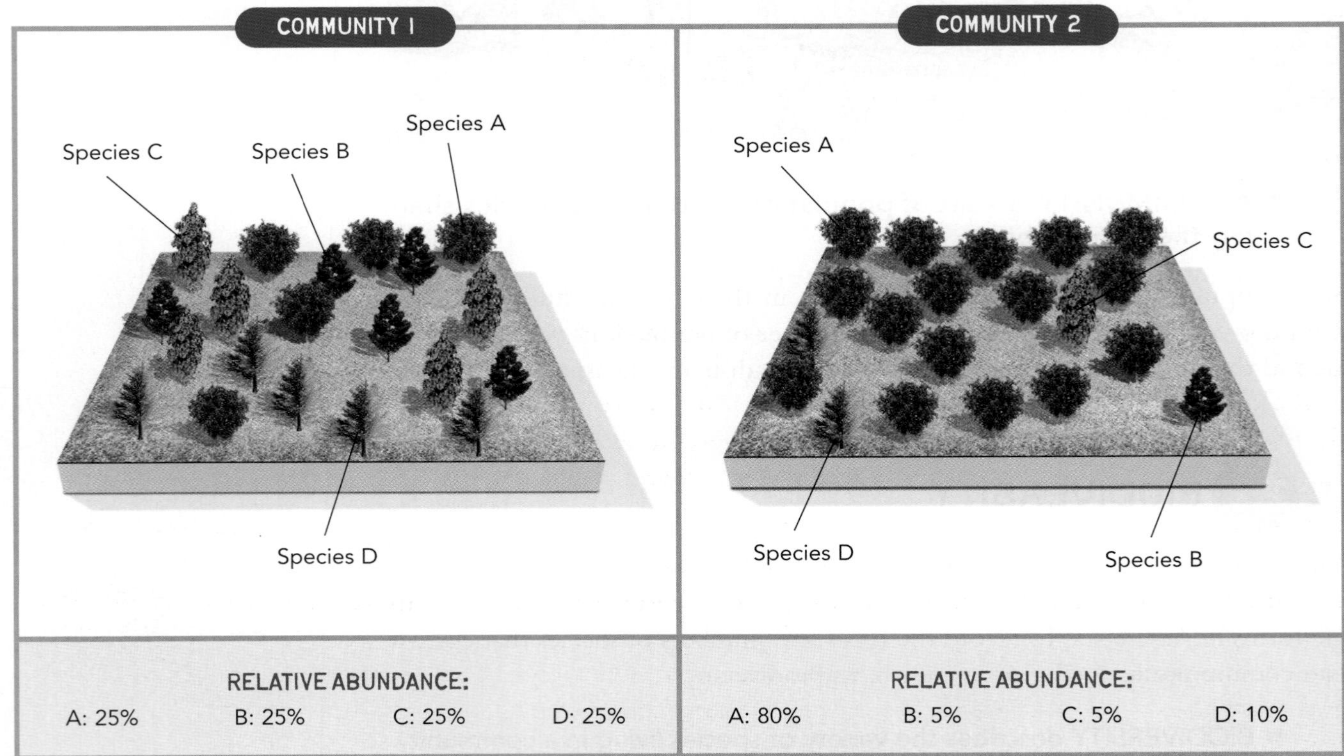

9.16 These two communities of trees have the same species richness, but the relative abundance of each species is different.

SPOTTING SPIDERS EVERYWHERE IS A GOOD SIGN

The province of Québec is home to more than 650 known species of spider. That is more than the total number of all mammal, bird, reptile and amphibian species in the province! Despite their unattractive appearance, spiders are very useful to us because they are such formidable predators. Without them, we would be overrun by flies.

During 2006, biologists compiled an inventory of the spiders living in the Parc national de la Yamaska, in Estrie. Eight thousand spiders, belonging to more than 210 species, were collected. Seven of these species were observed for the first time in the province. The most exciting discovery for the researchers was the collection of two species previously unknown both to Québec and to the world.

This research highlighted the biodiversity of Québec's natural heritage—a heritage whose full scope remains to be discovered.

Source: Adapted from Chantal Vallée, "Découvertes surprenantes," *La Voix de l'Est*, October 27, 2007. *[Translation]*

Spiders are formidable predators.

Briefly, the biodiversity of a community is high when the following two conditions are met:

- The number of species is high.
- The relative abundance of different species is similar.

In the example of Figure 9.16 (page 304), measuring biodiversity is simple. In real communities, however, the process proves much more difficult. It is nevertheless worth the effort when the time comes to plan for the conservation of natural habitats. With a measure of biodiversity, each of the species in a community can be taken into consideration.

According to a survey of species published in September 2007 by the International Union for Conservation of Nature (IUCN), global biodiversity is declining rapidly. Of the 41 415 species identified in this study, 16 306 are threatened with extinction, including one out of three amphibians, one out of four mammals, one out of eight birds and nearly three out of four plants. Fortunately, conservation measures have slowed the decline of some species, but these efforts must be sustained if they are to be effective.

ISLANDS TEEMING WITH LIFE

All the islands on Earth represent only three percent of its land mass, but they are home to 15 percent of all living species. Some of these species can be found on only one island or archipelago, like the archipelago of the Galápagos Islands.

2.2 INTERACTION BETWEEN INDIVIDUALS IN A COMMUNITY

Individuals and populations within a community do not live in isolation; they establish various relationships. A lion eating an antelope and a chickadee building its nest in the branches of a pine tree are two examples of interaction between individuals of different populations.

In the following sections, we will discuss the four main types of interaction that may occur between individuals of a community:

- competition
- predation
- mutualism
- commensalism

COMPETITION

Certain resources in a habitat are limited. In the desert, for example, all plant species compete for access to water and nutrients in the soil. In a forest, foxes, lynx and other predators compete for prey, such as hare. These species are said to be *in competition* with one another.

Competition comes from the Latin *competitio*, meaning "rivalry."

It is important to understand that, for competition to exist, an environmental resource must be limited in quantity. For a community living in a lake, for example, water is not a limited resource. For the trees of a forest, however, water can become a limited resource during periods of drought.

COMPETITION is the interaction between living organisms that seek access to the same resource in their habitat.

There are two types of competition:

- intraspecific competition, which occurs between individuals of the same species
- interspecific competition, which occurs between individuals of different species

1910
1997

Jacques-Yves Cousteau

This French oceanographer, with his team of researchers, explored the depths of the world's oceans for many years. He produced numerous films on the diversity of life in underwater communities.

9.17 In this desert, intraspecific competition for water occurs between cacti. Water is also the object of interspecific competition between cacti and other plant species.

PREDATION

ST EST

The word predation conjures up images of a crocodile killing and devouring a zebra that tries to cross a river, or other such violence. For scientists, however, predation is also the action of a deer quietly grazing. An organism does not necessarily have to die for predation to occur.

Predation comes from the Latin *praedatio*, meaning "pillage" or "robbery."

PREDATION is the interaction between two living organisms in which one feeds on the other.

The individual that feeds on another living organism is called the *predator*, while the individual being eaten, in part or in its entirety, is called the *prey*. In Figure 9.18 below, the lioness is the predator, and the kudu is the prey.

Parasitism is a form of predation. The predator-prey relationship in parasitism is described in terms of a *parasite* and a *host*. The parasite draws its food from the host by living either inside the host or on its surface. The parasite gains something from this interaction, but the host is harmed in some way. In Figure 9.19 below, the caterpillar is the parasite, and the tree is the host.

Parasitism comes from the Greek *parasitos*, made up of the words *para*, meaning "beside," and *sitos*, meaning "food."

9.18 This lioness hunting a kudu (a type of antelope) is an example of predation.

9.19 This caterpillar living on a tree and feeding on its leaves is an example of parasitism.

MUTUALISM

ST EST

In communities, two different species sometimes interact in a way that is beneficial to them both. This type of interaction is called *mutualism*.

Mutualism comes from the Latin *mutuus*, meaning "reciprocal" or "borrowed."

MUTUALISM is the interaction between two living organisms that benefits both organisms.

The relationship between the sea anemone and the clown fish is an example of mutualism. To feed, the anemone grabs its prey with its tentacles. It can also secrete venom to neutralize its prey. The clown fish, meanwhile, produces mucus on the surface of its skin, which protects it from the sea anemone's tentacles. The clown fish can take advantage of the anemone as a shelter while at the same time acting as bait for the anemone's prey, which helps the anemone. Both species thus benefit from their interaction.

Another very common example of mutualism occurs between flowering plants and pollinating species that feed off the nectar of flowers, such as hummingbirds, bees and butterflies. This interaction benefits the flowering plants, which reproduce through pollination, and the pollinators, which feed off the flowers.

9.20 The interaction between sea anemones and clown fish is a form of mutualism.

ST EST COMMENSALISM

In nature, some relationships between two species benefit one without affecting the other. This type of interaction is called *commensalism*.

Commensalism comes from the Latin *commensalis*, meaning "sharing a table."

COMMENSALISM is the interaction between two living organisms in which one organism benefits from the relationship, while the other remains unaffected.

The relationship that develops between human beings and some species of birds, such as sparrows, is an example of commensalism. These wild birds benefit from people (who are their "hosts"). The birds take advantage of the abundance of food in human-populated areas, but their presence is neither harmful nor beneficial to our species.

Similarly, when a bird or other animal builds a nest in a tree, the animal benefits from this association, while the tree is unaffected by it. Certain animals sometimes use the abandoned nest of another animal, which is also an example of commensalism.

9.21 This warbler's nest does not harm the pine tree where it is built, nor does it benefit the tree. The relationship between the warbler and its host, the pine tree, is therefore one of commensalism.

THE EFFECT OF INTERACTION BETWEEN POPULATIONS ON THEIR DENSITIES

In a community, populations interact in the same way as the individuals that form them. These interactions affect the population density.

Table 9.22 presents the four main types of interaction that can exist between the individuals of a community and the effect of these interactions on the densities of the populations concerned.

9.22 THE EFFECT OF INTERACTION BETWEEN POPULATIONS ON THEIR DENSITIES

Type of interaction	Effect on population A	Effect on population B
Competition	–	–
Predation and parasitism	+	–
Mutualism	+	+
Commensalism	+	0

- The "+" sign means the interaction tends to increase the population density.
- The "–" sign means the interaction tends to reduce the population density.
- The "0" sign means the interaction has no effect on the population density.

A VERY CLOSE RELATIONSHIP

The remora is a fish that can attach itself to animals like sharks, using a sucking disk on its head. It can thus travel long distances and avoid predators. Since it feeds off some of its host's parasites, the host also benefits from this interaction.

ENVIRONMENT EXTRA

Discovering marine communities

More than two thirds of the Earth's surface is covered in water, which harbours many different communities. For a long time, most of these communities were rarely visited by humans, and many were completely inaccessible.

The advent of scuba-diving equipment, developed in the mid-20th century by Jacques-Yves Cousteau and Émile Gagnan, opened marine biodiversity to human exploration. The "self-contained underwater breathing apparatus" (SCUBA) supplies divers with air so that they can swim freely in lakes and oceans.

More recently, the technology was further developed so that humans could study the ocean floor. For example, submersibles—small vessels designed to work under water—can dive as deep as 10 000 m. These vehicles have been essential in revealing the existence of communities in the ocean depths.

Thanks to scuba diving, humans can now explore the marine community of the St. Lawrence Estuary, at Les Escoumins.

CHECKUP

ST 1–19 and A–C.	AST None.
EST 1–19 and A–C.	SE None.

1 Studying populations (pp. 292–302)

1. What do the living organisms that form a population have in common?
2. Give two examples of a plant population and two examples of an animal population.
3. How can knowing the size of a wolf population be useful?
4. For each of the following examples, name the factor that makes the population size vary (births, deaths, immigration or emigration) and specify its effect.
   a) Every spring, Canada geese return to the shores of Lac Tranquille.
   b) During a logging operation, the noise from the forestry vehicles scared away the white-tailed deer in the vicinity.
   c) In the spring, a female bear nurses her three cubs in her den.
   d) Fish farmers stock a river with salmon fry.
   e) Cottage owners can eliminate voles by installing traps in the roof.

   Write your answers in a table like the one below.

Example	Factor	Effect on population size
a)		

5. What happens to a population when death and emigration rates are higher than birth and immigration rates?
6. The photos below show a slug (A), an American robin (B) and a bison (C). What would be the most appropriate method for measuring the size of a population of each of these species?

7. Scientists want to determine the size of a population of brook trout in a lake. First, they catch 50 trout, tag them and release them. A few days later, they catch 55 trout, including 11 tagged fish.
   a) Which method for measuring population size did the scientists use?
   b) What is the estimated population of brook trout in this lake? Show your calculations.

8. The twelve-spotted lady beetle feeds on the eggs of the Colorado potato beetle (a pest that attacks potato plants).

Biologists wanted to study the population of this type of lady beetle in a potato field of 10 000 m^2, so they counted the number of individuals in one-square-metre quadrats. The table below presents the results of this sampling.

Quadrat number	Number of twelve-spotted lady beetles	Quadrat number	Number of twelve-spotted lady beetles
1	2	6	0
2	1	7	0
3	0	8	1
4	1	9	1
5	0	10	0

a) What is the size of the population of twelve-spotted lady beetles in the field under study? Show your calculations.

b) What is the population density of twelve-spotted lady beetles in the field under study? Show your calculations.

c) If the population of twelve-spotted lady beetles were higher than the Colorado potato beetle population, what would happen?

9. The table below contains statistics on the human population and the area of Canadian provinces and territories (according to Statistics Canada, April 1, 2007).

Province or territory	Population	Total area (km^2)
Nfld.	506 548	405 212
P.E.I.	138 800	5 660
N.S.	932 966	55 284
N.B.	748 878	72 908
Québec	7 687 068	1 542 056
Ontario	12 753 702	1 076 395
Manitoba	1 182 921	647 797
Saskatchewan	990 212	651 036
Alberta	3 455 062	661 848
B.C.	4 352 798	944 735
Yukon	30 883	482 443
N.W.T.	41 795	1 346 106
Nunavut	31 216	2 093 190

a) In which province or territory is the population density the lowest?

b) In which province or territory is the population density the highest?

c) How does Québec rank in population density compared to the other provinces and territories?

10. a) What is the main factor affecting the density of any population?

b) Name two other factors that have an impact on population density.

11. Given that most of the Canadian population lives in cities, what is the pattern of population distribution in our country?

12. Which pattern of distribution is illustrated by each of the following situations?
   a) In a forest, the fir trees are scattered about at random.
   b) Fungi grow in colonies on the trunks of dead trees.
   c) Several clouds of mayflies hover over a lake.
   d) The hummingbirds in a valley aggressively defend their respective territories; they tend to build their nests at equal distances from one another.

13. Do the studies described below relate to a biotic or an abiotic factor?
   a) An ecologist studies the effect of hares' browsing on a population of fir trees.
   b) Chemists test the acidity of a soil sample.
   c) A water specialist assesses the amount of sunlight at different depths in a lake.
   d) Ecologists test a river for amounts of phosphorus from agricultural fertilizers.

14. Is the amount of oxygen in a lake a limiting factor for a population of fish (bass or trout, for example)? Explain your answer.

15. Why does the size of the hare population in Québec decrease when the size of the lynx population increases?

2 Studying communities (pp. 303–309)

16. The Earth is home to many communities.
   a) What do the living organisms that form a community have in common?
   b) What is a community composed of?

17. The Amazon Rainforest, in South America, is considered the most diverse forest habitat on Earth. What criteria do scientists use to establish the degree of biodiversity in a community?

18. Look at the photo below and answer the following questions.

   a) What is the interaction between the bee and the flower called?
   b) If a bumblebee flies up to the flower to feed on its nectar, how will the first bee and the bumblebee interact?
   c) If a bird eats the bee, what type of interaction would that be?
   d) If aphids attack the flower and damage its leaves, what would be the interaction between the aphids and the flower?
   e) If a spider spins a web, attaching one of its threads to the flower stem, what would be the interaction between the spider and the flower?

19. True or false? Explain your answers.
   a) The biodiversity of a community can be qualified as high when one species in the community is much more abundant than other species.
   b) In a relationship of parasitism, one of the living organisms is a parasite, and the other is its prey.
   c) When populations in a community interact through mutualism, this interaction tends to increase their population densities.
   d) Competition has a positive impact on population density.
   e) Parasitism and predation refer to exactly the same phenomenon.

review questions

A. The mark-recapture method was used to estimate the size of the groundhog population in a field. According to this estimate, the population was 50.

a) Subsequent studies of groundhog behaviour revealed that these animals can recognize a trap more easily if they have already been captured. In light of this new information, is the estimate of the size of the groundhog population too high or too low? Explain your answer.

b) Recapturing took place in May, when it was observed that many females were about to give birth. In light of this information, is the groundhog population more likely to grow or decrease?

c) Explain why quadrat sampling would not have been appropriate for estimating the size of the groundhog population.

B. During a study on a population of red fox, many of these animals are discovered to live near the groundhog population of the previous question.

a) Since foxes may feed on groundhogs, what type of interaction connects these two populations?

b) Do the fox and groundhog populations form a community? Explain your answer.

c) How does the presence of foxes affect the density of the groundhog population?

d) Explain why the size of the fox population could not be calculated using aerial photography and suggest an appropriate method for estimating the population size.

C. Prepare your own summary of Chapter 9 by building a concept map.

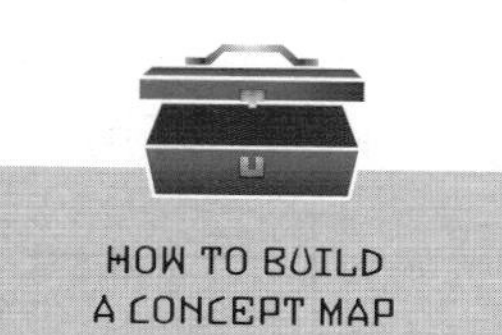

HOW TO BUILD A CONCEPT MAP

FOLLOW-UP

Saving a species at risk

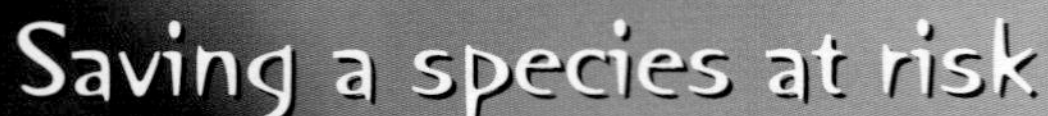

RESCUING THE PEREGRINE FALCON

The peregrine falcon is a bird of prey that can attack at more than 300 km/h. During World War II, the number of peregrine falcons dropped considerably: because their main prey is other birds, they were killed to protect the carrier pigeons used for sending messages. Later, over a period of about 20 years, peregrine falcons declined considerably in Canada due to the use of DDT, a very effective agricultural pesticide, which has now been banned. DDT caused the birds to lay eggs with thin, fragile shells that would break during incubation. The number of births fell. The species was in danger: it was time for a rescue.

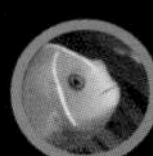

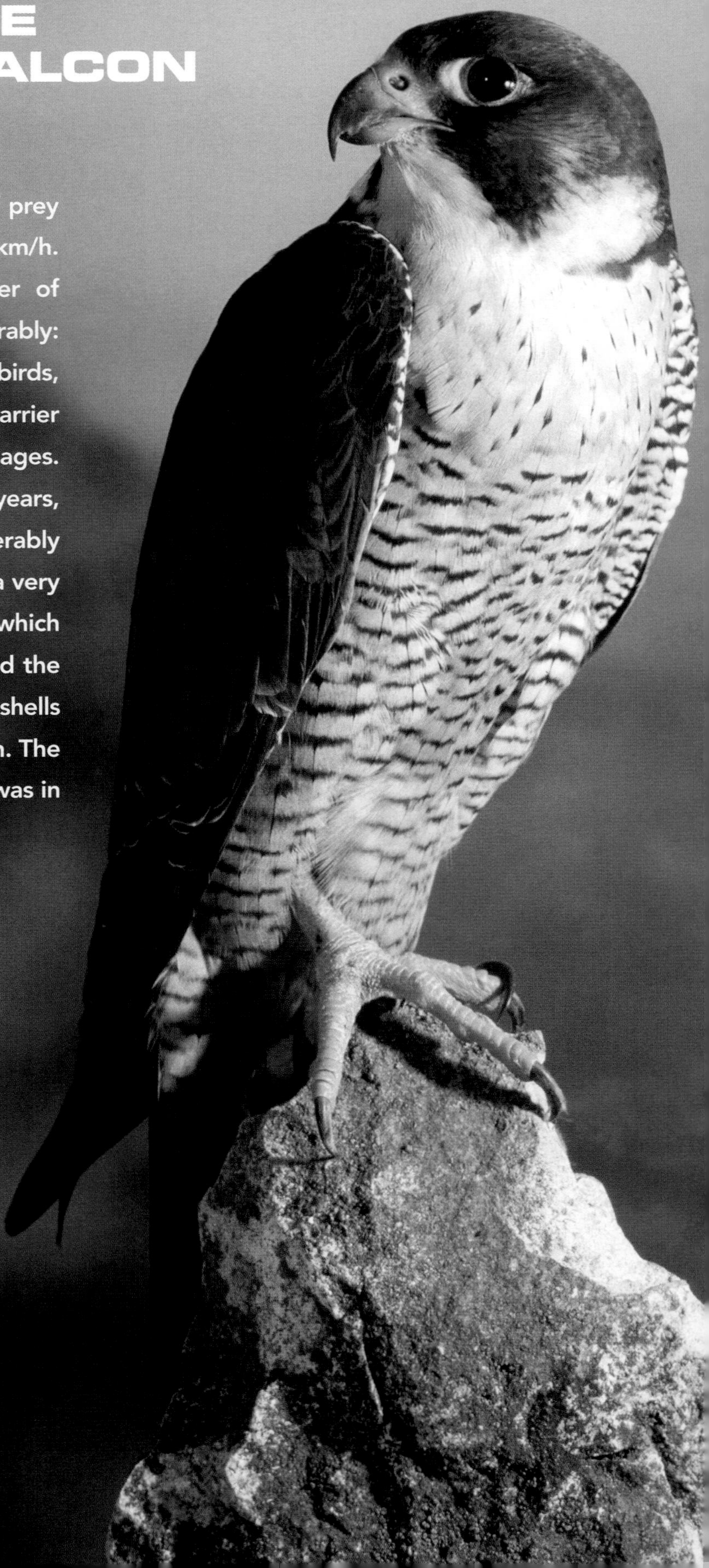

BIRTHS IN CAPTIVITY

In the early 1970s, the Canadian population of peregrine falcons had been reduced to 90 individuals. None lived in the south of the country, and only a few dozen pairs remained in the Yukon and the Northwest Territories. During this period, DDT use became severely restricted in farming because of its harmful effects on the environment, and specifically on peregrine falcons. Scientists observed, however, that DDT restrictions alone would not be enough to save the falcons. A greater effort was needed.

An innovative program was created, in which falcons were raised in captivity and then released back into their natural habitats. This was a new type of experiment, and many people simply did not believe it could work. The first attempts were met with problems, but scientists persevered. They found that if eggs were removed from the nest as they were laid, the females would rapidly lay more. Artificial insemination was used, to add to the number of births from natural mating. Little by little, researchers learned how to deal with young falcons. The research on falcons was applied elsewhere, expanding knowledge about how to raise various species in captivity.

It took almost 25 years to meet the challenge. At the end of the program, in 1996, more than 1600 falcons had been released into the Canadian wild from research facilities in Alberta and from universities in Québec and Saskatchewan. In the same year, the Canadian government drew up a national strategy for the protection of species at risk. In 1999, there were 600 peregrine falcon pairs in Canada, and that number had doubled by the following year. The Species at Risk Act, which called for collaboration between federal and provincial governments, was adopted in 2002. It included a ban on the killing, capture and harassment of peregrine falcons.

Today, the Committee on the Status of Endangered Wildlife in Canada (COSEWIC) makes regular scientific assessments of the evolution of different animal species. The *anatum* peregrine falcon, the most prevalent in the south of the country, was classified an "endangered species" in 1978. Thanks to conservation efforts, it now belongs to the "special concern" category. This means that

A peregrine chick

it is no longer endangered but still a cause for concern because of characteristics that make it vulnerable to human activity and certain natural phenomena.

THE FUTURE OF THE PEREGRINE FALCON

Today, the amounts of DDT in the Canadian environment are too low to be a threat to peregrine falcons. The future of the species could be secure as long as its habitat is preserved. Some peregrine falcons migrate to South America, however, where countries still use DDT to kill mosquitoes that transmit malaria to humans. The case of the peregrine falcon is thus another concrete example of how protecting biodiversity is a global issue.

1. Do you think that the methods used to save peregrine falcons could be applied to all other endangered species?
2. Peregrine falcons feed on other birds, especially pigeons. These birds of prey are now introduced into airports. Explain how they can be useful in such places.

2005 Granting of LEED certification (for green buildings) to the Biological Sciences building at UQAM

1998 Launch of the French satellite *Spot 4*, whose mission includes the observation of vegetation on Earth

1992 Definition of the concept of ecological footprint

1972 Ban on the use of DDT (dichlorodiphenyltrichloroethane) in Canada because of its harmful effects on ecosystems

1949 Publication of the Hodge and Sterner scale of contaminant toxicity

1939 Discovery of the insecticidal properties of DDT

1935 Coining of the term *ecosystem*

1931 Official founding of the Montréal Botanical Garden

1889 Construction of the world's first wastewater treatment plant

1866 Popularization of the term *ecology*

1864 Formulation of the equation for photosynthesis

CIRCA -500 Development of composting techniques

CIRCA -3000 Construction of early sewers and aqueducts

Nature contains many different habitats—deserts, seas, forests, ponds, etc.—and a multitude of living organisms and nonliving components can be found in each. All living organisms feed, grow and reproduce. To do this, they need energy.

Where do life forms find this energy? What happens when their habitats are disturbed? Humans produce a lot of waste: How does it affect the environment?

Studying ecosystems will help us answer these questions. But first, we must understand what an ecosystem is.

THE LIVING WORLD

10

Ecosystems

CONTENTS

ST
EST
AST

1 What is an ecosystem?

CONCEPT REVIEW

- Ecological niche
- Forms of energy (chemical, thermal, mechanical, radiation)

In the previous chapter, we discussed the first three levels of ecological organization occurring in nature: the individual, the **POPULATION** and the **COMMUNITY**. These three levels relate to organisms living in a single habitat.

Level 1:
Individual

Level 2:
Population

Level 3:
Community

Level 4:
Ecosystem

An environment does not consist solely of living organisms, however; it also contains nonliving components, such as temperature, light, soil elements, etc. These nonliving components can affect living organisms. When life and the nonliving are both taken into consideration in an environment, then its study has reached a fourth ecological level: the ecosystem.

10.1 After the individual, the population and the community, the fourth level of ecological organization is the ecosystem.

An ECOSYSTEM is a community of living organisms interacting with one another and with the nonliving components of the environment they inhabit.

Examples of ecosystems are many and varied: a forest, a lake, an aquarium, an island and a mountain all constitute ecosystems. The size and composition of an ecosystem vary from one example to another.

10.2 Ecosystems can be big or small, and very diverse.

ST EST AST 1.1 INTERACTIONS WITHIN AN ECOSYSTEM: TROPHIC RELATIONSHIPS

For scientists, ecosystems are natural "machines" that transform the matter and energy in an environment. All the living organisms in an ecosystem need energy to survive, and they obtain it by feeding on the matter (food) in their environment. The organisms in an ecosystem are thus connected by feeding relationships, which are referred to as *trophic relationships*.

Trophic comes from the Greek *trophē*, meaning "nourishment."

TROPHIC RELATIONSHIPS are the feeding connections among the living organisms in an ecosystem.

Trophic relationships between living organisms are often represented by a **FOOD CHAIN**. The chain is made up of a series of organisms, in which each member eats the preceding one. The position of each organism in a chain corresponds to its **TROPHIC LEVEL**. Food chains contain the following trophic levels:

- producers
- consumers
- decomposers

Figure 10.3 shows a food chain with examples of these three trophic levels.

1871
1955

Arthur George Tansley

This British ecologist coined the term *ecosystem* in 1935 to refer to the interaction between living organisms and their environment. Previously, ecology had been a science that sought to explain why species are present in a given environment.

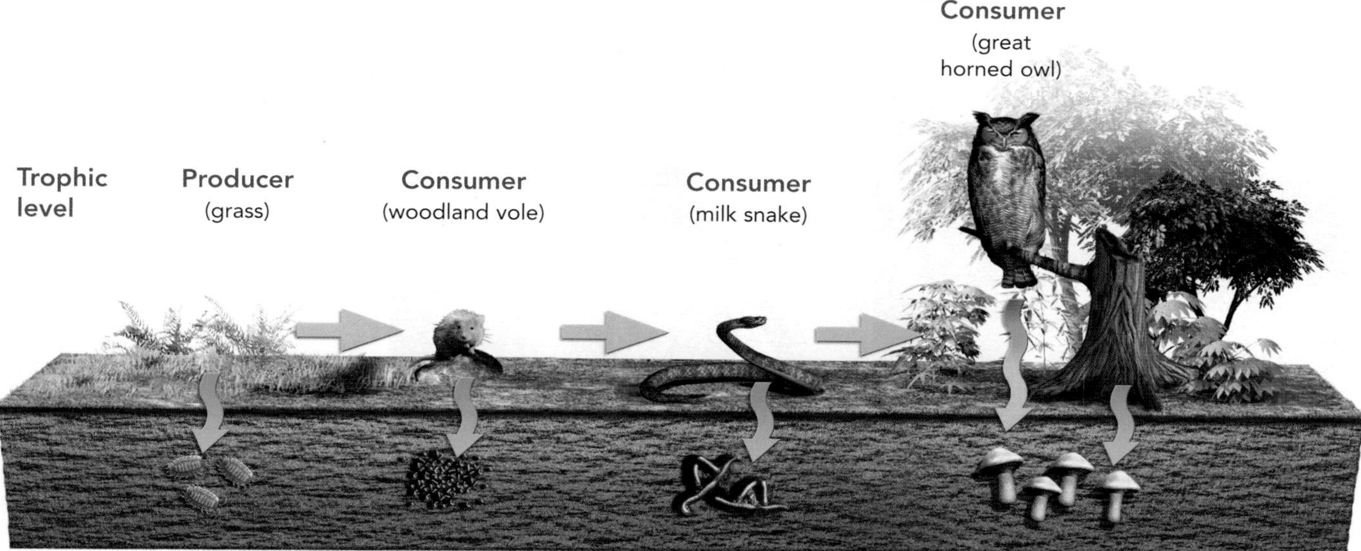

10.3 An example of a food chain in a woodland ecosystem. The arrows show the feeding relationships between the organisms.

ST
EST
AST

PRODUCERS

Organisms like plants, algae and certain bacteria can transform inorganic matter in the environment into organic matter. (Table 10.4 explains the difference between **ORGANIC MATTER** and **INORGANIC MATTER**.) This means that these organisms can use matter, such as water and soil elements, and energy, such as sunlight, to produce the material of life. They can thus feed themselves without having to ingest other organisms. They are called *autotrophs*.

Autotroph comes from the Greek words *autos*, meaning "self," and *trophē*, meaning "nourishment."

10.4 THE TWO CATEGORIES OF MATTER

Category	Description	Examples
Inorganic matter	Matter that is not necessarily produced by living organisms	Water, mineral salts
Organic matter	Matter that enters into the composition of living organisms and that is usually created by them	Proteins, lipids

AUTOTROPHS are at the bottom of the food chain because they are the organisms that introduce energy into the ecosystem. They use sunlight, carbon dioxide and soil nutrients, among other things, to produce organic matter. For this reason, they are called *producers*.

▶ **PRODUCERS are autotrophic organisms with the ability to create organic matter from inorganic matter in an ecosystem.**

10.5 Plants are the primary producers in terrestrial ecosystems. In aquatic ecosystems, the producers are mainly algae and microorganisms called *phytoplankton*.

In nature, **PHOTOSYNTHESIS** is the principal mechanism behind the transformation of inorganic matter into organic matter. By using sunlight to produce the energy they need, plants feed themselves and grow.

ST EST AST CONSUMERS

Many living organisms in an ecosystem are incapable of producing food themselves. They are called *heterotrophs*. The group is made up of organisms that obtain the energy they need by eating other living organisms or their products (eggs, fruit, etc.). In a food chain, **HETEROTROPHS** are called *consumers*.

> *Heterotroph* comes from the Greek words *heteros*, meaning "other," and *trophē*, meaning "nourishment."

CONSUMERS are heterotrophic organisms that feed on other living organisms.

Consumers can be divided into different types, as illustrated in Figure 10.3 (page 319):

- Primary, or *first-order*, consumers feed on producers or their seeds and fruit. Herbivores, including granivorous (seed-eating) and frugivorous (fruit-eating) species, are usually primary consumers. In Figure 10.3, the woodland vole is a primary consumer.
- Consumers of the second, third and fourth orders eat consumers of the respective preceding order. Species in the second order or higher are therefore usually carnivorous. In the food chain in Figure 10.3, the milk snake is a second-order (secondary) consumer, and the great horned owl, a third-order (tertiary) consumer.

Note that the same animal can be a consumer of a different order depending on its position in another food chain. For example, if the great horned owl had eaten the woodland vole, then it would be a secondary consumer.

10.6 A great horned owl

Some animals, called *omnivores*, are consumers of several orders at once. Bears, for example, feed on plants and other animals. They can thus be first-, second- or third-order consumers depending on what they eat.

> *Omnivore* comes from the Latin words *omnis*, meaning "all," and *vorare*, meaning "devour."

ST
EST
AST

DECOMPOSERS

Finally, a food chain also contains decomposers, which are connected to all the trophic levels. Decomposers feed on detritus, which is dead organic matter, such as fallen leaves, wood from dead trees, animal remains and excrement. Decomposers break down this organic matter into inorganic matter.

Decomposers are thus **DETRITIVORES**. Certain worms, all fungi, some bacteria and certain insects, such as sow bugs, are decomposers. They are heterotrophs and can be eaten by consumers.

> **DECOMPOSERS are organisms that feed on the waste and remains of other living organisms.**

More than one food chain is possible in an ecosystem. For example, various animals can graze on the grass in a forest, and those animals may be eaten by a number of different predators. An ecosystem thus contains many trophic relationships. A representation of all these relationships is called a **TROPHIC NETWORK** (or *food web*).

10.7 Consumers can feed on decomposers. For example, birds (like the American robin in this photo) eat earthworms.

10.8 This diagram represents the simplified food web of a woodland ecosystem. The arrows illustrate the various food chains possible. The white arrows show that decomposers are connected to all the trophic levels.

ST EST AST

1.2 ECOSYSTEM DYNAMICS

As we saw in the previous section, matter is transformed in an ecosystem. As a result, a transfer of energy takes place. Through trophic relationships, matter and energy within an ecosystem are exchanged from one organism to another in a process that is referred to as a *material and energy flow*.

> **The MATERIAL AND ENERGY FLOW is the exchange of matter and energy between the living organisms in an ecosystem and between those organisms and their environment.**

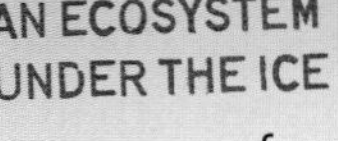

AN ECOSYSTEM UNDER THE ICE

A team of researchers has discovered a 10 000-year-old ecosystem in Antarctica, lying under 200 m of ice. It is home to a variety of about 1000 species, including spiders, small crustaceans, jellyfish and corals, which manage to survive in the freezing cold waters of the ocean depths.

ST EST AST

MATERIAL FLOW AND CHEMICAL RECYCLING

According to Antoine Laurent de Lavoisier's **LAW OF CONSERVATION OF MASS**, nothing is lost, and nothing is created; matter is *transformed*. The law is valid not only in the laboratory; it also applies to the matter in an ecosystem.

Producers are continually changing inorganic matter from the environment into organic matter. At this constant rate, all the inorganic matter might be expected to disappear with time, transformed into organic matter. Producers would no longer be able to find food and would die, putting the entire ecosystem at risk.

ENVIRONMENT EXTRA

Vermicomposting

In Québec, an estimated 40 to 50 percent of the volume of our household waste consists of table scraps and lawn and garden residue. Instead of sending this waste to the dump, homeowners can give it a second life by adopting a biotechnology called *vermicomposting*. This technique makes use of earthworms that can survive in boxes, such as *Eisenia foetida*, better known as *redworms*. The method is so clean and simple that it can even be used to make compost inside the home. All you need is a compost bin containing the worms and some food for them. They will eat just about any kind of kitchen or garden waste and turn it into compost.

Redworms are decomposers that can be used to make compost.

Two main reasons explain the growing popularity of composting organic waste. First, the process reduces the volume of our household waste. Second, it produces a natural and inexpensive fertilizer rich in the elements that our lawns, gardens and house plants need to grow.

However, decomposers break down the organic matter in the detritus they feed on, producing the inorganic matter that plants need, such as nitrogen, potassium and phosphorus. This is the process involved in composting. Producers thus have continual access to inorganic matter and so can create organic matter. This phenomenon of ecosystems is called *chemical recycling*.

CHEMICAL RECYCLING is a natural phenomenon by which decomposers make inorganic matter available in an ecosystem by breaking down organic matter.

Matter passes from one state to another, but it remains in circulation in the ecosystem. For example, when a hare grazes on clover, the substances contained in the clover are transferred to the hare. Then, if a lynx eats the hare, the predator gains access to the matter now in the hare, and so on. In the end, the matter in the detritus left by the living organisms becomes available to decomposers, which break it down into inorganic matter and return it to the ecosystem, where it can be used once again by the clover.

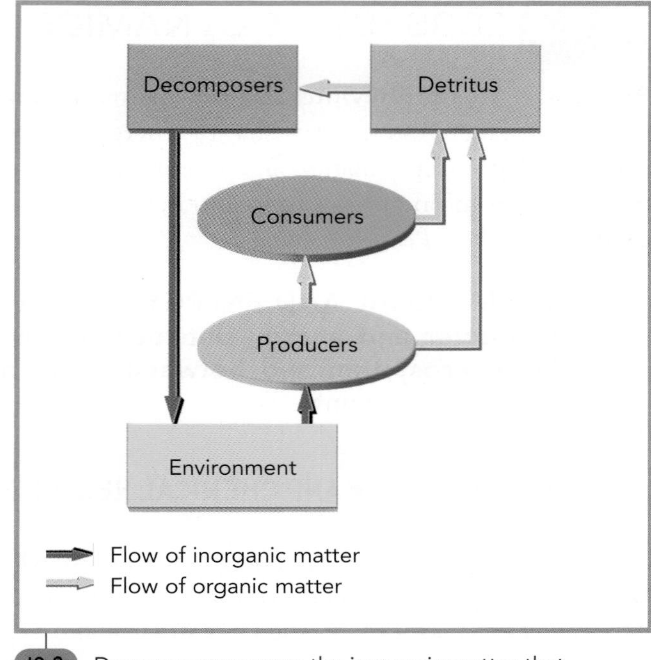

10.9 Decomposers renew the inorganic matter that producers use to create organic matter. This is the process of chemical recycling in an ecosystem.

ENERGY FLOW

Matter is not the only thing that circulates in an ecosystem. The energy stored in plants is also in flux.

Sunlight is usually the primary source of energy in an ecosystem. Through the action of autotrophic organisms, part of the radiation energy that enters the ecosystem is transformed into chemical energy and then passed on to consumers. At every trophic level, organisms obtain energy from their food and store it in their tissues.

A large part of this energy is always lost, however, as it passes from one trophic level to the next. At each level, organisms release some energy in the form of waste. They also use a considerable amount of energy to perform various activities, such as moving, growing or reproducing. Part of the energy loss takes the form of heat. For example, when we run for a certain length of time, we use a lot of energy and give off heat.

Unlike matter, the energy in an ecosystem is never recycled. Ecosystems must receive a continual supply of new energy from the sun.

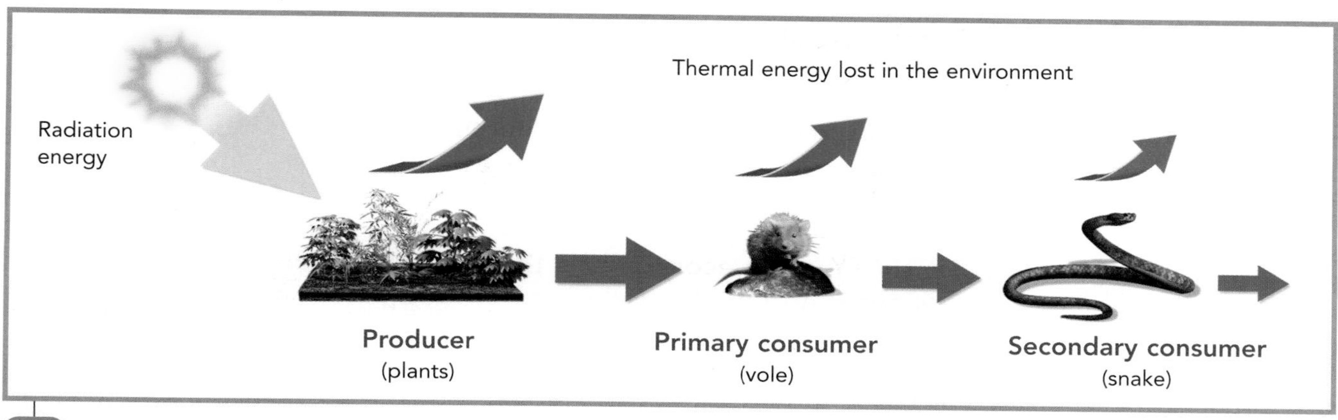

10.10 An example of energy flow in an ecosystem. The blue arrows illustrate the energy transfer from one trophic level to the next, and the red arrows, the energy loss at each level.

1.3 PRIMARY PRODUCTIVITY IN ECOSYSTEMS

One of the most important parameters in the study of ecosystems is the mass of new organic matter they produce. The total mass of all organic matter (plant and animal) in an ecosystem is called the *biomass*.

PHYTOPLANKTON UNDER THREAT

Satellite data show that the concentration of phytoplankton in the North Atlantic has plummeted by 30 percent since 1979. The drop is a serious cause for concern because these microorganisms living in the upper layer of ocean waters play an essential role in the food chain and in carbon dioxide (CO_2) recycling.

This satellite image shows the chlorophyll levels in the oceans, indicating the quantity of phytoplankton. The lighter the colour (yellow), the greater the concentration of phytoplankton in the zone. (Data collected by the MODIS instrument on the NASA *Aqua* satellite, between July 1, 2002 and December 31, 2004.)

Almost half of the photosynthesis on Earth is carried out by phytoplankton. It thus captures roughly one third of the CO_2 humans release into the atmosphere—between six and seven billion tonnes a year—and transforms it into the organic matter it needs to grow. Phytoplankton serve as food for zooplankton (another type of organism, without photosynthesis capacities), which, in turn, are eaten by many marine animals.

Scientists believe that two factors can explain the drop in phytoplankton levels: the rising temperature of surface waters in the oceans and the change in wind force.

The BIOMASS is the total mass of organic matter in an ecosystem at any given time.

As we saw previously, new organic matter is generated by producers. This matter is the new biomass of the ecosystem. Measuring the amount of new biomass reveals the primary productivity of the ecosystem.

The PRIMARY PRODUCTIVITY of an ecosystem is the amount of new biomass generated by its producers.

This measure is important because it represents the amount of energy available to primary consumers. It thus directly influences the number of living organisms that may inhabit an ecosystem. The more new organic matter created in an environment, the greater the capacity of the ecosystem to supply energy to many constituent organisms.

The primary productivity of an ecosystem may vary depending on several factors. Since primary productivity is associated with the creation of new biomass by producers, the growth of these producers (plants, phytoplankton, etc.) must be supported to maintain a high level of productivity. Factors that influence primary productivity in an ecosystem include the following:

- the amount of light because the radiation energy of the sun is necessary for photosynthesis
- the amount of water available because water, too, is necessary for photosynthesis
- access to essential nutrients for producers, especially carbon, nitrogen, phosphorus and potassium
- the temperature because some weather conditions promote the growth of producers

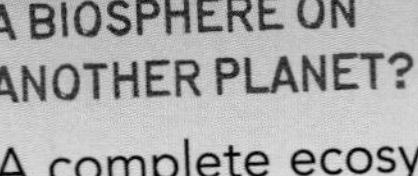
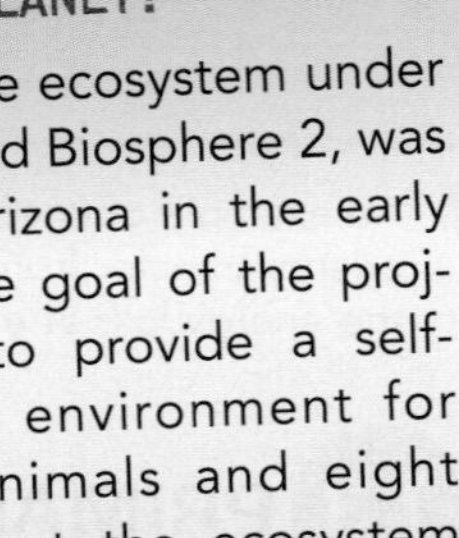
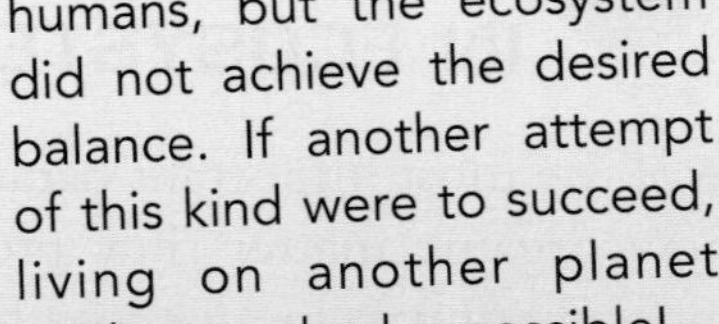

A BIOSPHERE ON ANOTHER PLANET?

A complete ecosystem under glass, called Biosphere 2, was built in Arizona in the early 1990s. The goal of the project was to provide a self-sufficient environment for plants, animals and eight humans, but the ecosystem did not achieve the desired balance. If another attempt of this kind were to succeed, living on another planet might one day be possible!

10.11 A polar terrestrial ecosystem is less productive than a forest ecosystem because the polar environment contains fewer plants. Weather conditions are not favourable to plant growth.

ST EST AST 2 Disturbances

Sooner or later, ecosystems are subjected to disturbances. A period of drought, a snowstorm or an oil spill, for example, will result in a change in the ecosystem dynamics.

A DISTURBANCE is an event that damages an ecosystem. It can lead to the elimination of organisms and alter the availability of resources.

10.12 An oil spill is a disturbance that can be disastrous for an ecosystem.

The type, frequency and seriousness of the disturbances to an ecosystem can vary depending on the situation.

- Disturbances can be of different types. In ecosystems like those in Québec, snowstorms are common. In other ecosystems, events such as sandstorms, hurricanes or volcanic eruptions may occur instead.
- Disturbances may vary in frequency. In Québec, some rivers tend to flood the surrounding land every spring, while other rivers only occasionally cause flooding, in the event of torrential rain.
- Disturbances can be more or less serious in nature. An ice storm will cause less damage to an ecosystem if it lasts only a few hours than if it lasts several days, like the storm in Québec in January 1998.

Disturbances can be of either natural or human origin, as you will see in the following two sections.

1911 –

Pierre Dansereau

Pierre Dansereau is one of the best-known ecologists in Canada. He was one of the first scientists to consider the role of humans in ecosystem dynamics. His expertise in ecology and research on ecosystems are recognized worldwide.

ST EST AST 2.1 NATURAL DISTURBANCES

Natural disturbances are many and varied. They are events triggered by environmental phenomena rather than by humans, but they damage ecosystems nonetheless.

Storms are natural disturbances. They can have an impact on almost every different type of ecosystem, even those at the bottom of the ocean. With the churning waves caused by a storm, surface and subsurface waters become mixed. Populations living in the ocean depths can thus be affected by storms at the surface.

In addition to storms, examples of natural disturbances include volcanic eruptions, forest fires, droughts, floods, periods of frost, and heat waves.

10.13 A hurricane is an example of a natural disturbance that can cause enormous damage to an ecosystem.

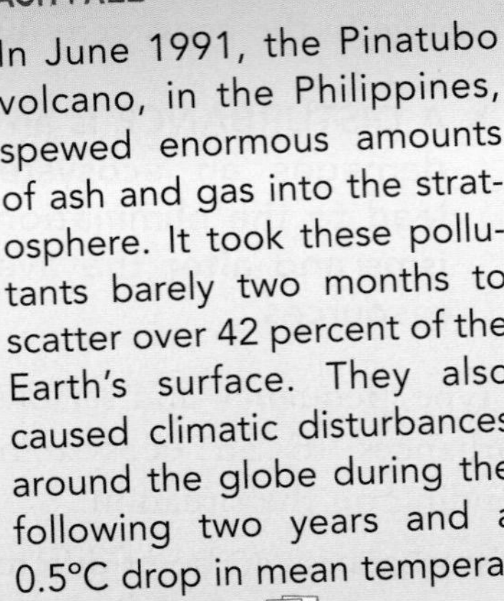

FAR-REACHING ASH FALL

In June 1991, the Pinatubo volcano, in the Philippines, spewed enormous amounts of ash and gas into the stratosphere. It took these pollutants barely two months to scatter over 42 percent of the Earth's surface. They also caused climatic disturbances around the globe during the following two years and a 0.5°C drop in mean temperatures in 1992. 14

HUMAN DISTURBANCES

Humans remain the principal source of environmental disturbances on Earth. Many human activities have a damaging effect on ecosystems, from individual acts like littering to large-scale projects.

For example, logging operations disrupt forest ecosystems. Oil spills at sea harm organisms living in marine ecosystems: aquatic plants, birds and marine animals die because of these incidents.

10.14 Mining is an example of a human disturbance in an ecosystem.

ST EST AST 2.3 ECOLOGICAL SUCCESSION

After suffering a disturbance, an ecosystem will undergo a series of gradual changes, sometimes spread out over hundreds of years, until it regains a state of balance. This series of changes in an ecosystem is called *ecological succession*.

ECOLOGICAL SUCCESSION is the series of changes that occur in an ecosystem after a disturbance and that continue until the balance of the ecosystem is restored.

Any alteration in an ecosystem leads to change, especially among animal and plant populations. For example, if a disturbance causes the trees in an area to disappear, the birds that used to nest in them will leave the habitat. Other species that were previously absent from the area—like field mice, for example—will appear because of the available resources (food and shelter). The presence or absence of living organisms also brings about change to an environment. The appearance of field mice in the ecosystem, for example, will attract their predators to it. Each change leads to another.

CONSERVATION QUANDARY: TREES OR OWLS?

It seems unusual for an ecologist to advocate clear-cutting, but that is exactly what a B.C. forest ecologist is suggesting for certain kinds of forest. Hamish Kimmins, a professor at the University of British Columbia, believes that different types of forest benefit from different kinds of management. Some may flourish with selective logging; others need clear-cutting, however destructive it may seem. The key, he believes, is to match the style of logging to the disturbances the forests would experience in nature. "Citizens have a responsibility to balance their emotional response to the forest against a respect for ecology, a respect for nature, so that we can maintain a wide range of resources and ecosystem conditions far into the future."

The northern spotted owl is a species vulnerable to logging operations.

Logging companies make money by selectively extracting red cedar, the most valuable species, but this system is flawed because cedar saplings need a lot of light to grow to maturity. Regeneration is actually more successful when a larger opening is made in the forest because the trees have the light they need to grow back naturally, without replanting. The second-growth stands will actually contain a similar mix to the original stand that was harvested, including red cedars.

On the other hand, clear-cutting is worse for wildlife. B.C. environmentalists are losing hope for Canada's population of northern spotted owls. The province was once home to several hundred breeding pairs, but numbers fell by half during the 1980s and are now estimated at only 17 individuals.

The threat to the spotted owl has been clearly identified: habitat destruction and logging. A special resource management area was identified for the species, but the government has allowed logging in that area, including clear-cutting. Here, sustainability of the local wildlife is being set against economic sustainability of the local community.

In British Columbia, it seems, society has yet to work out which values it wants most, and the clash between strands of society, and various definitions of sustainability, awaits resolution.

Source: Adapted from Richard Black, "Canada's search for sustainable logging," *BBC News* [online], October 4, 2006. (Accessed November 7, 2008.)

EST 2.4 ECOLOGICAL FOOTPRINTS

Many ecosystems on Earth are disturbed by humans because we need to develop part of the world's resources to survive. For example, to sustain human life, a certain area of the Earth's surface is used to cultivate fruit and vegetables, raise livestock, grow trees for timber and drill for oil. Moreover, all the waste we produce during our lifetimes, all the factories we build to manufacture goods and all the homes we live in take up space on Earth. By estimating the area that a person takes up and uses in his or her daily life, we can determine that person's ecological footprint. With this tool, we can measure the impact of human activities on ecosystems.

ECOLOGICAL FOOTPRINTS are estimates of the surface area individual humans or populations require to obtain the resources for satisfying all their needs and to ensure the disposal of their waste.

Ecological footprint of a population	=	Land and water occupied by the population	+	Land and water used to produce goods and services for the population	+	Land and water used to dispose of the population's waste

10.15 Equation for calculating the ecological footprint of a population

The resources available for development in the Earth's ecosystems correspond to the **ECOLOGICAL CARRYING CAPACITY**. According to the World Wildlife Fund, the Earth's carrying capacity in 2003 was approximately 1.8 hectares per person. In other words, by dividing the total surface area available on Earth to satisfy our needs by the number of humans (currently more than 6.5 billion), each person is estimated to have 1.8 hectares, or 18 000 m^2, at his or her disposal.

If the ecological footprint of each human were also 1.8 hectares, this would mean that all the Earth's surface is under development. If the individual footprint were greater, it would mean that the Earth is not big enough to meet our needs. If the footprint were smaller, the Earth would be able to satisfy both present human needs and those of future generations, and even those of populations of other species.

10.16 Example of a forest area developed for human use. In this case, an area of the Earth's surface is used to set up a logging camp, and another area is developed for its timber.

As shown in Graph 10.17, the average ecological footprint in Canada is 7.6 hectares per person—four times greater than the Earth's carrying capacity. According to the concept of ecological footprints, this means that if all humans were as avid consumers as Canadians are, the Earth's population would need four planets like its own to meet all its needs.

10.17 ESTIMATED ECOLOGICAL FOOTPRINT IN 2003, ACCORDING TO THE WORLD WILDLIFE FUND

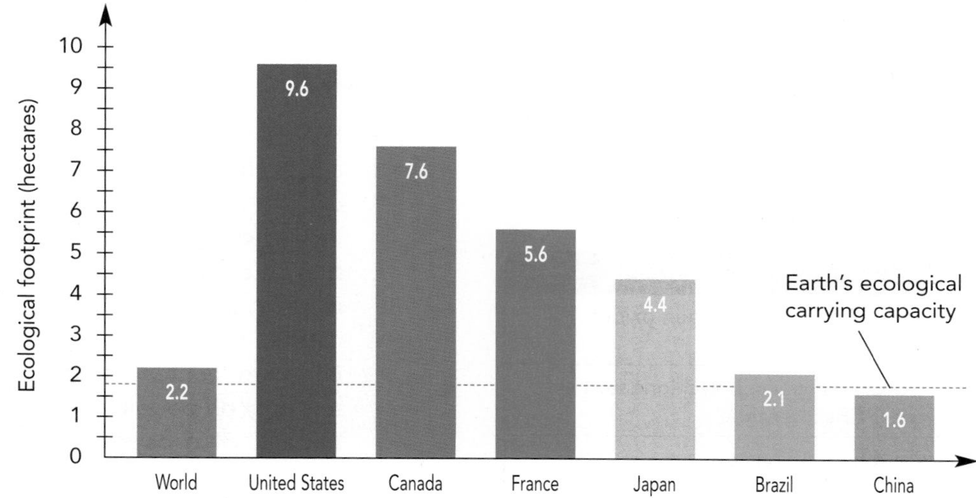

EST SE 3 Ecotoxicology

We have seen that humans disturb the world's ecosystems. Our industrial and agri-food activities, as well as some of our waste, release various substances or radiation into the environment, which can affect ecosystems. Ecotoxicology is the scientific study of the harm caused to ecosystems by such substances and radiation.

Ecotoxicology comes from the Greek *oikos*, meaning "house," the Latin *toxicum*, meaning "poison," and the Greek *logia*, meaning "theory."

ECOTOXICOLOGY is the study of the ecological consequences of polluting the environment with various substances and radiation, released by human activity.

10.18 Human activities affect ecosystems by polluting them with substances that do not occur there naturally or by significantly increasing concentrations of substances already present. This photo taken in China shows the discharge from a pulp and paper mill. In Québec, the government has gone to considerable length to avoid such situations.

EST SE 3.1 CONTAMINANTS

Any substance or radiation that is discharged into the environment and is likely to cause harm is referred to as a *contaminant*. Contaminants can be divided into four main classes depending on their nature. Table 10.19 presents these categories.

Contaminant comes from the Latin *contaminatio*, meaning "defilement" or "pollution."

A CONTAMINANT is any type of substance or radiation that is likely to cause harm to one or more ecosystems.

1909
1994

René Truhaut

Professor René Truhaut, a French toxicology expert, defined ecotoxicology as a branch of toxicology in 1969. Ecotoxicology aims to measure the impact of contaminants not only on people but also on ecosystems.

10.19 MAIN CLASSES OF CONTAMINANTS

Class of contaminants	Examples
Inorganic contaminants	Lead, arsenic, mercury, nitrogen oxides, phosphorus
Organic contaminants	Insecticides, pesticides, polychlorinated biphenyls (PCBs), benzene
Microbial contaminants	Viruses and harmful bacteria
Radioactive contaminants	Uranium, plutonium, radon

When a contaminant effectively harms an organism, it is said to be *toxic* to that organism. The toxicity of each contaminant depends especially on the following three factors:

- **Its concentration.** The more concentrated a contaminant, the higher the risk that it is toxic. For example, Québec regulations specify that the concentration of lead in drinking water must not exceed 0.01 ppm (0.01 mg/L). Above this level, the lead content is considered toxic and can cause human health problems.

10.20 In 1990, a fire at a used tire site in Saint-Amable, near Montréal, gave off a large amount of PCBs, among other pollutants. The water in the surrounding area, both above and below ground, was contaminated.

- **The type of organism it comes in contact with.** Certain contaminants are toxic to some organisms but not to others. For example, certain herbicides are toxic only to broad-leaved weeds.
- **The length of exposure.** Generally, the longer a contaminant is in contact with an organism, the greater the risk of toxicity. For example, the more people smoke or are exposed to secondhand smoke, the higher their risk of contracting lung cancer.

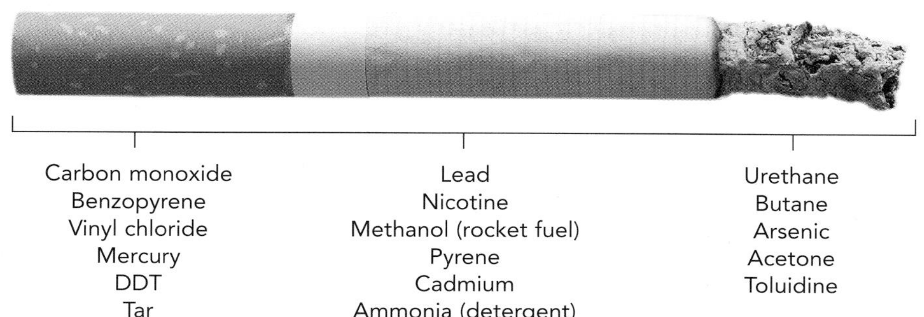

10.21 Cigarettes contain hundreds of toxic contaminants that are harmful to the health of humans and other organisms.

ENVIRONMENT EXTRA

DDT: threat or solution?

Dichlorodiphenyltrichloroethane used to be one of the most widely used chemicals in the world. It is an insecticide better known as *DDT*.

After Swiss chemist Paul Hermann Müller observed, in 1939, that DDT killed most insects, the chemical was widely used in farming to eradicate pests that destroyed crops.

By the end of the 1950s, however, there was a growing awareness of the harmful effects of DDT. Scientists observed that it also killed birds and other species, so the insect pests were losing their natural predators. The organisms originally targeted by the DDT also acquired some resistance to the chemical. The use of DDT was therefore banned in many countries, including Canada, in the early 1970s.

In spite of its harmful effects on the environment, some countries have not yet banned the use of DDT, particularly the developing countries of the world. DDT is one of the least expensive chemicals available to kill insects that may infect humans with disease. Malaria, for example, is transmitted by mosquitoes, such as those of the *Anopheles* genus. DDT is considered an agent of the eradication of malaria, as well as typhus, in Europe and North America.

In the 1950s and 1960s, DDT was used in Canada to protect crops from insect pests.

EST SE

TOXICITY THRESHOLD

LAB 69

To determine at what point a contaminant becomes toxic, scientists evaluate its toxicity threshold. The threshold is a minimal concentration of the contaminant that nonetheless produces a harmful effect on an organism.

The TOXICITY THRESHOLD is the level of concentration above which a contaminant causes one or more harmful effects in an organism.

For example, the World Health Organization sets the average toxicity threshold of sulphur dioxide (SO_2) for plants at 30 $\mu g/m^3$ of air. This means that above this level, sulphur dioxide can be harmful to vegetation.

10.22 Some cyanobacteria, commonly called *blue-green algae*, can release microcystins into the water. The toxicity threshold of these contaminants is set at 16 µg/L of water for humans. When this level of toxicity is reached or exceeded, the contaminants can cause nausea, vomiting and even jaundice. For this reason, beaches are sometimes closed when cyanobacteria are present.

Toxic contaminants can have many different effects on human health. In most cases, a contaminant has a specific toxic effect. For example, one may cause red patches on the skin, while another may provoke vomiting. Comparing the toxicity of contaminants by simply observing their effects therefore tends to be inconclusive.

To compare the toxicity of contaminants effectively, scientists can determine their **LETHAL DOSES**. This value indicates the amount of contaminant necessary, in a single dose, to cause the death of an organism.

Lethal comes from the Latin *letalis*, meaning "deadly."

Within a single species, some individuals have a higher resistance to a contaminant than others. The indicator used most often to compare the toxicity of contaminants is consequently the LD_{50}, which means the dose that causes death among 50 percent of individuals.

10.23 Rivers sometimes become so contaminated that many of their resident organisms die.

EST SE 3.2 THE BIOACCUMULATION AND BIOCONCENTRATION OF CONTAMINANTS

Many of the contaminants that result from human activities resist natural degradation once discharged and can thus pollute ecosystems for years. When these contaminants mix with inorganic matter such as water in an environment, living organisms can absorb the pollutants when they eat or drink.

Once inside an organism, certain contaminants, such as heavy metals, chemicals called *PCBs* (substances with insulating properties), and DDT (a powerful insecticide), cannot be eliminated. Over time, they accumulate in the tissues of affected organisms. This phenomenon is called *bioaccumulation*.

BIOACCUMULATION is the tendency among certain contaminants to accumulate over time in the tissues of living organisms.

10.24 Some of the waste we discharge into the environment leaks contaminants that can accumulate in the organisms of the surrounding ecosystem. In this photo, the bear may have ingested contaminated material in the dump.

In a food chain, an organism at a higher trophic level feeds on organisms from lower trophic levels. In the event of bioaccumulation, an organism will absorb the contaminants that have accumulated in the organisms from lower trophic levels. Consequently, the higher up the food chain an organism lies, the greater its concentration of such contaminants. This phenomenon is called *bioconcentration* (or *bioamplification*).

BIOCONCENTRATION (or bioamplification) is a phenomenon by which the concentration of a contaminant in the tissues of living organisms tends to increase with each trophic level.

Humans are no exception to this phenomenon. Since we occupy the highest trophic levels in food chains, we can be faced with high concentrations of contaminants in our bodies. For example, in Figure 10.25, pesticides applied in fields (contaminants) are carried by rainwater into rivers, where they are ingested day after day by phytoplankton. The phytoplankton are eaten by mayflies, which, in turn, are consumed by trout, which may be part of a human diet. Our bodies thus absorb a certain amount of contaminants.

1907
1964

Rachel Carson

In 1962, this American zoologist and marine biologist published a book on the side effects of DDT. Her book, *Silent Spring*, sparked fierce debate at the time and is now considered the starting point of the modern environmental movement.

Trophic level		
Third-order consumer	Human	
Second-order consumer	Trout	
First-order consumer	Mayfly nymphs	
Producer	Aquatic microorganisms (phytoplankton)	

Food chain
● = contaminant in tissues

10.25 Due to the phenomenon of bioconcentration, the higher an organism's trophic level in a food chain, the greater its concentration of contaminants.

EST 4 Biotechnology to the rescue

Many of the world's environmental problems are due to the discharge of contaminants from our industries, cars and household waste. Unfortunately, it is not always possible to simply remove contaminated water and earth from a polluted site.

Solutions in **BIOTECHNOLOGY** have been developed to counteract certain environmental problems. Living organisms are used either to limit contaminant discharge or to break it down. Pollution can thus be cleaned up through bioremediation or phytoremediation. Pollution can also be avoided by treating wastewater before it is discharged into an ecosystem.

Biotechnology comes from the Greek roots *bios*, meaning "life," *tekhnē*, meaning "art," and *logia*, meaning "theory."

EST 4.1 DECONTAMINATING SOIL THROUGH POLLUTANT BIODEGRADATION

We have seen that microorganisms in the soil, namely, bacteria and fungi, act as decomposers. To feed themselves, they break down organic matter into inorganic matter. In biotechnology, this process is called *biodegradation*.

BIODEGRADATION is the breaking down of organic matter into inorganic matter by microorganisms.

In their study of various types of bacteria and microscopic fungi, scientists have observed that some species can live in highly toxic environments and feed on contaminants by degrading them.

Introducing this type of microorganism into a polluted site is an effective method of decontaminating the soil. The organisms transform the pollutants into matter that is harmless to the environment. Scientists call this process *bioremediation*.

BIOREMEDIATION is a biotechnology for cleaning up a polluted site, using microorganisms that decompose the contaminants.

10.26 A worker sprays fertilizer on an oil-soaked beach. The fertilizer stimulates the growth of microorganisms that degrade the petroleum.

PLASTIC FEAST FOR FUNGI

A fungus that normally eats wood can also chew up some of the long-lasting plastic resins that clog landfill sites, researchers in the United States have found. This may offer an environmentally friendly way to recycle the waste.

Phenolic resins are widely used to glue together plywood and fibreboard and are commonly found in car mouldings. The resins are popular because they are so durable, but this also makes them difficult to recycle. Some scrap phenolic resins are simply ground up and used in other plastics. Another experimental recycling method uses heat and chemical solvents, but this is expensive and produces dirty by-products.

A team of researchers at the University of Wisconsin–La Crosse wondered whether white-rot fungi might be able to attack the resins. These fungi are commonly seen on rotting tree stumps and manufacture an array of enzymes able to break down the tough lignin in wood. Lignin has a similar chemical structure to phenolic resins.

The scientists fed chips of phenolic resin to five different species of white-rot fungus to see whether they could eat it. The team found that one species (*Phanerochaete chrysosporium*) turned from white to pink after a few days, suggesting that it had broken down the resin into smaller chemical components of the polymer known to be pink. Further tests confirmed that the fungus was indeed feasting on the plastic.

The idea of using the fungi to recycle plastic is a long way from being commercially viable, however. The team has not yet shown how efficiently or rapidly the fungus eats the resin but suspects that it might take the microbes a few months to finish a meal. The fungi's varied palate could still find a use. Researchers already know that white-rot fungi can digest other plastics such as polystyrene and that it can chew up pollutants such as polychlorinated biphenyls (PCBs).

The *Phanerochaete chrysosporium* fungus is often found on rotting tree stumps.

Source: Adapted from Helen Pearson, "Fungus eats enduring plastic," *Nature News* [online edition], June 6, 2006. (Accessed November 7, 2008.)

EST 4.2 PHYTOREMEDIATION

Microorganisms are not the only life forms that can be used to decontaminate sites; plants can also be helpful. Certain plants absorb the contaminants in soil, air or water and accumulate them in their systems. They can then be harvested so that the contaminants they have absorbed can be recovered and destroyed. This biotechnological process is called *phytoremediation*.

Phytoremediation comes from the Greek *phuton*, meaning "plant," and the Latin *remediare*, meaning "to heal."

PHYTOREMEDIATION is a biotechnology that uses plants or algae to eliminate contaminants from a site.

TREE PLANTING— AT THE PLANT!

In a Swedish example of a system of phytoremediation, willows were planted near a wastewater treatment station. The trees are irrigated with town wastewater and absorb its excess nitrogen. As well as acting as a natural water treatment facility, complementing the work done by the nearby plant, the trees take advantage of the fertilizing capacity of nitrogen, which stimulates their growth.

Cabbages, for example, can be used to remove heavy metals from the soil. The plants have the ability to absorb large quantities of heavy metals without harm to themselves. The cabbages do not degrade the metals, however; they simply concentrate the contaminants in their systems. It is important, therefore, to avoid any possibility of consumption and to harvest the cabbages before they die. Both the plants and the heavy metals they contain can then be eliminated safely.

10.27 Planting cabbages is one way to decontaminate soil containing heavy metals.

EST 4.3 WASTEWATER TREATMENT

We have seen that biotechnology can offer solutions for decontaminating a site, but methods also exist to limit the discharge of pollutants into the environment. These methods are applied mainly to treating wastewater.

Water is essential to many activities. Once used, it is discharged into the environment. In our homes, for example, we use water for household chores; in certain industries, water is used as a solvent for many chemicals. The water that is discharged after use is called *wastewater*.

WASTEWATER is water that is discharged after household or industrial use and that is polluted as a result of human activities.

Wastewater can contain the following undesirable elements:

- sand and other suspended particles
- pathogens (microorganisms that can cause disease)
- decomposing organic waste
- nutrients that stimulate the excessive growth of algae, cyanobacteria and aquatic plants
- chemicals

Pathogen comes from the Greek words *pathos*, meaning "suffering," and *genos*, meaning "origin."

To counter the presence of these elements, various biotechnological methods have been developed to treat and clean wastewater before returning it to the environment. Two main methods are commonly used:

- septic tanks, for homes that are not connected to a sewer system
- wastewater treatment plants, built near urban areas

IS CLEAN WATER A PRIVILEGE?

There are more than 50 000 water treatment plants in the world today. However, approximately 40 percent of the population does not yet have access to any kind of wastewater treatment system whatsoever. 

SEPTIC TANKS

EST

The principle behind septic tanks is quite simple. Wastewater from the house is drained into a container, the septic tank. Solid waste settles at the bottom of the tank and forms sludge. The sludge is occasionally collected by specialized companies, which treat it to make it harmless to the environment.

The liquid part of the wastewater can drain out of the septic tank into the surrounding land—the drain field. Microorganisms that are already present in the ground or that have been added to the soil can treat the liquids.

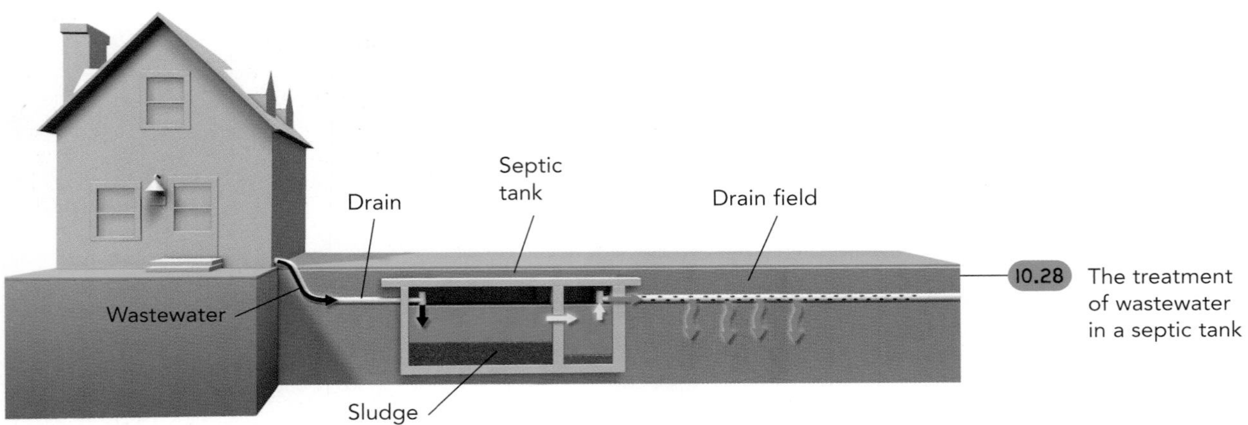

10.28 The treatment of wastewater in a septic tank

WASTEWATER TREATMENT PLANTS

EST

Wastewater treatment plants use various processes to clean wastewater. Since the plants are expensive to build and require a sewer system to pipe in the wastewater, they are usually found in urban areas only.

10.29 Some plants treat wastewater through lagooning. In the treatment ponds, solid particles settle at the bottom, and microorganisms oxidize the organic matter.

Inside a treatment plant, the wastewater usually undergoes three processes (illustrated below) before reentering the environment.

PRIMARY OR PHYSICAL TREATMENT

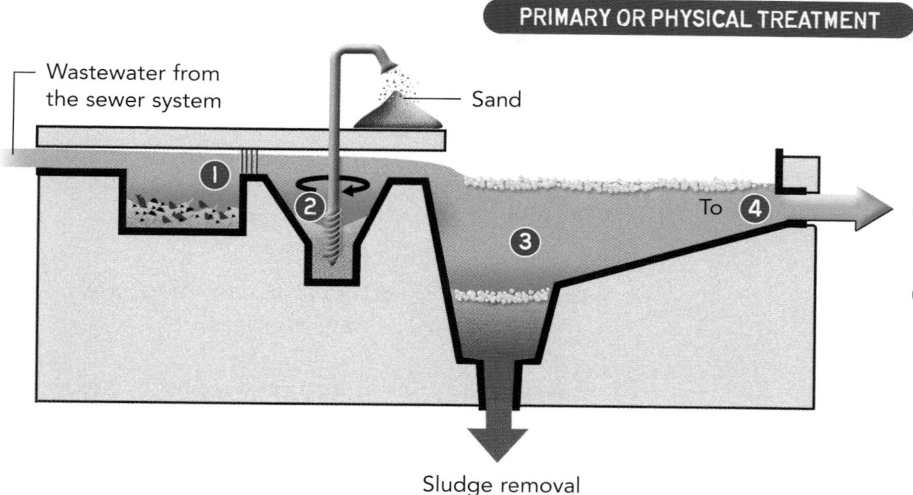

1. Screening of wastewater to remove large pieces of debris (plastic bags, rags, etc.)
2. Removal of sand and grit (fine inorganic matter) in a degritter
3. Primary sedimentation. Heavy organic matter collects in the settling tank. The scum (whitish foam floating on the surface) is pumped to the bottom, where it and the heavy organic matter form sludge, which is emptied out of the settling tank.

SECONDARY OR BIOLOGICAL TREATMENT

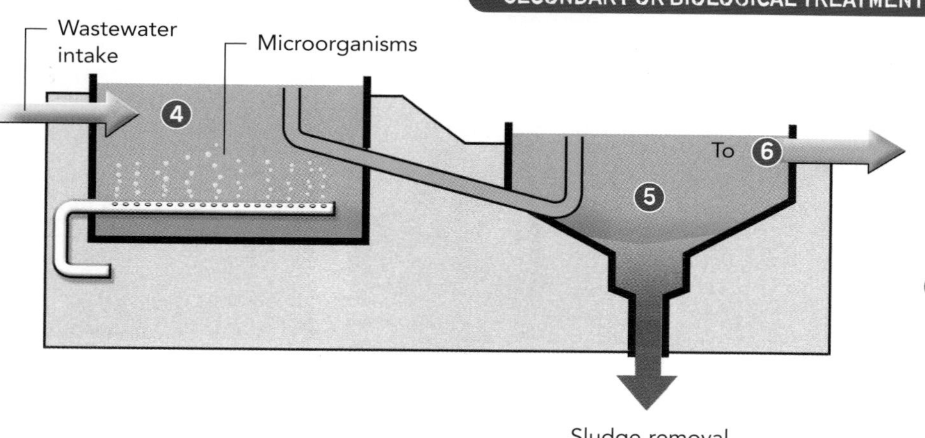

4. Transfer of wastewater into a tank where it is mixed with microorganisms and a large amount of air. The microorganisms digest the fine organic matter suspended or dissolved in the water, thus eliminating contaminants.
5. Secondary sedimentation. The solids that did not settle during primary sedimentation and those produced by the microbial action in Step 4 fall to the bottom of the secondary settling tank.

DISINFECTION

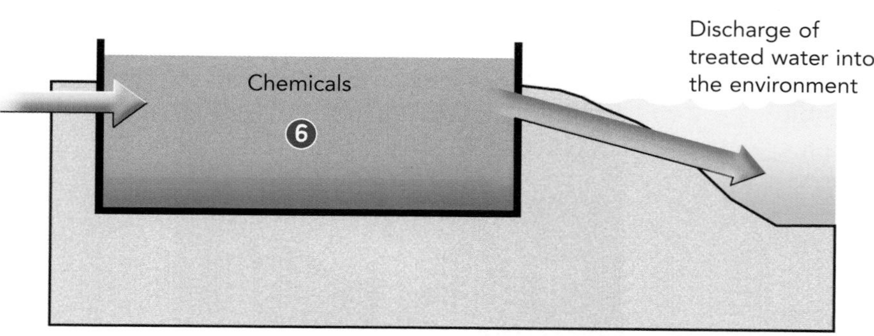

6. Treatment of water with chemicals or radiation to destroy disease-causing microorganisms. Chlorine compounds, ozone or ultraviolet rays are often used.

10.30 The main stages of wastewater treatment in a facility. In some treatment plants, the wastewater is not disinfected before being discharged into the environment.

CHECKUP

ST	1–15, A and C.	AST	1–15, A and C.
EST	1–26 and A–C.	SE	18–23 and B.

1 What is an ecosystem?

(pp. 318–326)

1. Which level of ecological organization do the following examples illustrate?
   a) a pack of wolves
   b) wolves hunting a caribou herd
   c) a lone wolf
   d) a pack of wolves drinking from a lake

2. What is the difference between a community and an ecosystem?

3. What is the name of the feeding relationships between the living organisms of an ecosystem?

4. A carnivore cannot be a primary consumer in a food chain. Why?

5. Which trophic level do detritivores belong to? Explain your answer.

6. What is transferred from one organism to another within each ecosystem?

7. Explain the role of decomposers in the material flow of an ecosystem.

8. What is the main source of energy in an ecosystem?

9. Approximately 10 percent of the energy absorbed by one consumer is available to the next consumer in a food chain. What happens to the energy that is lost at each level of a food chain? Give two explanations.

10. All the living organisms in an ecosystem need organic matter to survive.
    a) Which organisms are responsible for producing new organic matter (biomass)?
    b) What indicator is obtained by measuring the amount of new biomass produced by these organisms over a certain length of time?
    c) Name four factors that can affect the production of new biomass.

11. Build a food chain based on the photos below.
    a) Draw the food chain.
    b) Specify the trophic level for each of the living organisms in your food chain.

1

2

3

4

12. Look at the illustration opposite.

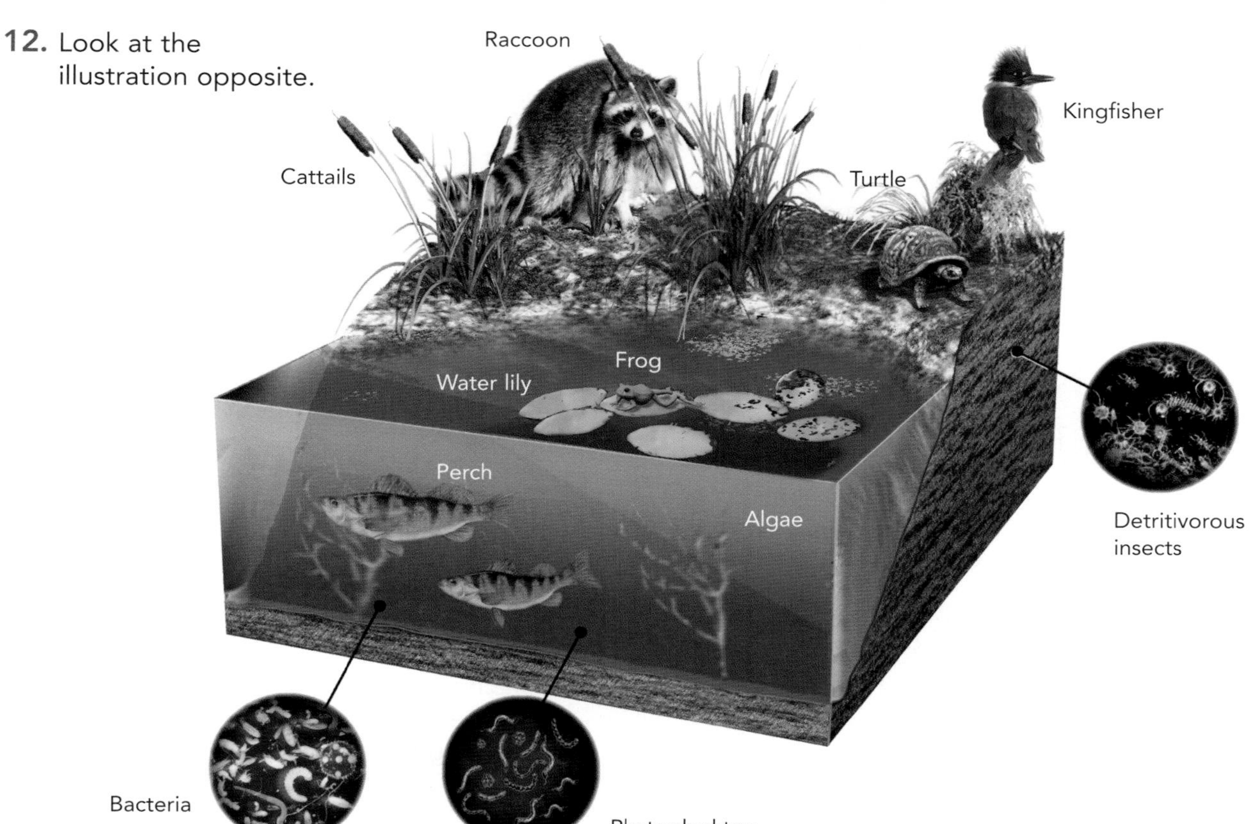

a) Among the organisms in the illustration, name those that are:
   - producers
   - consumers
   - decomposers

b) Draw a possible food chain containing the organisms in the illustration.

13. If you tried to establish the feeding relationships between all the organisms of the lake ecosystem illustrated in question 12, would you be drawing a food chain or a trophic network? Explain your answer.

2 Disturbances (pp. 327–331)

14. True or false? Explain your answers.
   a) The freezing of a lake can be considered a natural disturbance.
   b) Excessive hunting and fishing are human disturbances of ecosystems.
   c) All types of natural disturbance can occur in Québec.
   d) Ecological succession occurs only after a natural disturbance.
   e) Transforming forests into farmland constitutes a natural disturbance.
   f) A flood following heavy rain is a natural disturbance.

15. What is ecological succession?

16. What does the expression *ecological footprint* mean?

17. Which of the following statements about ecological footprints is correct according to the 2003 study by the World Wildlife Fund?
   a) The ecological footprint of North Americans does not exceed the Earth's carrying capacity.
   b) If all the people in the world had the same rate of consumption as the Japanese, we would need about 2.5 planets the size of the Earth to satisfy our needs.
   c) On average, the global human ecological footprint does not exceed the Earth's carrying capacity.

3 Ecotoxicology (pp. 331–336)

18. What is a contaminant?

19. What can make a contaminant toxic? Name at least two factors.

20. What is the toxicity threshold of a contaminant?

21. What does the LD_{50} of a contaminant indicate?

22. What is bioaccumulation?

23. Certain factories in Québec sometimes discharge low concentrations of contaminants into the environment. Explain why even small amounts of contaminants can nonetheless be hazardous to humans or other organisms at the top of food chains.

4 Biotechnology to the rescue

(pp. 337–341)

24. Which environmental biotechnology do the following statements describe? Is it bioremediation, phytoremediation or wastewater treatment?
   a) a biotechnology for cleaning the water we have used before returning it to the environment
   b) a biotechnology that involves a septic tank
   c) a biotechnology for cleaning up a polluted site, using microorganisms that degrade contaminants
   d) a biotechnology that uses plants or algae to eliminate contaminants from a site

25. Explain why it is dangerous to eat a cabbage that has been grown in soil containing a substantial amount of heavy metals.

26. Look at the position of the septic tank in relation to the well in the illustrations below. Which installation would be preferable? Explain why.

1

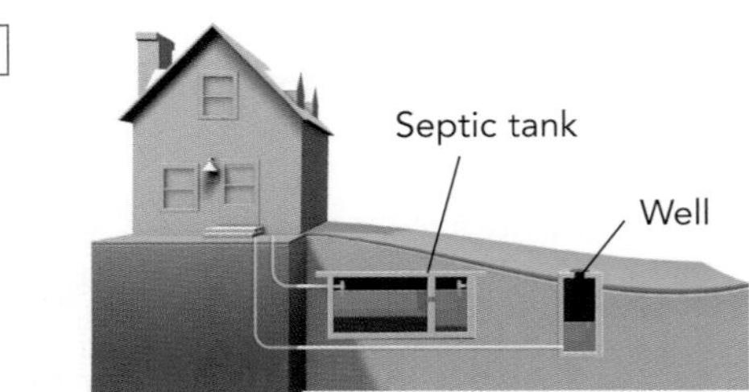

2

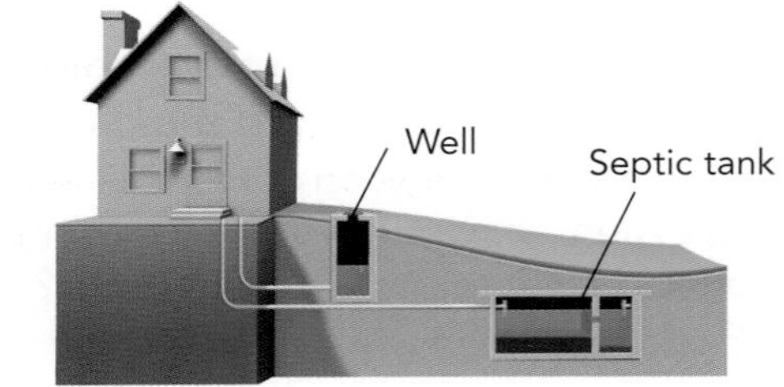

review questions

A. Look at the following three food chains.

Chain 1

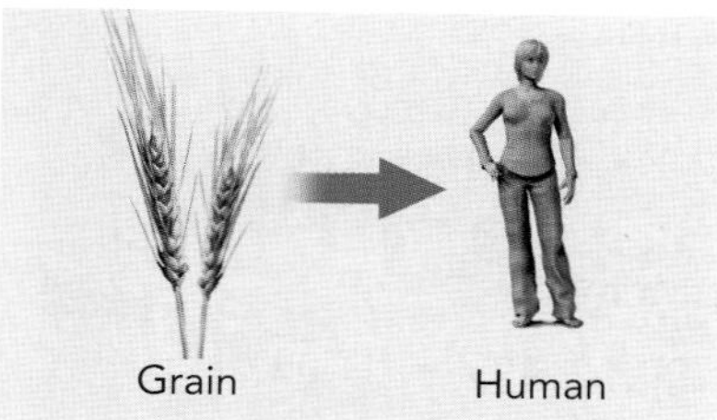

Chain 2

Chain 3

a) For each of the food chains, name the trophic level of the human.

b) Why is it correct to identify the phytoplankton in Chain 3 as producers?

c) Suppose that 10 percent of the available energy is converted into biomass at each change of trophic level. For each of the three food chains, calculate the percentage of the energy from the producers that the humans eventually convert into biomass.

B. Suppose that a contaminant is introduced into the environments of the three food chains in question A. This contaminant can accumulate in grain and in phytoplankton. In which food chain is the human health hazard the greatest? Explain your answer.

C. Prepare your own summary of Chapter 10 by building a concept map.

HOW TO BUILD A CONCEPT MAP

KEEPING THE RIVER CLEAN

For a long time, Canada showed little concern for preserving the quality of its natural waters, including the St. Lawrence River (Fleuve Saint-Laurent). Towns and villages, farms, chemical companies, oil refineries, foundries and other plants discharged their toxic waste directly into the river. Not until the 1970s, when environmental awareness took hold, did authorities take steps to protect the river, its wildlife and the residents along its shores. The federal and provincial governments as well as riverside municipalities passed legislation to this effect. Certain plants—particularly the large oil companies—built their own facilities to treat their wastewater before pouring it back into the river. However, thousands of other companies, and many private homes, could not take similar individual action.

TREATING WASTEWATER

In the early 1980s, Québec launched its water purification program with a budget of 6.4 billion dollars. The program rapidly bore fruit: between 1986 and 1992, the portion of the population along the St. Lawrence River (Fleuve Saint-Laurent) whose wastewater was treated in a plant rose from 10 to 65 percent.

Today, there are more than 600 wastewater treatment plants in operation in Québec, where more than 50 percent of the population lives along the riverbanks.

From Cornwall (Ontario) to Trois-Rivières, 42 treatment plants discharged almost four million cubic metres of water per day in 2006—enough to fill 1500 Olympic swimming pools. Nearly three quarters of the wastewater came from the municipalities on the Île de Montréal.

Since 1996, all the wastewater from the island has been treated at the plant in Rivière-des-Prairies. With a capacity of 7.6 million cubic metres per day, it is the largest wastewater treatment plant in North America—a huge system, in fact, for collecting, intercepting and purifying wastewater. Construction began in 1970, and it took 25 years and 1.4 billion dollars to complete the entire system, which treats half of all the wastewater in Québec. The water used by two million people and more than 4000 companies passes through this facility. It costs more than 50 million dollars a year to operate and requires a staff of 300 people.

GOING TO THE SOURCE

Although wastewater treatment plants are necessary, they are not the ultimate solution. The Montréal plant removes approximately 80 percent of the suspended matter and the phosphorus in the water. The remaining 20 percent ends up in the river, along with contaminants such as heavy metals, cyanides and antibiotic residues. Even if the quantities discharged each day are not alarming, researchers are concerned. Over time, the accumulation of small amounts of toxic products in an organism could nonetheless cause problems. Sébastien Sauvé, a chemist at Université de Montréal, believes that the antibiotics released into the environment could be the reason for increased bacterial resistance to them. Combined with chemical fertilizers, this waste could have an adverse effect on human fertility. We must focus our restoration efforts on the sources of river contamination, and the best way to do so is to discharge as little waste as possible into the water.

Rivière-des-Prairies wastewater treatment plant

Treating wastewater has restored the river's recreational appeal.

1. Tests conducted by Health Canada show that it is now possible to swim at several beaches along the St. Lawrence River (Fleuve Saint-Laurent). However, swimming on days after a heavy rainfall is not recommended. Explain why.
2. What precautions must be taken by riverside residents in areas where local wastewater is discharged into septic tanks rather than to a treatment plant?

2006 Successful treatment of Huntington's chorea in a mouse
2004 Publication of the complete human genome sequence
1996 First successful cloning of a mammal
1967 Deciphering of the entire genetic code
1953 Discovery of the structure of DNA
1952 Identification of DNA as the carrier of genetic information
1909 Earliest definitions of the terms *gene, genotype* and *phenotype*
1902 Discovery of the role of hormones
1900 Rediscovery of the laws of heredity
1896 Discovery of the four nitrogenous bases of DNA
1872 Description of Huntington's chorea, a genetic disease
1865 Formulation of Mendel's laws of heredity, subsequently forgotten until 1900
1839 Formulation of cell theory stating that cells are the basic units of life
1833 Discovery of the first enzyme
CIRCA 1830 Discovery of proteins

"She has her father's eyes." You have probably heard a description like this at some time. And you have undoubtedly noticed that members of the same family resemble one another in many ways. This is also true for the rest of the animal kingdom. But where do these similarities come from? How can they be explained? Why are birds of the same species all alike? How can brown-eyed parents have a blue-eyed child?

In this chapter, we will look at genetics. You will learn how resemblances are passed down from one generation to the next—and why individuals are nonetheless so different.

THE LIVING WORLD

11

Genetics

CONTENTS

EST

1 Factors responsible for character traits among living organisms

CONCEPT REVIEW
- Mitosis
- DNA
- Plant and animal cells
- Decomposition and synthesis

If you look at two birds of the same species, you will notice that they are enormously similar. Their feathers, the shape of their beaks and the position of their eyes, for example, are all very much alike.

The same phenomenon can be observed among individuals of the human species. Look at the people around you; they, too, appear very similar. For example, the position of our facial features—eyes, nose, ears and mouth—is roughly the same for everyone. In fact, humans have many characteristics in common.

Human beings are also different in many ways. For example, eye or hair colour can vary from one person to another. Such differences among members of the same species are called *character traits.*

Character comes from the Greek *kharactēr,* meaning "stamp" or "inscription."

A CHARACTER TRAIT is a physical, psychological or physiological attribute that may vary from one individual to another within the same species.

To understand why individuals have different character traits, we must first take a look inside their cells.

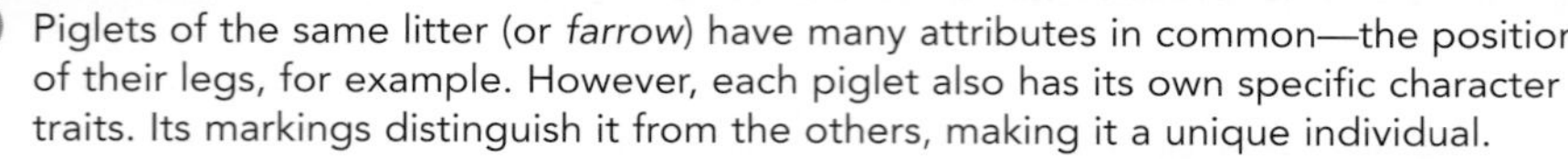

11.1 Piglets of the same litter (or *farrow*) have many attributes in common—the position of their legs, for example. However, each piglet also has its own specific character traits. Its markings distinguish it from the others, making it a unique individual.

EST 1.1 CHROMOSOMES

LAB 70

Most **EUKARYOTIC** cells contain a nucleus holding an individual's basic genetic information. The main component of the nucleus, chromatin, is made up of a molecule of DNA (deoxyribonucleic acid), combined with proteins. When chromatin is observed under the microscope, it appears as a mass of dispersed strands, as in the left-hand picture of Figure 11.2.

> **CHROMATIN is a mass of DNA and proteins within the nucleus of most cells not undergoing division.**

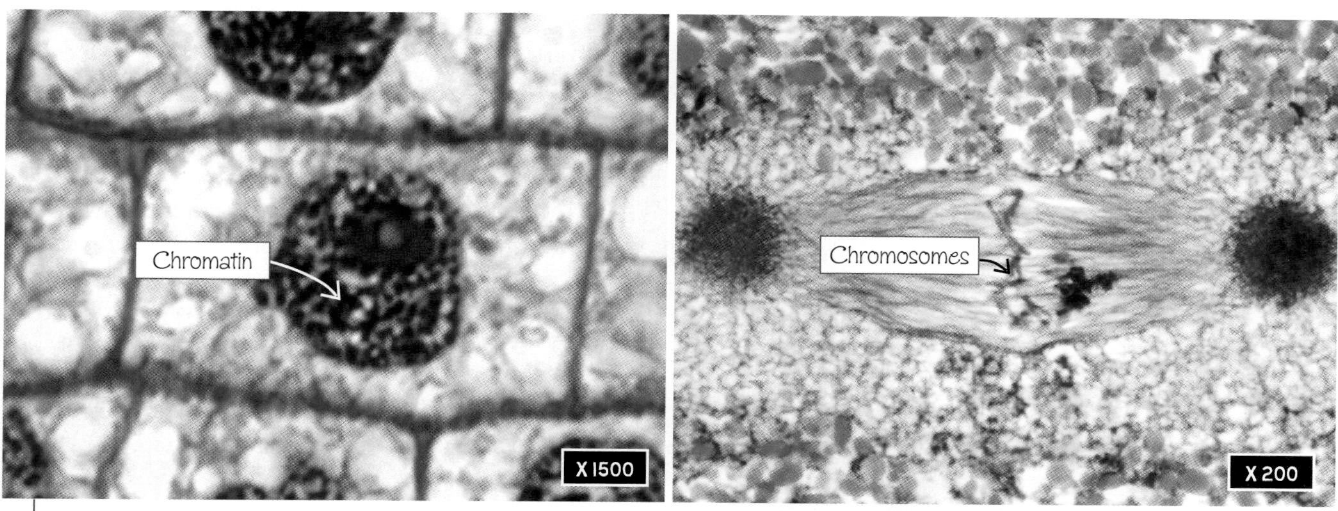

11.2 In the photo on the left the coloured chromatin appears under the microscope as a mass of dispersed strands. The photo on the right shows chromosomes during cell division.

When a cell is on the verge of dividing to reproduce or to form sex cells, however, the chromatin contracts, forming visible rods called *chromosomes*. The number of chromosomes is constant in each animal species. In humans, for example, a cell contains 46 chromosomes.

11.3 The number of chromosomes does not determine the complexity of an organism.

A CHROMOSOME is a structure that is formed when chromatin contracts. It is visible under the microscope.

The chromosomes in a cell can be classified according to size and their distinctive features. Each chromosome is then observed to have a partner of the same size and shape. The matching chromosomes are called *homologous chromosomes*. The 46 chromosomes in humans thus form 23 pairs of homologous chromosomes. Similarly, horses have 64 chromosomes, which form 32 homologous pairs. An ordered representation of an individual's chromosomes is referred to as its *karyotype*.

A KARYOTYPE is an ordered representation of an individual's chromosomes, obtained by grouping them into pairs according to size.

Normally, only one pair can contain chromosomes of different sizes: the pair of sex chromosomes. In humans, as in most animals, the two sex chromosomes are the same in the female (XX pair), while in the male, one of the two chromosomes is smaller (XY pair).

1927
2003

Martha Chase

The scientific community of the mid-20th century wondered whether the genetic information of an organism was contained in its DNA or in its proteins. While working as a laboratory assistant, Martha Chase conducted research with Alfred Hershey (1908–1997) that showed that an individual's genetic information is in fact contained in its DNA.

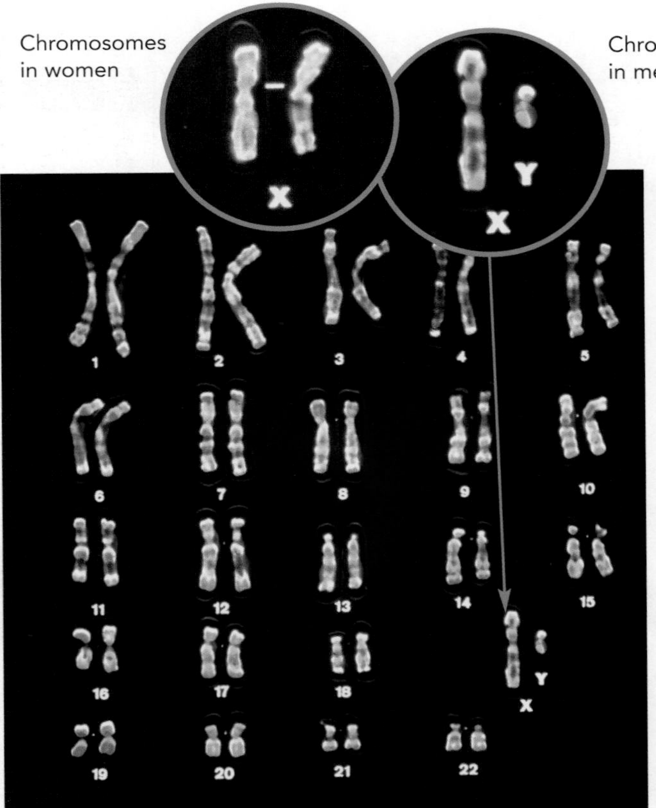

Chromosomes of a person with trisomy

II.4 These karyotypes show each of the 23 pairs of human chromosomes. Note that in the 23rd pair—the sex chromosomes—the shape of one of the chromosomes can vary. Also, chromosome 21 sometimes appears in threes, as in the picture on the right. When this happens, the person suffers from trisomy 21 (or Down syndrome). Trisomy of chromosomes other than 21 may also occur.

EST 1.2 DNA AND GENES

Each chromosome is made up of DNA. DNA is shaped like a twisting ladder, which is why it is often referred to as a double helix. It is composed of a series of chemical units called *nucleotides*. Each nucleotide contains three chemical components:

- a sugar: deoxyribose
- a phosphate group
- one of four nitrogenous bases: adenine (A), thymine (T), guanine (G) or cytosine (C)

As shown in Figure 11.5 (pages 354-355), the nucleotides in a DNA molecule form a sequence of pairs. Alternating sugars and phosphate groups make up the sides of the DNA ladder, while the nitrogenous base pairs make up the "rungs."

ENVIRONMENT EXTRA

DNA mutations of environmental origin

In biology, a mutation is a change in the sequence of DNA nucleotides. Most occurrences have no negative effect on the health of an organism because its cells have control mechanisms that counter the mutation. However, some mutations, such as cancer, can be harmful.

Many mutations in an organism occur when cells divide, as a result of errors during DNA replication. Others are caused by environmental agents, called *mutagens*. Since mutations can cause cancer, these agents are also known as *carcinogens*. Some of them, such as ultra-violet rays or certain forms of radioactivity, occur naturally in the environment.

Other environmental agents are the result of human activities, however, and they increase the natural rate of DNA mutation. Cells struggle to control all the mutations, which increases health risks. Common human-caused mutagens include nuclear waste, cigarette smoke, some types of pesticides and certain industrial waste, such as PCBs and other benzene derivatives. The discharge of such agents into the environment is increasingly regulated to preserve the integrity of DNA in humans and all other living organisms.

In the wild, some tigers are white because they carry a mutant gene that gives them a different fur colour.

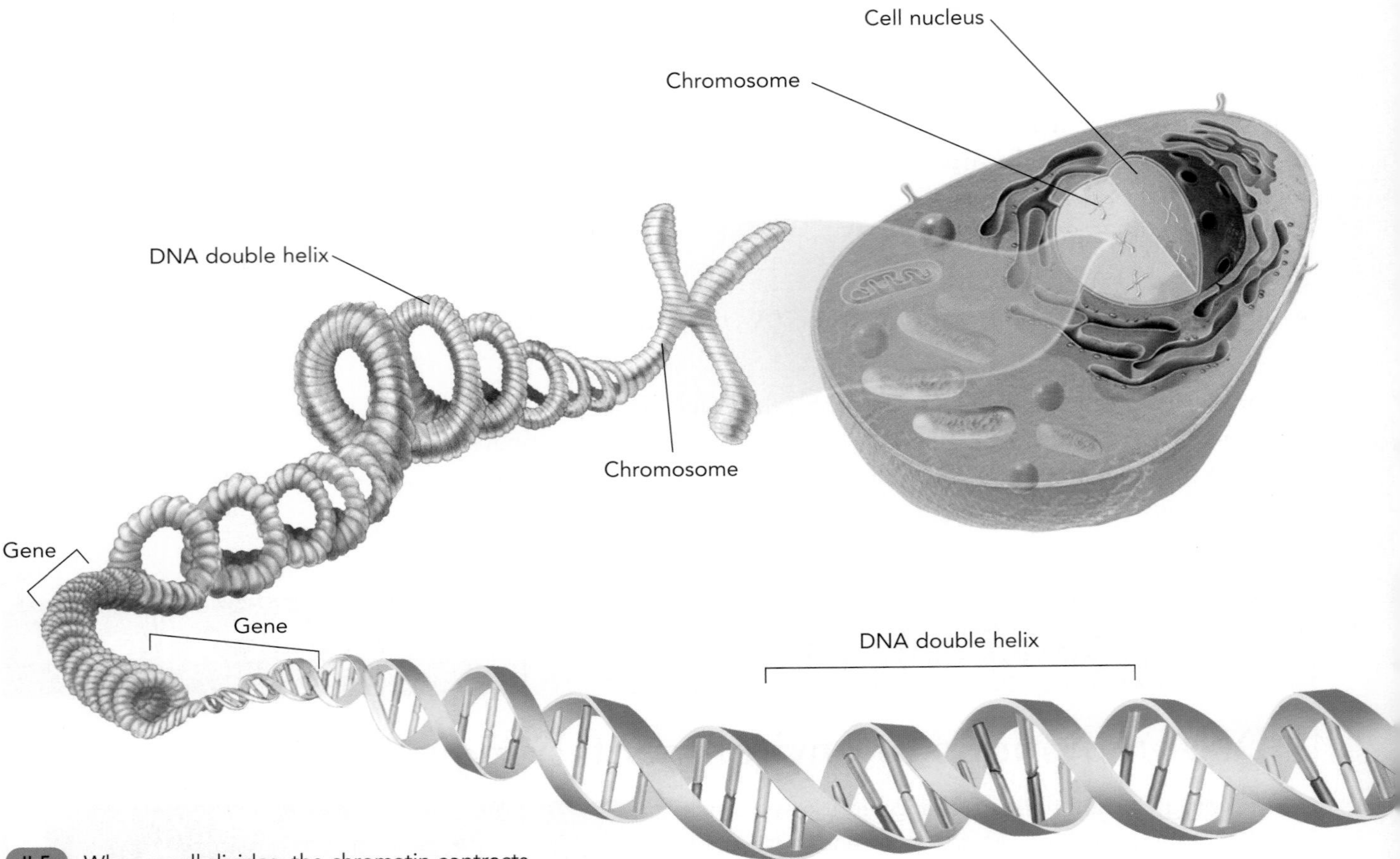

11.5 When a cell divides, the chromatin contracts into chromosomes. The chromosomes contain genes, which are segments of DNA.

The pairing of nitrogenous bases in DNA is not a matter of chance. Each base always pairs with its complementary base, according to the following pattern:

- Adenine always pairs with thymine, and vice versa, giving either A-T or T-A.
- Cytosine always pairs with guanine, and vice versa, giving either C-G or G-C.

A particular sequence of these bases constitutes a gene. A gene is therefore a segment of DNA containing its own chain of nitrogenous bases, which differentiates it from other genes. Just as words are formed with specific series of letters, a gene is made up of a specific sequence of nitrogenous bases.

A SUBTLE DIFFERENCE?

The difference between a human and a chimpanzee lies in only one percent of their genes. Nearly 99 percent of the two genomes are actually identical.

All the genes we receive from our mothers and fathers constitute our **GENOME**. Inside our cells, we have thousands of genes. They provide the instructions for making proteins, which determine such traits as a person's freckles, olive complexion or pointed nose.

A GENE is a DNA segment that contains information for making proteins.

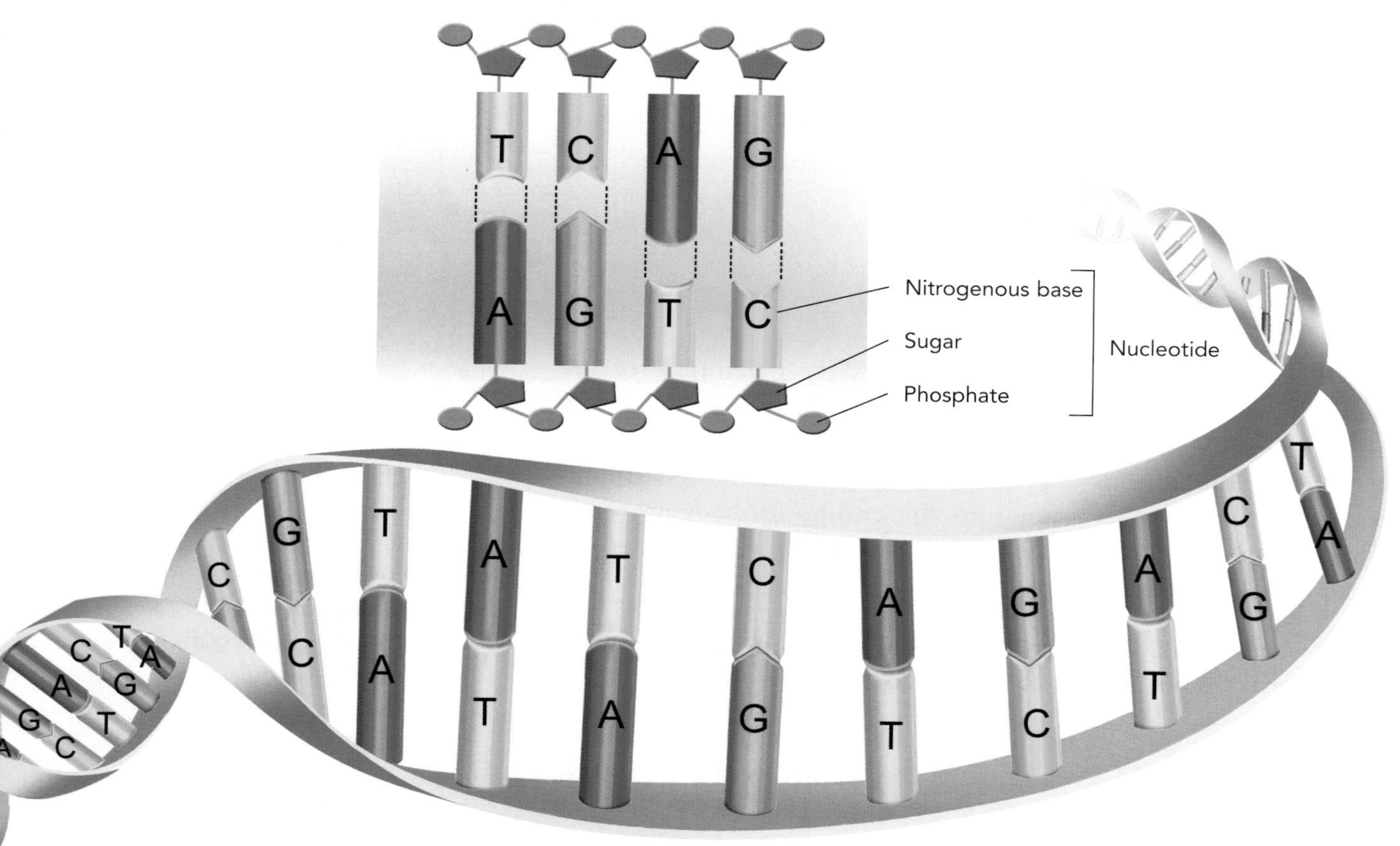

EST 1.3 PROTEINS

Proteins determine the character traits of an organism. These molecules are thus responsible for our physical appearance; they also enable our body to function. Table 11.6 presents some of the tasks performed by proteins.

- **A PROTEIN is a molecule that plays a specific role in the functioning of an organism and in the expression of its character traits.**

11.6 EXAMPLES OF TASKS PERFORMED BY PROTEINS IN ORGANISMS

Task	Example
Support	Elastin is a protein that makes the skin firm yet elastic.
Transport of substances	Hemoglobin is a protein that carries oxygen in the blood.
Control and message relay	Hormones are proteins that control cell functions and relay messages in the body. For example, insulin helps to control the amount of sugar in the blood.
Immunity	Antibodies are proteins that protect us from disease.
Catalysis	Enzymes are proteins that speed up biochemical reactions in the body. For example, amylase breaks down starch to speed up digestion.

The human body contains more than 100 000 different proteins, each with a very specific role in the organism, as demonstrated by the examples in Table 11.6 (page 355). But what determines the role of each protein?

EST PROTEIN STRUCTURE

The role a protein plays is determined by its structure. Proteins are molecules composed of one or more chains of small units called *amino acids*. The sequence of amino acids in a chain determines the function of a protein. In all, 20 different naturally occurring amino acids enter into the composition of proteins. The name and symbol for each of these acids are provided in Appendix 4 of this textbook.

An AMINO ACID is a molecule that can combine with other amino acids to form proteins.

Some chains are extremely long, containing more than 600 amino acids. More often, however, proteins contain an average of 100 to 200 amino acids.

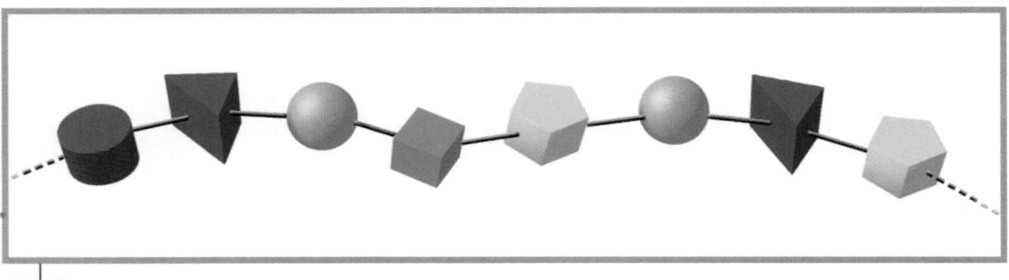

11.7 Proteins are made up of a chain of amino acids. This illustration shows part of an amino acid chain in a protein.

1802 / 1880

Gerardus Mulder

In the 1830s, this Dutch chemist analyzed the composition of egg whites. He thus discovered that egg white consisted primarily of molecules containing mostly carbon, hydrogen, oxygen and nitrogen, as well as small amounts of sulphur and phosphorus. He had discovered the composition of proteins. Further research led him to conclude that all living organisms are made up of proteins.

In the previous section, we saw that genes, which are segments of DNA, contain the instructions for making proteins. Protein structure is very different from DNA structure, however: proteins are composed of amino acids, while DNA is made up of nucleotides. How then can a cell produce proteins using DNA? This is the topic of the next section.

EST 1.4 PROTEIN SYNTHESIS

One of the distinctive features of cells is that they have the ability to produce the proteins they need. The genes containing the instructions for protein manufacture are in the cell nucleus, while the actual process is carried out by ribosomes, which are outside the nucleus. Scientists usually describe this process as *protein synthesis*.

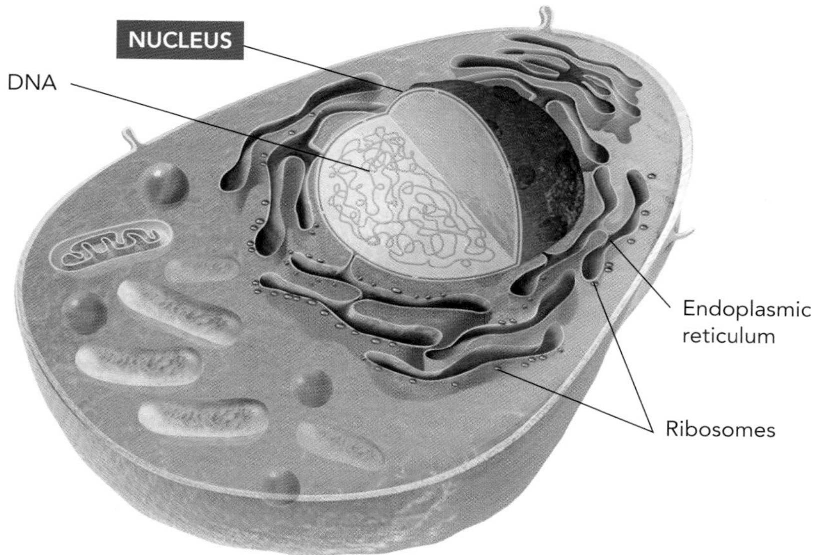

11.8 In cells that contain a nucleus, genes are DNA segments inside the nucleus, while ribosomes are located outside the nucleus, usually on the surface of the endoplasmic reticulum.

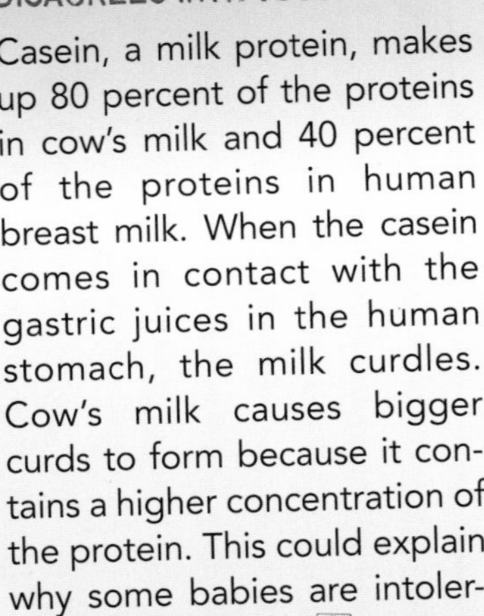

A PROTEIN THAT DISAGREES WITH YOU?

Casein, a milk protein, makes up 80 percent of the proteins in cow's milk and 40 percent of the proteins in human breast milk. When the casein comes in contact with the gastric juices in the human stomach, the milk curdles. Cow's milk causes bigger curds to form because it contains a higher concentration of the protein. This could explain why some babies are intolerant to cow's milk. 16

PROTEIN SYNTHESIS is the creation of proteins by cells.

Since DNA cannot leave the nucleus, a messenger must carry the information from the DNA to the ribosome. This messenger is a molecule of RNA: ribonucleic acid. The structure of an RNA molecule is very similar to that of a DNA molecule, with a few important differences. Figure 11.9 explains these differences.

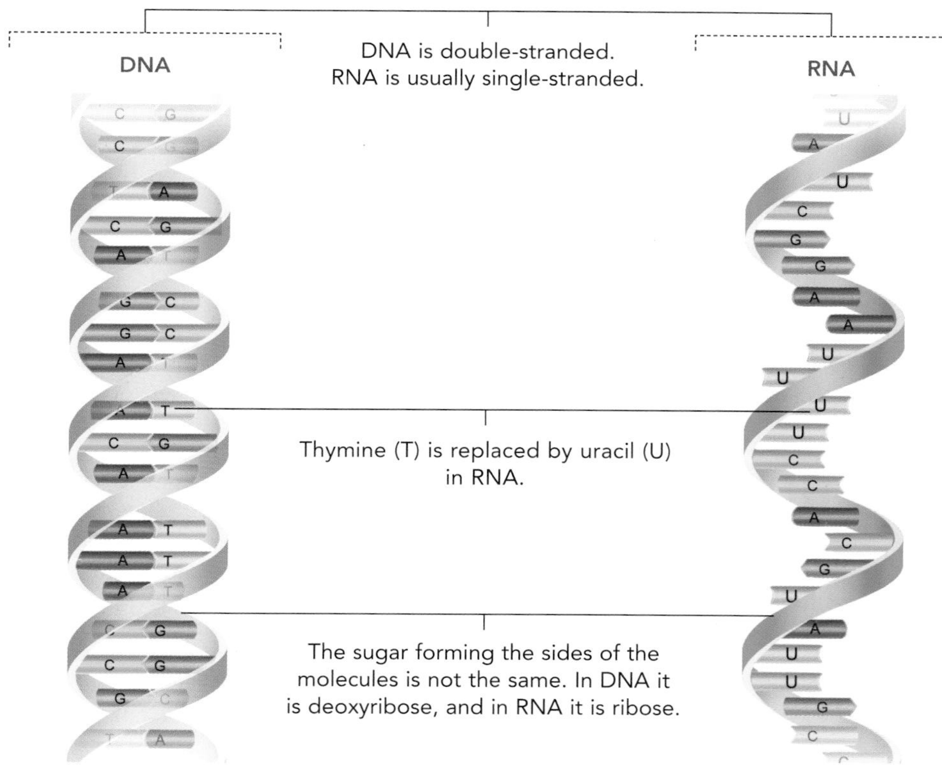

11.9 The differences between DNA (deoxyribonucleic acid) molecules and RNA (ribonucleic acid) molecules

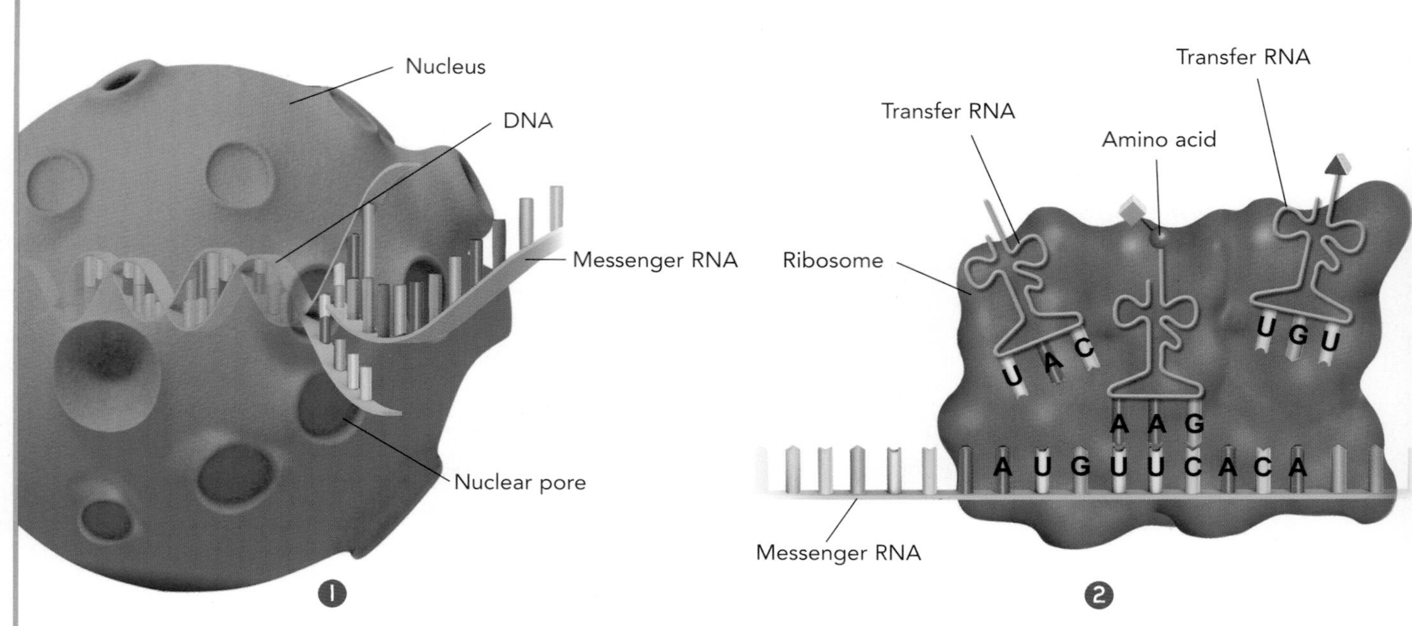

11.10 Protein synthesis

Two types of RNA are involved in protein synthesis:

- messenger RNA, or *mRNA*, which, as its name implies, acts as a messenger for carrying instructions about the gene to the ribosome
- transfer RNA, or *tRNA*, which transfers the amino acids in the cell's cytoplasm to the ribosomes in order to make proteins

Now that we have described cell structures and the molecules involved in protein synthesis, let's see how a ribosome accomplishes its task of producing a protein by "reading" genetic information from the nucleus. Figure 11.10 illustrates this process.

EST 2 Principles of heredity

Living organisms and their offspring share common traits. Children's frequent resemblance to their parents is a well-known phenomenon. However, explaining certain obvious differences is not so straightforward. Why, for example, do some children have blue eyes when both their parents have brown eyes?

CONCEPT REVIEW

- Asexual and sexual reproduction
- Meiosis and sexual development (meiosis, fertilization)

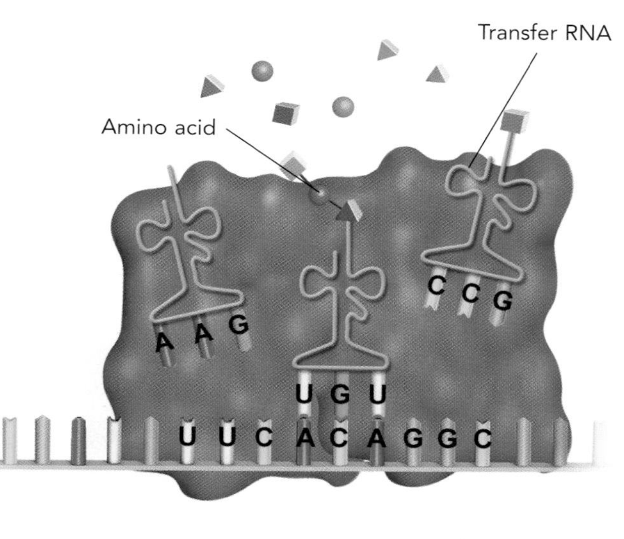

③

TRANSLATION OF THE MESSENGER RNA INTO A PROTEIN

The ribosome reads the nucleotide triplets one after another. Each triplet determines the amino acid that must be added to the chain according to a code called the *genetic code*, described in Appendix 4 of this textbook. The amino acids are brought to the chain by transfer RNA molecules, which carry the nucleotide triplet complementary to that of the messenger RNA on one side and the appropriate amino acid on the other. The amino acids then link together, and the RNA is released.

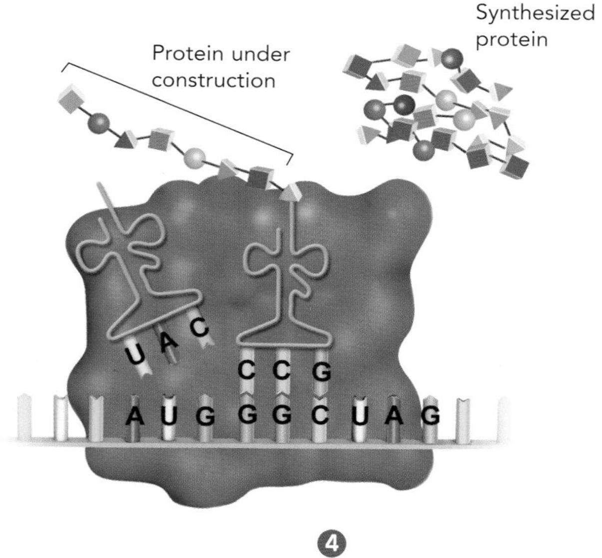

④

END OF PROTEIN SYNTHESIS

When the ribosome encounters a UAA, UAG or UGA nucleotide triplet, the amino acid chain is complete. The protein is then released from the ribosome, folds into its functional shape and performs its role in the body.

The way in which parents' character traits are passed on explains the differences as well as the similarities between members of the same family. This phenomenon of transmission is called heredity.

Heredity comes from the Latin *hereditas*, meaning "inheritance."

HEREDITY is the transmission of parents' character traits to their offspring.

11.11 The phenomenon that explains why members of the same family look alike is called *heredity*.

When a character trait is said to be *hereditary*, this means that it can be passed on from the parents to their offspring. For example, eye colour in humans and the colour of pea blossoms are hereditary traits.

EST 2.1 CROSSBREEDING

The scientist Gregor Mendel was the first to understand how character traits are passed on from one generation to the next through **SEXUAL REPRODUCTION**. Through his experimentation with cross-pollination in pea plants, he defined the basic laws of heredity.

Mendel chose the pea plant for his research because it is a plant that can pollinate itself, a phenomenon called **SELF-POLLINATION**. This means that a flower from a pea plant can be pollinated with pollen from the same flower. Pure lines of the plant can thus be produced, in which a particular trait is passed down from one generation to the next, without variation.

> **A PURE LINE is a group of individuals of the same species, which, for a specific character trait, produces only offspring with the same trait, without variation.**

Mendel decided to study a specific characteristic of pea plants that "breed true": the colour of their blossoms. He chose plants with white flowers and plants with purple flowers. To understand how colour was passed down from one generation to the next, he cross-bred plants, which means that he exchanged **GAMETES** between the plants.

> **CROSSBREEDING is the exchange of gametes between two different individuals during sexual reproduction.**

11.12 Mendel used pea plants for his research on the mechanisms of heredity.

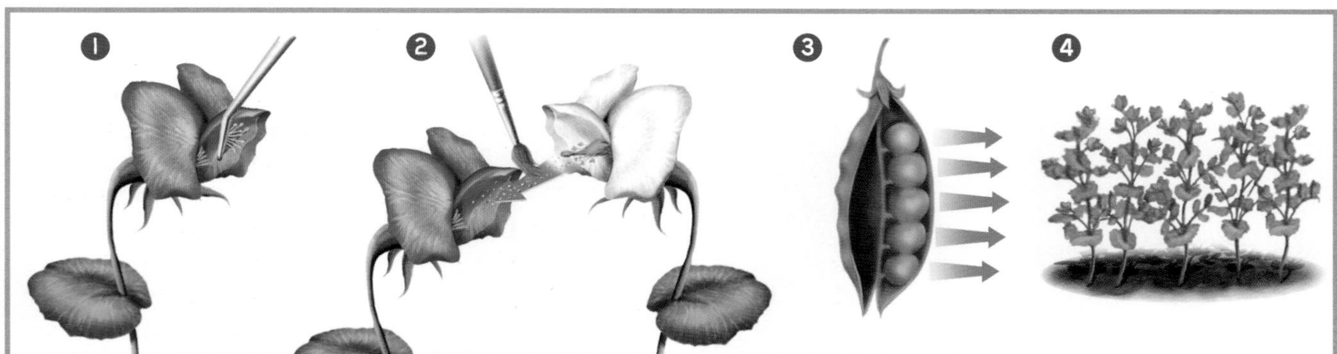

11.13 Mendel cross-pollinated purple-flowered pea plants with white-flowered pea plants.

As Figure 11.13 shows, to guarantee cross-pollination between the purple-flowered and the white-flowered plants, Mendel had to make sure that self-pollination was impossible. He cut the stamens (male organs that produce pollen) off the purple flowers and, using a paintbrush, deposited pollen from the white flowers onto the carpel (female organ that contains ovules) of the same purple flowers. He observed that all the pea plants obtained by this cross-pollination were plants with purple flowers. The plants were hybrids since they were the product of the crossbreeding of two genetically different plants.

A HYBRID is an individual obtained by the crossbreeding of two genetically different individuals.

To continue his research, Mendel left the hybrids to reproduce with one another. As Figure 11.14 shows, his work spanned three generations: the first generation (the generation of pure-line parent plants) and then the second and third generations.

A GENERATION is a group of individuals descended from common parents.

Mendel observed that white blossoms reappeared in the third generation. Out of the 929 third-generation plants he obtained, 705 had purple flowers, while 224 had white flowers. He therefore had three times as many purple-flowered plants as white-flowered plants.

To explain the reappearance of white blossoms among the pea plants, Mendel assumed that cells contain information that is passed down from one generation to the next.

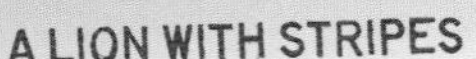

A LION WITH STRIPES

Have you ever heard of a liger? It is the animal that results from the crossbreeding of a female tiger with a male lion. It weighs around 450 kg and is four metres long, making it almost twice as big as its parents.

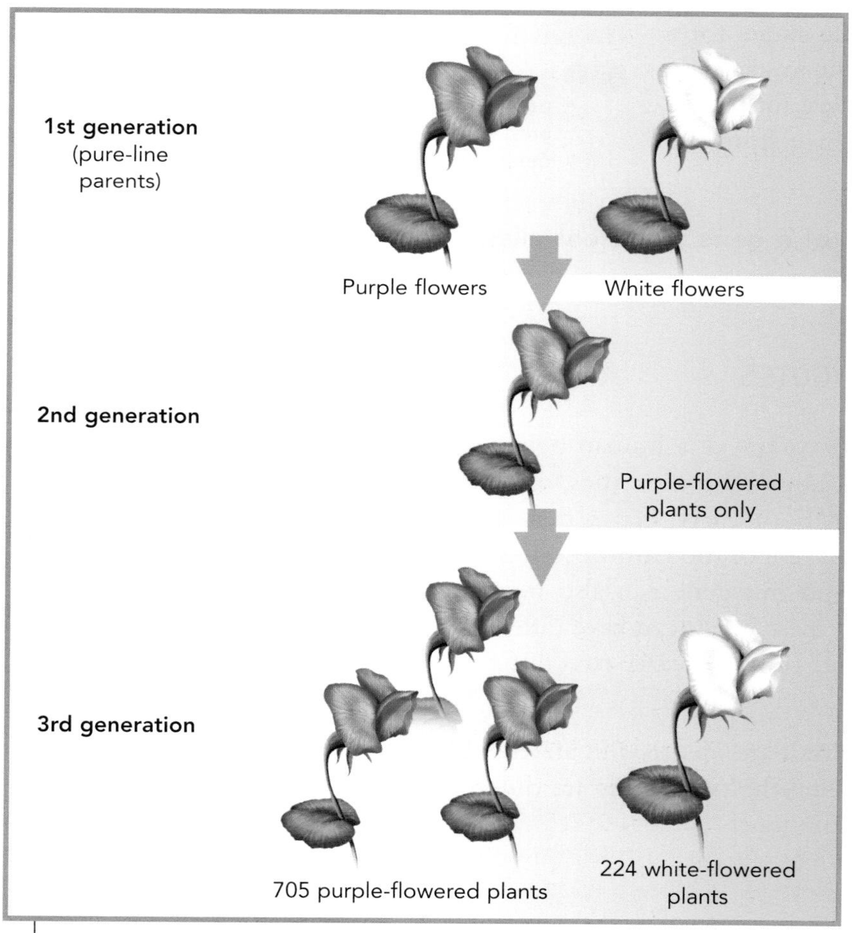

11.14 A summary of Mendel's work on the colour of pea blossoms

1822
1884

Gregor Mendel

This Austrian botanist and monk is considered the founding father of genetics. He established the fundamental laws of heredity, now referred to as "Mendel's laws." The laws were published in 1865 but went unnoticed at the time. It was only in 1900 that scientists realized their significance for the field of heredity.

EST 2.2 THE PRESENCE OF ALLELES

At the time Mendel was studying the mechanisms of heredity, he and his fellow scientists did not know that chromosomes existed, and they had certainly never heard of genes. Nevertheless, he understood that some type of information unit, which he named a *hereditary factor,* must be responsible for the expression of character traits in living organisms. Since human understanding of genetics has evolved considerably since Mendel's day, we now know that his "hereditary factors" are, in fact, genes. For this reason, we will use the term *gene* when referring to his work even though it had not yet been coined.

11.15 Eye colour is a character trait that can vary from person to person. The difference is explained by the presence of different alleles for this same trait among the human population.

To understand how Mendel succeeded in discovering some of the mechanisms of heredity, let's go back to the colour of the pea blossoms that he used in his research. Two different versions of this character trait appeared: white and purple. To explain why it is possible to have more than one version of a particular trait, Mendel assumed that there must be several possible alternatives for each of the genes responsible for a single trait. These different forms are called the *alleles* of a gene.

Today we know that the various possible alleles for a gene are the result of differences in the nucleotide sequence. In the case of pea plants, the allele for purple flowers has a different nucleotide sequence from the allele for white flowers.

An ALLELE is a possible form of a gene. Different alleles have different nucleotide sequences.

EST HOMOZYGOTES AND HETEROZYGOTES

As we saw earlier in this chapter, the karyotype of a human being contains 23 pairs of homologous chromosomes. These chromosomes, one from the father and the other from the mother, both carry genes that determine the same character traits. For example, on one of the chromosomes from the father, there is a gene for eye colour, and this gene can also be found on the chromosome from the mother. Since these genes can have different alleles (brown, blue, etc.), it is possible for an individual to carry two distinct alleles for the same character trait.

When both alleles for a given character trait are identical in an individual, it is said to be *homozygous* for the trait. When the two alleles are different, the individual is said to be *heterozygous* for the trait.

- **A HOMOZYGOTE is an individual with two identical alleles for a given character trait.**
- **A HETEROZYGOTE is an individual with two different alleles for a given character trait.**

Let's go back to the example of the pea blossoms, further illustrated in Figure 11.16. The gene for their colour is on a pair of homologous chromosomes in the cells of the pea plant. The gene exists in two different forms: the allele for the colour purple and the allele for the colour white. A homozygous plant can bear white or purple flowers, while a heterozygous plant will necessarily bear purple flowers. The reason for this single possibility in heterozygous plants can be explained by the existence of dominant and recessive alleles.

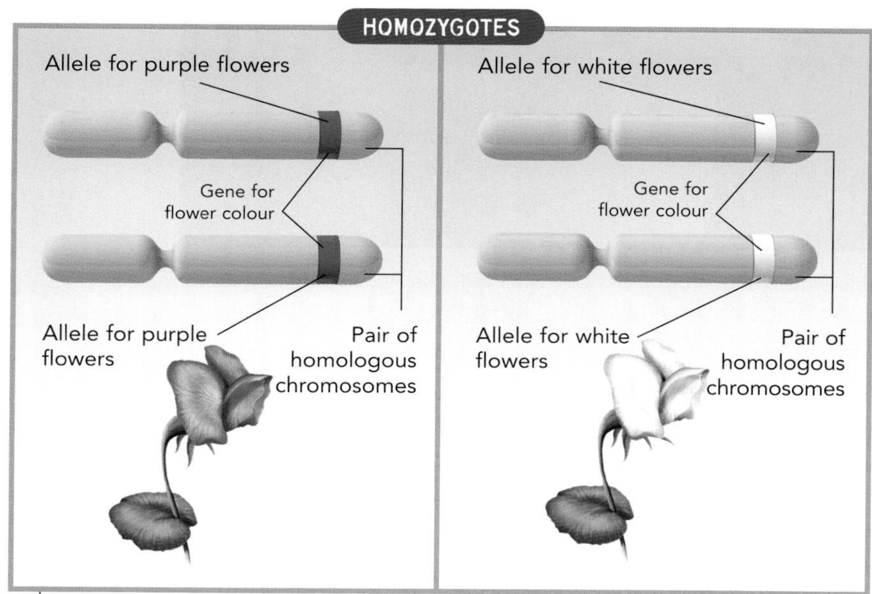

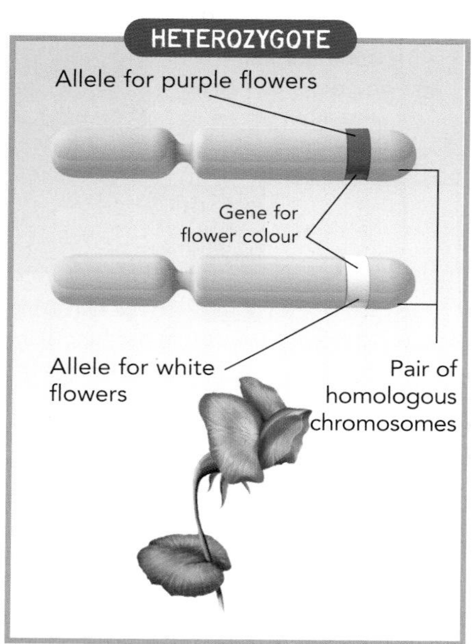

11.16 The gene for flower colour occupies a specific position on a certain chromosome and on its matched pair in the pea plant cells. Two alleles are possible for this character trait. A homozygous individual can bear either purple or white flowers, while a heterozygous individual necessarily bears purple flowers.

EST DOMINANT AND RECESSIVE ALLELES

Through his work, Mendel discovered that certain alleles are dominant, while others are recessive. When an individual carries two different alleles, the one that is expressed is considered dominant. An allele is said to be expressed when it affects how an organism looks or functions. For example, if an individual carries two different alleles for eye colour—one for blue eyes and the other for brown—and if that individual has brown eyes, the brown allele is said to be *dominant*. An individual carrying a dominant allele thus expresses the dominant character trait. For that trait, then, the individual can be either heterozygous or *homozygous dominant*.

11.17 These two African girls are sisters, but one of them is albino. She has no pigmentation in her hair, skin and eyes. The allele causing albinism is recessive. To be albino, the girl must therefore carry two recessive alleles.

A DOMINANT ALLELE is an allele that is expressed when an individual carries two different alleles for a given gene.

On the other hand, the allele that is not expressed when two different alleles are present is said to be *recessive*. Consequently, for a recessive allele to be expressed in an individual, the two alleles for the particular character trait must be identical. The individual is then said to be *homozygous recessive* or to carry a recessive trait.

A RECESSIVE ALLELE is an allele that is not expressed when an individual carries two different alleles for a given gene.

EST 2.3 GENOTYPES AND PHENOTYPES

Due to the phenomena of dominance and recessivity in alleles, all of an individual's alleles may not be expressed, meaning that they do not affect the individual, but the individual carries them nonetheless. This is the case for the non-albino sister in Figure 11.17, for example. Although she may be carrying a gene with the allele for albinism, she is not affected by the condition.

Scientists distinguish between an individual's phenotype and genotype. The genotype describes all of the alleles an individual possesses, while the phenotype describes the way in which the genotype expresses itself.

A GENOTYPE is an individual's genetic inheritance. It describes all of an individual's alleles for specific genes.

A PHENOTYPE is the way in which a genotype expresses itself. It describes the appearance or state of the individual for one or more character traits.

To describe an individual's genotype, scientists usually apply the following rules:

- Each allele is represented by a letter. The selected letter is usually the first letter of the adjective qualifying the character trait expressed by the dominant allele. For example, *P* stands for the colour purple among the pea blossoms.
- To represent a dominant allele, a capital letter is used; the corresponding recessive allele is represented with the lowercase form of the same letter.

Table 11.18 presents a few character traits of the pea plants that Mendel studied, using the notation just described.

11.18 HEREDITARY CHARACTER TRAITS IN PEAS, AS STUDIED BY MENDEL

Character trait	Dominant allele	Recessive allele	Phenotypes	Genotypes
Flower colour	P	p	Purple flowers	PP or Pp
			White flowers	pp
Seed colour	Y	y	Yellow seeds	YY or Yy
			Green seeds	yy
Seed shape	R	r	Round shape	RR or Rr
			Wrinkled shape	rr
Stem length	L	l	Long stem (about 3 m)	LL or Ll
			Short stem (about 30 cm)	ll

EST 2.4 THE LAW OF SEGREGATION OF ALLELES

Gametes are formed during sexual reproduction through a phenomenon of cell division called **MEIOSIS**. This cell division leads to the creation of gametes containing half the chromosomes normally present in the cells of the organism. Instead of carrying pairs of chromosomes, gametes thus contain only one chromosome from each pair. Consequently, only one allele is present instead of two.

Since an offspring results from the fusion of a gamete from the father and a gamete from the mother, half of its chromosomes will come from the father, and the other half, from the mother. However, even if half the genes in the offspring's chromosomes come from one parent, and the other half, from the other parent, the offspring will not *half* resemble the father and *half* resemble the mother. Why not?

Without even knowing about meiosis, Mendel's research nonetheless led him to formulate the law of segregation of alleles. This law states that the two alleles for a particular character trait separate when gametes are formed. Half of the gametes thus receive one of the two alleles, and the other half receive the second allele. For example, in the case of flower colour (Figure 11.19), homozygous individuals produce gametes—shown here in circles—that all have the same allele, while in a heterozygous individual, 50 percent of the gametes carry the *P* allele, and 50 percent, the *p* allele.

Segregation comes from the Latin *segregare*, meaning "to set apart."

1902
1992

Barbara McClintock

This scientist focused her research on the structure of the corn genome. She developed techniques to visualize the behaviour of chromosomes and their genes during gamete formation. Her work earned her a Nobel Prize in 1983.

Phenotype	Purple flowers	Purple flowers	White flowers
Genotype	Homozygote PP	Heterozygote Pp	Homozygote pp
Gametes	(P) 50% (P) 50%	(P) 50% (p) 50%	(p) 50% (p) 50%

11.19 Alleles for flower colour as they occur in gametes, according to the different genotypes possible and the law of segregation of alleles

EST 2.5 DETERMINING POSSIBLE GENOTYPES AND THEIR PROBABILITY

During reproduction, gametes join at random. Many different combinations of alleles are thus possible. Certain researchers wanted to study all the genotypes that could occur during gamete fusion and evaluate the probability of each occurrence. One of those scientists devised a grid for this purpose, called the *Punnett square* in his honour. To use this tool properly, four steps must be followed:

1. Determine the genotype of the two parents.
2. Find all the possible genotypes for the gametes of each parent and write them in circles. These circles represent the possible gametes.
3. Place the possible gametes from one parent at the top of a Punnett square, and the possible gametes from the other parent, on the left side of the same grid.
4. Indicate, inside the Punnett square, all the possible gamete combinations; enter the resulting genotypes and phenotypes.

Figure 11.20 shows the results of crossing a heterozygous purple-flowered pea plant with a homozygous white-flowered pea plant. There is a 50-percent chance of obtaining plants with purple flowers and a 50-percent chance of obtaining plants with white flowers.

This example shows what happens when the transmission of a single character trait is studied. The next step would be to consider the transmission of several character traits at once. This is what Mendel did in fact, and it led him to state the second law of heredity: the law of independent assortment of character traits.

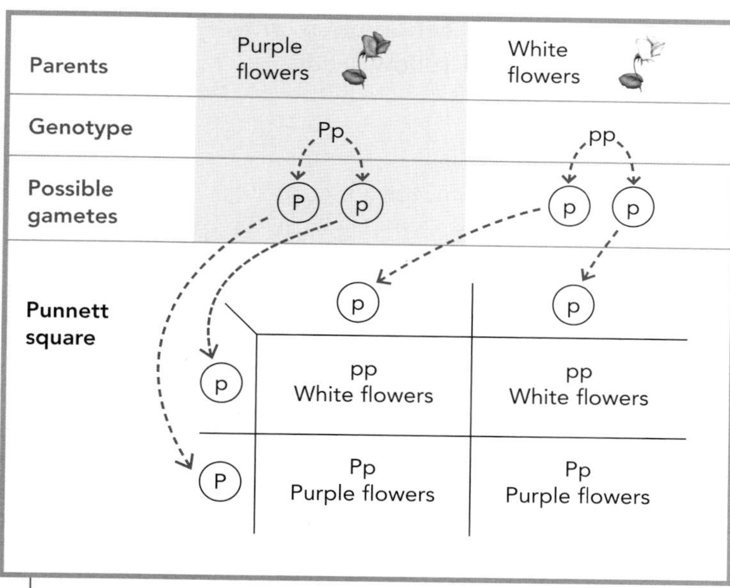

11.20 Example of crossbreeding with regard to a single character trait

EST 2.6 THE LAW OF INDEPENDENT ASSORTMENT OF CHARACTER TRAITS

During gamete formation, the alleles for different character traits, which up until then had been in pairs, become separated. To find out the genotype of the different gametes that could be obtained when considering more than one trait at a time, all the possible combinations of the alleles must be taken into account.

Let's look at Figure 11.21 to understand how to predict the genotype or phenotype of offspring when considering more than one character trait. It is important to specify in this example that two colours of seed are possible, yellow or green, and that yellow-coloured seeds are dominant. In addition, the seeds can come in two shapes, round or wrinkled, and the round shape is dominant. The other possible alleles for these two character traits (green and wrinkled) are necessarily recessive.

First, using the parents' genotypes, the possible gametes are identified. In this example, a pea plant with the genotype RrYy—a plant with round yellow seeds—is crossed with a plant whose genotype is rrYy—a plant with wrinkled yellow seeds.

Parents	Round yellow seed	Wrinkled yellow seed
Genotype	Rr Yy	rr Yy
Possible gametes	(RY) (rY) (Ry) (ry)	(rY) (rY) (ry) (ry)

Punnett square

	(rY)	(rY)	(ry)	(ry)
(RY)	RrYY Round yellow	RrYY Round yellow	RrYy Round yellow	RrYy Round yellow
(rY)	rrYY Wrinkled yellow	rrYY Wrinkled yellow	rrYy Wrinkled yellow	rrYy Wrinkled yellow
(Ry)	RrYy Round yellow	RrYy Round yellow	Rryy Round green	Rryy Round green
(ry)	rrYy Wrinkled yellow	rrYy Wrinkled yellow	rryy Wrinkled green	rryy Wrinkled green

11.21 Example of crossbreeding with regard to more than one character trait

PICKY EATERS? IT'S IN THEIR GENES!

For parents who worry that their children will never eat anything but chocolate milk, Gummi vitamins and the occasional grape, a new study offers some relief. Researchers examined the eating habits of 5390 pairs of twins between 8 and 11 years old and found children's aversions to trying new foods are mostly inherited.

The message to parents: It's not your cooking, it's your genes.

The study, led by Dr. Lucy Cooke of the department of epidemiology and public health at University College London is believed to be the first to use a standard scale to investigate the contribution of genetics and environment to children's reactions to new foods.

Most children eat a wide variety of foods until they are around two, when they suddenly stop. The phase can last until the child is four or five. It's an evolutionary response, researchers believe: a natural skepticism of new foods is thought to be a healthy part of a child's development.

Even though fear of new foods appears to be genetic, doctors say parents of picky eaters can't just surrender and boil another pot of pasta. People who study children prone to flinging themselves on the floor at the mere mention of broccoli agree that calm, repeated exposure to new foods every day for between five days to two weeks is an effective way to overcome a child's fears.

How a child reacts to a plate of spinach may depend on her genes.

Source: Adapted from Kim Severson, "Picky Eaters? They Get It From You," *The New York Times* [online edition], October 10, 2007. (Accessed November 11, 2008.)

After entering all the possible combinations and the resulting genotypes and phenotypes, we can see that, for example, there are two chances in 16 of obtaining a plant with wrinkled green seeds.

EST 3 Cloning

There are two natural methods of reproduction: sexual reproduction and asexual reproduction. The principles of heredity we have just seen concern sexual reproduction, which involves two members of the same species. Since the resulting offspring inherit a unique combination of genes from both parents, sexual reproduction creates greater genetic diversity. Each offspring is genetically unique, with the exception of identical twins.

CONCEPT REVIEW
- Genetic diversity
- Cell cultures
- Genetic transformation (GMOs)

Asexual reproduction, in contrast, involves one parent only. The offspring are therefore identical copies of their single parents, with the same genetic makeup. Creating identical versions of an individual, part of an individual or one of its genes is called *cloning*. An individual created by cloning will be genetically identical to its only parent. It is referred to as a *clone*.

CLONING is the reproduction of an individual, part of that individual or one of its genes in order to obtain an exact copy.

EST 3.1 NATURAL CLONING

When cloning occurs in nature, without any human intervention, it is called *natural cloning*. Table 11.22 presents a few forms of this type of cloning.

NATURAL CLONING produces genetically identical individuals through asexual reproduction.

11.22 EXAMPLES OF NATURAL CLONING

Form of asexual reproduction	Description
Budding	In this form of reproduction, a new individual develops from a protrusion that eventually detaches itself from the parent.
Layering	In this form of reproduction, which is specific to plants, roots—called *stolons*—develop from a branch in contact with the ground. If the stolon detaches itself from the parent plant, it becomes a new individual.
Propagation by cutting	In this form of reproduction, which is also specific to plants, a new individual is formed from a separated section of the plant (other than its seeds), which falls to the ground.

EST 3.2 ARTIFICIAL PLANT CLONING

Layering and cutting techniques, based on natural propagation in plants, have been used by humans for centuries. People often take a cutting from a plant and put it in water until roots grow. Once the roots have formed, the new plant can be transferred into a pot. Since this technique involves human participation, the process is referred to as *artificial plant cloning*.

The artificial cloning of plants is an increasingly widespread agricultural practice. It allows farmers and florists to obtain identical copies of individuals with desirable characteristics. For example, a farmer might be tempted to clone a plant that produces big tasty orange carrots. Figure 11.23 (page 371) illustrates the *in vitro* method for cloning a carrot.

ENVIRONMENT EXTRA

Farmers' fields or pharmaceutical factories?

There is nothing new about plants with medicinal properties. Just think of the sailors in Jacques Cartier's crew, who, in 1536, were saved from scurvy by drinking an Aboriginal brew of spruce bark and needles.

Until recently, people were content to extract the medicines they needed from plants. Now, the science of genetics makes it possible to use plants to manufacture remedies they do not produce naturally. Scientists develop genes containing the instructions for the required drug and insert them into plants, which can be farmed. This manufacturing process is called *molecular farming*.

One day, perhaps, corn grown in fields like this one may be used to manufacture drugs, but first any risk of food contamination must be eliminated.

Molecular farming can also have undesirable effects. A case study presented by the Québec government reveals that in 2001, corn containing a vaccine against a particular disease among pigs was grown in a field in the United States and then harvested. The following year, soybean was grown in the same field, but this time the crop was meant for human consumption.

Corn shoots appeared among the soybean, which was harvested nonetheless. Humans were then at risk of eating food that contained a drug for pigs. Fortunately, the American authorities became aware of the problem and took the crop off the market.

Modern society thus faces a challenge: establishing regulations to reduce to a minimum the effects of molecular farming on our diet, health and environment, while still encouraging this technological innovation that can ultimately provide low-cost medication.

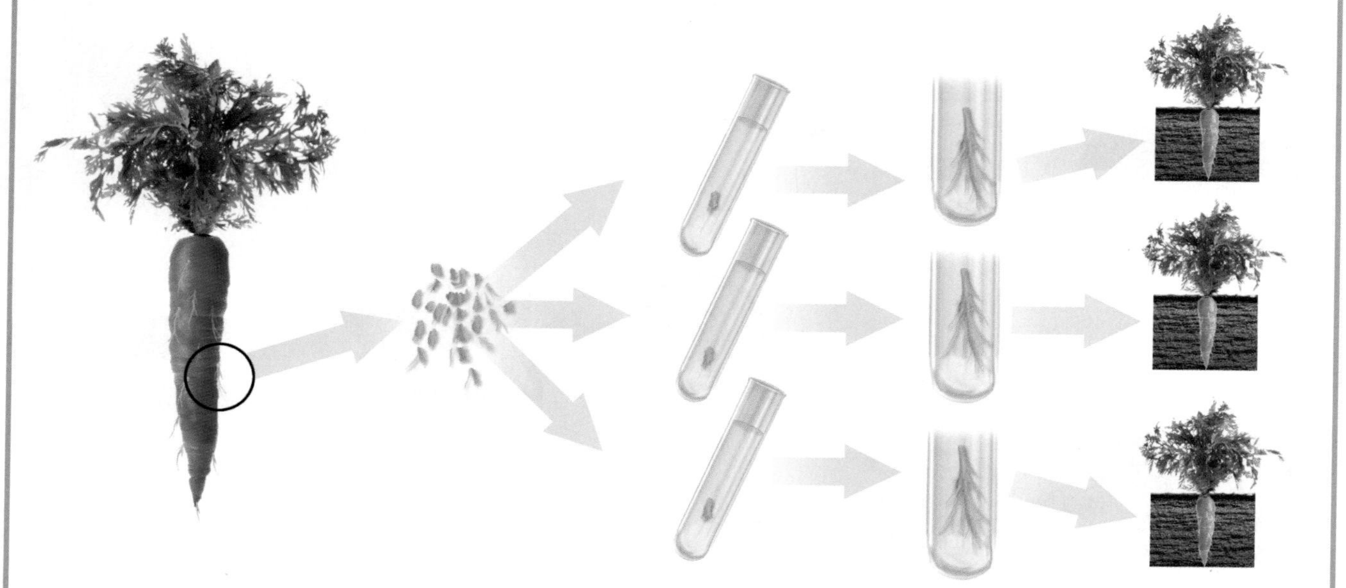

Carrot root

Fragments of carrot root

Culture in test tubes

Plants cultivated *in vitro*

Crop of carrots that are genetically identical to the original plant

11.23 In agronomy, a plant with desirable characteristics can be cultivated *in vitro* to produce many identical copies.

EST 3.3 ANIMAL CLONING

Unlike plants, the animals we raise for meat, such as beef, or for useful materials, such as the wool from sheep, cannot reproduce asexually. It is therefore impossible for them to clone naturally. A technique has been developed, however, for cloning animals artificially. In mammals, the technique consists of:

1. removing a cell from the individual to be cloned
2. taking an ovum from another individual and removing its nucleus—thus, its DNA
3. combining the cell and the ovum without a nucleus, which results in an embryo with the same genetic material as the original individual
4. implanting the embryo into the uterus of a surrogate mother. The embryo will develop there, and the surrogate mother will give birth to a clone of the targeted individual.

Figure 11.24 (page 372) illustrates this technique as it was applied to the cloning of a bull; the resulting offspring was called Starbuck II. The practice of cloning mammals has been a source of controversy in modern society. Since we are mammals ourselves, cloning raises the theoretical possibility of copying human beings.

A LION-HEARTED MOUSE?

Who has ever heard of a mouse that is not afraid of cats? Japanese researchers successfully created such a fearless beast in 2007 by modifying the genes responsible for the mouse's sense of smell. The mouse no longer recognized the characteristic scent of its predators, so it stopped running away from cats on the prowl.

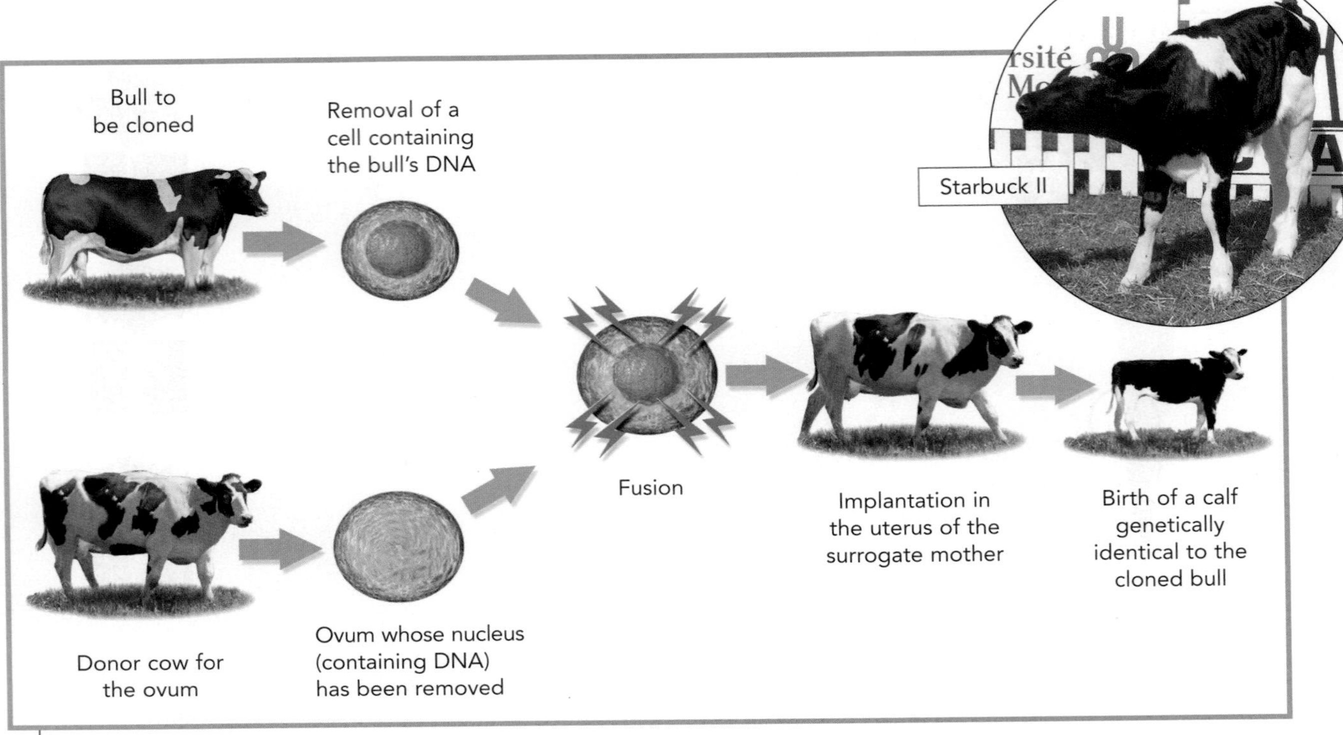

11.24 Starbuck the bull, who is reported to have more than 200 000 descendants throughout the world, was cloned two years after his death. His clone—Starbuck II, born in September 2000—possesses the same genetic material as his famous father.

HORSES STRAIGHT OUT OF THE LAB

Thirteen cloned horses were born in 2006 using the same technique as for Dolly the sheep. Five of them were sired by the same stallion, Smart Little Lena, a star of western riding in the United States. Katrin Hinrichs, in charge of the Equine Embryo Laboratory at Texas A&M University, is still surprised by the lab's success: "Our objective was to obtain just one clone, but the technique was more effective than we anticipated."

Calvaro V. In a few years' time, show-jumping competitions may feature clones of this horse.

Scientists remove skin cells from the animal to be cloned. They then procure ova, usually from slaughterhouses. They remove the nuclei from the ova and replace them with the nuclei from the cells of the horse to be cloned. The cost of each cloned foal is over $100 000.

The team's next objective is to produce a clone of Calvaro V, the legendary show jumping champion, who died in 2003 but whose cells have been preserved.

EST 3.4 HUMAN CLONING

Human cloning may take one of two forms:

- reproductive cloning
- therapeutic cloning

The aim of reproductive cloning is to produce babies that are genetically identical to the people being cloned. This form of cloning, and any form of experimentation in this direction, is currently prohibited in Canada and many other countries.

REPRODUCTIVE CLONING is the application of cloning techniques to obtain a new individual genetically identical to the one being cloned.

Therapeutic cloning aims to produce human tissues or organs for replacement. Since these tissues or organs contain the same genetic information as the person receiving them, the risk of rejection is nil.

THERAPEUTIC CLONING is the application of cloning techniques to obtain tissues or organs genetically identical to those of a person in need of a transplant or medical grafting.

EST 3.5 MOLECULAR CLONING

We have seen that cloning is used to produce complete individuals, such as new plants, or parts of individuals, such as organs or tissues, to treat people who are ill or have suffered an accident. Cloning has yet another application. Many illnesses have genetic causes, which means they are due to defective genes. For this reason, scientists want to clone genes so they can obtain multiple copies and study them more closely. This is called *molecular cloning* (also *DNA* or *gene cloning*).

MOLECULAR CLONING is the production of multiple copies of the same gene.

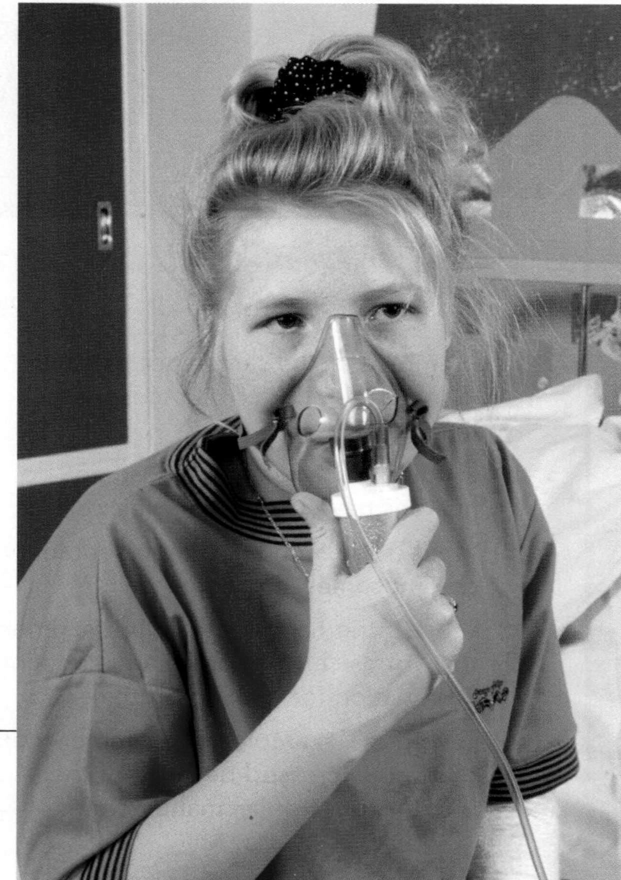

II.25

Cystic fibrosis is a disease affecting one child in 2500. It is caused by a defective gene in the body. The airways of children with the disease are clogged with mucus, which creates an ideal environment for bacterial growth. With molecular cloning, scientists hope one day to find a treatment for cystic fibrosis.

CHECKUP

ST	None.	AST	None.
EST	1–17, A and B.	SE	None.

1 Factors responsible for character traits among living organisms (pp. 350–358)

1. Look at the two cells below.

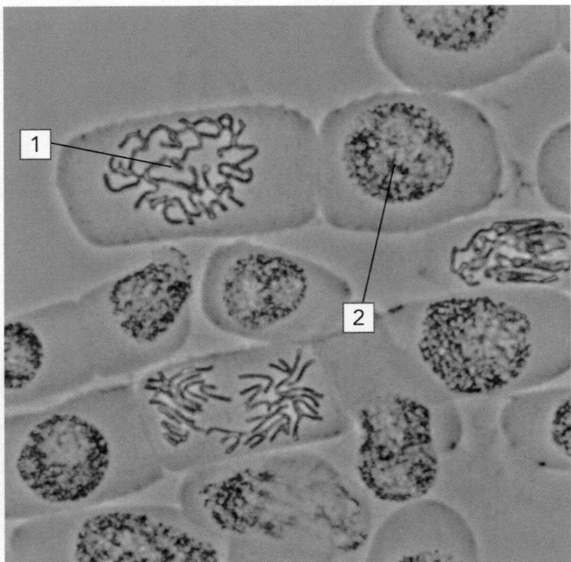

a) What is the form of the DNA in cell 1?

b) What is the form of the DNA in cell 2?

2. All members of the same species have an identical number of chromosomes in their cells.

a) In total, how many chromosomes do humans have in most of their cells?

b) What is the name of a representation of chromosomes in ordered pairs?

c) What is the name of the DNA segment that forms chromosomes and contains information for making proteins?

d) Give three examples of character traits that are expressed because of the proteins our bodies manufacture.

3. Look at the illustration below representing DNA in a simplified form.

Use the information in the illustration to answer the following questions.

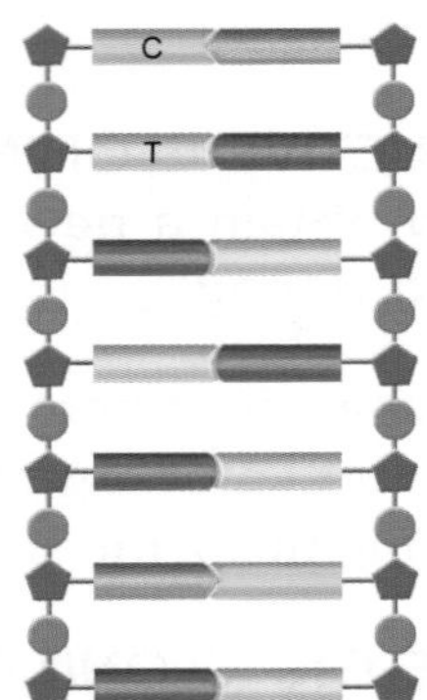

a) Name the nitrogenous base represented by the following shape: (Write its full name.)

b) Name the nitrogenous base represented by the following shape: (Write its full name.)

c) Name the nitrogenous base represented by the following shape: (Write its full name.)

d) Name the nitrogenous base represented by the following shape: (Write its full name.)

e) If ● represents a phosphate group, what does ⬟ represent?

4. We know that letters are the building blocks for forming words.

a) What are the building blocks for making proteins called?

b) The alphabet contains 26 letters. How many different building blocks can be used to make proteins?

c) True or false? The building blocks for forming proteins in bacteria and fungi are different from those we use to make our own proteins. Explain your answer.

5. The growth hormone stimulates growth and metabolism, among other things. This molecule is a sequence of 191 amino acids.
   a) Why can this hormone be identified as a protein?
   b) The growth hormone controls functions and carries messages in our bodies. Name four other roles proteins can play in the human body.

6. Protein synthesis occurs as a result of certain processes in a cell. Place the following steps in the correct order.
   A. An mRNA is formed.
   B. tRNA bond with the mRNA. Amino acids are joined together.
   C. The synthesized protein detaches itself from the ribosome and folds into its final shape.
   D. The two strands of DNA separate.
   E. An mRNA attaches itself to a ribosome.

7. Does each of the following statements refer to DNA or RNA?
   a) My full name is ribonucleic acid.
   b) The sugar I contain is deoxyribose.
   c) I do not contain any thymine.
   d) Most of the time, I am a molecule made up of two complementary strands.
   e) One of my nitrogenous bases is uracil.
   f) I act as a messenger during protein synthesis.

2 Principles of heredity (pp. 358–369)

8. Fruit flies are often used for experiments in genetics. To reproduce, sperm from the male flies fertilize the ova of the female flies, which then lay eggs. Why can fruit flies be said to reproduce by crossbreeding?

9. Among the character traits studied in fruit flies is the length of their wings. Two shapes are possible for this character trait: normal wings and miniature wings.

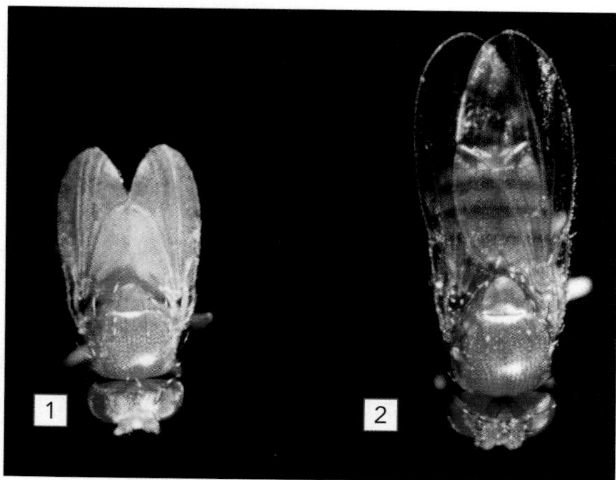

1. Fruit fly with miniature wings
2. Fruit fly with normal wings

If two pure-line individuals with normal wings are crossbred, what proportion of the offspring will also have normal wings? Explain your answer.

10. When a fruit fly has an allele for normal wings and an allele for miniature wings, its phenotype for this character trait is "normal-winged."
   a) Is this individual homozygous or heterozygous for the character trait? Explain your answer.
   b) Which of the two alleles is dominant?
   c) Which of the two alleles is recessive?
   d) What would be the possible genotype or genotypes for a fruit fly with normal wings?
   e) What would be the possible genotype or genotypes for a fruit fly with miniature wings?

11. Is each of the following character traits hereditary or not?
    a) the tendency to tan in the sun
    b) eye colour
    c) hair length
    d) the presence of a scar
    e) hand size
    f) occurrence of cystic fibrosis
    g) infection with the flu

12. In guinea pigs, the allele for black-coloured fur (B) is dominant over the allele that produces white fur (b). A pure-line individual with black fur is crossbred with an individual with white fur. What is the probability that a black-haired offspring from this cross will be heterozygous for the character trait? Support your answer with a Punnett square.

13. In rabbits, the allele for black hair (B) is dominant over the allele for tan-coloured hair (b). Second, the allele for short hair (S) is dominant over the allele for long hair (s). A long-haired male rabbit that is heterozygous for hair colour is crossbred with a black short-haired female that is homozygous for both character traits. Using a Punnett square:
    a) Specify the possible genotype or genotypes of the offspring from this crossbreeding.
    b) Specify the possible phenotype or phenotypes of the offspring from this crossbreeding.

14. In tomatoes, the allele for purple stems (P) is dominant over the allele for green stems (p). Second, the allele for red fruit (R) is dominant over the allele for yellow fruit (r). Two tomato plants that are heterozygous for the two character traits are crossbred. Supposing that 160 new plants are obtained, use a Punnett square to show how many of them, in theory, will have:
    a) a purple stem and yellow fruit
    b) a purple stem and red fruit
    c) a green stem and yellow fruit
    d) a green stem and red fruit

3 Cloning (pp. 369–373)

15. Why can identical twins be described as clones of each other?

16. Distinguish between natural cloning and artificial cloning. Give an example of each.

17. Look at the figures below.

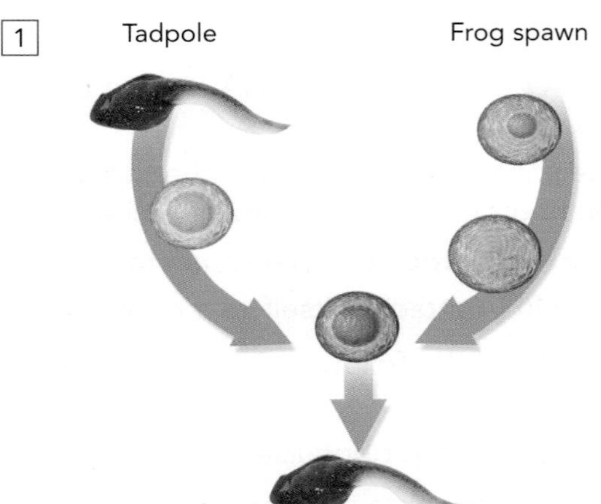

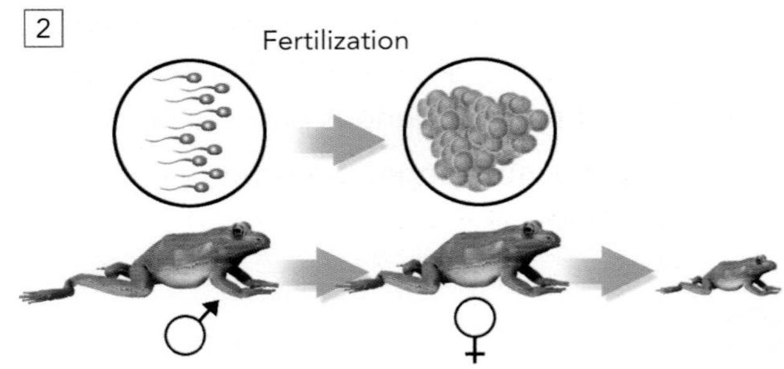

    a) Which of the two figures illustrates cloning? Explain why.
    b) Is this natural or artificial cloning? Explain your answer.

review questions

A. Read the following text and then answer the questions below.

In Canada, one in 10 000 people suffers from Huntington's chorea, which causes neurons in the brain to decay. Patients typically have difficulty controlling their movements; eventually they become completely immobile and die.

On our fourth pair of chromosomes, we all have a gene called the *Huntington gene*. It contains instructions for synthesizing a protein called *huntingtin,* whose exact function in our neurons remains unexplained. It is known, however, that a particular amino acid is repeated in its structure. If this amino acid is repeated fewer than 35 times in a row, the carrier does not normally suffer from Huntington's chorea. When there is a sequence with more than 35 repetitions, the person has the disease.

Unfortunately, people who carry the allele causing Huntington's chorea in their DNA are inevitably afflicted with the disease. The first symptoms of this hereditary disease usually appear between the ages of 30 and 45 years, so affected adults may already be parents before realizing that they are sick.

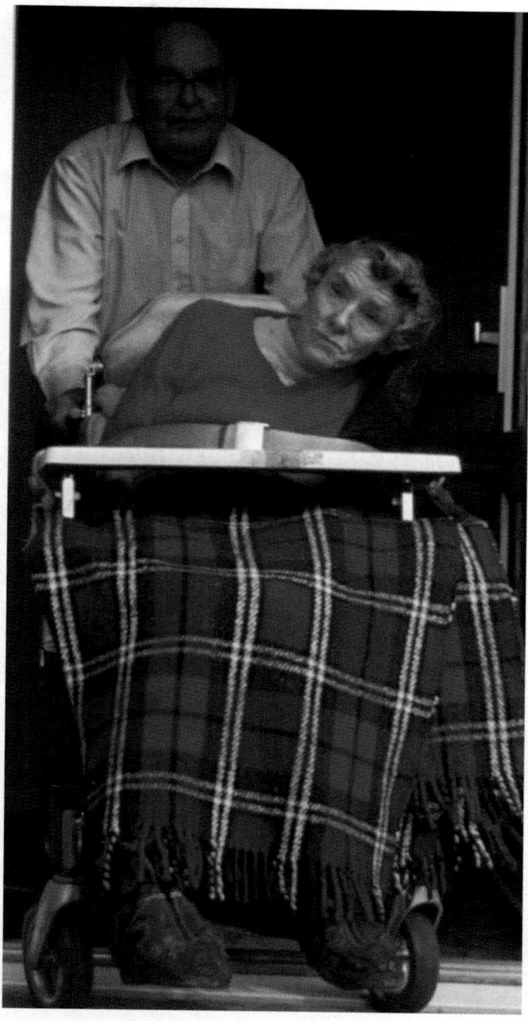

Since people suffering from Huntington's chorea have difficulty controlling their movements, they are often confined to a wheelchair.

a) Which mRNA has the longer nucleotide sequence: the one copied from the mutant allele associated with Huntington's chorea or the one copied from the normal allele? Explain your answer.

b) Which of the two alleles is dominant: the one that causes the disease or the one that does not? Explain your answer.

c) What are the possible genotypes for a person with this disease?

d) If the father of a child is heterozygous for this character trait and the mother does not have Huntington's chorea, what is the probability that the child will have the disease? You can use a Punnett square to answer this question.

B. Prepare your own summary of Chapter 11 by building a concept map.

HOW TO BUILD A CONCEPT MAP

SAVING LIVES AND PRESERVING BIODIVERSITY

The Pacific yew, also known as the *Western yew*, is a conifer that grows very slowly in the wild. It can reach up to 40 cm in diameter and 15 m in height. It is found mostly along the Pacific coast, from Alaska down to central California. First Nations people used its very hard wood to make lances, arrows, bows, paddles, snowshoe frames, etc.

In the 1960s, the American government, in its determination to find a cure for cancer, organized a vast collection of plant samples across the country. The Pacific yew (*Taxus brevifolia*) was discovered to hold a secret—a surprising property. One of its genes contains the recipe for manufacturing a molecule called *taxol* that can fight cancer. By breaking down the bark many times and analyzing each of the fractions, biologists succeeded in isolating the taxol, which is still used today to treat a wide range of cancers.

Taxol represents only a tiny proportion of yew bark—between 0.01 and 0.03 percent of its dry mass. To prolong the life of just one patient by about a year, almost 30 kg of bark must be harvested, which means cutting down four to six century-old trees. The yew underwent a period of intensive harvesting, to the extent that, by the early 1990s, the species was threatened with extinction. Environmentalists sounded the alarm, pointing to the importance of preserving this species for its genetic and molecular potential for human use. An alternative source of taxol had to be found.

DIVERSIFYING SOURCES OF TAXOL

American authorities were the first to respond to the problem, which was especially acute in their country. To protect the Pacific yew and to control waste in the forest industry, logging became regulated. But this measure did not resolve the question of taxol supply. In 1992, the drug called Taxol was approved for treating ovarian cancers that were not responding to chemotherapy. The demand for taxol grew. The pharmaceutical giant Bristol-Meyers Squibb, which held the rights to the drug, reached an agreement with the forest industry to increase the supply of yew bark, but the company quickly realized that it would be in its best interest to diversify its sources. Two solutions were possible: find more trees or synthesize the drug in the laboratory.

In 1994, two research teams, one in Florida and the other in California, succeeded almost simultaneously in synthesizing the anticancer molecule. The process was interesting from a scientific point of view but too complex to be profitable. The pharmaceutical company decided instead to manufacture its drug from the Himalayan yew (*Taxus wallichiani*), a more common variety. By using the twigs and needles of this tree, the new manufacturing process also avoided harming the environment.

At the same time, in France, a team of researchers managed to obtain a molecule similar to taxol, called *taxodere,* using needles from the English yew (*Taxus baccata*). Other varieties of yew that are easy to cultivate have been identified, particularly in Italy.

The needles of some species of yew can be used to manufacture anticancer drugs.

In Canada, regulations and research projects have protected the Pacific yew. Meanwhile, another variety of yew (*Taxus canadensis*) has been identified in the east of the country and is being harvested under sustainable forest management, meaning that both trees and forest are protected. More recently, the anticancer molecule has also been discovered in various parts of the hazel tree and even in the fungi that grow on it.

MONITORING OUR GLOBAL GENETIC HERITAGE

Thanks to these valuable discoveries, the Pacific yew is no longer at risk. However, the plundering of natural resources, especially plants that may contain drugs, remains a cause for concern. Plants and trees carry information in their genes, which—as in the case of the Pacific yew—can be turned to our advantage in the production of food, drugs or other material. Preserving our natural heritage and biodiversity worldwide is therefore of the utmost importance, even if we have not yet realized all their potential benefits. Norms must be established, pharmaceutical companies must be monitored, and research must continue.

1. Why were researchers interested in the nucleotide sequence of the gene responsible for taxol synthesis?
2. In Québec, phytotherapy, which is the treatment of diseases with plants, is becoming increasingly popular. Explain why protecting genetic diversity is important for this industry.

Science at work IN...

A CENTRE FOR COLLECTING AND PROCESSING RECYCLABLE MATERIALS

It takes about 19 mature trees to produce one tonne (1000 kg) of paper. Every one of seven million Quebeckers uses an average of 210 kg of paper each year. To prevent deforestation, all this paper must be effectively recycled. This task falls to the personnel in many recycling centres across the province, which also process all the other recyclable materials collected. In Québec, millions of tonnes of recyclable materials are recovered each year.

Let's meet a few of the people who work in centres for collecting and processing recyclable materials.

Jennifer Smith,
sales coordinator

Marie Nguyen,
computer support technician

Marc-André Gouin,
plant manager

Patrice Hamel,
operations supervisor

Véronique Laroche,
human resources and
labour relations coordinator

Claude Daoust,
maintenance and
purchasing supervisor

Occupation	Education	Length of study	Main tasks
Sales coordinator	DCS in business management	3 years	• Ensure that sales objectives are reached • Promote and market products or services
Operations supervisor	Undergraduate certificate in operations management	1 year	• Supervise plant operations • Plan employee training
Human resources coordinator	Bachelor's degree in industrial relations	3 years	• Manage human resources • Represent the employer in relations with employees
Maintenance supervisor	AVS in preventive and prospective industrial maintenance mechanics	450 hours	• Identify problems and solutions when machinery breaks down • Maintain various systems
Computer support technician	DVS in computing support	1800 hours	• Help computer users experiencing difficulties • Consult user guides, technical manuals and other documentation to repair equipment and apply solutions
Plant manager	Master's degree in business administration	5 years	• Plan, coordinate and manage operations

THE TECHNOLOGICAL

WORLD

FOR CENTURIES, HUMANS HAVE BEEN APPLYING THEIR INTELLIGENCE TO DESIGNING INCREASINGLY INGENIOUS TECHNOLOGICAL OBJECTS AND SYSTEMS.

Some, like the hammer or the electric light bulb, were invented a long time ago but are still in use today.

To design objects and systems for contemporary society, we produce standardized drawings, work with a greater diversity of materials and use increasingly sophisticated manufacturing techniques. Every part of an object or system has a specific function essential to the proper working of the combined whole.

Technology is fundamental to the entire process of designing, manufacturing, maintaining and repairing objects and systems. And it is thanks to technology that we succeed ever better in fulfilling our many needs and desires.

CONTENTS

2000 — Adoption of a regulation in Québec targeting the recovery of discarded paint containers and paints

1989 — Invention of the first biodegradable plastics

1933 — Invention of polyethylene, a thermoplastic widely used to manufacture bags

1915 — Invention of Pyrex, an extremely heat-resistant glass

1886 — Discovery of the electrolytic process for manufacturing aluminum

1865 — Synthesis of celluloid, the first plastic

1836 — Invention of fibreglass

1650 — Manufacture of varnish, wax, grease and lamp oil from petroleum

1311 — Construction of first blast furnaces for iron extraction

CIRCA 620 — Earliest production of porcelain, a type of ceramic

CIRCA -100 — Invention of glassblowing

CIRCA -1500 — Earliest iron quenching

CIRCA -3500 — Invention of welding

CIRCA -4000 — Discovery of glass

CIRCA -5000 — First lead, copper and tin mines

CIRCA -10 000 — Earliest manufacture of ceramic pots

Since the beginning of human history, people have continually sought to improve their living conditions. In the pursuit of a better world, they have imagined, designed and created a multitude of tools and objects of all kinds. Now, at the dawn of the 21st century, modern life brings us constant reminders of the many ingenious inventions of humankind—inventions that we will refer to here as *technical objects*.

What materials are used most often to manufacture these objects? What types of drawings do we usually work with to determine the shape and assembly of the parts in a technical object? Finally, which manufacturing techniques, tools and machines are used most frequently to produce technical objects? This chapter will provide the answers to these questions.

Manufacturing technical objects

CONTENTS

ST EST AST

1 Materials

In our daily lives, we are becoming increasingly dependent on various technical objects. The textbook you are reading, the chair you are sitting on and the shoes you are wearing are examples of technical objects. All technical objects, whatever they may be, are made of one or more *materials*.

Material comes from the Latin *materia*, meaning "matter" or "substance."

CONCEPT REVIEW
- Material
- Constraints (tension, compression, torsion)
- Mechanical properties

Technical objects are designed for specific purposes. Their uses expose them to different types of stress, which can cause the materials they are made of to deform. To decide which materials are suitable for making technical objects, manufacturers must first determine the stress the objects will be exposed to and the possible resulting deformations. The manufacturers must also know the properties of the selected materials.

ST EST AST

1.1 CONSTRAINTS AND DEFORMATIONS

The parts of a technical object may be subjected to one or more external **FORCES**. These forces tend to deform the parts. To consider the effects an external force can have on a material is to study the different types of stress the material undergoes, referred to as *constraints*. The weight of the building in Figure 12.1, for example, is causing compression (a constraint) on the columns. In Figure 12.2, the mountain climber's weight will tighten the rope (tension).

12.1 The columns of this building are subjected to compression.

12.2 The mountain climber is applying tension to the rope attached to the mountain.

A CONSTRAINT describes the effect of external forces on a material.

The main types of constraints are presented in Table 12.3.

12.3 THE MAIN TYPES OF CONSTRAINTS

Type of constraint	Description	Symbol	Examples
Compression	A material subjected to forces that tend to crush it is undergoing compression.	⇨ ⇦	• hands squeezing a wet sponge • a foot crushing a can
Tension	A material subjected to forces that tend to stretch it is undergoing tension.	⇦ ⇨	• copper stretched into wire • two teams in a tug of war
Torsion	A material subjected to forces that tend to twist it is undergoing torsion.		• an earthquake twisting a bridge • hands wringing a wet towel
Deflection	A material subjected to forces that tend to bend it is undergoing deflection.	⇩ ⇧ ⇩	• a fish bending a fishing rod • clothes weighing down a clothesline
Shearing	A material subjected to forces that tend to cut it is undergoing shearing.		• scissors cutting paper • metal cutters trimming shapes from metal

Depending on the constraints on the constituent materials of an object, three types of **DEFORMATION** can take place. They are presented in Table 12.4.

12.4 THE THREE TYPES OF MATERIAL DEFORMATION

Type of deformation	Description
Elastic	The constraint leads to a temporary change in the shape or dimensions of the material. When the constraint is removed, the material returns to its original form.
Plastic	The constraint leads to a permanent change in the shape or dimensions of the material. Even when the constraint is removed, the material remains deformed.
Fracture	The constraint is so intense that the material breaks.

In the example of the rope pulled tight by the mountain climber's weight (Figure 12.2, page 386), the deformation is elastic because the rope will normally return to its original form once released. However, as soon as the rope begins to fray or no longer returns to its original shape when it is untied, it becomes an example of plastic deformation. Finally, if the rope breaks, the stress on it has led to its fracture.

ST EST AST 1.2 PROPERTIES

As we saw in the previous section, not all materials react in the same way to the constraints they undergo. The reaction of a material under stress often depends on its properties. By defining these properties, experts can predict how a material will behave when subjected to various constraints. For example, before a bridge is built, an engineer must compare the properties of various materials to select the most suitable for the construction project. Among other concerns, the engineer must ensure that the bridge will not collapse under the deflection caused by crossing vehicles.

12.5 This snowboard is elastic enough to return to its original shape.

ST EST AST MECHANICAL PROPERTIES

When engineers compare the ability of materials to resist deflection, for example, they are comparing the mechanical properties of the materials because deflection is a mechanical constraint.

The MECHANICAL PROPERTIES of a material describe how it reacts when subjected to one or more constraints.

Table 12.6 presents a few examples of mechanical properties.

12.6 MECHANICAL PROPERTIES OF MATERIALS

Mechanical property	Definition
Hardness	Ability to resist indentation or abrasion
Elasticity	Ability to return to their original shapes after undergoing a constraint
Resilience	Ability to resist shocks without breaking
Ductility	Ability to be stretched without breaking
Malleability	Ability to be flattened or bent without breaking
Stiffness	Ability to retain their shapes when subjected to various constraints

12.7 This motorcycle helmet is resilient enough to resist shocks.

ST
EST
AST

OTHER PROPERTIES

We have just seen that materials can exhibit mechanical properties, but the ability to resist constraints is not the only aspect of a material that may be of value. For example, an engineer who has to design a corrosion-resistant object will look for a material possessing this quality. Table 12.8 presents other interesting properties engineers may take into account when choosing materials.

12.8 OTHER PROPERTIES OF MATERIALS

Property	Definition
Resistance to corrosion	Ability to resist the effects of corrosive substances (such as water, various salts and some components of fumes), which cause the formation of rust, for example
Electrical conductivity	Ability to carry an electric current
Thermal conductivity	Ability to transmit heat

12.9 These copper wires are excellent conductors of electricity.

12.10 These hubcaps are made of a material that resists corrosion.

12.11 The stainless steel of this pot transmits heat evenly.

ST
EST
AST

1.3 DEGRADATION AND PROTECTION

All materials degrade, although at different rates. Sooner or later their original properties are attacked and diminished by the surrounding environment. If nothing is done to counteract these damaging effects, the materials are doomed to eventual destruction.

- **The DEGRADATION OF A MATERIAL is the decline in some of its properties due to the effects of the surrounding environment.**

12.12 The rust on this car body is a sign that its materials are degrading.

Although all materials deteriorate, whether rapidly or slowly, there are nonetheless ways to prevent or delay their degradation. Methods of protection vary according to the materials in question. For example, some cars are treated with rustproofing to prevent or delay the formation of rust on the body.

The PROTECTION OF A MATERIAL is the application of procedures that prevent or delay its degradation.

ST EST AST 2 Categories of materials and their properties

CONCEPT REVIEW
- Wood and modified wood
- Nonferrous metals and alloys
- Ferrous alloys
- Plastics (thermoplastics) (AST)

Wood was one of the first materials humans used to improve their living conditions. Early in their history, however, people had to use their imaginations to find other materials to satisfy other needs; they invented ceramics. Later, they discovered uses for metals. For a long time, humans made do with these basic materials and their derivatives and with textiles. Centuries later, the arrival of plastics marked a turning point in the manufacture of technical objects. Composites, made by combining materials from different categories, were then added to the list. In the following sections, we will take a look at these different types of materials, their properties and some ways to protect them.

ST EST AST 2.1 WOOD AND MODIFIED WOOD

Wood was one of the first materials to be put to use by humans.

WOOD is a material obtained by harvesting and processing trees.

Wood is generally divided into two categories. Wood with a high degree of hardness is called *hardwood*. It usually comes from deciduous trees, such as oak or maple. Wood with a lower degree of hardness is called *softwood*. This type of wood usually comes from conifers, such as pine or spruce.

The mechanical properties of wood vary with the type of wood. The variations are mainly due to the following factors:

- the species of tree from which the wood originates
- the speed of growth of the tree and any injuries it may have sustained
- the water content of the wood

12.13 Many people appreciate the aesthetic qualities of wood, which is why it is still widely used to make furniture.

Wood is often used to make objects such as cabinets or furniture because of its aesthetic appeal. However, many other properties may also influence the choice of this type of material, such as:

- its hardness, elasticity, resilience and toughness (resistance to fracture)
- its low thermal and **ELECTRICAL CONDUCTIVITY**
- the ease with which it can be shaped and assembled
- its colours and shades
- its lightness

Modified wood

The majority of the trees harvested in our forests today are no longer shaped into wooden planks, boards or beams but used to make materials called *modified wood* instead. As its name suggests, modified wood consists mainly of wood but also contains other substances, such as glue, plastics and preservatives.

MODIFIED WOOD is treated wood or a material made from wood mixed with other substances.

Most modified wood is made by gluing together pieces, sheets or residues of wood left over after timber harvesting. Common products include plywood, particleboard and fibreboard. While the properties of different woods vary enormously from one species to another, the properties of modified wood products are usually more consistent.

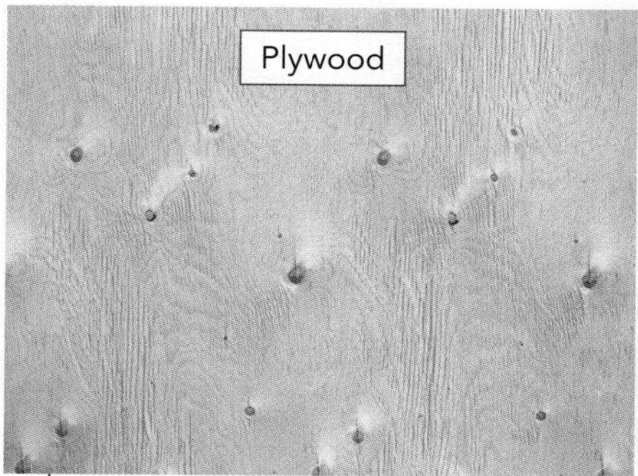

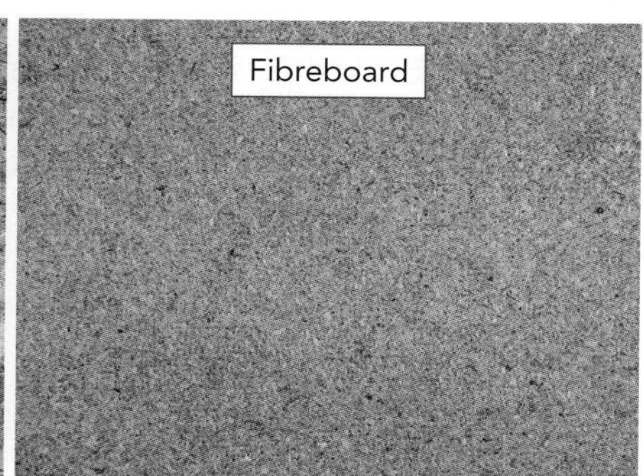

12.14 Plywood, particleboard and fibreboard are types of modified wood.

ST
EST
AST
THE DEGRADATION AND PROTECTION OF WOOD AND MODIFIED WOOD

Wood is a material that can degrade swiftly. One of the main reasons for its rapid deterioration is its organic origin: it comes from a living organism. Many fungi, microorganisms and insects can infest the wood, feed off it and cause it to rot, thus reducing its mechanical properties. Rotten wood, for example, is not as hard as wood that is intact.

Various means exist to protect wood from the effects of organisms that degrade it. For example, it can be varnished, painted or treated with protective coatings.

Many types of wood that have been treated to prevent degradation are also available on the market. This wood is called *treated wood* and is prepared in one of the following two ways:

- by dipping it in an alkaline solution containing copper. Wood treated in this way has a greenish colour.
- by heating it to a high temperature. The change in appearance of the wood is less pronounced, but the procedure is usually more expensive.

12.15 Wood exposed to water is more likely to be damaged by rot-causing organisms.

ST
EST
AST
2.2 CERAMICS

Although humans have been using wood longer than any other type of material, our use of ceramics also has a long history. Ceramics are obtained by heating inorganic raw materials containing various compounds, usually **OXIDES**, such as silicon dioxide (SiO_2).

When the raw material is heated, the water in it evaporates, and the bonds between the constituent compounds are rearranged. A ceramic is always solid at room temperature.

A CERAMIC is a solid material obtained by heating inorganic matter containing various compounds, usually oxides.

12.16 Figures of the life-size Terracotta Army, made in China around 210 BCE

Traditionally, ceramic objects were made with pottery techniques; products included dishes, pots and works of art. Most of these objects were made out of clay, which was shaped and then baked. Sand was another common raw material, particularly for glassmaking.

Ceramic comes from the Greek *keramikos*, meaning "of potter's clay."

Clay and sand are still widely used because they are plentiful and inexpensive. Industries have also turned to other raw materials, both natural and artificial, to manufacture ceramics.

12.17 Some examples of the many ceramics that have been commercialized

The properties of ceramics vary with the raw materials used to make them and with the baking method. Certain properties make one or another type of ceramic especially suitable for a particular application.

- Because of their low electrical conductivity, ceramics are often used as insulators in the electronics sector.
- Because of their generally high degree of hardness, ceramics are in great demand as building materials (bricks, tiles, etc.) and for use in certain cutting tools (titanium carbide or quartz blades, etc.).
- Because of their heat resistance and low thermal conductivity, ceramics are found in the kitchen—in dishes and as thermal insulators, especially in ovens.
- Because of their resistance to corrosion, ceramics can be used in ducts for fumes or water.
- Most ceramics are fragile. However, by carefully controlling the raw materials used and the baking method, some industries manage to manufacture ceramics that are so resilient they can be used in engines, in spite of the frequent shocks engine materials undergo.

FRAGILE YET RESISTANT

American space shuttles are built with a heat shield containing nearly 24 000 ceramic tiles. The tiles are designed to resist temperatures up to 1650°C as the shuttle reenters the atmosphere. Although they are thin, light and fragile, the tiles are nonetheless highly heat-resistant. Damage to the heat shield could jeopardize a shuttle's return to Earth.

ST EST AST

THE DEGRADATION AND PROTECTION OF CERAMICS

In general, ceramics are very durable. Archaeologists frequently discover ancient pottery that is remarkably well preserved.

However, some **ACIDS**, such as sulphuric acid (H_2SO_4), and some **BASES**, such as calcium hydroxide ($Ca(OH)_2$), can have a degrading effect on ceramics. Furthermore, when ceramics are subjected to a thermal shock (a sudden variation in temperature), the properties of the material tend to deteriorate.

Since ceramics are very durable, little thought is given to protecting them. Nevertheless, exposure to acids, bases or thermal shocks should be avoided whenever possible. In addition, as we have seen, certain properties of ceramics can be further enhanced by choosing suitable raw materials and baking temperatures.

TRADE ESSENTIALS

In antiquity, ceramics were essential to trade. They were used especially to make amphorae, the jars in which many types of food were stored and transported. However, the first century BCE saw the advent of glassblowing and kilns powerful enough to liquefy sand. These innovations led to the large-scale production of another type of ceramic—glass.

2.3 METALS AND ALLOYS

While ceramics are made from clay or other inorganic matter, metals are produced from substances extracted from **MINERAL ORE**. These materials are usually shiny in appearance and exhibit good thermal and electrical conductivity. Certain metals are valued for their ductility and malleability; iron and aluminum are the two most commonly used metals in this category. Other frequently used metals are presented in Appendix 5.

- **A METAL is a material extracted from a mineral ore. Metals are usually shiny in appearance and are good conductors of electricity and heat.**

Metallic materials are rarely made of pure metal. They are usually mixed with other substances, metallic or otherwise, which enhance their properties. These mixtures are called *alloys*.

- **An ALLOY is a mixture of a metal with one or more other substances, which may be metallic or nonmetallic.**

Alloys can be divided into two types. The most common are **FERROUS ALLOYS**, whose main component is iron. All other alloys (whose main component is a metal other than iron) are called **NONFERROUS ALLOYS**. The most commonly used alloys are presented in Appendix 5.

1945
1995

Marianne Mareschal

Marianne Mareschal was a Belgian-born geophysicist. In 1987, she joined the Institut de recherche minérale at the École Polytechnique de Montréal as a researcher. She eventually became a professor at the school, in 1989, while continuing her research work. She pioneered the use of electromagnetic methods to detect mineral ores—methods that she perfected herself.

THE DEGRADATION AND PROTECTION OF METALS AND ALLOYS

The main cause of metal and alloy degradation is **OXIDATION**, which causes corrosion.

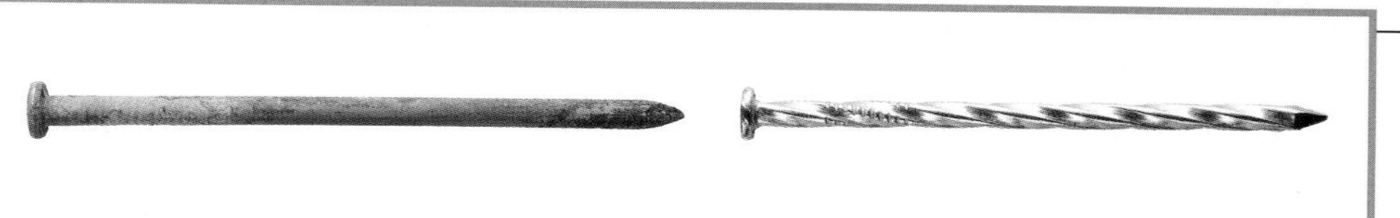

12.18 These two nails are made of iron. The nail on the right has been galvanized, which means it has been coated with zinc. It degrades much more slowly than the ungalvanized nail on the left.

To protect metals and alloys from degradation, coatings and surface treatments are often used. The material is isolated from its surroundings, and then the surface is treated so that a protective coating can adhere to it (Table 12.19).

12.19 COATINGS USED TO PROTECT METALS

Type of coating	Examples
Metallic coatings	Zinc, chrome, gold, silver, nickel, aluminum, lead
Other coatings	Paint, enamel, grease, resin

1813
1898

Henry Bessemer

This British engineer figures prominently among the scientists who contributed to developing steel as a material. In the 1850s, he invented the revolutionary Bessemer converter, which opened the way to industrial mass production of the alloy.

Some techniques even enhance the properties of metals and alloys. One example is the heat treatments used on steel.

STEEL HEAT TREATMENTS are methods of enhancing certain mechanical properties of steel through periods of heating.

Steel is an alloy made mostly of iron and carbon. Heat treatment causes the various atoms inside the material to rearrange themselves.

Harder steels are obtained through the processes of **QUENCH HARDENING** and **TEMPERING**.

12.20 STAGES AND EFFECTS OF QUENCH HARDENING AND TEMPERING STEEL

No.	Stage	Description	Effect
1	Heating (quench hardening)	Elevation of furnace temperature to more than 800°C	The atoms inside the piece of steel are rearranged.
2	Cooling (quench hardening)	Rapid drop in temperature through quenching in a solution (bath quench or spray quench)	The new arrangement of atoms becomes set. The steel is harder, but more brittle.
3	Heating (tempering)	Elevation of furnace temperature, but to a lower level than that of the quenching temperature	The atoms inside the piece of steel are rearranged, making it less brittle.

ANNEALING, another type of heat treatment, restores the original properties of steel after it has been deformed—by welding, for example.

ST EST AST

2.4 PLASTICS

TECH 3

Plastics are materials developed mainly from petroleum and natural gas. From these **FOSSIL FUELS**, basic units called *monomers* are extracted industrially and used in the synthesis of plastics. Monomers are arranged in chains to form polymers. Plastics are thus made up of different polymers, which vary with the type of plastic. The most widely used plastics are presented in Appendix 5, at the end of this textbook.

Monomer comes from the Greek words *monos*, meaning "single," and *meros*, meaning "part."

Polymer comes from the Greek words *polus*, meaning "many," and *meros*, meaning "part."

Various substances can be added to polymers to produce plastics with certain desirable properties.

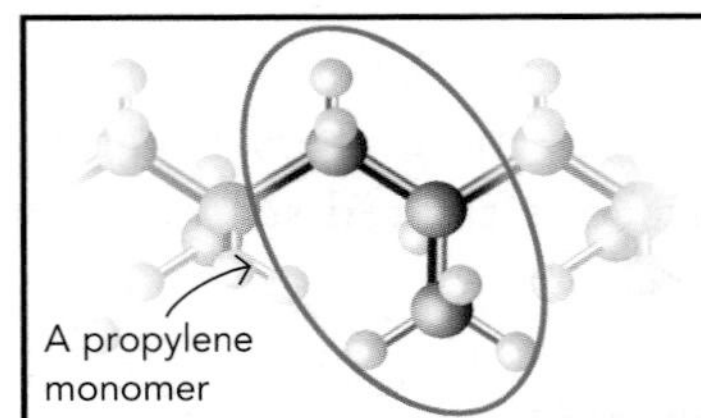

12.21 Polypropylene is a polymer formed from an arrangement of many propylene monomers. It is often used to make food containers.

ENVIRONMENT EXTRA

Plastic bags: good for shopping, bad for the environment

When Quebeckers go shopping, they usually leave the store with a plastic bag. Most plastic bags are made of low-density polyethylene, a recyclable thermoplastic. Few of them are actually recycled, however, and few are even reused, which means that roughly a billion bags end up in Québec landfills every year. Since the bags are hardly biodegradable, they take many years to decompose. They pile up in landfills, where the wind often catches them and blows them away, scattering them about the environment, even as far as the Arctic. In the wild, animals, especially marine species, may swallow the bags and die.

There are alternatives to using low-density polyethylene bags. Bags made of paper or fabric are two examples. Increasing numbers of biodegradable plastic bags are also becoming available, but the decomposition of these bags produces methane, a powerful greenhouse gas. All plastic bags may therefore be harmful to the environment in some way. The clearest path to reducing their environmental impact is to reuse them as many times as possible before throwing them away.

Many of the plastic bags piling up in dumps are scattered by the wind, littering the environment.

A PLASTIC is a material made of polymers, to which other substances may be added to obtain certain desirable properties.

The invention of plastics marked a veritable revolution in the world of materials. Their popularity is unquestionable: they are used to manufacture many technical objects. Plastics are generally divided into two subcategories: thermoplastics and thermosetting plastics. Let's look at the characteristics of these two types of plastics.

Thermoplastics

Thermoplastics soften when heated and harden when cooled. When a thermoplastic becomes soft, it can be given a new form. When it is cooled, its form is set.

A THERMOPLASTIC is a plastic that becomes soft enough when heated to be moulded or remoulded and that hardens enough when cooled to hold its shape.

This subcategory of plastics unites more than three quarters of all the plastics produced in the world, including all kinds of containers. Some thermoplastics are recyclable, where facilities exist. They then carry a recycling code (Appendix 5, page 530).

Thermosetting plastics

Unlike thermoplastics, which soften when heated, thermosetting plastics form a group of plastics that remain permanently hard, even when heated. If heat is applied to a thermosetting plastic, it keeps the same stiffness until it reaches its decomposition temperature.

A THERMOSETTING PLASTIC is a plastic that remains permanently hard, even when heated.

Clearly, the term *thermosetting* does not mean that this group of plastics can be hardened with heat. It refers instead to the manufacturing process. Thermosetting plastics are obtained by mixing monomers in a hot mould. Once the material has hardened, its form can no longer be altered. Although they are sold in various forms, such as melamine and polyesters, thermosetting plastics are used less than thermoplastics partly because they cannot be reshaped.

A MORE "SENSITIVE" PLASTIC WRAP

Brazilian researchers are working on the development of a new type of biodegradable, and even edible, plastic wrapping for food. This plastic film, reportedly made from cassava and sugar, would change colour when it comes in contact with microorganisms, thus indicating whether the food is contaminated. 17

1896
1937

Wallace Carothers

This American chemist invented a thermoplastic of the polyamide family that would revolutionize the world of materials: in 1935, he synthesized nylon. Today, many variants of nylon are manufactured and used to make clothing and fabric, among other products.

Certain mechanical properties of thermosetting plastics nevertheless give the materials several advantages over thermoplastics. For example, thermosetting plastics are often harder and more resilient than thermoplastics.

Furthermore, when a manufacturing process calls for materials that are poor conductors of electricity and heat, both thermosetting plastics and thermoplastics are usually good choices. In Québec, however, thermosetting plastics are not recyclable, which puts them at a considerable disadvantage environmentally, compared to many thermoplastics. Figure 12.22 shows one use of thermosetting plastics.

12.22 The hulls of the kayaks on this beach are made of thermosetting plastic.

ST EST AST

THE DEGRADATION AND PROTECTION OF PLASTICS

Plastics tend to degrade over time. Their deterioration can be observed most often in the appearance of cracks or a change in colour. The process is frequently slow, but always irreversible.

Table 12.23 presents three causes of plastic degradation. The effects depend on the type of plastic. For example, a concentrated solution of sulphuric acid will tend to degrade nylon rapidly but will have practically no effect on polystyrene; yet both materials are thermoplastics. For each cause of degradation in the table below, a means of protection is proposed.

12.23 THE MAIN CAUSES OF PLASTIC DEGRADATION

Cause	Description	Example of a method of protection
Penetration by a liquid	Substances in the liquid state (such as water) or solutions (such as an acid) can penetrate certain plastics and cause them to degrade.	Protection with a waterproof coating
Oxidation	Oxygen and other gases with similar properties can react with the polymers in certain plastics and cause the material to degrade.	Addition of antioxidants, such as carbon black
Ultraviolet rays	Ultraviolet rays, especially those from the sun, can damage plastic polymers.	Addition of pigments that absorb ultraviolet rays

ST EST AST

2.5 COMPOSITES

Sometimes, to obtain a material with the desired properties, materials from different categories are combined. The result is a composite, whose properties are enhanced in comparison to those of the original materials.

A COMPOSITE is formed by combining materials from different categories to obtain a material with enhanced properties.

A composite has two main components: the matrix and the reinforcement. The matrix constitutes the skeleton of the material and gives it its shape. It surrounds and supports the reinforcements, which are inserted into the matrix to strengthen it.

Matrix is a Latin word meaning "source" or "origin."

For example, plastic reinforced with fibreglass (a type of ceramic) is used in many airplanes. The plastic is the matrix while the fibreglass constitutes the reinforcement. The properties of the two basic materials are thus combined. While plastics are usually not very stiff, they are resilient. Fibreglass, on the other hand, is usually not very resilient, but extremely stiff. By combining the two, airplane manufacturers obtain a composite that is both stiff and resilient.

A NEW LIFE FOR FIBREGLASS

Unlike plastics, composite materials that are reinforced with fibreglass—used to make kayaks, showers, bathtubs and boat hulls, for example—are not recyclable. The only prospect for used fibreglass composites at present is disposal in a landfill. The Regroupement des Industries des Composites du Québec (RICQ) would like to change this state of affairs. Association members have been racking their brains to find ways to shred, neutralize and recycle these materials. Several options are under study.

"Even if this waste isn't considered hazardous to the environment, we would like to be proactive," declared RICQ President, François Chevarie. In his opinion, manufacturers could kill two birds with one stone. They could reduce the cost of their waste disposal and, at the same time, lower their production costs by reusing recycled materials.

Rather than making its way to a landfill, fibreglass waste, such as the material piling up in this factory in the Beauce region, will soon be given a new lease on life.

Source: Adapted from Gilbert Leduc, "Seconde vie pour la fibre de verre," *Le Soleil*, December 4, 2007, *Affaires*, p. 39. *[Translation]*

Table 12.24 presents the main matrices and reinforcements used in composites. The name of a composite is usually based on the type of reinforcement used. In surfboards, for example, the composites are often made of plastic matrices combined with fibreglass reinforcements. This type of surfboard is then said to be made of fibreglass.

12.24 THE MAIN MATRICES AND REINFORCEMENTS USED IN COMPOSITES

		Description	Properties often sought in composites
Matrices	Plastic matrices	Thermosetting plastics are preferred for plastic matrices, although thermoplastics are also used. Thermosetting plastic matrices are often called *resins*.	• Durability • Lightness • Resilience • Low cost
	Metallic matrices	Made from metals or alloys	• Ductility • Thermal and electrical conductivity • Stiffness
	Ceramic matrices	Made from ceramics, often glass	• Durability • Heat resistance
Reinforcements	Fibreglass	Made of glass (a ceramic) in the form of fibres. Their length and diameter, as well as the type of glass used, may vary.	• Stiffness • Corrosion resistance
	Aramid fibres	Known by the trade name *Kevlar* and one of the few plastics used as a reinforcement	• Low density • Resilience
	Carbon fibres	Obtained by carbonizing polymers, mostly polyacrylonitriles	• Stiffness • Low density • Electrical conductivity

12.25 The surfboard and the hull of the sailboat are both made of composites.

Each composite thus has its own characteristics, depending on the matrix and the type of reinforcement. Composites are present in an increasing number of sectors, including:

- the aeronautical industry—in the wings of an airplane, for example
- the sports sector, especially in the manufacture of swimming pools, bicycle helmets and frames, rackets, hockey equipment and sticks, sailboards, etc.
- the arts—for example, in violin bows
- the mechanical industry, especially in engines and high-performance brakes
- the military and police sectors, notably in bulletproof vests

12.26 The sports sector is making increasing use of composites to enhance equipment performance.

ST EST AST

THE DEGRADATION AND PROTECTION OF COMPOSITES

Like the other categories of materials, composites may also deteriorate. Their degradation usually takes one of two forms:

- the deformation or fracture of the matrix or the reinforcements
- a loss of adherence between the matrix and the reinforcements

The speed at which degradation occurs depends on the type of matrix in the composite, its reinforcements and the conditions of its use. For example, a plastic-matrix composite will normally tend to degrade more quickly if it is immersed in salt water than if it is simply left in the open air.

To protect composites from degradation, it is important to ensure that their constituent materials are not likely to become deformed or break under the conditions of their intended use. Assuring a strong adherence between the matrix and the reinforcements is also essential.

EST AST 3 Technical drafting

After choosing suitable materials for a technical object, and before proceeding with its manufacture, the forms and dimensions of the different parts of the object must be determined. One way of establishing this information is through drafting, which is the process of creating technical drawings. More and more, drafters are using computers to produce the types of drawings needed to manufacture technical objects. To understand the meaning of these drawings, we must know how to recognize and analyze different projections.

CONCEPT REVIEW

- Geometric lines
- Basic lines
- Scales
- Dimensioning
- Sections

EST AST 3.1 PROJECTIONS

The main difficulty in drafting lies in a contradiction: the objects being drawn have three dimensions, while the drawing is done on a surface with only two dimensions, such as a piece of paper. To overcome this difficulty, drafters use projections.

A PROJECTION is the representation of a three-dimensional object on a two-dimensional surface.

Among all the possible projections in drafting, two types are the most commonly used: isometric projections and multiview projections.

CONCEPT REVIEW

- Forms of representation (sketch, perspective drawing, oblique projection)
- Orthogonal projections (multiview, isometric)

EST AST ISOMETRIC PROJECTIONS

When an object is drawn so that the lines representing its length, height and depth form 120° angles on the paper, the drawing is an isometric projection. Figure 12.27 illustrates an isometric projection.

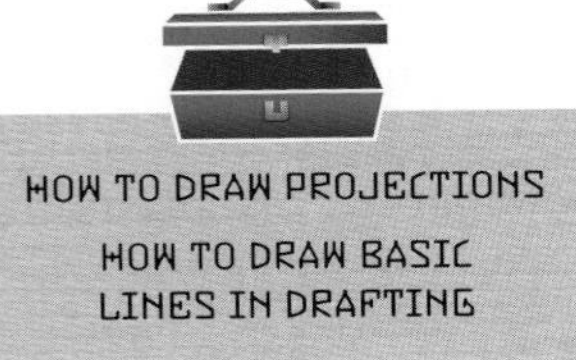

HOW TO DRAW PROJECTIONS

HOW TO DRAW BASIC LINES IN DRAFTING

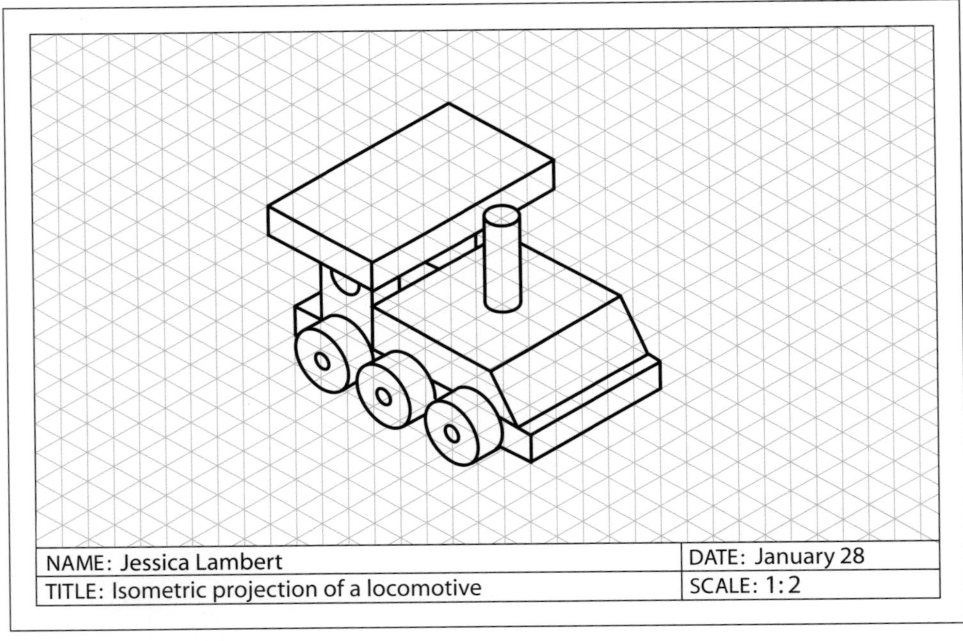

12.27 An isometric projection of a locomotive

EST AST MULTIVIEW PROJECTIONS

To create a multiview projection of an object, the drafter must visualize the object in the middle of a transparent cube. Using basic lines, the drafter draws the different views of the object as they would appear on the sides of the cube. The result is a multiview projection. Usually, only the front, top and right-side views are illustrated in a multiview projection.

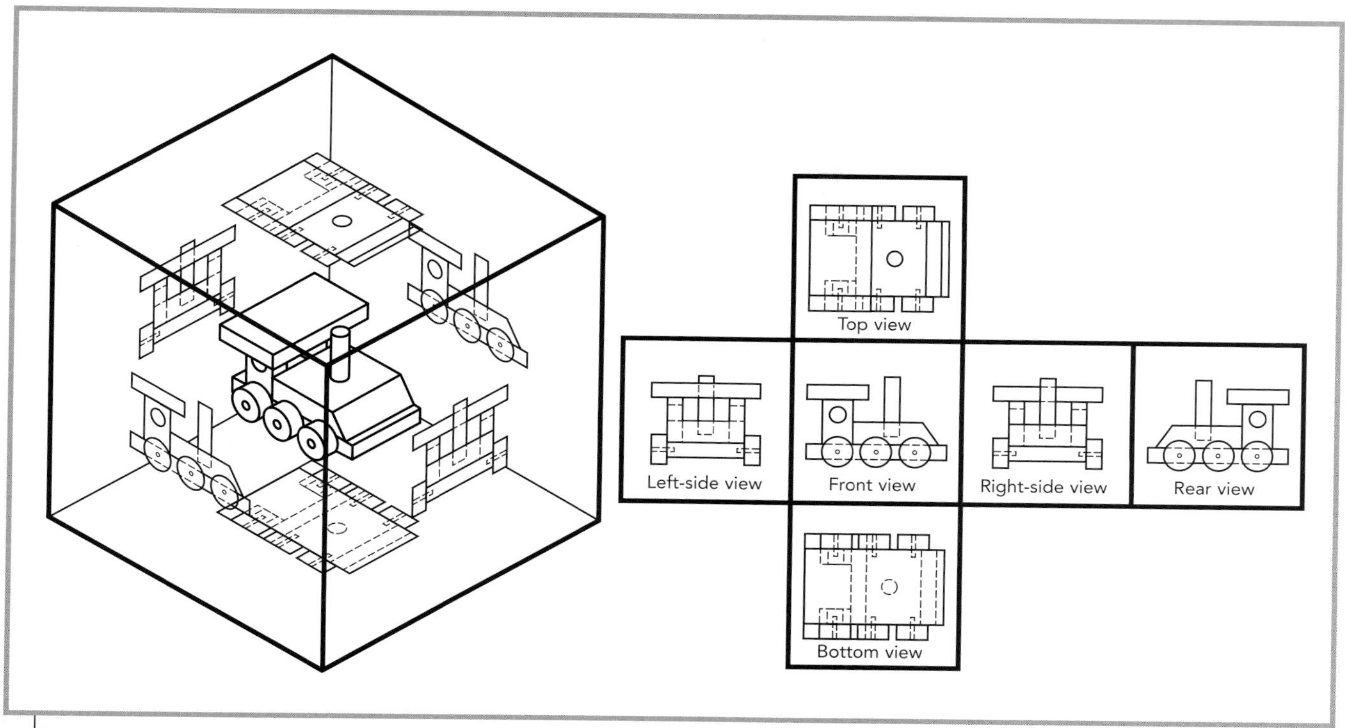

12.28 A multiview projection of a locomotive

Isometric and multiview projections each meet a specific need when it comes to manufacturing an object. An isometric projection shows the object in **PERSPECTIVE**: it represents the three dimensions of the object in a single view. With a multiview projection, on the other hand, at least three views are required to represent the object in its entirety. However, multiview projections have the advantage of providing greater detail without distortion.

Now that we have presented the two main projections used in drafting, let's see how they actually appear in technical drawings.

EST AST 3.2 ENGINEERING DRAWINGS

CONCEPT REVIEW
Axonometric projection: exploded view (reading) (AST)

To manufacture an object, it is often useful to have a drawing that depicts the general appearance of that object. The type of drawing that performs this function is called a *general arrangement*. It is usually drawn to **SCALE**.

> **A GENERAL ARRANGEMENT is a technical drawing representing the overall appearance of an object.**

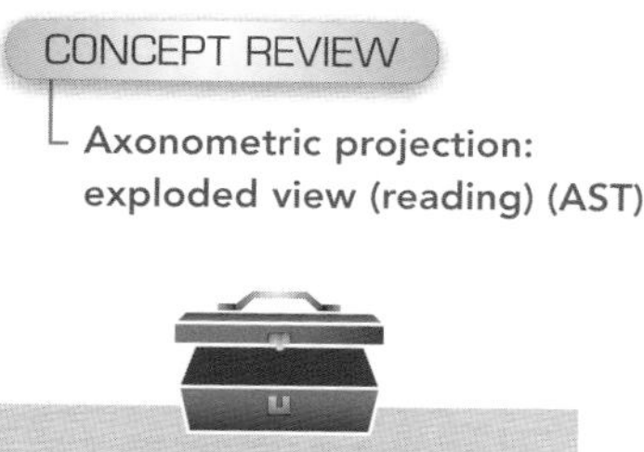

Multiview projections are suitable for drawing general arrangements because they contain many details of the object. An isometric projection is often added because it offers the advantage of showing the object, in perspective, in a single view. Figure 12.29 (page 404) shows a general arrangement drawing, including a **TITLE BLOCK**.

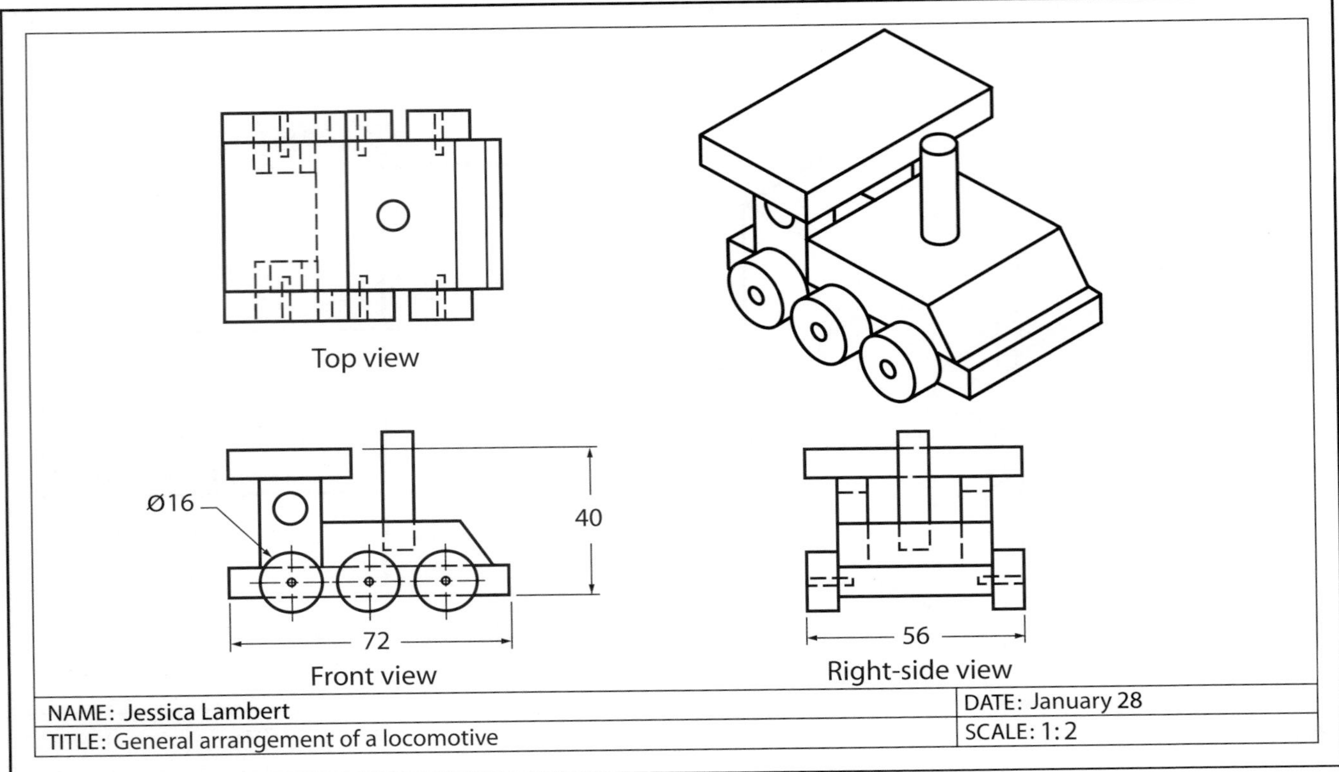

12.29 A general arrangement drawing of a locomotive

EST AST

EXPLODED VIEWS

An exploded view is useful for visualizing all the component parts of an object. The entire object is shown in an isometric projection, but the parts are separated from one another. Exploded views are usually drawn to scale.

- **An EXPLODED VIEW is a drawing in which the various parts of the object are separated from one another.**

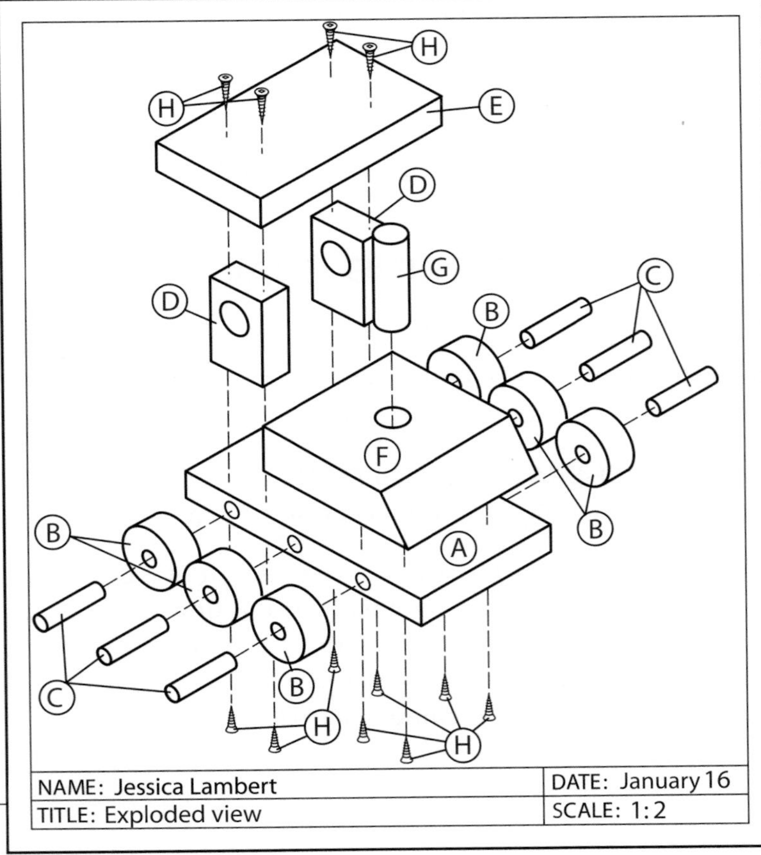

12.30 An exploded view of a locomotive

This type of drawing is often included in instruction leaflets describing the steps for do-it-yourself assembly of an object. The drawing is accompanied by a list of the parts, indicating their names and the numbers of parts provided. Figure 12.30 (page 404) shows an exploded view of a locomotive.

EST AST DETAIL DRAWINGS

To manufacture an object, it is essential to know the dimensions and all the other details for each of the parts. This information is provided in detail drawings, which are almost always made to scale and show one or more views of the part in question.

A DETAIL DRAWING is a drawing specifying all the relevant information for manufacturing a part.

Figure 12.31 shows a detail drawing of a part for a decorative locomotive. Two views of the part are presented.

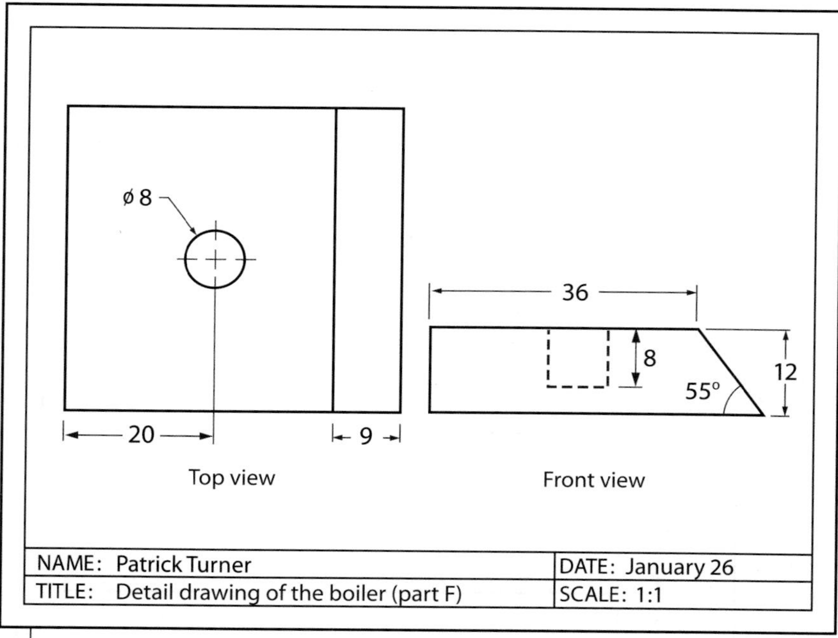

12.31 A detail drawing provides complete information for manufacturing a part.

Dimensional tolerances

Since the machines, tools and instruments used to manufacture objects are not perfect, the actual size of parts often differs from that indicated in the detail drawing. To set an acceptable margin of error between a **DIMENSION** in the drawing and the actual measurements of a part after it has been manufactured, engineers establish a tolerance.

1895
1985

Esther Marjorie Hill

Drafting is not used only in engineering; it is also essential to architecture. In 1920, Esther Marjorie Hill became the first Canadian woman to obtain a degree in architecture in the country. After a difficult start, her career reached its peak in the 1950s and early 1960s. She set up her own practice, doing all the design work and drawings for her projects herself.

CONCEPT REVIEW
Tolerances (AST)

A DIMENSIONAL TOLERANCE is an indicator of the maximum acceptable difference between a specified measurement and the actual measurement on the finished object.

For example, if the diameter of the inner hole in the wheels of the locomotive is too large, the axle will tend to slip. If the hole is too small, it will be impossible to attach the wheels to the axle. It is therefore important for the drafter to indicate the tolerance for the diameter of the hole. If a tolerance applies to all the dimensions in a drawing, it is written in the title block. Figure 12.32 shows another way of indicating the tolerance for the hole in the wheel.

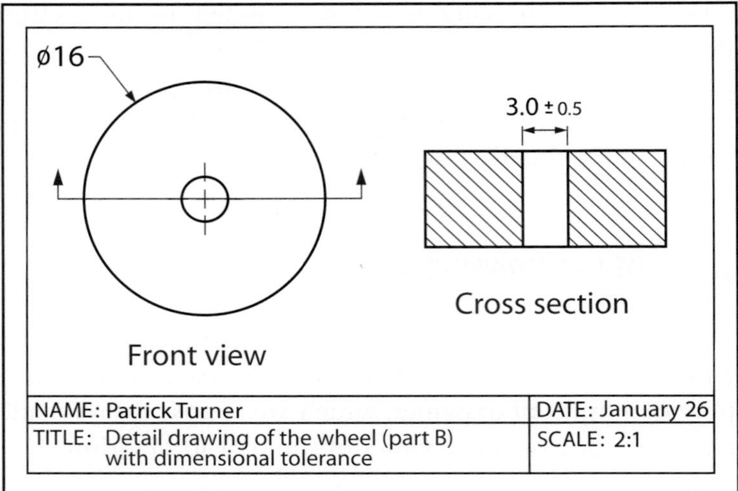

12.32 In a technical drawing, a dimensional tolerance can be indicated by a measurement preceded by a ± sign.

Functional dimensioning

To ensure that certain technical objects or systems work, their various parts must be assembled according to specific instructions. These operating conditions may be indicated in the detail drawing with dimensions referred to as *functional dimensions*. Functional dimensioning thus involves the inclusion of operational information about an object in a drawing.

The FUNCTIONAL DIMENSIONING of a drawing specifies the information required for the object to work.

Let's consider the example of a retractable utility knife. For the blade to move along the slide that is holding it, there must be a certain space, called the *play*, between the blade and the slide. When a drafter indicates a piece of information like the play of the blade, the drawing then features functional dimensioning. To determine the functional dimensions of an object, engineers must analyze how the object works.

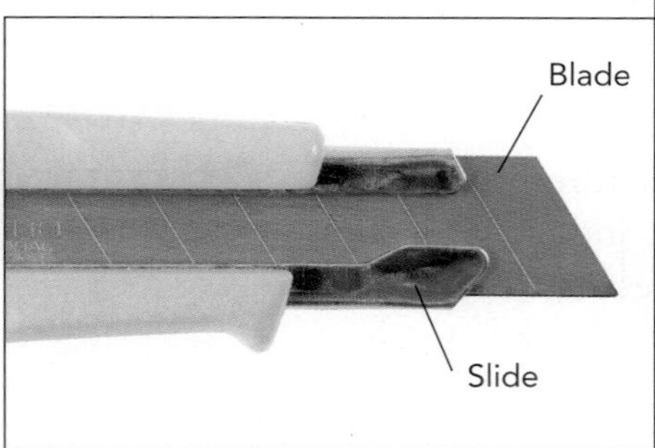

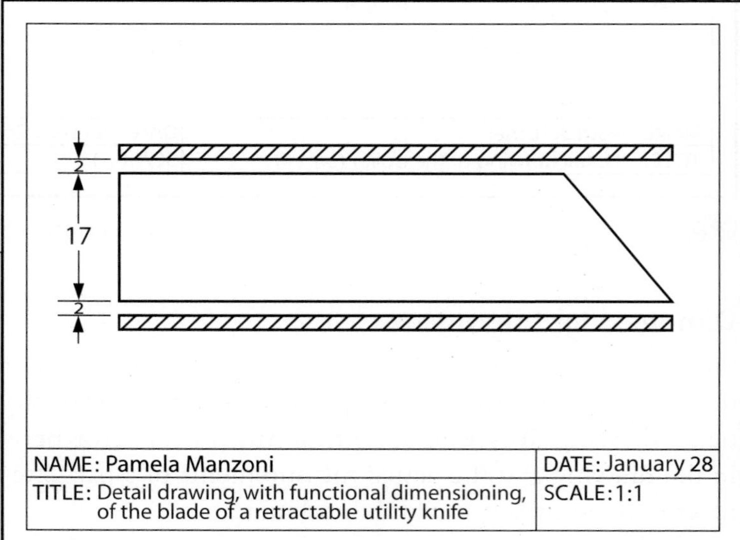

12.33 This drawing indicates functional dimensioning: it shows the space required between the blade and the slide for the knife to work.

Developments

Sheet metal is used to manufacture some technical objects. It can be bent to form parts of various shapes. A detail drawing that shows the surface area of material needed to make a part by bending is necessarily drawn as a development. Figure 12.34 illustrates examples of developments for parts in the shape of a cuboid, a cone, a square pyramid and a cylinder.

A DEVELOPMENT is the representation of the surface area required to make a part by bending.

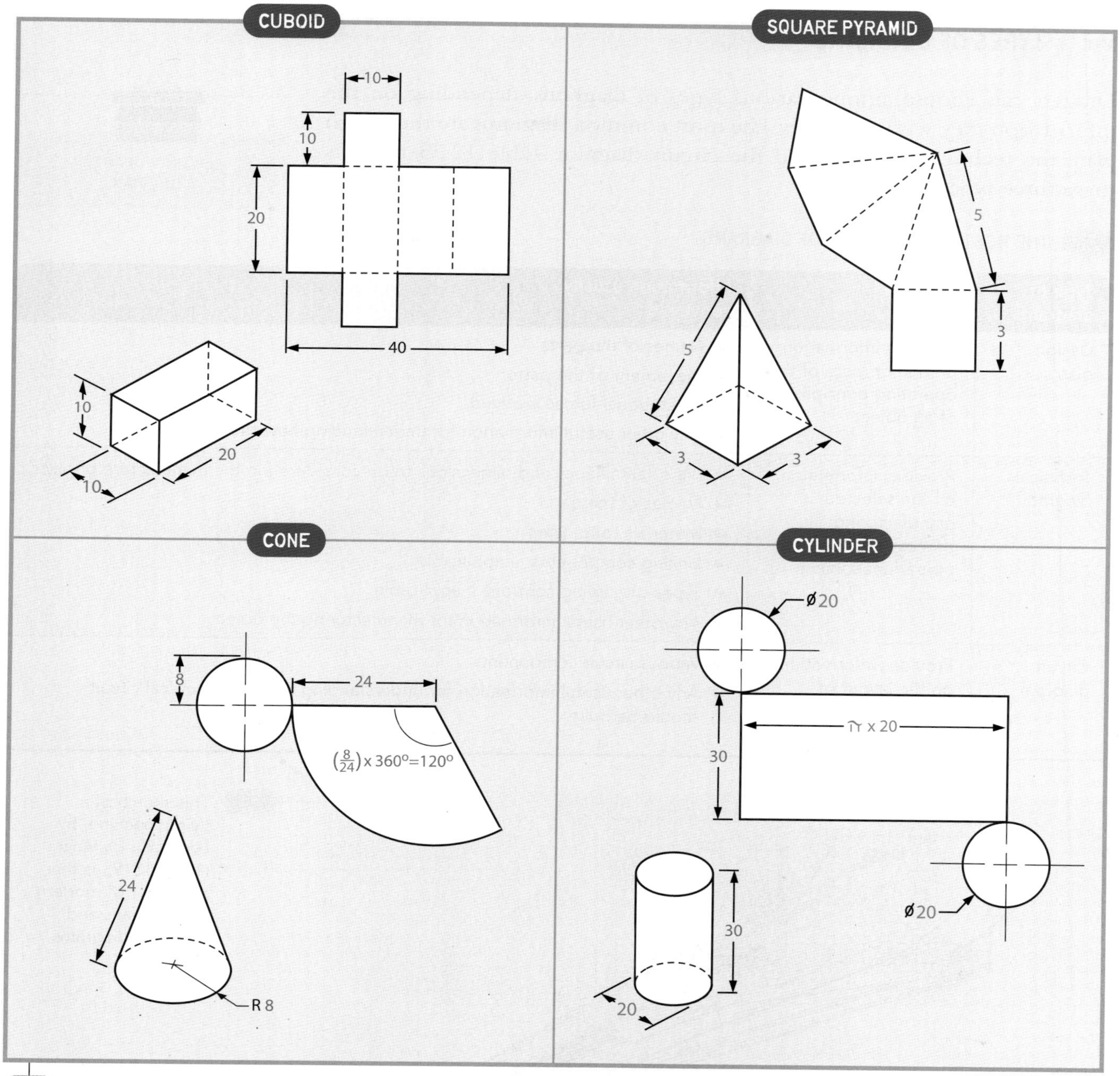

12.34 The developments for four differently shaped parts

AST 3.3 DIAGRAMMATIC REPRESENTATIONS

In addition to knowing the shapes and dimensions of the parts of an object, it is often useful to understand its operating principles and any specific characteristics that should be taken into account during the manufacturing process. This information can be obtained from drawings called *diagrams*.

CONCEPT REVIEW
Standards and representations (diagrams, symbols)

A DIAGRAM is a simplified representation of an object, a part of an object, or a system.

AST TYPES OF DIAGRAMS

Drafters can choose among various types of diagrams, depending on the information they wish to convey. The most common diagrams are the design plan, the technical diagram and the circuit diagram. Table 12.35 presents these three types.

12.35 THE MOST COMMON TYPES OF DIAGRAMS

Type of diagram	Purpose	Information usually conveyed
Design plan	Provides information on one or more of the operating principles of an object.	• Names of the parts • Movement of the parts • Operational forces involved • Any other useful information for understanding how the object works
Technical diagram	Provides information on the selected manufacturing process of an operational object.	• Important shapes and dimensions to be considered in the manufacture of parts • Names of the parts • Materials to be used • Linking components, if applicable • Types of guiding controls, if applicable • Any other useful information for manufacturing the object
Circuit diagram	Provides information on the layout of various components of an electrical circuit.	• Various circuit components • Any other useful information for understanding how the electrical circuit should be built

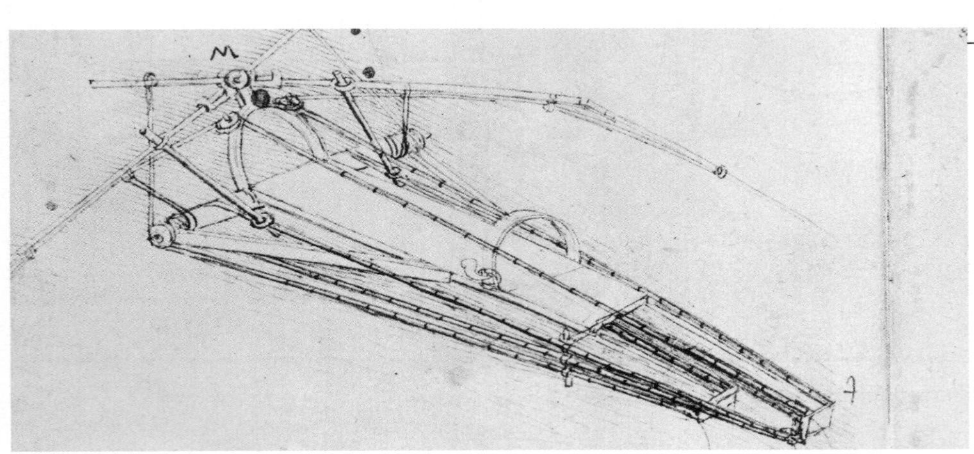

12.36 This sketch of a flying machine, by Leonardo da Vinci (1452–1519), is the precursor of modern design plans and technical diagrams.

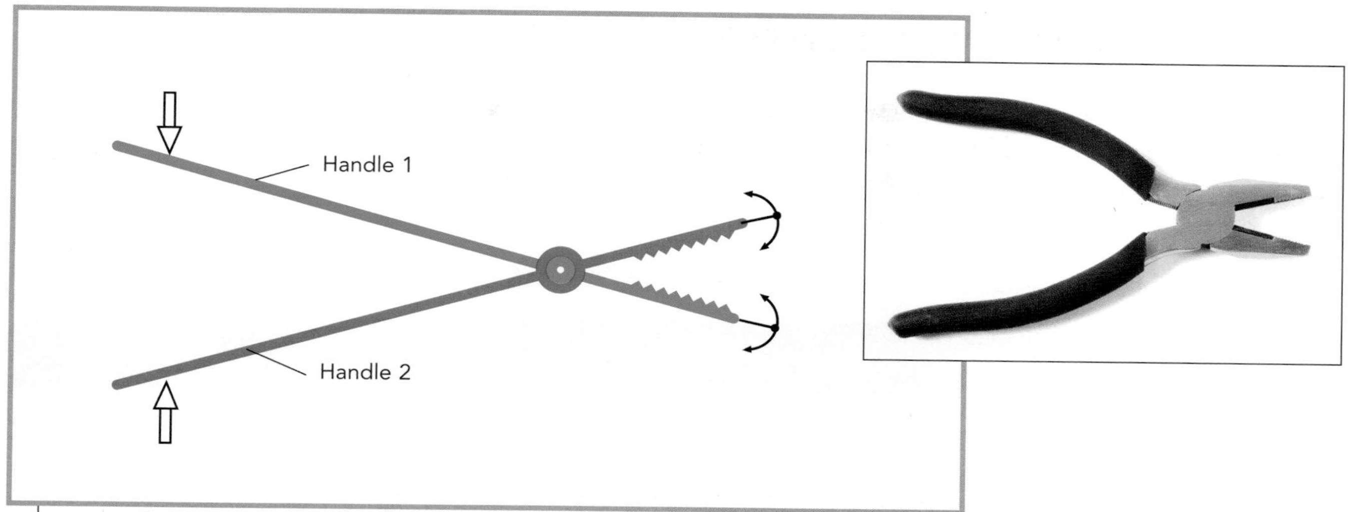

12.37 Design plan for a pair of pliers

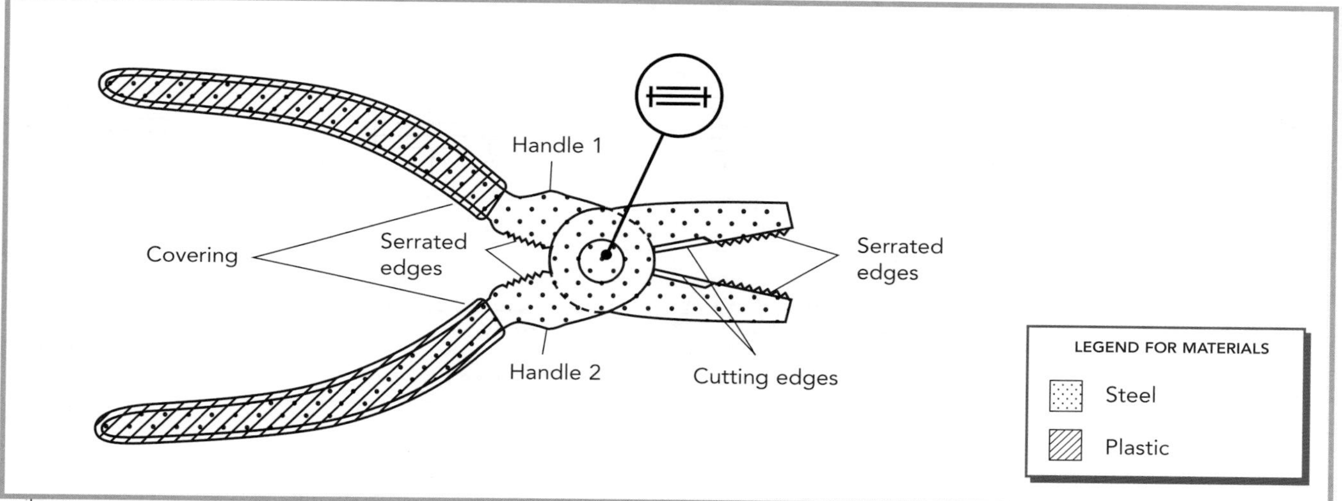

12.38 Technical diagram for a pair of pliers

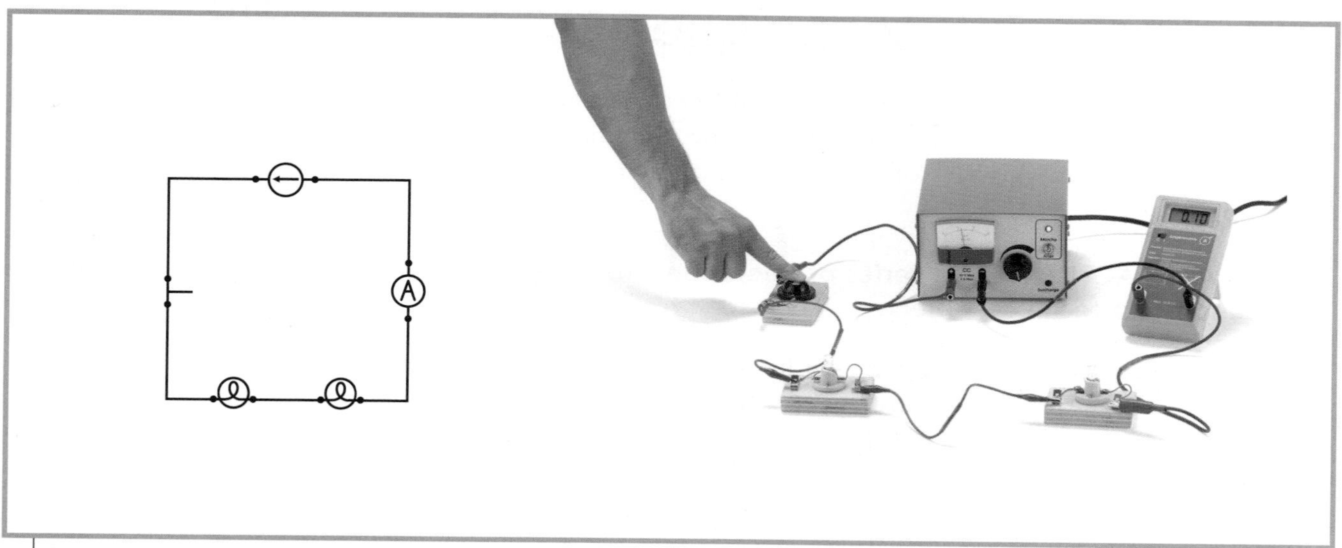

12.39 Circuit diagram for an electrical circuit assembly

AST STANDARDIZED SYMBOLS IN DIAGRAMS

Standardized symbols are used in diagrams to convey information as simply as possible. The symbols represent forces and motion in objects, electrical components, types of guiding controls, etc. Table 12.40 presents some examples of symbols.

12.40 SYMBOLS USED IN DIAGRAMS

Elements symbolized	Examples			
Forces and constraints	Force	Compression	Tension	Shearing
Motion	Unidirectional translation	Bidirectional translation	Unidirectional rotation	Bidirectional helical motion
Links and guiding controls	Complete link	Translational guiding control	Rotational guiding control	Translational and rotational guiding control
Electrical components	Battery	Light bulb	Electrical wire	Push-button switch

EST AST 4 Manufacturing: tools and techniques

Once suitable materials have been selected and the shapes and dimensions of the parts have been determined and drawn, the manufacture of a technical object can begin. A series of operations is carried out to obtain the target object.

MANUFACTURING is a series of operations resulting in the creation of a technical object.

The various operations essential to manufacturing a functional object require the use of a number of instruments. First, we will look at several examples of these instruments, and then we will describe various manufacturing techniques.

CONCEPT REVIEW

- Manufacturing process sheet
- Machines and tools (AST)
- Roughing and finishing (AST)
- Characteristics of laying out (AST)
- Direct measurement (ruler) (AST)

Any instrument used to accomplish a task in the manufacture of an object is called a *tool*. For example, a backsaw is a tool used to cut out wooden parts, and a screwdriver is a tool for screwing different pieces together.

A TOOL is an instrument used in the manufacture of an object.

Tools can be divided into two categories: hand tools and machine tools. Hand tools must be held and operated by the force of the person using them. For example, to saw wood with a backsaw, the sawer provides the force needed to apply a back-and-forth movement to the tool. Other tools can be held and operated by devices that keep them in motion. In a band saw, for example, a motor causes the movement of the saw. Tools like these are referred to as *machine tools*.

A MACHINE TOOL is a tool that is held and operated by forces other than human force.

Illustration 12.41 below shows some examples of the hand and machine tools required to manufacture a part.

Many hand and machine tools may be used to produce technical objects. The manufacturing process is usually divided into three stages:

- measuring and laying out the parts
- machining the parts
- assembling and finishing the parts

Let's see how an object is made by following these three steps.

1856
1915

Frederick Winslow Taylor

This American engineer is considered a pioneer in the organization of factory and workshop production, for which he developed methods of analysis. With these methods, engineers were able to assign each worker limited and specific responsibilities in the manufacturing process and provide workers with the appropriate tools for their tasks.

12.41 A workshop is equipped with a variety of hand and machine tools.

THE ALL-PURPOSE MACHINE

Some science-fiction fans dream of a futuristic household appliance that can manufacture any object its owner desires. Users would simply have to select a nutcracker, an MP3 player or a toaster, for example, on their computer screens. As easily as a printer sprays ink onto paper, the all-purpose machine would produce a stream of matter forming three-dimensional components.

Perhaps this dream is not as completely unrealistic as it sounds. Neil Gershenfeld, professor and researcher at the Media Lab of the famous Massachusetts Institute of Technology (MIT), considers "the development of this type of personalized factory inevitable." He believes that the technologies for creating such machines already exist. Will industries and mass production become obsolete one day?

Source: Adapted from Jean-François Arnaud, "Chacun pourra enfin satisfaire toutes ses envies," *Le Figaro*, October 20, 2007, *Économie*, p. 20. *[Translation]*

Neil Gershenfeld, professor and researcher at the Media Lab of the famous Massachusetts Institute of Technology (MIT)

EST AST 4.1 MEASURING AND LAYING OUT

To begin manufacturing a technical object, the position of the markings or reference points for each part must first be determined and then laid out on the materials. The information needed for this measuring can be found in the detail drawings of the object or on its **MANUFACTURING PROCESS SHEET**.

- **MEASURING is the act of determining the size or position of a marking.**
- **LAYING OUT is the act of tracing markings or reference points onto a material.**

Measuring involves more than determining the length of a marking. For example, when manufacturing an object, the size of an angle or the depth of a hole may also need to be measured. Different tools are used depending on the type of measurement to be made.

The next step, the layout, is a delicate operation. In fact, if this step is not done properly, the configuration of the part may be faulty, which could cause problems during the manufacturing process and result in wasted materials. It is important, therefore, to make precise markings that show clearly and accurately where machining operations such as sawing or drilling should be done. Although measuring tools can be used to indicate the position of markings, more specific layout instruments, such as combination squares, bevel squares and punches, may be more suitable.

12.42 Measuring and layout are two important steps in the process of manufacturing a technical object.

EST AST 4.2 MACHINING

Once the parts have been laid out on the appropriate materials, machining can begin. Normally, the first step in machining a part is to cut it out roughly, in an approximate shape of the finished part. This operation is called **ROUGHING**. Then various techniques are applied to give the part its desired configuration. Throughout the machining process, the part is inspected several times to ensure that the configuration corresponds to the plan.

HOW TO MANUFACTURE AN OBJECT - MACHINING PARTS

MACHINING consists in shaping a material into a desired configuration.

The most common machining techniques used in manufacturing technical objects are cutting, drilling, tapping, threading and bending. Let's look at these techniques in greater detail.

12.43 Factory personnel are assigned different predefined tasks.

EST AST CHARACTERISTICS OF CUTTING

Cutting materials is frequently part of the manufacturing process of a technical object. Cutting gives a material the shape needed to make a particular part.

CUTTING consists in giving a material a desired shape.

A variety of tools can be used for cutting. Choosing the right one depends on several factors, including the type of material and its thickness. For example, a relatively thin piece of metal can be cut with aviation shears, while metal that is too thick for shears must be cut with a band saw. For a piece of plastic, a retractable knife with a suitable blade or a band saw may be used, depending on the thickness of the material.

12.44 Safety glasses should always be worn when cutting.

EST AST CHARACTERISTICS OF DRILLING

During the manufacture of a technical object, it is often necessary to make holes in a material. To do this, a craftsperson uses drilling techniques.

DRILLING consists in making a hole in a material.

Drilling is usually carried out with a bit mounted on a tool such as a hand or an electric drill. Bits can be distinguished by the shank—the end that is inserted into the drill. A straight shank is cylindrical, while a taper shank has a non-cylindrical shape (Figure 12.45).

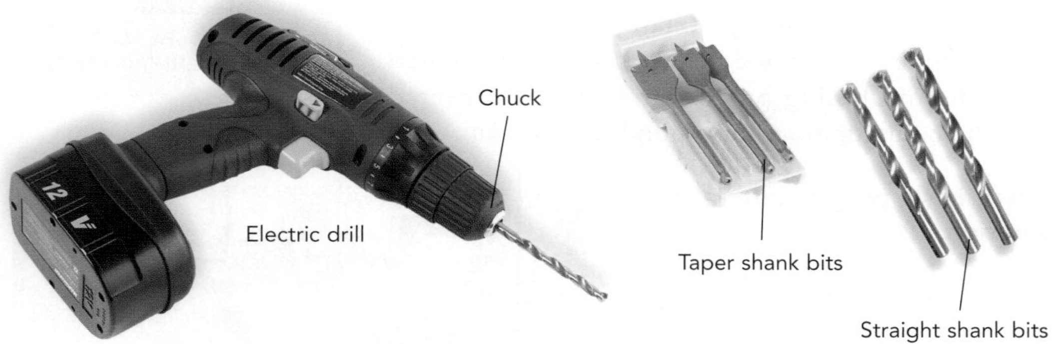

12.45 Straight shank and taper shank bits can be distinguished by examining the end of the bit that is inserted into the drill chuck.

The drill bit to be used is not chosen at random. The choice depends first on the diameter of the hole to be drilled. Second, it is always advisable to consider the type of material in which the hole is being made. Different drill bits are designed specifically for certain types of materials, such as wood or metal. The rotation speed of the drill bit also depends on the type of material and the diameter of the hole to be bored.

EST AST

CHARACTERISTICS OF TAPPING AND THREADING

Tapping and threading are machining techniques that produce threaded parts. For some technical objects, such as nuts, screw threads must be formed inside a hole. This process is known as *tapping* and is accomplished with a tool called a *tap*, as shown in Figure 12.46.

TAPPING is a machining technique in which screw threads are formed inside holes drilled into a material.

In other technical objects, such as screws, the threads must be machined around a rod. This process is known as *threading* and is carried out with a tool called a *die*, mounted on a diestock, as shown in Figure 12.47.

THREADING is a machining technique in which screw threads are formed around a rod.

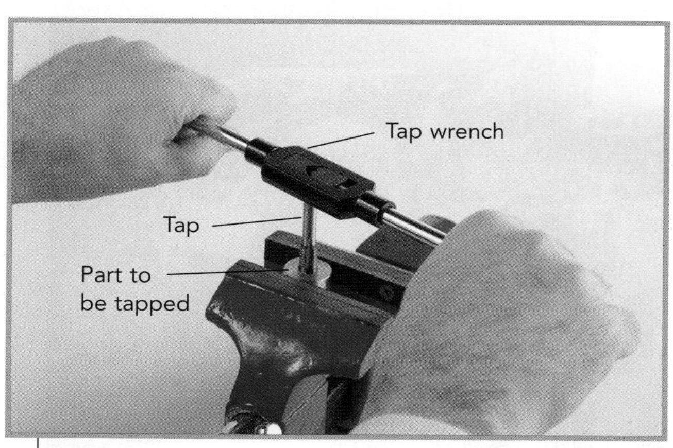

12.46 Tapping a part

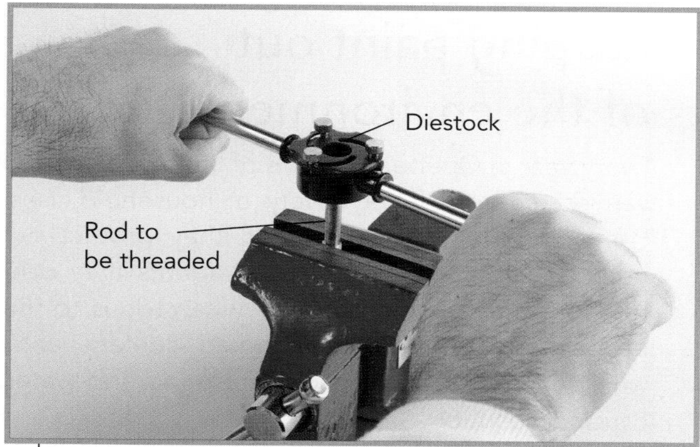

12.47 Threading a part

AST

CHARACTERISTICS OF BENDING

Parts are frequently shaped by bending during the machining process. With this technique, a material is curved into a particular form. The materials most likely to be machined by bending are metals and thermoplastics.

BENDING is a machining technique in which a material is curved into a certain shape.

AST INSPECTING PARTS

Parts are checked in various ways during machining to ensure that the configuration matches the detail drawing. Inspecting a part may include:

- checking its length, width and thickness
- ensuring that any holes are the right size and in the correct places
- checking that it has the right shape (square, hexagonal, triangular, etc.) and is bent at the correct angle
- ensuring that surfaces are level

Different techniques, such as sanding or filing, can be used to correct certain errors that may occur in the process of manufacturing parts.

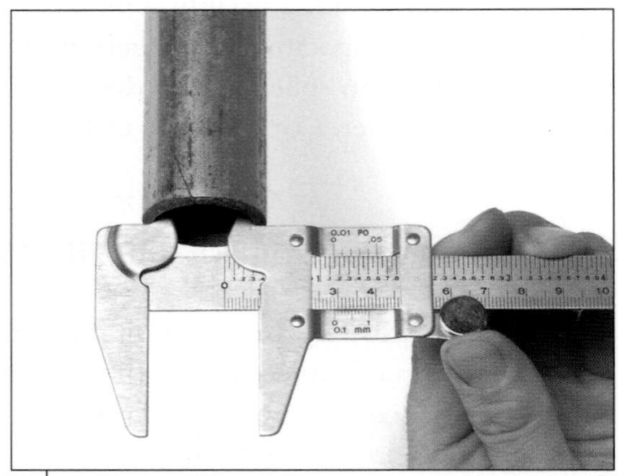

12.48 A vernier caliper is often used to check parts.

ENVIRONMENT EXTRA

Recycling rainbow: keeping paint out of the environment

Every year in Québec, millions of litres of paint and varnish are sold for a variety of household uses. Paints brighten our walls, and they protect our homes thanks to the antimould agents they contain, but they remain potentially hazardous to the environment. They contain liquid contaminants, which can enter easily into the ground and water, causing pollution.

Unfortunately, once our renovations are completed, we often find ourselves with leftover paint that we no longer want. Even empty paint containers still contain residues that are harmful to the environment. Since June 1, 2000, however, a regulation adopted by the government agency Recyc-Québec requires every company that sells paint in Québec to set up a system for recycling discarded surplus paint. To comply with the regulation, most companies have chosen to work with Éco-peinture, an organization that sorts the discarded paints, checks and adjusts their composition and filters them. The leftover paint is thus recycled and prepared for resale.

Municipal site for recovering discarded paint and paint cans

Between 1998 and 2004, paint and varnish recycling increased almost fivefold. For 2008, the Recyc-Québec target was to recover 75 percent of discarded paint and paint containers.

EST AST 4.3 ASSEMBLING AND FINISHING

Once the various parts of an object have been formed, inspected and adjusted, they must be assembled.

HOW TO MANUFACTURE AN OBJECT - ASSEMBLING AND FINISHING PARTS

ASSEMBLING is a set of techniques by which various parts are united to form a complete technical object.

There are numerous assembly techniques, including:

- nailing
- screwing
- bonding
- riveting
- joining
- bolting
- welding

To complete the manufacturing process, an object undergoes finishing. The main reasons for finishing are to protect the materials from the elements or from wear and to enhance the appearance of the object.

FINISHING is a set of techniques that complete the manufacture of the parts of a technical object.

Finishing techniques are also numerous and include polishing, varnishing, staining and dyeing. Finishing is usually done after assembling the parts. However, since some parts can be difficult to reach once assembled, they may be finished before assembly.

12.49 Varnishing a table

1879
1951

Peter Lymburner Robertson

After cutting his hand with a flat-headed screwdriver, this Canadian engineer invented the square-headed screw and screwdriver. His invention met with great success because a person could drive the screw in more rapidly, using only one hand. In workshops, the new tools increased the rate of production and reduced the number of damaged parts. Square-headed screwdrivers are still called *Robertson screwdrivers* today.

CHECKUP

ST 1–5, A and D.

EST 1–7, 9, 11, 14, A, B and D.

AST 1–14 and A–D.

SE None.

1 Materials (pp. 386–390)

1. Depending on how they are used, technical objects are likely to be subjected to stress. Name the constraint at work in the part of the object indicated in the photos below.

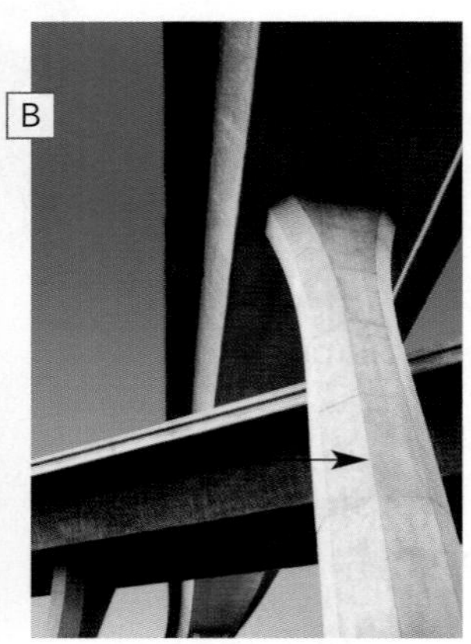

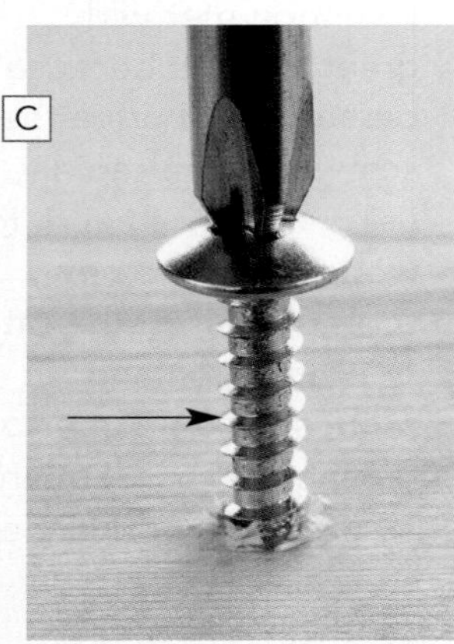

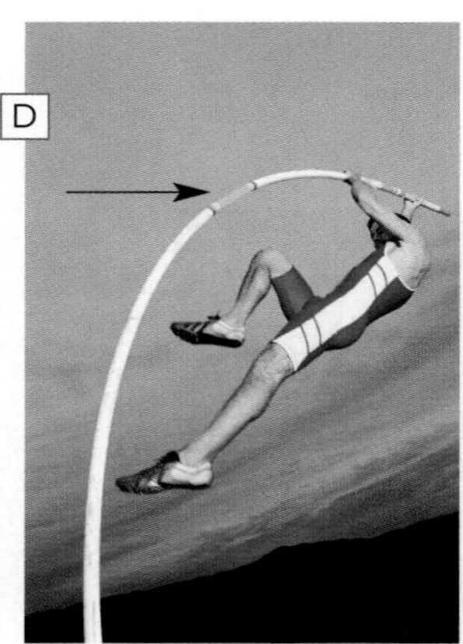

2. When manufacturing a technical object, it is often necessary to define the mechanical properties of different materials in order to make the most suitable choice. Which mechanical property is sought in each of the following examples?
   a) a plastic that keeps its shape even when twisted
   b) wooden flooring that resists indentation by pointed objects, such as shoe heels
   c) a metal that stretches well to make wire
   d) a boat hull that resists shocks caused by running into shoals
   e) a material that bends easily, without breaking, to make eavestroughing

2 Categories of materials and their properties (pp. 390–401)

3. Identify the category of material used to make the following objects. Choose from the following categories (each category may be used only once):
   – wood and modified wood
   – plastics
   – composites
   – metals and alloys
   – ceramics
   a) coins
   b) a sheet of plywood
   c) a pane of glass
   d) a soft-drink bottle
   e) a bulletproof vest
4. Which category of material would you suggest to meet the following needs? Choose from the same categories as in question 3 (each category may be used only once).

a) a shiny material that conducts electricity well
b) a light, durable and inexpensive material
c) a material that combines the properties of several categories of materials
d) a natural-looking material, with variations in colour and shade, that can be shaped and assembled easily
e) a durable material with low electrical conductivity and high degrees of heat resistance and hardness

5. During an experiment, a student puts two iron nails in a beaker containing an aqueous solution. One of the two nails was previously coated in grease. Which of the two nails will take longer to rust? Explain your answer.

6. In the Middle Ages, when knights had swords forged, the steel blades were heated then dipped in water.

Name the thermal treatment just described and identify the main advantage of the treatment for the eventual properties of the blade.

3 Technical drafting (pp. 401–410)

7. Look at the following two drawings of a compact disk storage tower.
   a) Name the type of projection used in each drawing.
   b) Could these two drawings be called general arrangements? Explain why or why not.

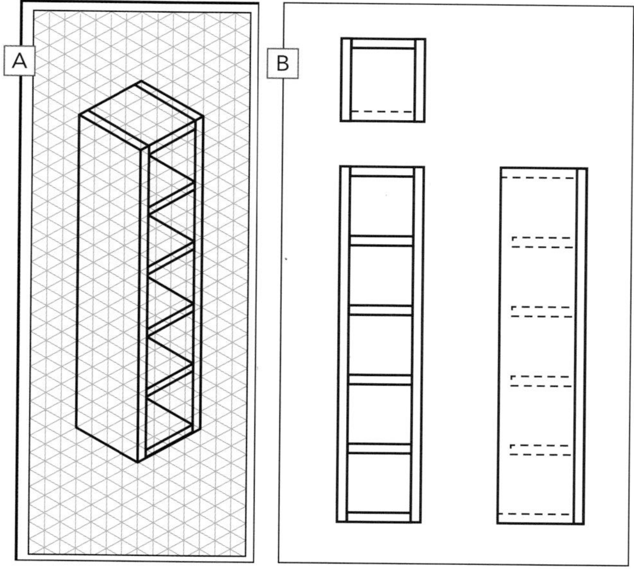

8. Look at the drawing below, which represents a three-ski sled.

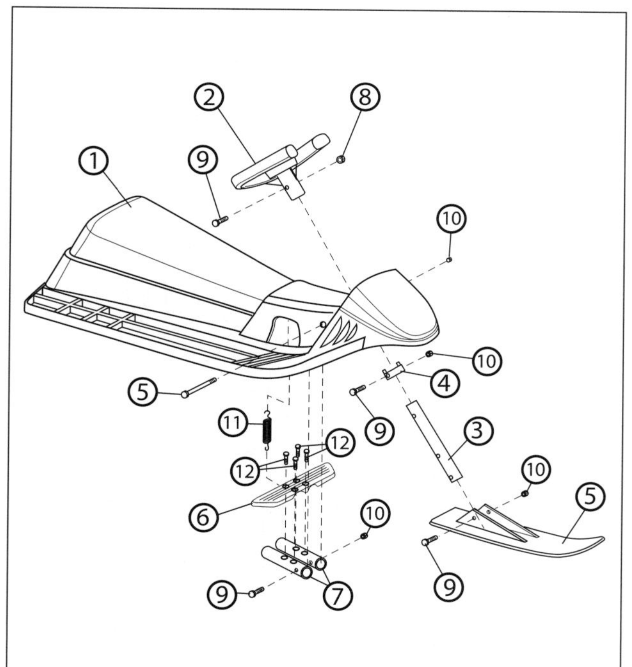

a) What type of drawing is it?

b) The number 12 parts are metal screws. Determine how many of these screws are needed to assemble this technical object.

c) If we wished to represent all the parts with detail drawings, what is the minimum number of drawings we would have to make? Explain your answer.

d) Part number 3 can be machined by bending. How can we represent, in a detail drawing, the surface area required to manufacture this part?

9. To manufacture a part, a student relies on the drawing below.

a) When the actual part dimensions are checked, the width of the indentation is found to measure 22 mm. Does this part comply with the drawing? Explain your answer.

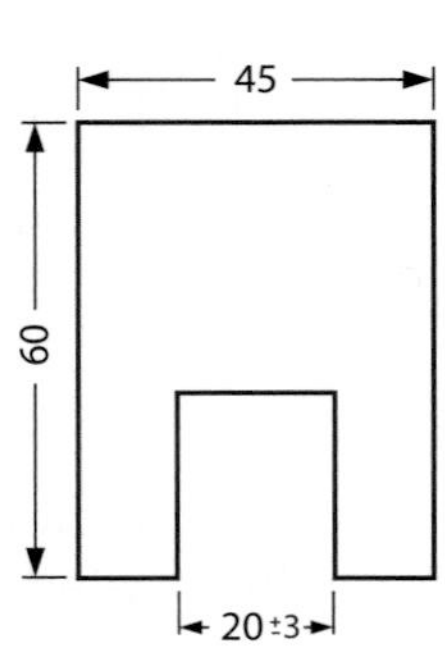

b) What is the minimum width the indentation could have?

10. Match each solid below with the correct development.

Solids

1

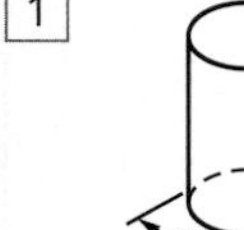

2

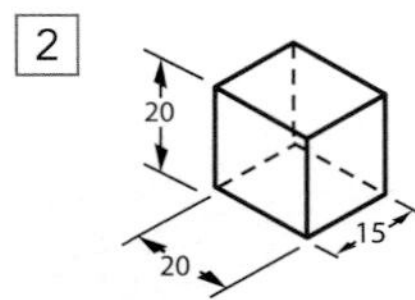

Developments

A

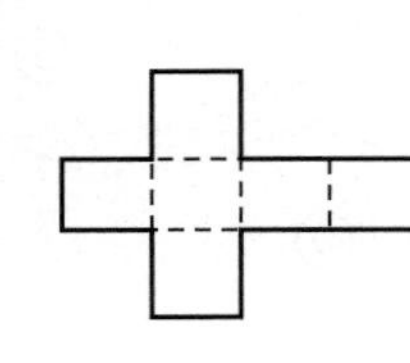

B

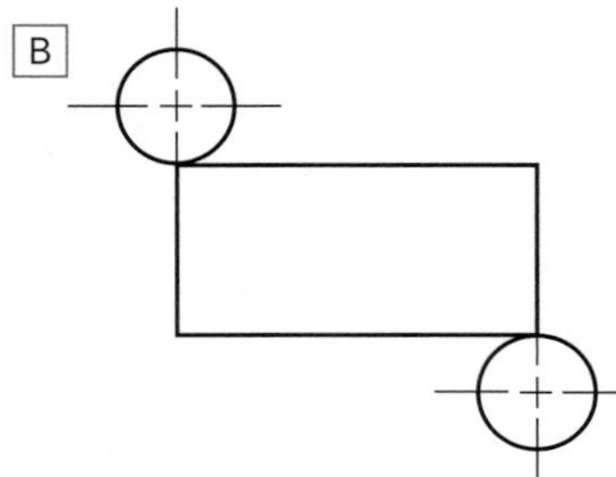

4 Manufacturing: tools and techniques (pp. 410–417)

11. Drilling is one of the most frequently used techniques in the manufacture of technical objects.

a) What is the purpose of drilling?

b) What are the two main factors to consider when choosing a drill bit?

c) Must the two factors in question b) also be considered when determining the speed of rotation of the drill bit? If not, what should be considered instead?

12. The roof of the birdhouse below has been covered in aluminum, obtained from a single sheet of metal. Which machining technique was used to shape the sheet of aluminum? Explain your answer.

13. Name three ways to inspect parts for a technical object.

14. For which assembly technique is each of the following tools most often used?

a) a hammer

b) carpenter's glue

c) a soldering iron

d) a screw

review questions

A. The photo below shows a handsaw, a tool often used to saw wood. The cutting part of this tool is made out of steel, while the handle is made of acrylonitrile butadiene styrene (ABS).

a) Which category of material does the cutting part belong to?

b) Since ABS can be remoulded when heated, which subcategory of plastics does this material belong to?

c) When the saw is used, the blade sometimes bends and then returns to its original shape. Which constraint is this part being subjected to and which mechanical property allows it to return to its original shape?

d) One of the important features of the handle is that it is difficult to deform permanently. Which mechanical property does the handle exhibit?

B. The steel used to manufacture the blade of the saw in question A has been quenched. What was the purpose of this treatment?

C. Look at the drawing opposite.

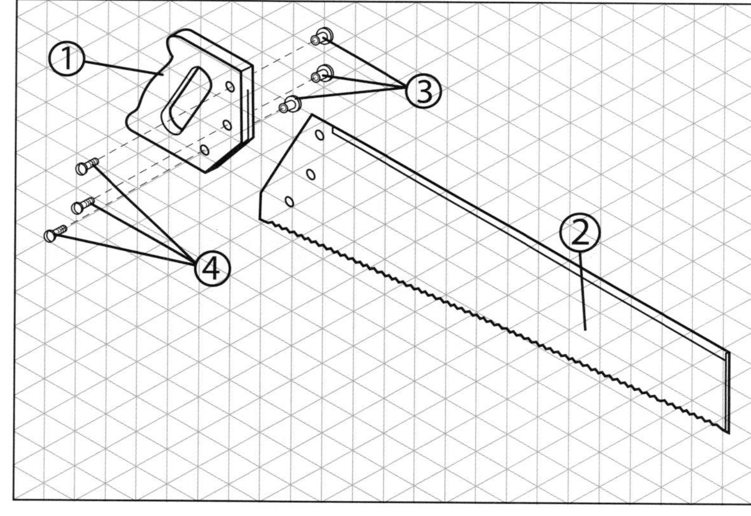

a) What type of drawing is it?

b) Make a technical diagram for the handsaw.

c) Can the handsaw be considered a machine tool? Explain your answer.

d) At which stage of the manufacturing process is this tool mainly used?

D. Prepare your own summary of Chapter 12 by building a concept map.

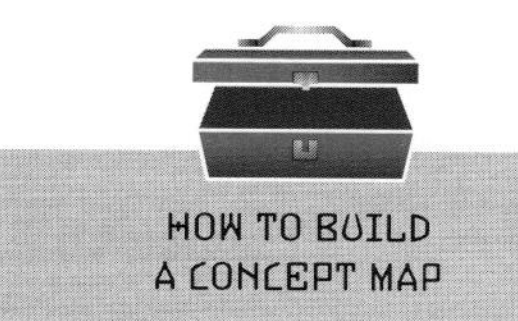

WORKING TOWARD SUSTAINABLE FORESTRY

Logging is posing problems all over the world because in many cases, the *use* of forest resources actually constitutes *overuse*. From clearcutting to extensive farming based on the "slash-and-burn" method of agriculture, from destroying unique ecosystems to replanting mainly fast-growing varieties, the issues of forest management had gained sufficient importance by 1992 to capture the attention of the world during the Rio Earth Summit, in Brazil.

FSC CERTIFICATION

After the Earth Summit in Rio, environmental groups, retailers, industry representatives and community organizations came together to find concrete solutions to forest management problems. They wanted to find ways to encourage large corporations to implement sustainable logging practices that respect the ecological, economic and social environment. They began by founding the Forest Stewardship Council (FSC) in 1994. One of its first initiatives was to establish an international certification standard based on 10 fundamental principles of sustainable forestry (some of these principles are presented in the box opposite). These principles are broad enough to apply to tropical, temperate and boreal forests. Individual countries can add or adapt criteria specific to their climates. In Canada, for example, a boreal standard was created in 2004, covering logging in 85 percent of Canadian forestland, which is located in this type of region.

The FSC standard is generally well accepted by environmentalists primarily because it depends on the evaluation of outside experts. Other, less impartial standards are based on objectives and evaluation that a company pursues internally. For FSC certification, a company requests an evaluation by independent inspectors, who assess the company's practices and grant the certification if FSC standards are met. Consumers who then buy the wood can be certain that it was harvested under sustainable management.

PROMOTING THE FSC STANDARD

Since Richard Desjardins's film *L'erreur boréale* (translated as *Forest Alert*) was released in 1999, sustainable forestry has made progress. The population must remain vigilant, however; many forestry operators still need to be prompted to take sustainable development seriously. It is equally important to convince consumers to request and buy wood certified by the FSC or approved by some other certifying organization.

Some of the FSC principles of responsible forest management

1. The legal and customary rights of Aboriginal peoples to own, use and manage their lands, territories and resources shall be recognized and respected.
2. Forest management operations shall maintain or enhance the long-term social and economic well-being of forest workers and local communities.
3. Forest management shall conserve biological diversity and its associated values, water resources, soils and unique and fragile ecosystems and landscapes.
4. Plantations shall be planned and managed in accordance with the principles of sustainable development. They should complement the management of natural forestland, reduce pressures on natural forests and promote forest restoration and conservation.

Planned reforestation is a crucial step toward sustainable forestry.

1. If you were planning to buy some wooden boards, how could you make sure that the lumber you choose was harvested according to sustainable development practices?
2. Paper is one of the main products derived from logging. Suggest several ways in which we could limit our paper consumption.

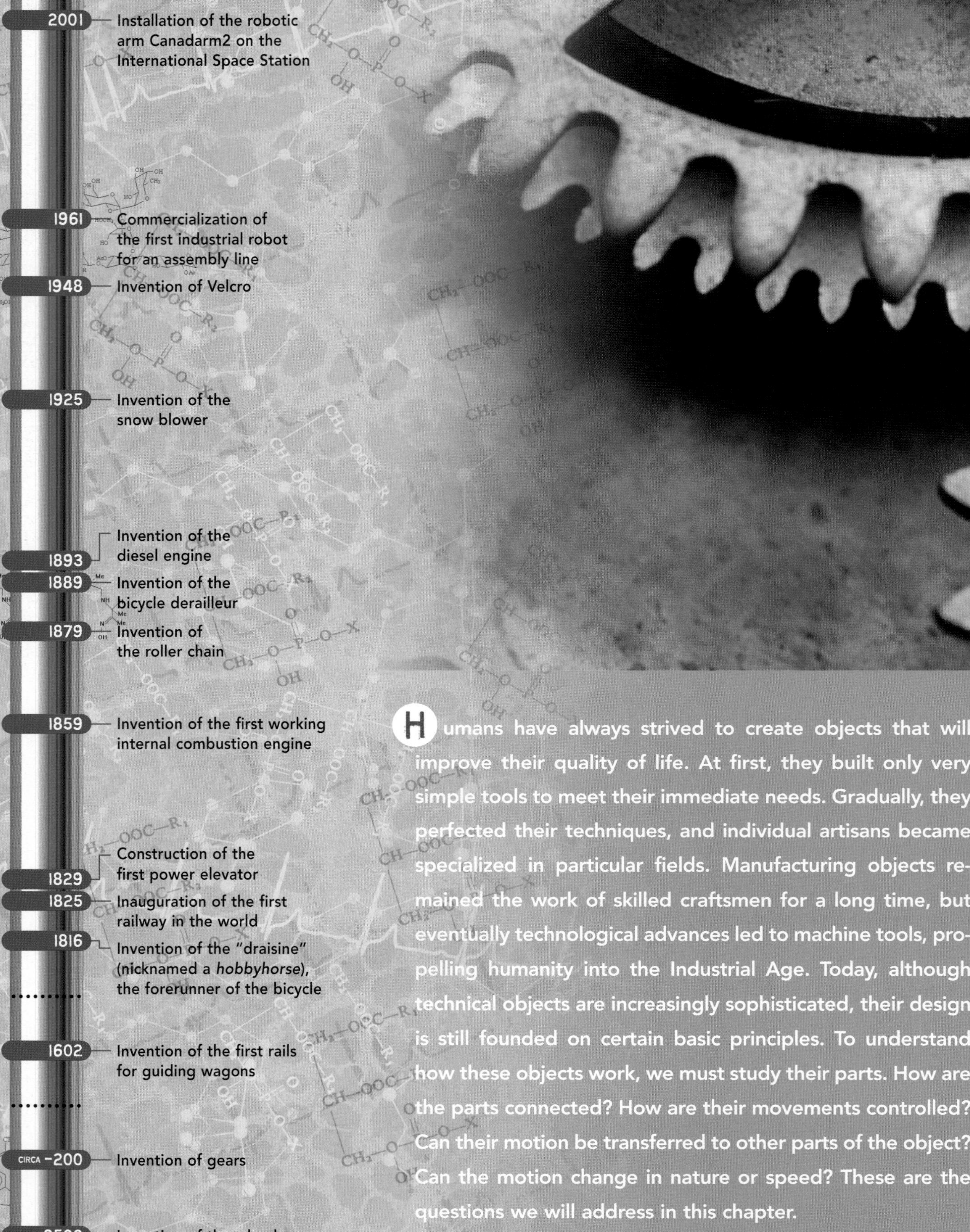

Humans have always strived to create objects that will improve their quality of life. At first, they built only very simple tools to meet their immediate needs. Gradually, they perfected their techniques, and individual artisans became specialized in particular fields. Manufacturing objects remained the work of skilled craftsmen for a long time, but eventually technological advances led to machine tools, propelling humanity into the Industrial Age. Today, although technical objects are increasingly sophisticated, their design is still founded on certain basic principles. To understand how these objects work, we must study their parts. How are the parts connected? How are their movements controlled? Can their motion be transferred to other parts of the object? Can the motion change in nature or speed? These are the questions we will address in this chapter.

Mechanical engineering

CONTENTS

ST
EST
AST

1 What is mechanical engineering?

Among the fields of study in science and technology, one branch focuses particularly on the analysis and execution of technological projects, such as building bridges, roads, bicycles, cars, televisions, etc. This branch is called *engineering*.

Engineering comes from the Latin *ingenium*, meaning "talent" or "ability."

Engineering is divided into various areas of specialization, including civil engineering, which deals with infrastructure such as roads, bridges and overpasses; computer engineering, which covers computer systems; and electrical engineering, which concentrates on electrical circuits. This chapter is on mechanical engineering, a branch that focuses mainly on objects whose working depends on moving parts.

MECHANICAL ENGINEERING is a branch of engineering that focuses on the design, production, analysis, working and improvement of technical objects with moving parts.

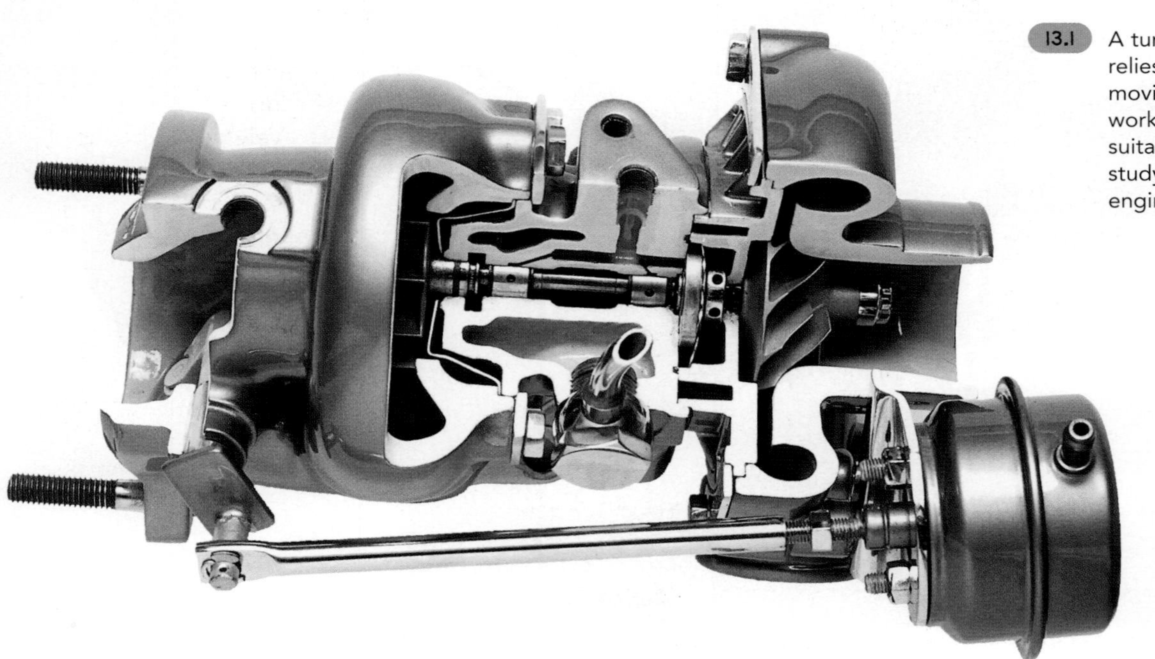

13.1 A turbocharger relies on many moving parts to work, so it is a suitable object of study for mechanical engineers.

Mechanical engineering must take into account all aspects of motion in an object, namely, the guiding, transmission and transformation of that motion as well as changes in its speed. Before discussing these subjects, however, we must understand how the parts of an object are connected and how free they are to move.

ST EST AST

2 Linking in technical objects

CONCEPT REVIEW

- Basic mechanical functions (links, guiding control)
- Types of motion

As soon as a technical object contains two or more parts, an engineer must find a way to hold them together—to *link* them. Any part, such as a nail, or any fluid, such as glue, that holds together a technical object performs a mechanical function called *linking*. The part or fluid is referred to as a **LINKING COMPONENT**. A technical object may involve more than one type of link.

- **In mechanics, a COMPONENT is a part or fluid that performs a mechanical function.**
- **LINKING is the mechanical function performed by any component that connects different parts of a technical object.**

13.2 In these natural gas pipes, many parts are connected with nuts and screws, which thus perform the mechanical function of linking.

1907
1990

George de Mestral

One everyday example of linking can be seen in the Velcro strips used to fasten shoes. George de Mestral, a Swiss engineer, invented Velcro in the early 1940s. The story goes that he was inspired by the burrs stuck to his dog's fur and his own jacket after a walk.

ST EST AST

2.1 CHARACTERISTICS OF LINKS

Technical objects may be held together in many different ways. Despite the multitude of possibilities, every link displays four basic characteristics: direct or indirect, rigid or flexible, removable or non-removable, and complete or partial. These characteristics are described in Table 13.3 (page 428).

13.3 CHARACTERISTICS OF LINKS

Direct	Indirect
A link is direct when two parts hold together without a linking component.	A link is indirect when the parts require a linking component to hold them together.
Rigid	**Flexible**
A link is rigid when the linking component or the surfaces of the linked parts are rigid.	A link is flexible when the linking component or the surfaces of the linked parts can be deformed. Springs and rubber are often used in flexible links.
Removable	**Non-removable**
A link is removable when the linked parts can be separated without damaging either their surfaces or the linking component (if present). Nuts and screws, for example, are used in removable links.	A link is non-removable when separating the linked parts damages their surfaces or the linking component.
Complete	**Partial**
A link is complete when it prevents the linked parts from moving independently of one another.	A link is partial when at least one part can move independently of the other parts.

LINK BETWEEN THE TIRE AND THE WHEEL
Characteristics: direct, flexible, removable, complete

LINK BETWEEN A WHEEL AND THE FRAME
Characteristics: indirect, rigid, removable, partial

13.4 Characteristics of two different links

2.2 DEGREES OF FREEDOM OF MOVEMENT

In a technical object, linking limits the possibility of independent motion of one part in relation to another. As we saw in the previous section, a complete link—for example, between the bicycle tire and wheel in Figure 13.4—totally restricts the motion of one part in relation to the other. The tire will always follow the motion of the wheel.

In a partial link, however, as in the rollerblade wheel and frame, the possibility of independent movement of one part in relation to the other is only partly restricted. The wheel can turn even if the frame is immobile.

Figure 13.5 shows the six possibilities of independent motion: three translational motions and three rotational motions, in relation to the three axes commonly used to define dimensions (*x*, *y* and *z*).

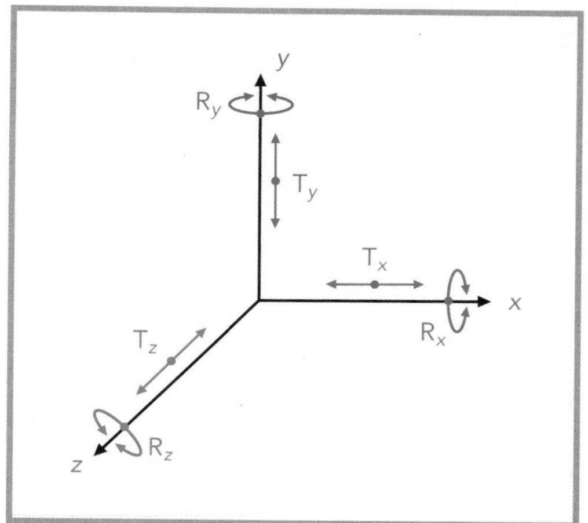

	Possibilities	Notation
Translational motion	Translation from left to right or from right to left	T_x
	Translation from top to bottom or from bottom to top	T_y
	Translation from front to back or from back to front	T_z
Rotational motion	Rotation about the *x* axis	R_x
	Rotation about the *y* axis	R_y
	Rotation about the *z* axis	R_z

13.5 The six possibilities of independent motion

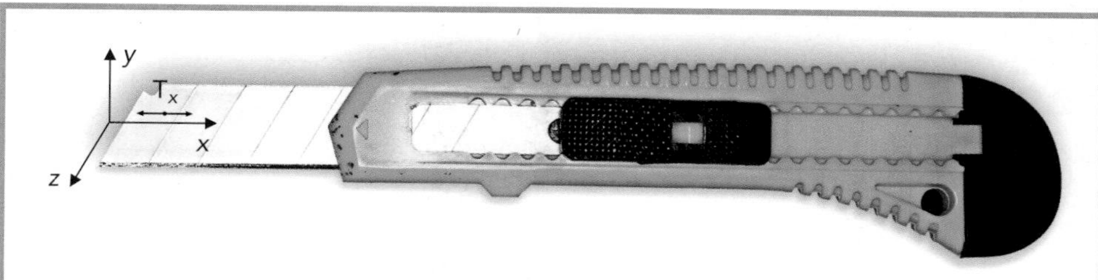

13.6 The blade of this retractable utility knife has only one independent motion: a bidirectional translation along the *x* axis.

13.7 This filing cabinet drawer also has only one independent motion: a bidirectional translation along the *z* axis.

When the possibilities of independent motion are analyzed for a linked part, the resulting description is its degree of freedom of movement. A part may therefore have a maximum of six degrees of freedom, corresponding to the six possibilities of independent motion. Figures 13.8 and 13.9 illustrate the degrees of freedom of two different parts.

The DEGREES OF FREEDOM are the set of independent movements that are possible for a given part in a technical object.

13.8 The door connected to the wall has only one degree of freedom because the only independent motion it can have is a rotation about the *y* axis.

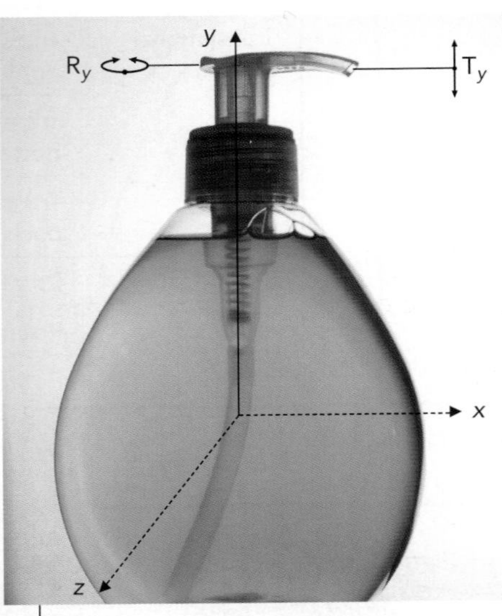

13.9 To pump soap from this dispenser, we can turn and press the spout. The spout thus has two degrees of freedom: one translation along the *y* axis and one rotation about the same axis.

TOYOTA PRODUCES ROBOTIC LEG

The Toyota group, known mainly as an automobile manufacturer, is also at the forefront in the field of robotics. The company's engineers have developed a robotic leg that can jump up to four centimetres in the air and land on its foot. The action may seem simple for humans, but it is actually a complex motion whose reproduction represents a breakthrough in humanoid robotics.

The one-metre-high autonomous leg is mounted on a foot with jointed toes. The leg can hop along using the degrees of freedom of its foot to propel itself forward.

"Movements of the leg and foot are difficult to robotize," a Toyota spokesperson explained. "Developing the leg required a series of prototypes." The company hopes to integrate this type of leg into more complex robots that will walk exactly like humans.

Source: Adapted from Agence France-Presse, "La jambe robotisée de Toyota," *Le Soleil*, September 14, 2006, *Affaires*, p. 50. *[Translation]*

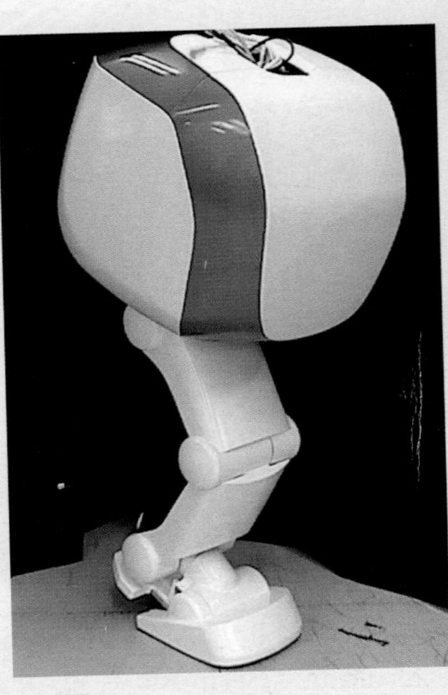

ST
EST
AST

3 Guiding controls

In many technical objects, the function of certain components is to force moving parts to follow a specific trajectory. These components are said to act as *guiding controls*.

> **GUIDING is the mechanical function performed by any component that controls the motion of one or more moving parts.**

As in the example of Figure 13.10, many pieces of furniture contain slides for opening and closing drawers. The slides guide the motion of the drawers. Since the slides perform a guiding function, they are considered guiding components or controls.

> **A GUIDING COMPONENT or CONTROL is a component whose mechanical function is to guide the motion of moving parts.**

In technical objects, there are three main forms of guiding: translational, rotational and helical. Let's take a closer look at these three types.

13.10 The slides on the sides of this drawer perform a guiding function. They are therefore guiding controls.

3.1 TYPES OF GUIDING

When a guiding control allows only the translational motion of a part, the guiding is described as *translational*. Drawer slides and other grooved components are particularly suited to this type of guiding.

> **TRANSLATIONAL GUIDING ensures the straight translational motion of a moving part.**

13.11 Grooves on either side of this hung window ensure translational guiding when the window is opened and closed.

When a guiding control allows only the rotational motion of a part, the guiding is described as *rotational*. Cylindrical components are particularly suited to this type of guiding.

ROTATIONAL GUIDING ensures the rotational motion of a moving part.

13.12 An axle attached to the fork guides the wheel hub in a rotational motion.

When a guiding control allows for a rotational motion combined with a translational motion along the same axis of a part, the guiding is described as *helical*. Threaded components are especially suitable for this type of guiding.

HELICAL GUIDING ensures the translational motion of a moving part while it rotates about the same axis.

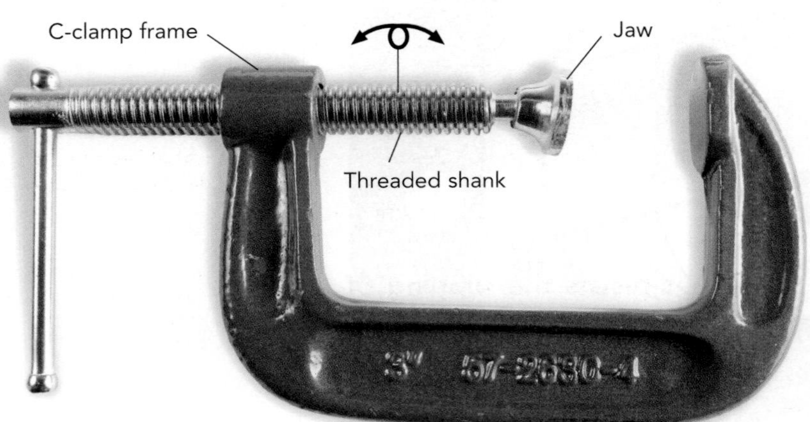

13.13 Threads inside the frame of the C-clamp control the helical guiding of the threaded shank.

1811
1861

Elisha Graves Otis

Elevator cars are among the many parts that are subjected to translational guiding. Before a certain modification by Elisha Graves Otis, an American mechanic, people were reluctant to trust these machines to carry them from floor to floor in a building. In 1852, Otis invented a device that locks the elevator car in place if the supporting cable breaks. His invention was among the reasons for the increased popularity of skyscrapers.

EST AST

3.2 ADHESION AND FRICTION OF PARTS

TECH 10

When a car stops on the way up a hill, the tires keep the vehicle on the road and prevent it from sliding. The phenomenon that holds the tires on the road is called *adhesion*. Without adhesion between the tires and the road, the car would start to slide as soon as it stopped on a slope. Adhesion decreases when roads are icy, often causing car accidents.

ADHESION is the phenomenon by which two surfaces tend to remain in contact with each other without slipping.

The strength of adhesion between two surfaces depends mainly on five factors:

- the nature of the materials in contact. For example, adhesion between rubber and asphalt differs from that between steel and asphalt.
- the presence of a lubricant. Adhesion is usually reduced by the presence of a lubricant. For example, a tire will not adhere well to the road if there is an oil spot on the asphalt.
- temperature. Adhesion between two surfaces tends to diminish with colder temperatures. For example, the colder the weather, the weaker the adhesion of a tire to the road.
- the state of the surfaces in contact. Usually, the rougher a surface, the better its adhesion to another surface. This explains why the adhesion of a tire to asphalt decreases with wear.
- the perpendicular **FORCE** exerted by one surface on another. Adhesion increases as this force increases. For example, it is more difficult to pull a loaded sleigh than an empty one.

13.14 If the soles of these boots did not adhere to the ground properly, the hiker would slip as he would on an icy surface in winter.

A moving part in a technical object is usually guided by another part. Surfaces of the moving part and the guiding component thus slip over one another. However, adhesion tends to make the parts hold together, so an opposing force forms, resisting the slipping movement. This force is called *friction*. The greater the adhesion between two parts, the greater the friction when they move against each other.

In mechanics, FRICTION is a force that resists the slipping of one moving part over another.

One of the main means of reducing friction between parts is to apply a lubricant so that the surfaces in contact can slip more easily over one another. The mechanical function of these substances is called *lubrication*. Oils, such as the motor oils used in combustion engines, are examples of lubricants.

LUBRICATION is the mechanical function performed by any component that reduces friction between two parts.

13.15 As the piston moves back and forth inside the guiding cylinder, its outer surface slides over the inner surface of the cylinder, causing friction.

TIRE AND TRACK: A STICKY BUSINESS?

In Formula One racing, victory hinges on adhesion. The team engineers can think of nothing else. Between Grand Prix races, they spend countless days assessing tires, testing the bands of natural or synthetic rubber where the tire meets the track. A softer rubber, with greater adhesion, can help a car gain a second or more per lap.

Let's picture exactly what is happening: at 300 km/h, the wheels are turning so fast that a single point on the tire tread touches the track for only two thousandths of a second, 40 times per second. In each of these brief instants, the tread must adhere to the track. If we could observe this process under a microscope, we would see tire molecules literally catch on the uneven surface of the asphalt. The car can thus adhere to the track and make turns.

The obsession of racing teams about tires eventually became so acute that the FIA (Fédération internationale de l'automobile) decided to tighten the regulations. Since 2008, teams are allowed to do business with only one tire manufacturer.

Source: Adapted from Luc Domenjoz, "Entre la gomme at la piste, c'est la magie noire," *La Presse*, June 25, 2006, p. 58. *[Translation]*

A Formula One racing car in a turn

13.16 EXAMPLES OF LUBRICANTS

Lubricant type	Examples
Liquid	Water, oil (vegetable, animal and mineral)
Semisolid	Suet, Vaseline, animal fat, vegetable fat
Solid	Graphite, paraffin

Another method of reducing friction is polishing. Under a microscope, the surfaces of most materials prove to have minuscule ridges that cause adhesion and friction since they tend to catch on the surface of another part when they move against it. When a surface is polished, some of these tiny ridges are eliminated, reducing friction.

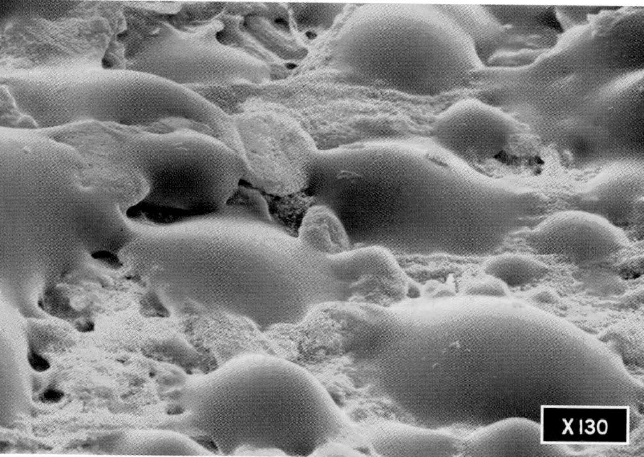

13.17 The illustration on the left shows a self-adhesive label as seen by the naked eye. On the right, a magnified view of part of the sticky side of the same label shows its roughness—a surface covered in uneven ridges.

Motion transmission systems

CONCEPT REVIEW

- System (overall function, inputs, processes, outputs, control)
- Components of a system
- Function, components and use of motion transmission systems (friction gears, pulleys and belt, gear assembly, sprockets and chain, worm and worm gear)

In many technical objects, it is useful to transmit the motion of one part to one or more other parts. Components that accomplish this transfer in a technical object perform the mechanical function of motion transmission.

> **MOTION TRANSMISSION is the mechanical function of relaying a motion from one part to another without altering the nature of the motion.**

For example, in the bicycle illustrated in Figure 13.19 (page 436), the rotational motion applied by the cyclist's legs to the crankset is transferred to the rear wheel by a set of three components: a sprocket linked to the crankset, a sprocket linked to the rear wheel, and a chain. Since the three components all contribute to the same function—transmitting motion—they form a motion transmission system.

A MOTION TRANSMISSION SYSTEM is a set of components that perform the function of transmitting motion.

As shown in Table 13.18, any mechanical system contains a driver (component) and at least one driven component. In addition, some systems, such as the motion transmission system in a bicycle, also contain an intermediate component.

13.18 TYPES OF COMPONENTS IN A MECHANICAL SYSTEM

Type of component	Description
Driver component	Component that receives the force required to activate the system
Driven component	Component that receives the motion and transfers it to another part
Intermediate component	Component located between the driver and driven components. Not all systems contain an intermediate component.

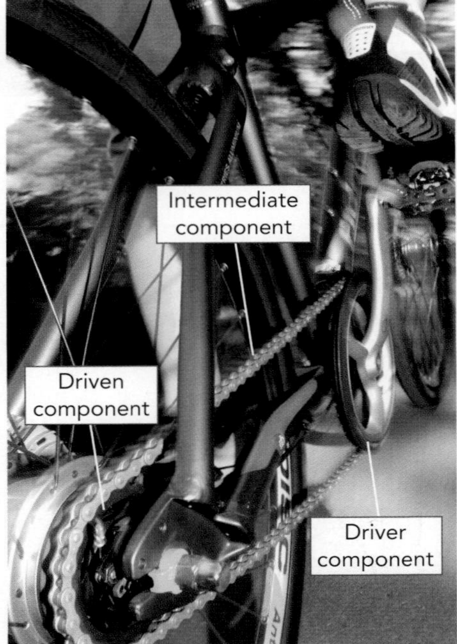

13.19 The motion transmission system in a bicycle contains a chain and sprockets.

ST EST AST 4.1 CHARACTERISTICS OF MOTION IN TRANSMISSION SYSTEMS

In mechanical engineering, motion transmission systems are often applied to technical objects. The most common systems are:

- gear trains
- chain and sprocket systems
- worm and worm gear systems
- friction gear systems
- belt and pulley systems

While all these systems transmit rotational motion, they differ in their specific characteristics. First, as shown in Figure 13.21 (page 437), the direction of rotation of the various components is sometimes identical throughout the entire system and sometimes different. Figure 13.20 illustrates the two directions of possible rotation.

Clockwise

Counterclockwise

13.20 The two directions of rotational motion are described as *clockwise* and *counterclockwise.*

Second, reversing the system may not always be possible. In mechanical engineering, a system is described as *reversible* when a driven component can become a driver, and vice versa. Among the systems in Figure 13.21 below, only the worm and worm gear is irreversible.

13.21 Characteristics of motion in the main motion transmission systems

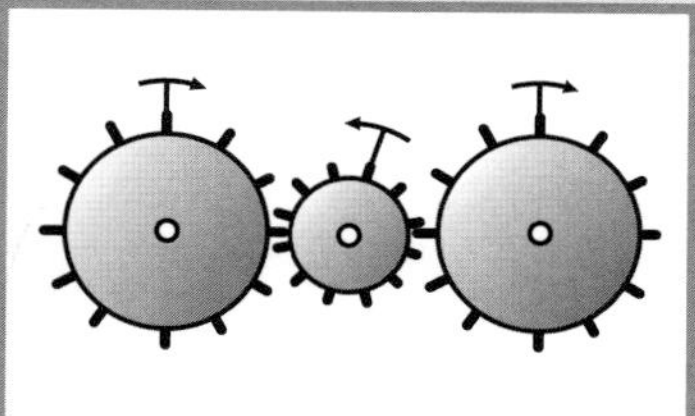

GEAR TRAINS

DIRECTION OF ROTATION OF COMPONENTS
Alternates from one gear to another.

REVERSIBILITY
Yes

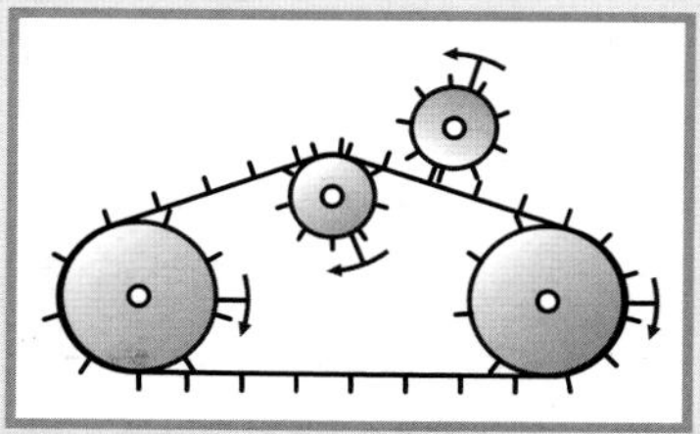

CHAIN AND SPROCKET SYSTEMS

DIRECTION OF ROTATION OF COMPONENTS
Depending on the configuration, identical only for sprockets touching the same side of the chain

REVERSIBILITY
Yes

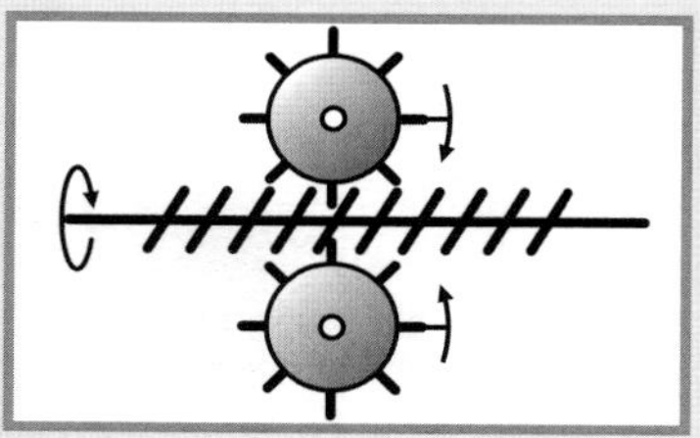

WORM AND WORM GEAR SYSTEMS

DIRECTION OF ROTATION OF COMPONENTS
Varies with the direction of the threads on the worm screw shaft.

REVERSIBILITY
No

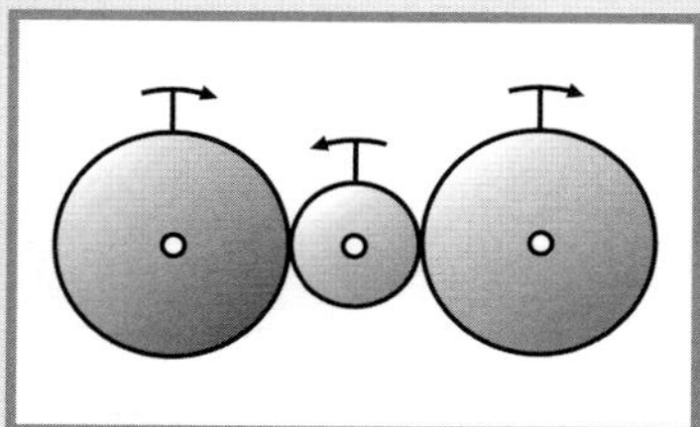

FRICTION GEAR SYSTEMS

DIRECTION OF ROTATION OF COMPONENTS
Alternates from one gear to another.

REVERSIBILITY
Yes

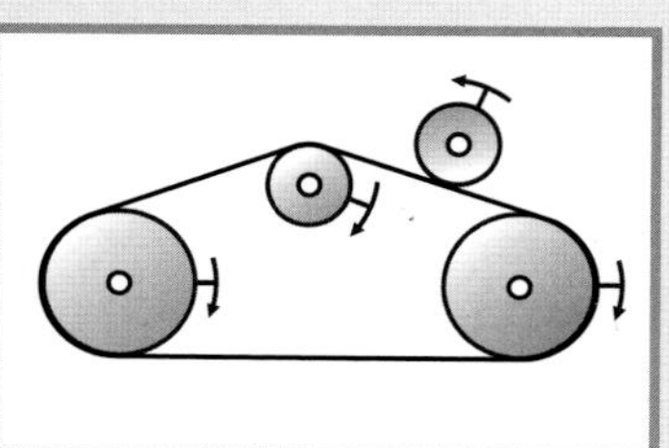

BELT AND PULLEY SYSTEMS

DIRECTION OF ROTATION OF COMPONENTS
Depending on the configuration, identical only for pulleys touching the same side of the belt

REVERSIBILITY
Yes

PEDALS TO PUSH

Did you know that the "draisine" (nicknamed a *hobby-horse*), the forerunner of the modern bicycle, did not even have pedals? Its motion was generated by the cyclist's feet pushing against the ground. The first pedal bicycle was invented in 1839, but it still did not involve rotary motion. The cyclist's feet pushing on the pedals produced a back-and-forth motion that activated rods attached to the rear wheel. Various mechanical systems were tested until the arrival, in 1880, of bicycles with chain and sprocket transmission systems, which are still in use today.

ST EST AST 4.2 CONSTRUCTION CONSIDERATIONS FOR MOTION TRANSMISSION SYSTEMS

Engineers must take various elements into account when building motion transmission systems, depending on the type of system they wish to develop. Let's look at the main elements that engineers must consider as they design the more common motion transmission systems.

ST EST AST GEAR TRAINS

Gear trains consist of at least two gears that meet and mesh with each other. The systems are used to transmit motion between two or more closely positioned parts.

Particular attention is given to certain elements when building a gear train. These elements are presented in Table 13.22.

13.22 ELEMENTS TO CONSIDER WHEN BUILDING A GEAR TRAIN

Element	Description
Gear teeth	The teeth of all the gears in the system must be identical: they must have the same shape and direction and be equally spaced. Figure 13.23 illustrates the two main types of teeth (straight and helical) in gear trains.
Gear type	In a gear train, the rotational axis of the gears can be positioned in different ways. As shown in Figure 13.24 (page 439), when rotational axes are parallel, straight gears are commonly used. When the axes are perpendicular, bevel gears are preferred.
Gear size	The higher the number of teeth, the lower the speed of rotation. Consequently (since gear teeth are all identical in gear trains), the larger the diameter of a gear, the slower its rotation.

13.23 The two main types of teeth in gear trains. In gears with straight teeth, the teeth grooves are parallel to the rotational axis. In gears with helical teeth, the grooves are not parallel to the axis. Gears with straight teeth are noisier than gears with helical teeth, but more efficient.

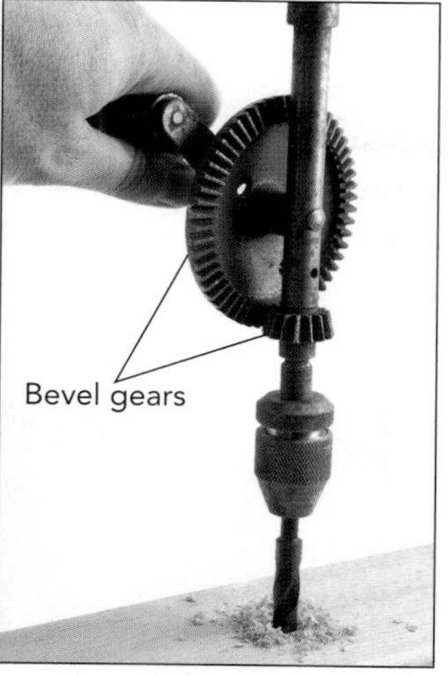

13.24 In the gear train of a watch, the rotational axes of the gears are parallel, so straight gears are used. In a hand drill, the rotational axes of the gears are perpendicular, so bevel gears are preferred.

Archimedes

This Ancient Greek scientist is widely considered the father of mechanics. He assembled gear trains in machines of war to defend his homeland. He is also credited with the invention of the screw and the nut as well as with many other contributions to various branches of science.

ST EST AST

CHAIN AND SPROCKET SYSTEMS

Like gear trains, chain and sprocket systems consist of at least two gears. However, the gears do not mesh; they are connected by a chain, and they are referred to as *sprockets*. Since sprocket teeth do not meet directly but mesh with a chain, chain and sprocket systems are used to transmit motion between two or more distant parts. The main elements to consider when building a chain and sprocket system are presented in Figure 13.25.

13.25 The main elements to consider when building a chain and sprocket system

- **A** The teeth on the system sprockets must be identical.
- **B** The chain links must mesh easily with the sprocket teeth.
- **C** The system requires frequent lubrication to avoid the rapid wear of the teeth and chain.
- **D** The smaller a sprocket, the faster it turns.

ST EST AST

WORM AND WORM GEAR SYSTEMS

Worm and worm gear systems consist of a single worm (screw) whose rotational motion is transmitted to one or more worm gears. The worm is also called an *endless screw* because it can drive the worm gear indefinitely. The elements to consider when building a worm and worm gear system are described in Figure 13.26.

A The groove of the worm must fit the gear teeth so that they can mesh.

B The driver (to which the force is applied) must be the worm.

13.26 The main elements to consider when building a worm and worm gear system

ST EST AST

FRICTION GEAR SYSTEMS

Friction gear systems are similar to gear trains except that the friction gears do not have teeth. Instead, motion is transmitted by friction between the gears. Another similarity is that friction gear systems are also used to transmit a rotational motion between two or more closely positioned parts.

Since friction gears do not require teeth, the gear systems are more economical and less complicated to produce than gear trains. However, friction gear systems are also less efficient than gear trains because the gears can slip. Table 13.28 (page 441) describes the main elements to consider when building a friction gear system.

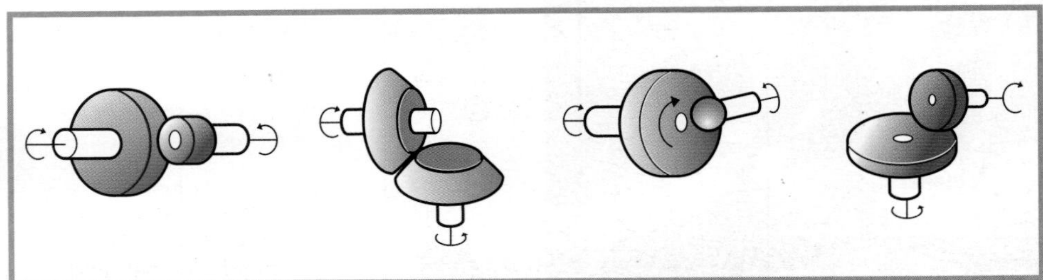

13.27 Various gear types. Straight gears are in red, bevel gears are in blue, and the gear in green is spherical.

13.28 ELEMENTS TO CONSIDER WHEN BUILDING A FRICTION GEAR SYSTEM

Element	Description
Gear type	As shown in Figure 13.27 (page 440), the three main types of friction gears are straight, bevel and spherical. The three types may be positioned along parallel, perpendicular or other rotational axes.
Gear size	In a friction gear system, the larger the diameter of a gear, the slower its rotation.
Adhesion of materials	For a friction gear system to be efficient, friction between gears must be high. For this reason, the gear rims must be made of materials that adhere well to one another.

ST
EST
AST

BELT AND PULLEY SYSTEMS

Belt and pulley systems are similar to chain and sprocket systems. However, the toothless gears are referred to as *pulleys,* and they are connected by a belt instead of a chain. Like chain and sprocket systems, belt and pulley systems are used to transmit a rotational motion between two or more distant parts. The main elements to consider when building a belt and pulley system are described in Figure 13.29.

Ⓐ Pulleys must contain a groove where the belt can fit. The groove must be smooth to prevent damage to the belt.

Ⓑ The belt must adhere to the pulleys to avoid slipping as much as possible.

Ⓒ The smaller a pulley, the faster it turns.

13.29 The main elements to consider when building a belt and pulley system

ST EST AST

4.3 SPEED CHANGES IN MOTION TRANSMISSION SYSTEMS

The systems we have just discussed relay motion from a driver to one or more driven components without altering the nature of the motion. However, as Figure 13.30 below shows, the systems can change the speed of the motion during its transmission.

CONCEPT REVIEW
Speed changes (AST)

A SPEED CHANGE occurs in a motion transmission system when the driver does not turn at the same speed as the driven component or components.

Let's see how the main motion transmission systems effect changes in speed.

ST EST AST

SPEED CHANGES IN WORM AND WORM GEAR SYSTEMS

Worm and worm gear systems are the system of choice for dramatically reducing the speed of a rotational motion during transmission. As illustrated in Figure 13.30, for each full turn of the worm, the worm gear moves a distance equivalent to the width of only one tooth. The greater the number of teeth on the gear, the greater the decrease in speed.

CHANGING GEARS

Several decades separate the invention of the first bicycle and the launch of the first derailleur. In the 1890s, racing cyclists had to turn their rear wheels to change speeds. Then, in the early 20th century, the modern-day derailleur appeared on the market. It was, and remains, a mechanism for changing speed on a bike by shifting the chain from one sprocket to another. 18

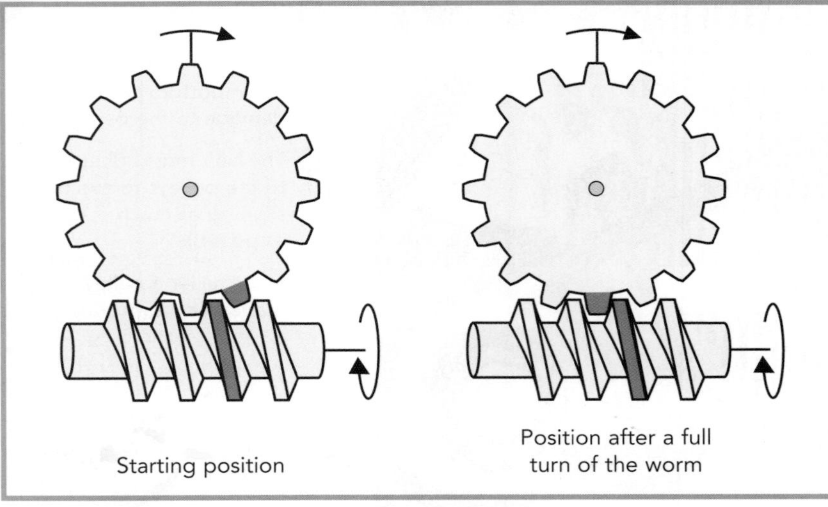

13.30 Speed change in a worm and worm gear system

ST EST AST

SPEED CHANGES IN OTHER MOTION TRANSMISSION SYSTEMS

In the other motion transmission systems we have studied, speed changes occur when the gear diameters vary. Since the gear teeth must all be identical in both gear trains and chain and sprocket systems, the gear diameter varies with the number of teeth. Speed changes in these two types of systems therefore depend on the number of teeth on the gears or sprockets. Table 13.31 explains how rotational speed can vary in these two systems as well as in friction gear and belt and pulley systems.

13.31 SPEED CHANGES IN MULTIPLE-GEAR MOTION TRANSMISSION SYSTEMS

Speed change	Friction gear systems Belt and pulley systems	Gear trains Chain and sprocket systems
Increase	Motion is transmitted from one gear or pulley to a gear or pulley of smaller diameter.	Motion is transmitted from one gear or sprocket to another with fewer teeth.
Decrease	Motion is transmitted from one gear or pulley to a gear or pulley of larger diameter.	Motion is transmitted from one gear or sprocket to another with more teeth.
No change	Motion is transmitted between two gears or pulleys of the same diameter.	Motion is transmitted between two gears or sprockets with the same number of teeth.

It is often useful to know the ratio of speed increases or decreases in motion transmission systems. The ratio is equivalent to the ratio between the gear diameters or between the numbers of teeth on each gear.

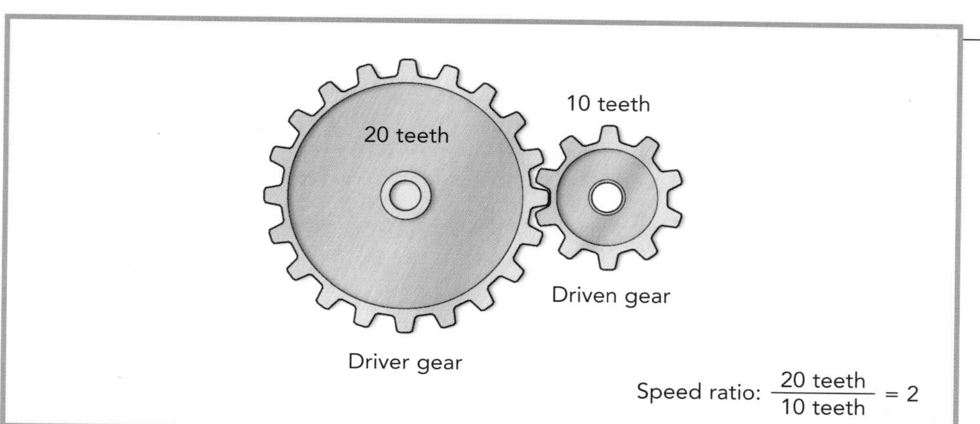

13.32 In this gear train, the rotational speed of the driven gear is twice the speed of the driver gear.

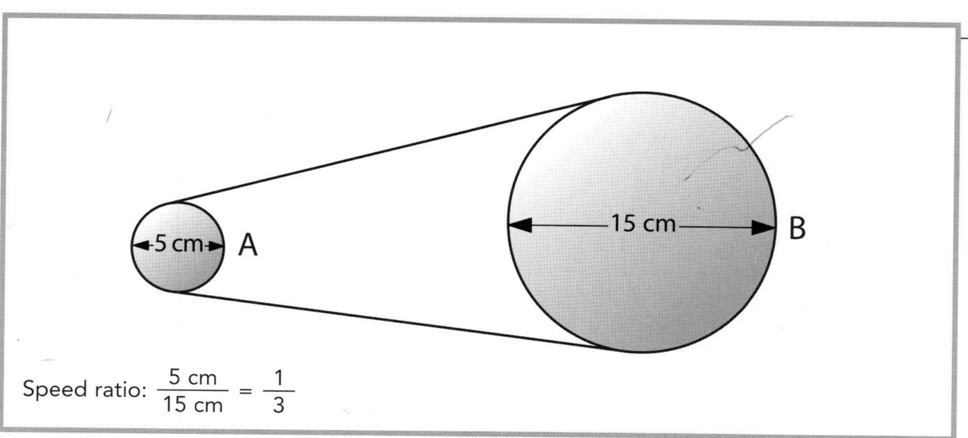

13.33 In this belt and pulley system, the rotational speed of pulley B is three times slower than the speed of pulley A.

ENVIRONMENT EXTRA

Speed changes in wind turbines

In Québec, wind turbines are becoming an increasingly popular means to generate electricity. Wind energy makes the blades of the turbine spin. This rotational motion is transmitted to the generator, which transforms the wind energy into electrical energy. The motion transmission system is illustrated opposite.

With winds of 50 to 60 km/h, the rotational speed of the blades of Hydro-Québec wind turbines is about 20 to 30 revolutions per minute. To produce an electric current equivalent to current from other sources in the Hydro-Québec network, rotational speeds have to reach about 1800 revolutions per minute. A gear train, located between the blades and the generator, is responsible for increasing the rotational speed.

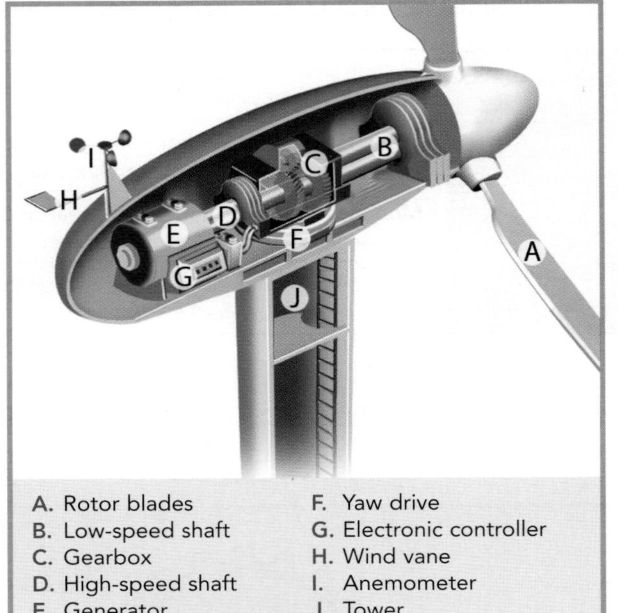

Principal components of a wind turbine

AST 4.4 TORQUE

To produce a rotational motion about an axis, two forces of equal strength but applied in opposite directions are required. These two forces are referred to as *torque*. Figure 13.34 explains how torque is applied.

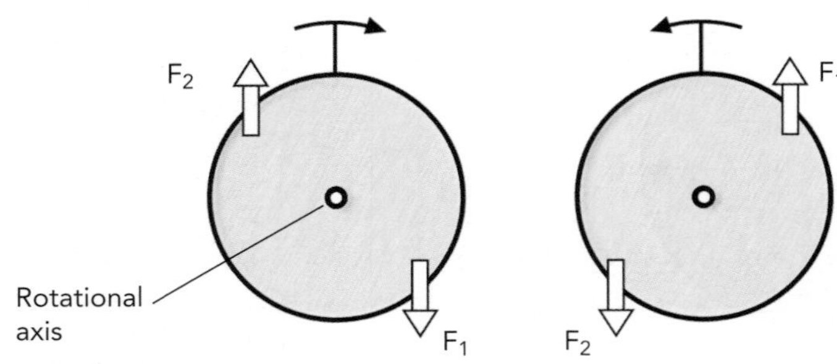

13.34 Torque applied to the left wheel causes a clockwise rotation, while torque applied to the right wheel causes a counterclockwise rotation.

TORQUE involves two forces of equal strength but applied in opposite directions, which cause a component to rotate about an axis.

In motion transmission systems, when torque increases the rotational speed of components, it is called *engine torque.* When torque reduces or stops the rotational motion of components, it is called *resisting torque.*

ENGINE TORQUE increases the rotational speed of components in mechanical systems.

RESISTING TORQUE slows or stops the rotation of components in mechanical systems.

To operate a motion transmission system or to increase the rotational speed of its components, the engine torque must therefore be greater than the resisting torque. For example, when a cyclist rides up a hill, the engine torque applied by the cyclist's legs must be greater than all the forces behind the resisting torque, including ground friction, air resistance and gravitational force.

13.35 In this logging truck, the engine generates the forces responsible for engine torque, and the truck can accelerate. The weight of the logs contributes to the resisting torque.

13.36 ROTATIONAL SPEED CHANGES CAUSED BY STRENGTH DIFFERENCES BETWEEN ENGINE TORQUE AND RESISTING TORQUE

Comparison of torque strength	Effect on speed of components
Engine torque = resisting torque	No change
Engine torque > resisting torque	Increased speed
Engine torque < resisting torque	Reduced speed

ST EST AST

5 Motion transformation systems

CONCEPT REVIEW

Function, components and use of motion transformation systems (screw gear systems, cams, connecting rods, cranks, slides, slider-crank mechanisms, rack and pinion systems)

The systems we have studied to this point are systems that transmit motion without altering its nature. In many technical objects, however, it is often useful to modify a motion while transferring it. These cases call for motion transformation systems.

MOTION TRANSFORMATION is the mechanical function of relaying a motion from one part to another while altering the nature of the motion.

ST EST AST

5.1 CHARACTERISTICS OF MOTION IN TRANSFORMATION SYSTEMS

The most common motion transformation systems in technical objects are described below.

13.37 Characteristics of motion in the main motion transformation systems

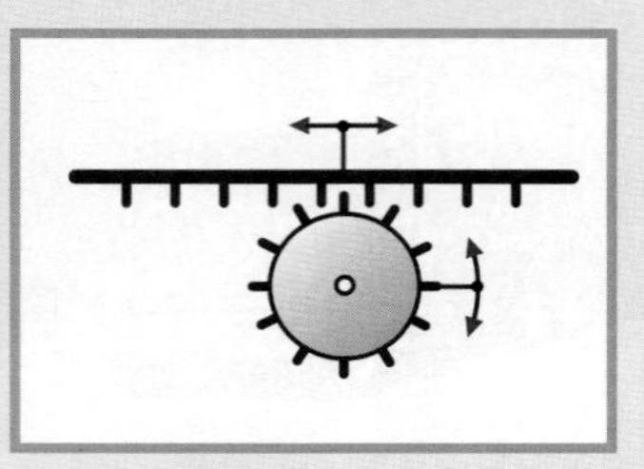

RACK AND PINION SYSTEMS

POSSIBLE TRANSFORMATIONS

Rotation → Translation
or Translation → Rotation

REVERSIBILITY

Yes

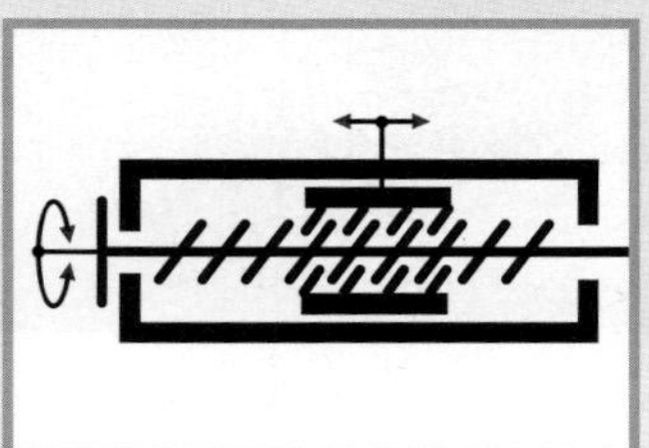

SCREW GEAR SYSTEMS, TYPE I

POSSIBLE TRANSFORMATION

Rotation → Translation

REVERSIBILITY

No

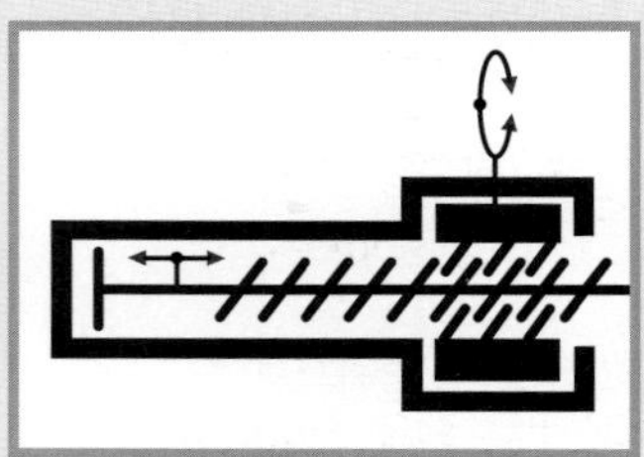

SCREW GEAR SYSTEMS, TYPE II

POSSIBLE TRANSFORMATION

Rotation → Translation

REVERSIBILITY

No

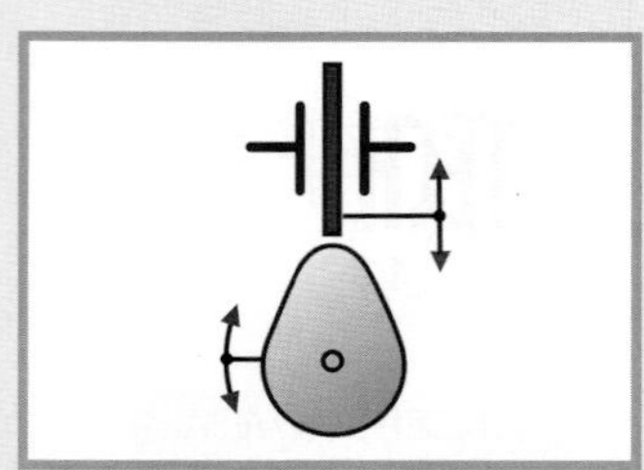

CAM AND FOLLOWER SYSTEMS

POSSIBLE TRANSFORMATION

Rotation → Translation

REVERSIBILITY

No

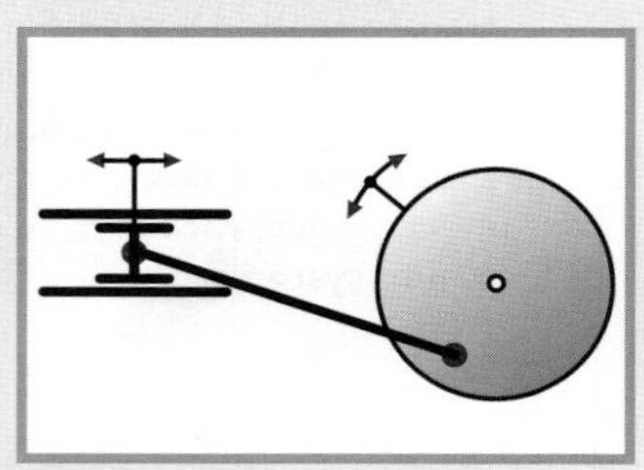

SLIDER-CRANK MECHANISMS

POSSIBLE TRANSFORMATIONS

Rotation → Translation
or Translation → Rotation

REVERSIBILITY

Yes

Figure 13.37 (page 446) illustrates the movement of parts in each of these systems and the motion transformations that the systems can perform. When a motion transformation system can be used to convert rotational motion into translational motion and vice versa, then the system is reversible.

13.38 The windmill, forerunner of the modern wind turbine, is sometimes equipped with a motion transformation system.

ST EST AST 5.2 CONSTRUCTION CONSIDERATIONS FOR MOTION TRANSFORMATION SYSTEMS

Engineers must consider various factors when building motion transformation systems, depending on the type of system they are designing. Let's look at the main elements to consider when designing the most common motion transformation systems.

ST EST AST RACK AND PINION SYSTEMS

Rack and pinion systems contain at least one gear, called a *pinion,* and one straight bar with teeth, called a *rack*.

13.39 The main elements to consider when building a rack and pinion system

- **A** The teeth on the rack and on the pinion must be identical.
- **B** The system requires frequent lubrication to prevent wear.
- **C** The greater the number of teeth on the pinion, the slower its rotation.

ST EST AST

SCREW GEAR SYSTEMS

There are two types of screw gear systems that can transform motion. In the first type, the screw is the driver, and its rotational motion is transformed into the translational motion of the nut. An example of this type of system is found in jacks for lifting cars.

In the second type of system, the nut is the driver, and its rotational motion is transformed into the translational motion of the screw. This type of system is used in pipe wrenches. Figure 13.40 describes the elements to consider when building screw gear systems.

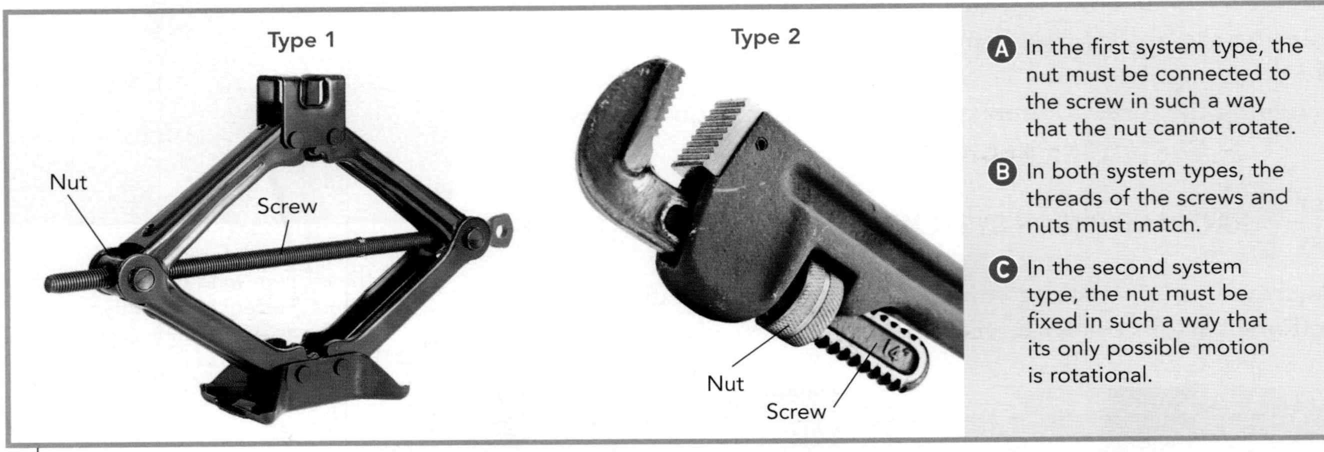

13.40 The main elements to consider when building screw gear systems

ST EST AST

CAM AND FOLLOWER SYSTEMS AND ECCENTRICS

Cam and follower systems transform the rotational motion of a cam into the reciprocating translational motion of a follower—in other words, a back-and-forth movement like that of a sewing machine needle. Figure 13.41 describes the main elements to consider when building cam and follower systems.

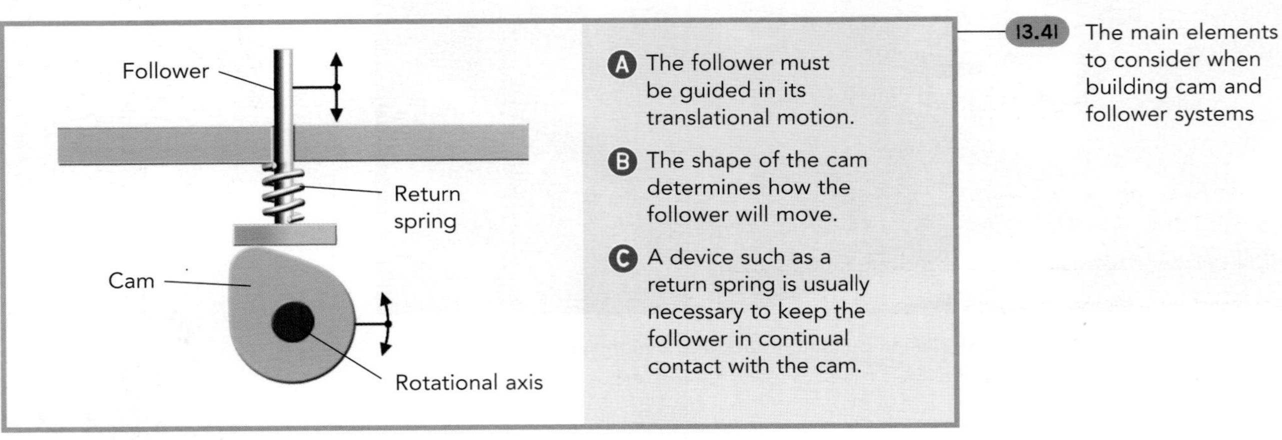

13.41 The main elements to consider when building cam and follower systems

Special cams called eccentrics are sometimes used in this type of system. Figure 13.42 shows that the rotational axis of cams is centred, while in eccentrics, the rotational axis is off-centre.

Eccentric comes from the Latin *eccentricus*, meaning "not having the same centre."

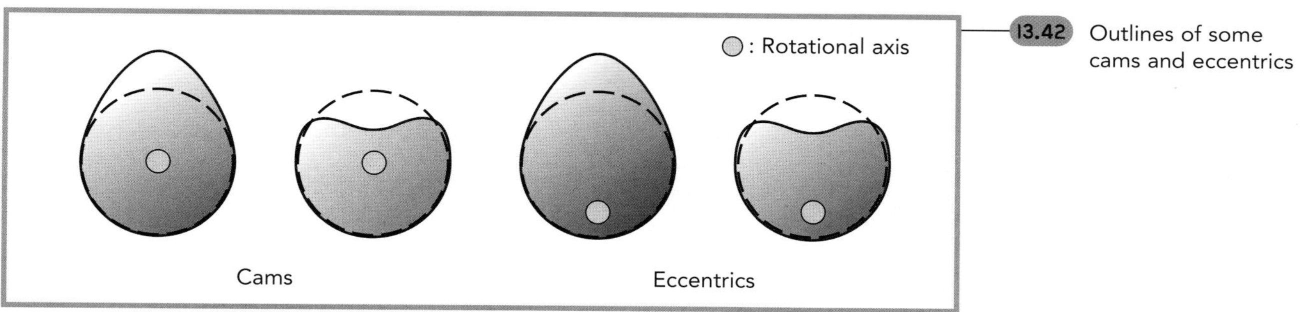

13.42 Outlines of some cams and eccentrics

ST EST AST

SLIDER-CRANK MECHANISMS

Slider-crank mechanisms are used in internal combustion engines, for example, to transform the translational motion of the pistons into the rotational motion of the crank, causing the wheels to turn. Figure 13.43 describes the main elements to consider when building slider-crank mechanisms.

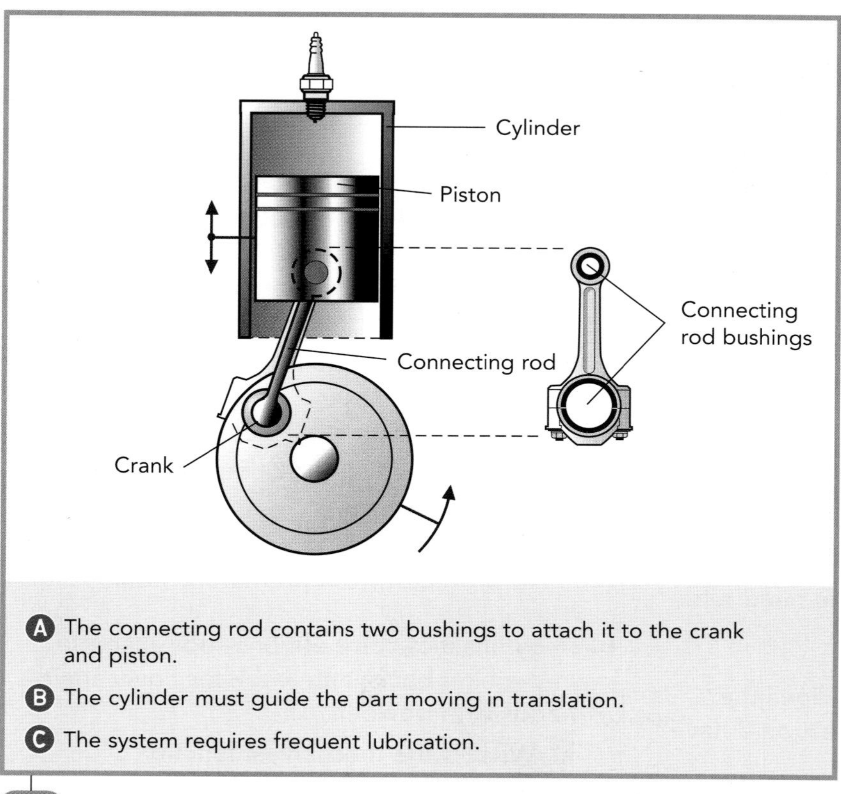

A The connecting rod contains two bushings to attach it to the crank and piston.

B The cylinder must guide the part moving in translation.

C The system requires frequent lubrication.

13.43 The main elements to consider when building slider-crank mechanisms

1858
1913

Rudolph Diesel

Diesel engines are among the technical objects that contain a slider-crank mechanism. The invention was named after German engineer Rudolph Diesel, who designed the first engine of this type, in which combustion occurs not by firing a spark plug but by compressing a mixture of air and vapourized oil.

CHECKUP

ST 1, 2, 4, 7–13, 15–17, A, C and E.
EST 1–13, 15–17 and A–E.
AST 1–17 and A–E.
SE None.

1 What is mechanical engineering? (p. 426)

1. Name the branch of science and technology that focuses specifically on the study of technical objects with moving parts.

2 Linking in technical objects (pp. 427–430)

2. Look at the bicycle below.

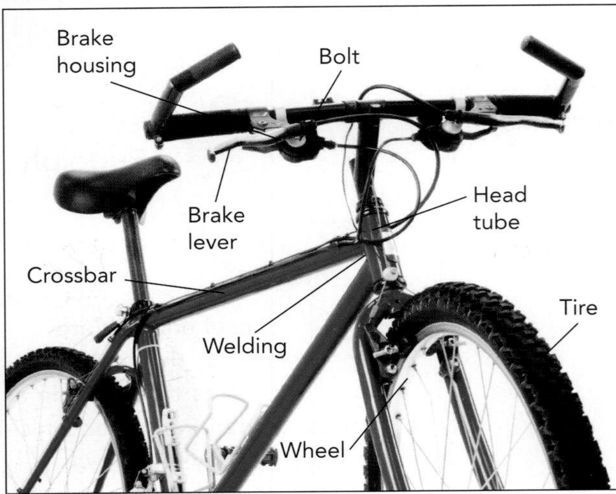

a) Name the four characteristics of the link between the tires and their respective wheels. Explain each characteristic.
b) Name the four characteristics of the link between the brake housing and lever. Explain each characteristic.
c) Name the characteristics of the link between the crossbar and the head tube. Explain each characteristic.

3. How many degrees of freedom does the front wheel of the bicycle in question 2 have? Explain your answer.

3 Guiding controls (pp. 431–435)

4. Look at the three objects below.

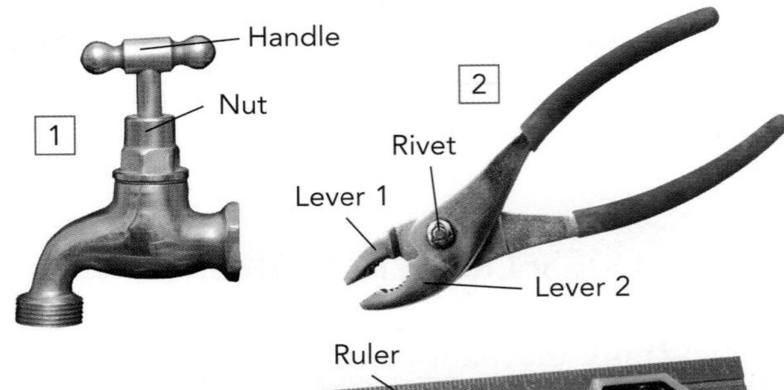

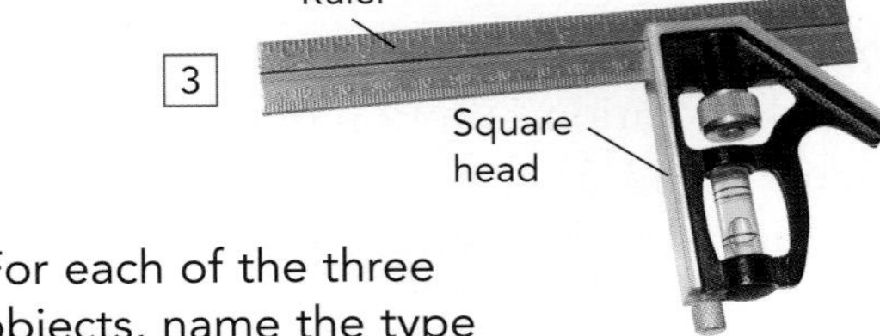

a) For each of the three objects, name the type of guiding involved.
b) Identify the guiding component in each object.

5. In each of the following statements, what factor causes the strength of the adhesion between two surfaces to vary?
   a) Nonslip stair treads are installed in a staircase to prevent accidents.
   b) Cross-country skis usually glide better in colder weather.
   c) To avoid injury, it is best not to wear leather-soled shoes when playing sports in a gym.
   d) Each spring, Yuri oils his bicycle chain to protect it from premature wear.

6. In gymnastics competitions—for example, in the high bar event—athletes cover their hands with powder.
   a) What is the mechanical function of the powder?
   b) How is the powder useful during this event?

4 Motion transmission systems (pp. 435–445)

7. The motion transmission system opposite is used to direct the chute of a snow blower.

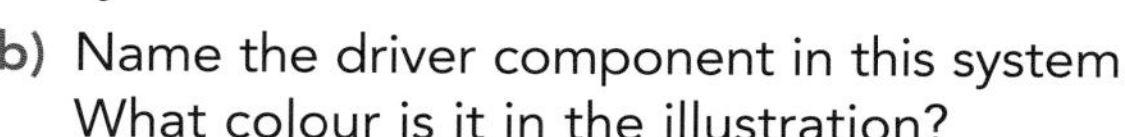

   a) What is this type of motion transmission system called?
   b) Name the driver component in this system. What colour is it in the illustration?
   c) Name the driven component in this system. What colour is it in the illustration?
   d) Does the system contain an intermediate component? If so, what is it called?
   e) If the snow blower user decides to turn the chute manually, the motion transmission system could be damaged. Explain why.

8. Antonia is asked to build a gear train using two of the gears illustrated below.
   a) Which gears should she choose for her system?
   b) Which characteristic of the gears would motivate her choice?

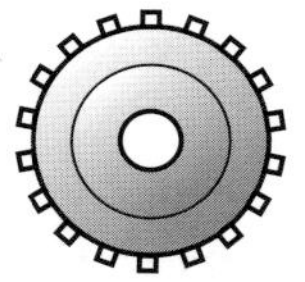

A

9. Among the motion transmission systems below, identify those whose rotational motions are correctly illustrated.

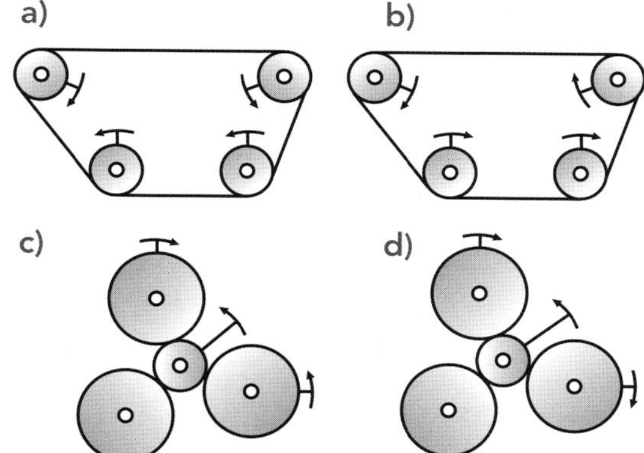

10. Look at the mechanism opposite.
    a) Which type of motion transmission system is used in this technical object?
    b) Which type of gear is used in this system?

11. Based on the information provided, calculate the ratio of the gear speeds for each of the motion transmission systems below.

a)

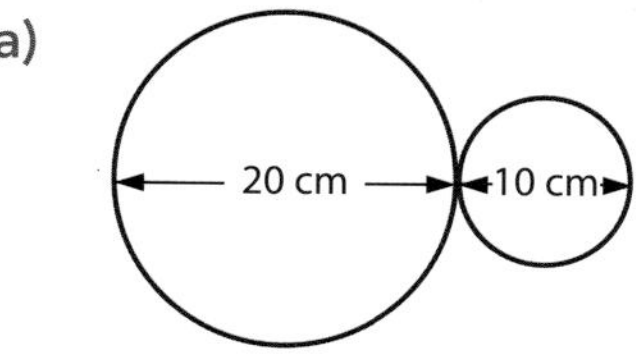

b)

20 cm

4 cm

12. Look at the two worm and worm gear systems below.

a) 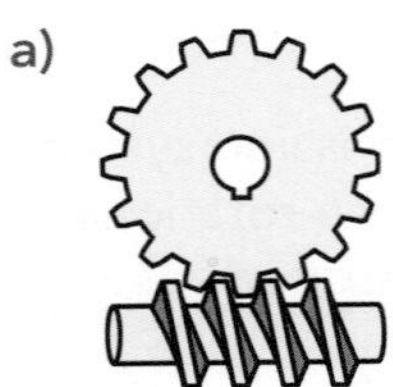

b) 

In which system will the rotational speed be more greatly reduced? Explain your answer.

13. In the chain and sprocket system below, the rotational speed of the driver sprocket is 60 revolutions per minute. Based on the information provided by the illustration, calculate the rotational speed of the other sprocket. Express your answer in revolutions per minute.

14. The object below is a hand drill. By turning the crank, a person can use the drill to bore holes.

a) What colour is the gear that receives the engine torque when the drill is used?

b) Given that steel is harder than spruce wood, will the resisting torque be stronger when drilling a hole in a piece of steel or in a piece of spruce? Explain your answer.

5 Motion transformation systems (pp. 445–449)

15. Look at the motion transformation system below.

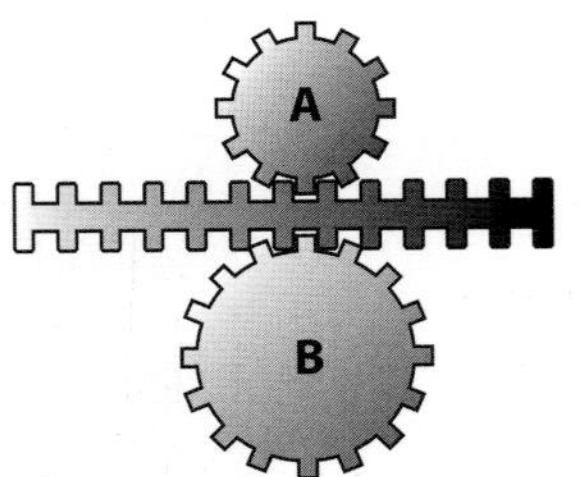

a) What is this type of motion transformation system called?

b) Which of the two gears will turn faster? Explain your answer.

16. A tensioner is used to tighten the wire or rope of a clothesline, as in the illustration below. Which type of motion transformation system is at work here?

17. Look at the motion transformation systems below.

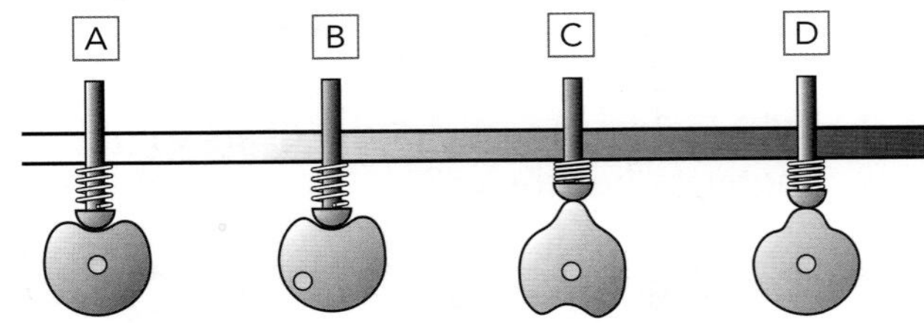

a) What are these motion transformation systems called?

b) Which of the four systems involves an eccentric? Explain your answer.

c) What does the spring do in these systems?

d) In which of the four systems will the rod rise the highest?

review questions

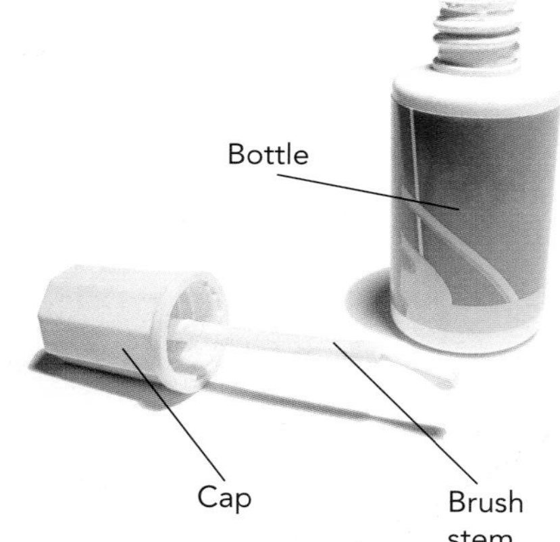

A. Look at the bottle of correction fluid opposite.

a) Name the characteristics of the link between the cap and the brush stem.

b) Name the characteristics of the link between the cap and the bottle.

c) Which part acts as a guiding control in this object?

d) Which type of guiding is involved?

e) What characteristic of the guiding component controls the guiding?

B. Referring to the correction fluid bottle in question A, how many degrees of freedom do the following parts have?

a) the cap when screwed on the bottle

b) the brush stem when attached to the cap

C. Glue sticks are among the most popular types of glue. In the tube, the glue stick is attached to a nut. Twisting the screw at the base of the tube will make the glue stick move up or down.

a) What is the usual mechanical function of glue in technical objects?

b) Which part guides the glue stick motion, and which type of guiding is involved?

c) Is the system for raising or lowering the glue stick a motion transmission system or a motion transformation system? Identify the type of system at work.

d) Name the four characteristics of the link between the cap and the tube.

D. Referring to the glue stick in question C, answer the following questions.

a) How many degrees of freedom does the nut in the tube have? Describe them.

b) How many degrees of freedom does the cap have when it is placed on the tube? Describe them.

c) Explain why it is important for there to be adhesion between glue and parts to be glued.

E. Prepare your own summary of Chapter 13 by building a concept map.

HYBRID CARS

In the 19th century, the invention of the automobile was welcomed as an important improvement to the human environment. Gone were the days of picking up piles of horse manure that stank, carried disease and posed a constant, disagreeable risk to unwary pedestrians. Barely 100 years later, we now realize that cars present an even greater environmental problem. The gases they emit contribute significantly to global warming. In Canada, transportation alone is responsible for approximately 25 percent of greenhouse gas (GHG) emissions, which increased by 27 percent between 1990 and 2004.

ALTERNATIVE FUELLING

By the end of the 20th century, automobile manufacturers were trying to find solutions to this problem. Most vehicles, such as cars, motorcycles and trucks, run on an internal combustion engine, which transforms the thermal energy released by fuel combustion into mechanical energy that drives the wheels. To reduce GHG emissions from motor vehicles, engineers turned to other energy sources. In hybrid cars, an electric motor takes over from the conventional combustion engine at certain times.

The first hybrid car appeared on the Japanese market in 1997, signalling a change in the automotive industry. From the low-performance, high-cost vehicles of their early days, hybrid cars have now become near-equals to their traditional counterparts, and engineers continue to improve the technology.

Different hybrid vehicles work in different ways, but they all make use of two power sources. At high speeds, on the highway, a hybrid car runs on its combustion engine. At the same time, it recharges the battery of the electric motor, recovering and storing the surplus energy. If the car accelerates abruptly, both engines work simultaneously, ensuring performance that is at least equal to that of a gas-powered car. The electric motor functions alone at speeds of 50 km/h or less and for starting and stopping. Hybrid cars are thus ideal for city driving, reducing GHG emissions by 50 percent, compared to a 10-percent reduction for highway driving.

RENEWABLE ENERGY FOR CARS

Despite government subsidies, hybrid cars are still expensive—more expensive than their conventional counterparts. Prices are expected to drop, but meanwhile the overall number of cars around the world is rapidly increasing. Experts predict that their number will have doubled by 2025, due primarily to massive industrialization in China. Eliminating GHG emissions from cars is an uphill struggle, and hybrid vehicles will not solve the problem completely. In addition, hybrid SUVs emit even more GHGs than small gas-powered cars, so another approach would be to reduce the size of vehicles. This, however, is not the current trend in North America.

Hybrid cars, especially compact ones, represent one solution to the ongoing problem of increasing pollution from transportation, which contributes significantly to global warming.

Many automobile manufacturers are presently studying the possibility of commercializing, by 2012, rechargeable hybrid models, which could travel up to 60 km on a single charge. The cars would be recharged at home overnight and ready to go back to work the next morning. Engineers hope one day to eliminate gas engines entirely and replace them with motors that run exclusively on renewable energy sources such as electricity.

1. Why is the mechanical energy from an electric motor considered "greener" than energy from a combustion engine? Give at least two reasons.
2. How can you counteract the harmful effects of combustion engines when you choose a means of transportation? Give several examples.

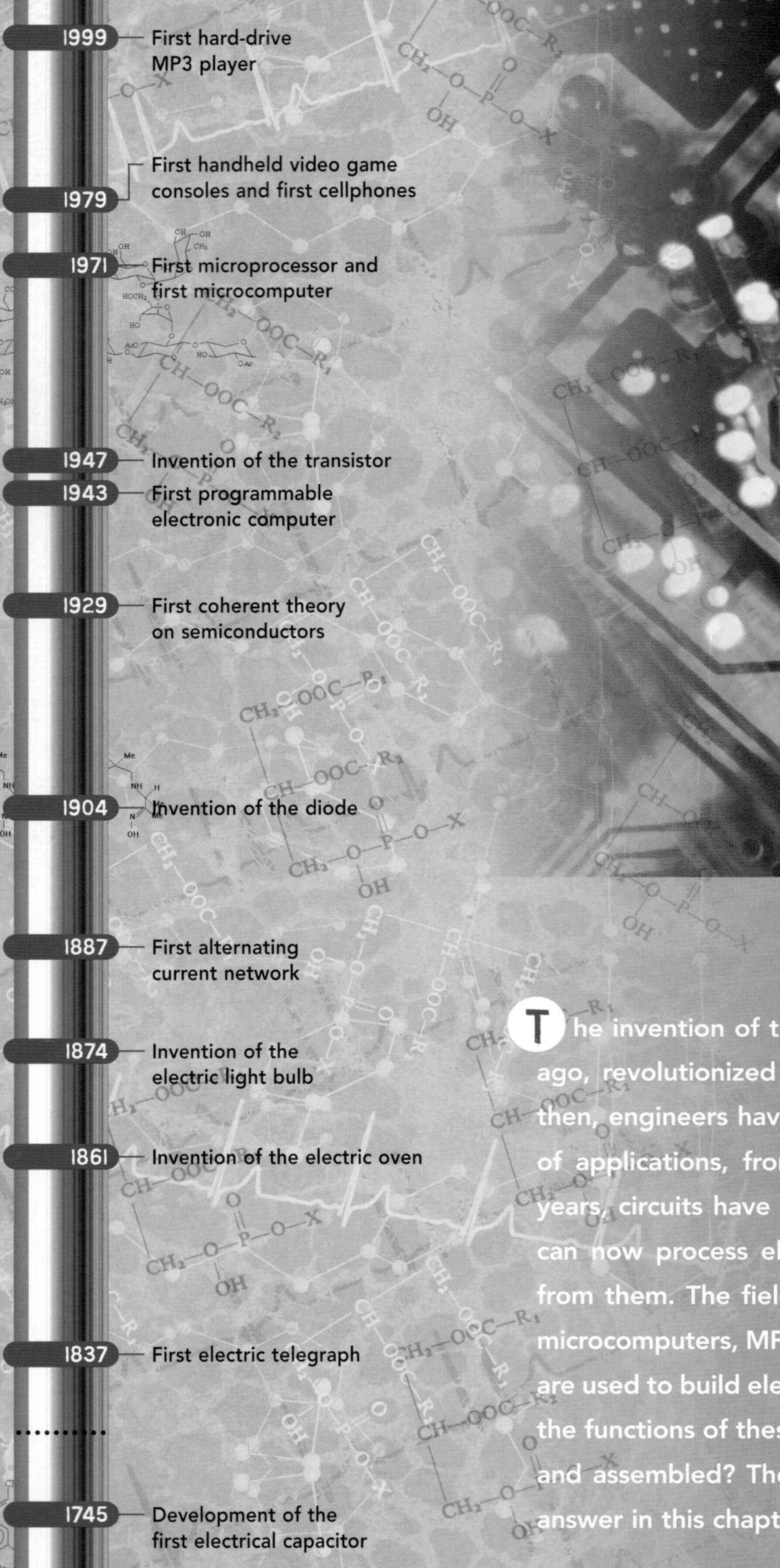

The invention of the electric light bulb, nearly 150 years ago, revolutionized the lifestyle of modern society. Since then, engineers have used electrical circuits in a multitude of applications, from toasters to refrigerators. Over the years, circuits have been perfected to the point that they can now process electrical signals to extract information from them. The field of electronics was born, bringing us microcomputers, MP3s and DVD players. What components are used to build electrical and electronic circuits? What are the functions of these components? How are they selected and assembled? These are some of the questions we will answer in this chapter.

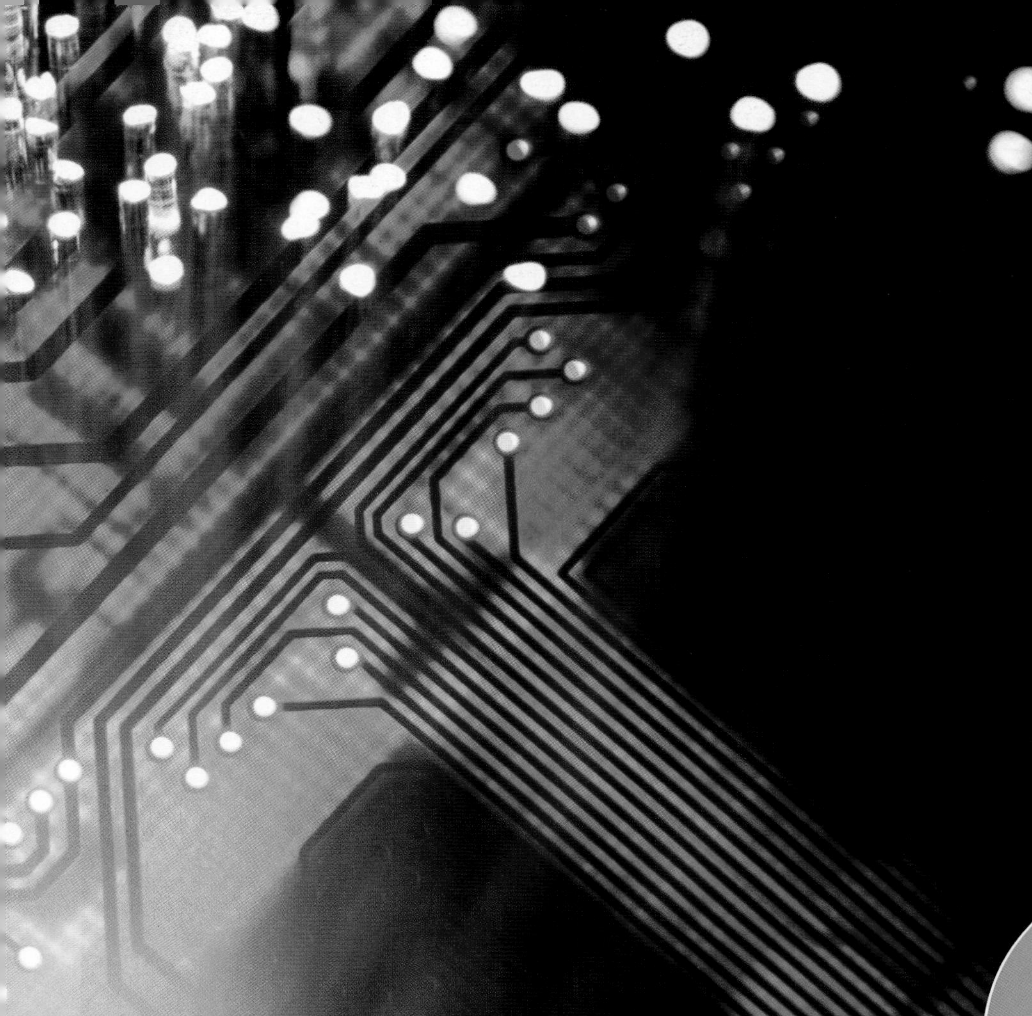

THE TECHNOLOGICAL WORLD

14

Electrical engineering

CONTENTS

ST EST AST 1 What is electrical engineering?

It would be difficult to imagine modern life without electricity. A power shortage of just a few hours shows us exactly how dependent we are on our electrical distribution system. Without electricity, our homes fall into cold darkness, and we lose our household appliances and electronic equipment, including televisions, cellphones and computers.

CONCEPT REVIEW
- Components of a system
- Standards and representations (diagrams, symbols)

Designing and developing all these objects, as well as electrical systems, is the work of electrical engineers. The science of electrical engineering covers a vast range of applications, from systems for producing, transporting and using electrical power to communications systems and avionics (aviation electronics).

Electrical engineering covers two main areas: electricity and electronics. The difference between the two is discussed in the next section.

14.1 Electrical engineering includes the design and development of power grids.

ST EST AST 1.1 ELECTRICITY AND ELECTRONICS

All electrical appliances (such as toasters) and electronic devices (such as computers) depend on **ELECTRICAL CIRCUITS**. The main difference between electricity and electronics lies in the design of the circuit components.

- Electronic components (diodes, transistors, etc.) are made with a particular type of material called a **SEMICONDUCTOR** (usually silicon). On the other hand, **CONDUCTORS**—metals and alloys (especially copper)—are generally used for electrical components.
- Electronic components are distinctive in their high degree of miniaturization and their low-intensity currents. Most electrical components are designed for more powerful circuits, such as electric motors.
- In electronics, electrical conduction can be more finely controlled than in electrical components, which makes it possible for electronic devices to process information.

Despite these important differences, electronic components nonetheless follow the general laws of electricity.

14.2 Installing an electrical circuit in a house belongs to the field of electricity.

14.3 Working on computer circuits belongs to the field of electronics.

ST EST AST 1.2 ELECTRICAL CIRCUITS

An electrical (or electronic) circuit consists of a simple or complex set of conductors and components carrying an **ELECTRIC CURRENT**. Figure 14.4 presents an example of an electrical circuit. As the illustration shows, the **CONVENTIONAL CURRENT DIRECTION** flows from the positive terminal of the power supply to the negative terminal. In fact, the electrons move in the opposite direction (see page 150).

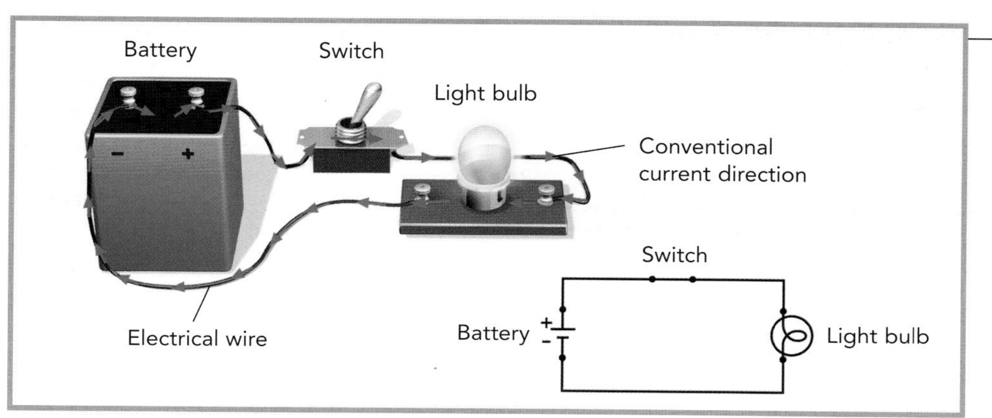

14.4 Example of an electrical circuit (on the left) and its corresponding diagram (on the right)

Figure 14.4 (page 459) also shows the diagram for the illustrated circuit. The role of circuit diagrams in electricity is much like that of scores in music. They are symbolic representations showing how different components fit together to form a whole. Conventional symbols are used to represent the components. Table 14.5 contains some of the symbols for circuit components.

14.5 SYMBOLS FOR CIRCUIT COMPONENTS

Name	Symbol	Name	Symbol
Source of direct current		Protective device (fuse, breaker)	
Source of alternating current		Resistance or electrical appliance	or
Battery	− +	Light bulb	or or
Photoelectric cell		Capacitor	
Switch		Diode	
Electrical outlet		Light-emitting diode (LED)	
Electrical wire		Transistor	

ST EST AST

DIRECT CURRENT AND ALTERNATING CURRENT

Electric current can be described as *direct* or *alternating* depending on the way **ELECTRONS** flow through the circuit.

In direct current (DC), the electrons move continuously in the same direction. A battery is one example of a source of direct current.

> **DIRECT CURRENT is an electric current in which the electrons are continuously moving in the same direction.**

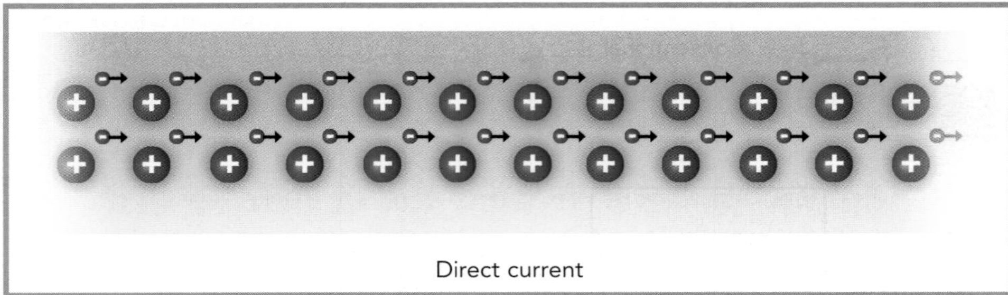

Direct current

14.6 In direct current, the electrons move in only one direction.

CONTACT LENSES OF THE FUTURE

A team of researchers at the University of Washington has successfully implanted an electrical circuit into a contact lens, a technology that might eventually let users see data while leaving their regular vision unchanged.

The device might enable drivers to see their speed, video gamers to get even more involved with their virtual worlds and other people to surf the web on a midair virtual display screen that only they would be able to see. The device might even be used to correct vision defects. Wireless communication through the lens is also a possibility, although it is only at the prototype stage.

The lens does not obstruct the wearer's view because there is a large area outside the transparent part of the eye, where instrumentation could be placed.

A full-fledged display will not be available soon, but a basic lens with a few pixels could be operational "fairly quickly," according to Babak Parviz, an electrical engineering professor who heads the group. The researchers tested a lens—an electrical circuit and a diode that emits red light for displays—on rabbits for 20 minutes without problems.

Source: Adapted from "A circuit for the eye," *CBC News* [online], January 18, 2008. (Accessed January 28, 2009.)

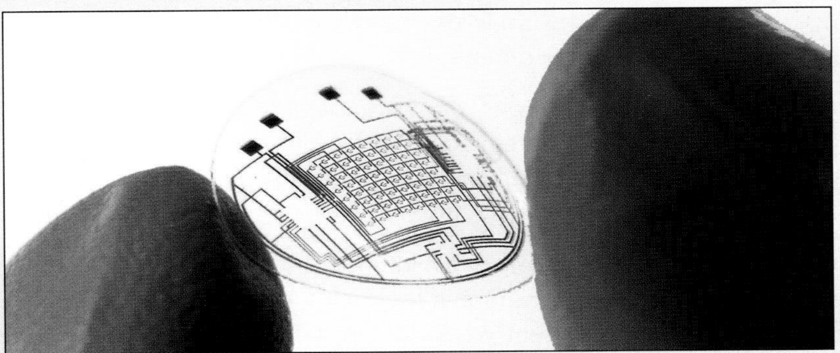

In the future, contact lenses might contain integrated electrical circuits.

In alternating current (AC), the electrons change direction many times per second. Power plants generate alternating current. In North America, the frequency of this current is 60 Hz (hertz), which means that the electrons move back and forth 60 times per second.

ALTERNATING CURRENT is an electric current in which the electrons move back and forth in a regular pattern.

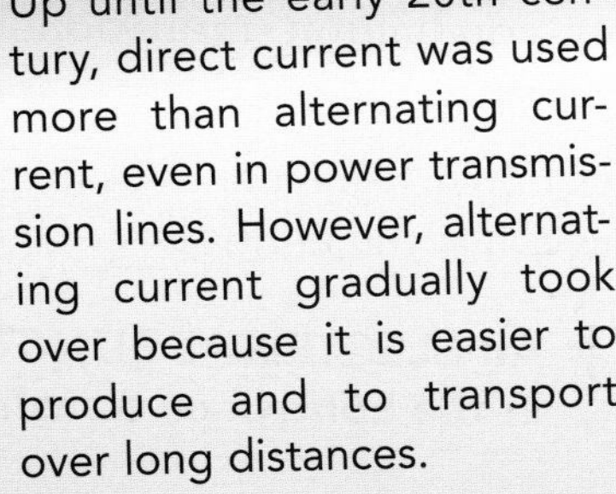

ELECTRICAL TAKEOVER

Up until the early 20th century, direct current was used more than alternating current, even in power transmission lines. However, alternating current gradually took over because it is easier to produce and to transport over long distances.

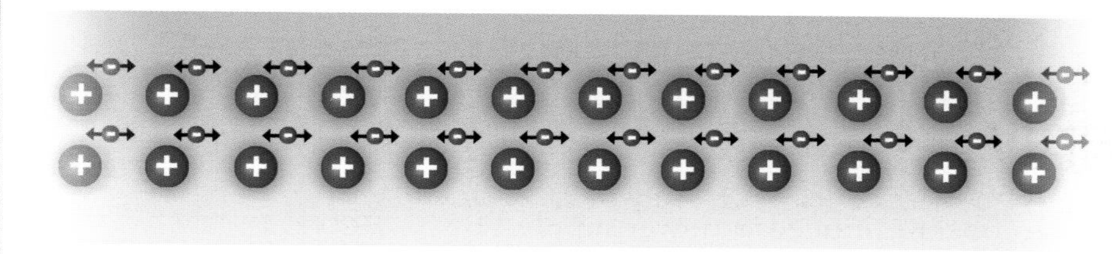

Alternating current

14.7 In alternating current, the electrons move back and forth.

ENVIRONMENT EXTRA

Biologists and electrical engineers team up for the environment

Biologists and electrical engineers have come up with an original way to measure the toxicity of pollutants in natural waters.

In this method, bacteria of the species *Vibrio fischeri* are added to a sample from the affected body of water. These bacteria are luminescent, which means they have the ability to emit light. When they are immersed in a toxic environment, however, this light becomes dimmer.

To measure the level of light, the water sample is placed in a device containing a light-sensitive diode (an electronic component). The diode is connected to an electrical circuit.

When the diode is exposed to intense light, it induces a strong electric current in the circuit. When the light is low, the current weakens. An ammeter inserted into the circuit measures the current intensity. This measurement is then converted to a corresponding toxicity value.

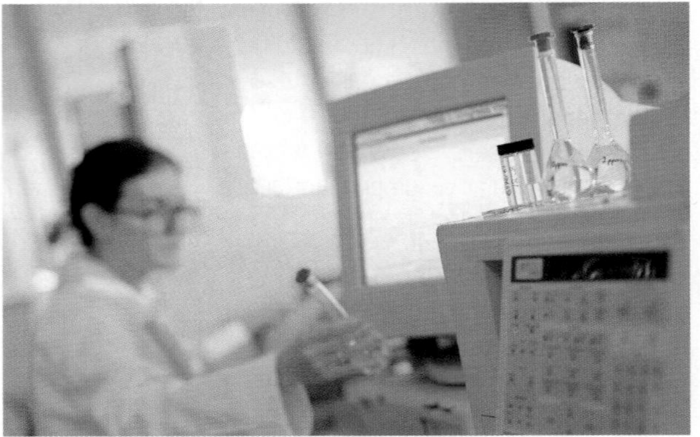

Electronic devices can be used to discover the level of toxicity of natural waters by measuring the luminescence of certain aquatic bacteria.

1.3 ELECTRICAL FUNCTIONS

An electrical or electronic circuit is made up of components that all have a specific function. Components may thus serve purposes such as power supply, conduction, insulation, protection, control or the transformation of energy.

For example, in Figure 14.4 (page 459), the battery is the power supply, and the switch is the control.

An ELECTRICAL FUNCTION is the role that a component plays in the control or transformation of electric current.

The following sections in this chapter will deal with various electrical functions and some of the components that play these roles in circuits.

2 Power supply

For an electrical or electronic circuit to operate, it needs a power supply. The power supply provides the energy that makes a current flow through the wires and components of the circuit. Figure 14.8 (page 463) presents some examples of electrical power supplies.

Power supply (AST)

POWER SUPPLY is the electrical function performed by any component that can generate or provide an electric current in a circuit.

BATTERY

The battery (technically, an electrochemical cell) is a device that transforms the energy from a chemical reaction into electrical energy.

ADVANTAGES AND DISADVANTAGES

Appliances that run on batteries are portable, but the batteries must be replaced after a certain time. When people throw out used batteries, the cells can contaminate the environment around the landfill by leaking heavy metals.

EXAMPLES OF APPLICATIONS

MP3 players, watches, remote controls

ELECTRICAL OUTLET

An outlet is designed to receive the prongs of an electric plug. The outlet contains contacts and is permanently connected to an electrical network.

ADVANTAGES AND DISADVANTAGES

Appliances that are plugged into a wall outlet have the advantage of a stable and long-lasting power supply. In Québec, where electricity is supplied mainly by hydroelectric dams, power generation creates very little greenhouse gas, although it does cause flooding of vast areas of land. On the other hand, the appliances cannot be moved far from the wall outlet, and they stop working in the event of a power shortage.

EXAMPLES OF APPLICATIONS

Televisions, refrigerators, computers

PHOTOVOLTAIC CELL

The photovoltaic cell (often called a *solar cell*) is an electronic device that generates an electric current when exposed to light.

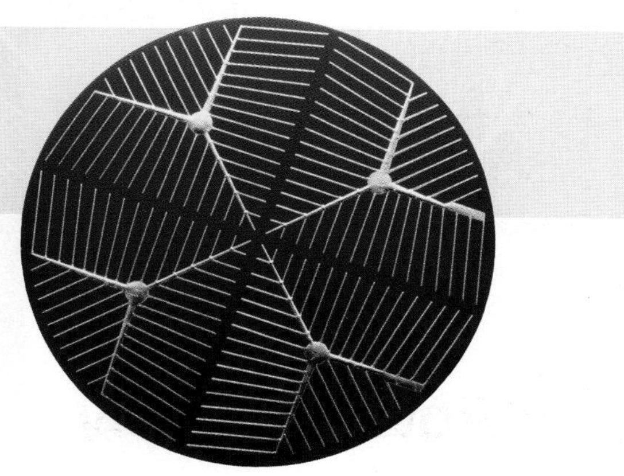

ADVANTAGES AND DISADVANTAGES

Solar cells can power equipment in isolated areas without access to the power grid. They can also power portable or mobile devices and machines, such as calculators and cars. They do not cause greenhouse gas emissions and have a life span of 20 to 30 years. However, their operation depends on sunny conditions. They are also much more expensive to install than other sources of power.

EXAMPLES OF APPLICATIONS

Solar homes, calculators, solar cars

14.8 A few examples of power supplies

ST EST AST

3 Conduction, insulation and protection

Electric current travels from the power supply through wires. This movement is called *conduction*. The wiring must be insulated with nonconductive material to avoid accidents such as electric shocks and **SHORT CIRCUITS**. Protective devices such as fuses are also often added to circuits. In the following sections, we will take a closer look at conduction, insulation and the protection of electrical circuits.

CONCEPT REVIEW
- Conduction, insulation and protection (AST)

ST EST AST

3.1 CONDUCTION

Electricity is conducted primarily through wiring. The wires carry the electrons, which form the electric current, throughout the circuit. Wiring is made of conductive material, usually copper.

Components other than wires can also act as conductors. For example, a current can pass between two pieces of metal that come into contact. The human body can also conduct electricity, which is why people must be careful when working with electrical circuits.

CONDUCTION is the electrical function performed by any component that can transmit electric current from one part of a circuit to another.

COPPER: STILL USEFUL AFTER ALL THESE YEARS

Copper is an exceptionally good conductor of electricity. Since the invention of the telephone, it is the material of choice for communication networks. Although it is now being replaced with optical fibres for some applications, copper is still the preferred material for manufacturing underground cables. 19

14.9 Copper is the most commonly used metal for making electrical wires.

EST AST

PRINTED CIRCUITS

Since the dawn of the electronic era, engineers have been locked in a race for ever greater miniaturization. Thick copper wires wrapped in rubber and connected to switches are not suitable for cellphones, MP3 players and portable video game consoles. The wires have been replaced by printed circuits.

A printed circuit is essentially a board about one millimetre thick, often made of plastic and covered with a thin layer of copper. The circuit board is etched, and then the excess copper is leached (removed through dissolution), leaving only the electrical circuit printed on the board. Small holes are then drilled in the board to solder on the electric and electronic components the circuit needs to operate.

A PRINTED CIRCUIT is an electrical circuit printed on a solid support called a *circuit board*.

The latest boards can carry several layers of circuits, separated by an insulating material.

14.10 Nearly all electronic devices are built with printed circuits.

WIRELESS RECHARGING FOR WIRELESS PHONES

After wireless remote control devices, wireless phones and wireless computers, will we soon see wireless battery chargers? Researchers say that we will.

For more than 200 years, scientists have known that contact between systems is not necessary for energy to be transferred from one system to another. For example, a current in one coil can induce a current in a second coil even without contact between the two.

Of course, these wireless transfers take place over very short distances—a few millimetres at most. Researchers are working on a similar system that would work over longer distances. This new system would make use of the energy from electromagnetic waves that would be perceptible to the target device only.

The present trend is toward wireless electronic devices.

ST
EST
AST

3.2 INSULATION

Since the human body is a good conductor of electricity, we try to prevent shocks by covering wires with an insulating material such as plastic. **INSULATORS** are poor conductors, so they prevent electrons from leaving the wires. This not only protects people but also avoids short circuits by preventing wires from coming in contact with one another.

Other components, such as ceramic and plastic housings, may also isolate electrical circuits from their surroundings.

- **INSULATION is the electrical function performed by any component that prevents an electric current from flowing.**

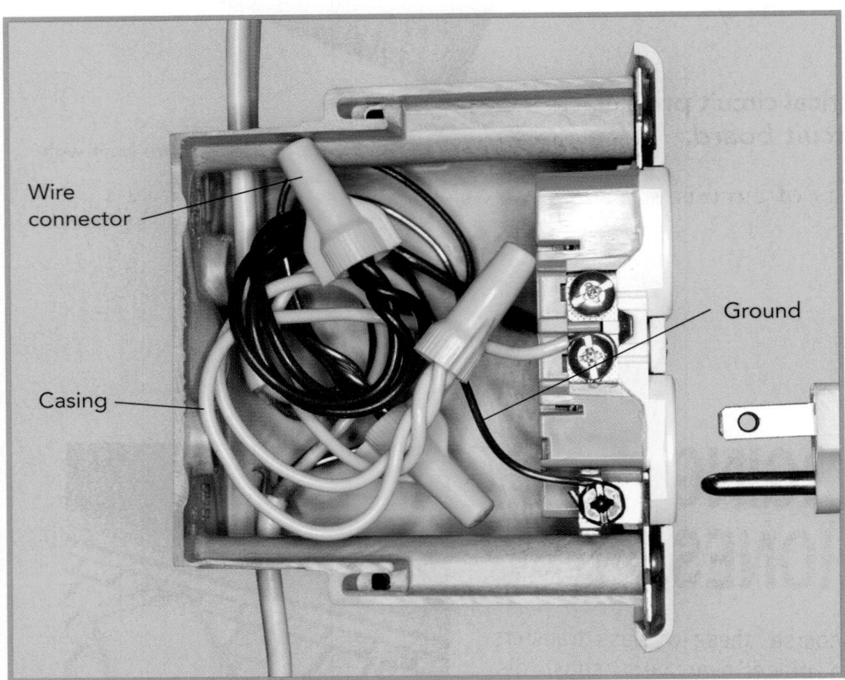

14.11 Inside this electrical outlet, all the wires are insulated with casings or connectors. The ground wire is not insulated because it is a safety device that does not usually carry a current.

1683
1744

Jean Théophile Désaguliers

Born in France and raised in England, Jean Théophile Désaguliers made a name for himself with his scientific research, especially in the field of electricity. He was the first scientist to use the terms *conductors* and *insulators* to distinguish between materials that conduct electricity and those that do not.

ST
EST
AST

3.3 PROTECTION

An electrical circuit may malfunction: a short circuit or an overload (when too many appliances are plugged into one outlet, for example) may occur. To avoid serious accidents (fires or electric shocks), protective devices, such as fuses or circuit breakers, can be connected to the electrical circuit.

PROTECTION is the electrical function performed by any component that can automatically cut current flow in the event of a power surge.

Figure 14.12 describes how fuses and breakers work.

Fuse comes from the Latin verb *fundere*, meaning "pour" or "melt."

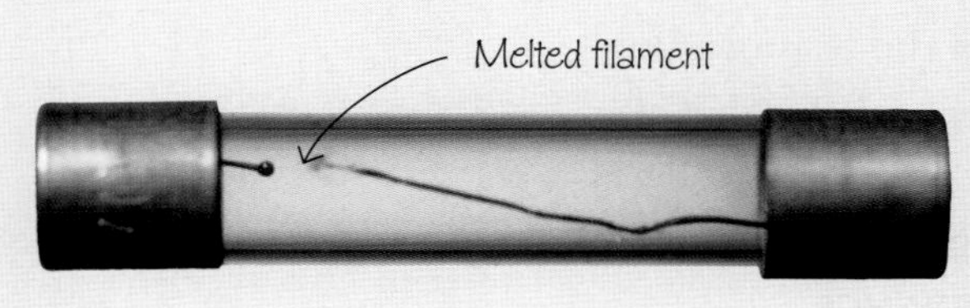

FUSES

When a circuit is functioning normally, the electric current crosses the fuse through a conductive filament.
If the current intensity exceeds a certain level, the filament melts and breaks, preventing the current from flowing through the fuse. Once a fuse has blown, it must be replaced.

BREAKERS

A breaker is a protective device that can be reset as many times as necessary. In some breakers, the current passes through a bimetallic strip. When the current intensity exceeds a certain level, the strip becomes hot, it bends, and the connection is broken. A switch is thrown to restore circuit operation. Other breakers use an electromagnetic mechanism.

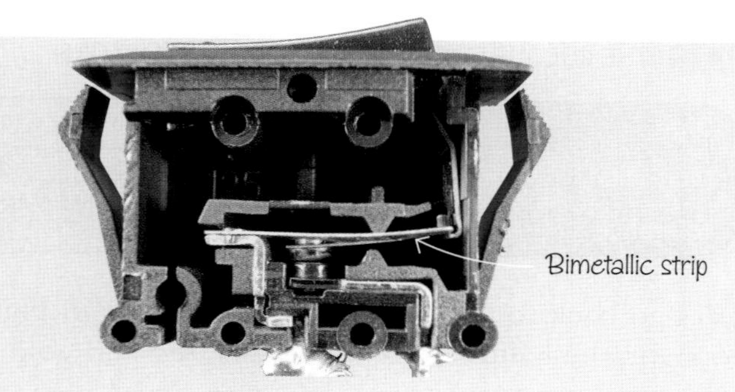

14.12 Protective devices

EST AST 3.4 ELECTRICAL RESISTANCE

A resistor is a component that limits the flow of electrons in an electrical circuit. It acts like a small-diameter pipe in a water supply system. Even if a pump can inject a large volume of water into the system, the water flow will be restricted by the size of the small pipe. Resistors function in a similar way, by hindering the flow of electrons through a circuit.

A RESISTOR is a component designed to limit the flow of electrons through an electrical circuit.

Resistors do not all have the same limiting capacity; some control electron flow more than others. Electrical resistance is expressed in ohms (see page 153), represented by the Greek letter omega (Ω).

Resistance is usually indicated with a colour code. Four coloured bands appear on the resistor, as shown in Figure 14.13 (page 468).

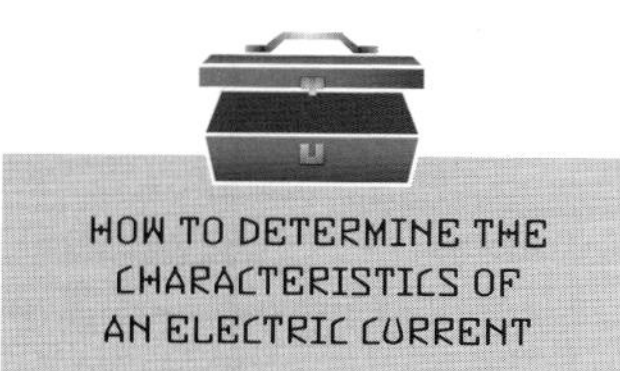

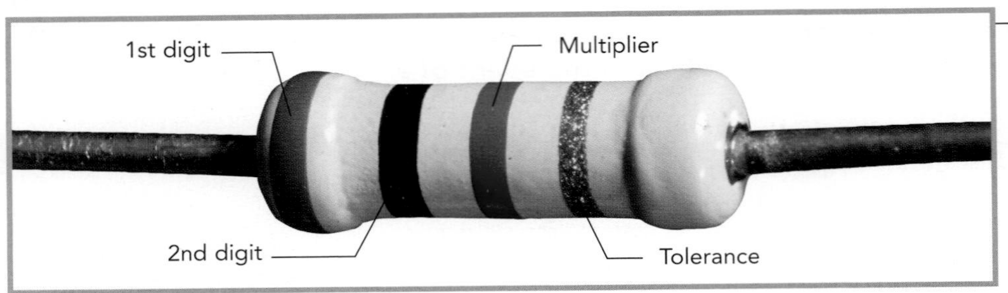

14.13 Electrical resistance is indicated with a colour code.

- The colour of the first band corresponds to the first digit of the resistor value.
- The colour of the second band corresponds to the second digit of the resistor value.
- The colour of the third band corresponds to the multiplier.
- The colour of the fourth band corresponds to the **TOLERANCE**.

Table 14.14 shows the value for each colour.

14.14 THE COLOUR CODE FOR ELECTRICAL RESISTORS

Digit	0	1	2	3	4	5	6	7	8	9	Gold	Silver
Multiplier	1	10	10^2	10^3	10^4	10^5	10^6	10^7	10^8	10^9		
Tolerance	± 20%										± 5%	± 10%

Let's go back to the example of the resistor in Figure 14.13 above. From left to right, the bands are brown, black, red and gold.

- The brown band corresponds to the number 1, and the black, to 0. Together, they indicate a value of 10.
- The red band corresponds to a multiplier of 10^2. The resistor thus has a value of 10 x 100, or 1000 Ω.
- The last band, which is gold, corresponds to a tolerance factor of 5%. In fact, the value of a resistor is not 100-percent precise. In this case, its value is 1000 Ω ± 5%, which means that it falls somewhere between 950 Ω and 1050 Ω.

In an electrical circuit like the one in Figure 14.15 below, the required current intensity may vary from one section to another. The resistors control the current intensity in different parts of the circuit. They also protect the more sensitive elements of the circuit by limiting the current that flows through those components.

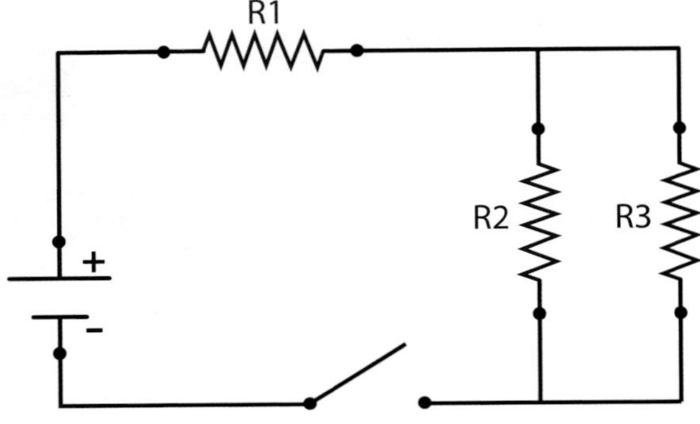

14.15 This circuit contains several resistors with different values (R1, R2 and R3).

ST
EST
AST

4 Control

CONCEPT REVIEW

Typical controls (lever, push button, flip-flop, magnetic controller) (AST)

For electric current to flow through a circuit, the circuit must form a closed loop. The electrons can then travel throughout the entire circuit. Figure 14.16 shows a closed circuit.

A CLOSED CIRCUIT is a circuit in which electric current flows in a loop.

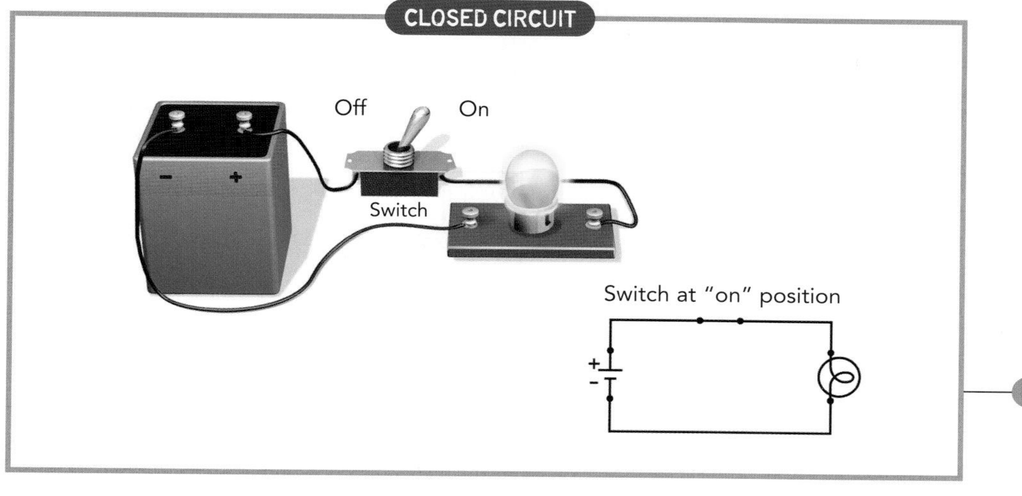

14.16 When the circuit is closed, the current can flow. Here, the light bulb is on.

When the loop is not complete, the circuit is open. In this case, the electric current cannot flow through the entire circuit, as in Figure 14.17.

An OPEN CIRCUIT is a circuit in which electric current cannot flow in a loop.

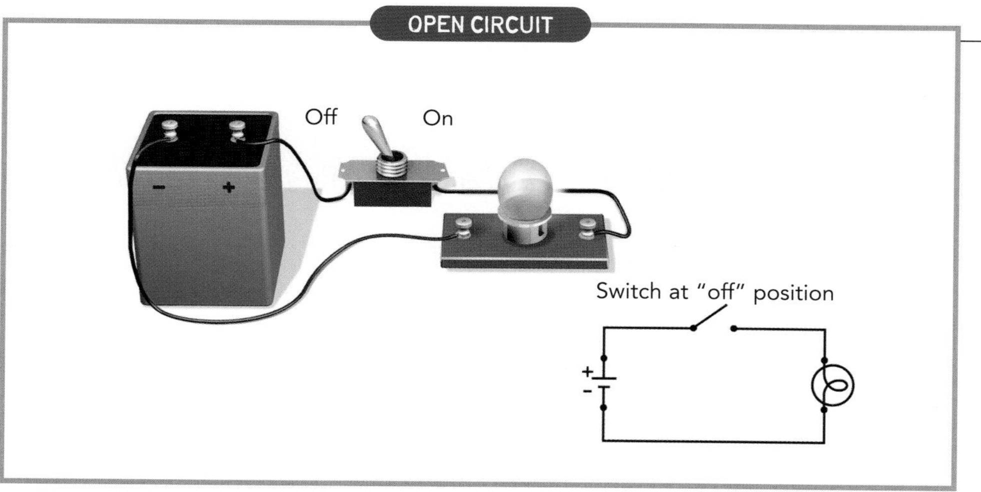

14.17 When the circuit is open, the current cannot flow. Here, the light is off.

With a control component, we can open and close a circuit as we wish. In the examples above, the control depends on a switch.

CONTROL is the electrical function performed by any component that can open and close a circuit.

EST AST 4.1 TYPES OF SWITCHES

There are several types of switches. For example, the switch in Figure 14.16 (page 469) is a single-pole, single-throw switch. Let's take a closer look at what this means.

- The term *single-pole* means that the switch opens or closes one contact at a time. Some switches are double-pole and so can open or close two contacts at once. For example, if the "on" position in Figure 14.16 allowed current to flow in two different circuits, the switch would be double-pole.
- In certain circuits, the electrons can follow only one path. In this case, the switch is said to be *single-throw*.
- In more complex circuits, where the electrons may follow one of two distinct paths, a double-throw switch is called for. The position of a double-throw switch determines the path that the electrons will take. Figure 14.18 illustrates this type of circuit: a double-throw switch directs the current to light bulb 1 or light bulb 2, depending on the switch position.

Table 14.19 presents the different types of switches.

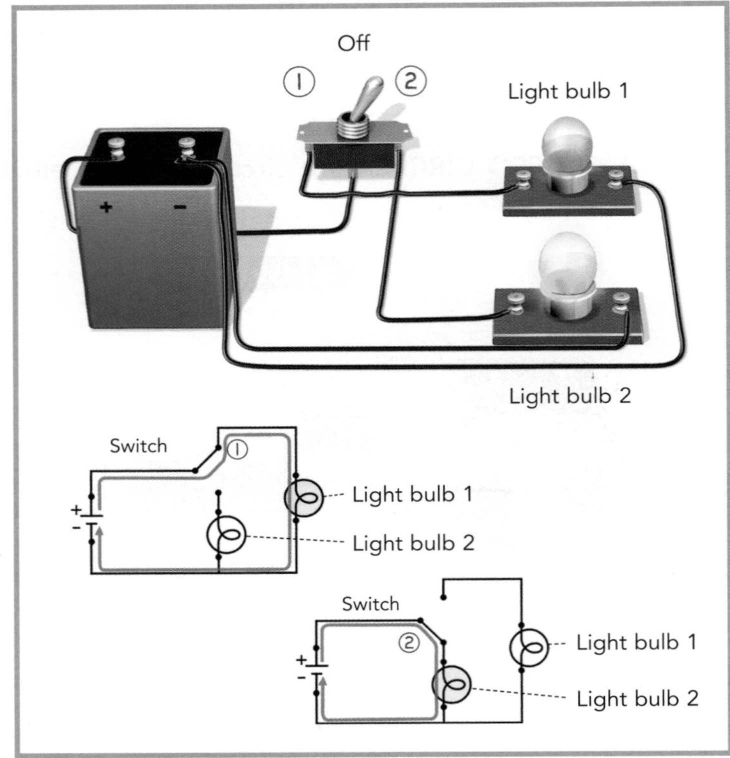

14.18 Depending on the position of this single-pole, double-throw switch, the electrons can take either path 1 to lightbulb 1 or path 2 to lightbulb 2, but only one contact can be made at a time.

14.19 DIFFERENT TYPES OF SWITCHES

Switch	Number of contacts that are opened or closed at a time	Number of possible paths for the electrons	Diagram	Example
Single-pole, single-throw	1	1		Figure 14.16
Single-pole, double-throw	1	2		Figure 14.18
Double-pole, single-throw	2	1		Figure 14.16, but with 2 circuits
Double-pole, double-throw	2	2		Figure 14.18, but with 2 circuits per position (1 or 2) of the switch

Rocker switch

Toggle switch

Push-button switch

14.20 Different types of switches

Magnetic contact switch

Switches can take many different forms. The most common type of switch is the rocker switch. The toggle switch and the push-button switch are also popular. By changing the position on any one of these three types of switches, a contact is made or broken, closing or opening the electrical circuit.

The magnetic contact switch is less common but still frequently used in alarm systems, to detect an open door, for example. A magnet in the mechanism keeps the system armed. When the door opens, the magnet is pulled away from the other part of the switch, which sets off the alarm.

The transformation of energy

CONCEPT REVIEW
- Energy transformations
- Forms of energy (chemical, thermal, mechanical, radiation)

Many electrical circuits convert electrical energy into another form of energy for human use. In this way, we obtain luminous energy (light), thermal energy (heat) or mechanical energy.

> **The TRANSFORMATION OF ENERGY is the electrical function performed by any component that can convert electrical energy into another form of energy.**

Figure 14.21 (page 472) presents some examples of electrical components that are used to transform electrical energy.

INCANDESCENT LIGHT BULBS

The electrons that make their way to the light bulb must flow through a tungsten filament. The filament resists the current, heating up to the point of emitting white light.

FORM OF ENERGY OBTAINED	EXAMPLES OF APPLICATIONS
Luminous energy	Flashlights, ceiling lamps

HEATING ELEMENTS

As in light bulbs, the electrons must pass through a material that resists the current. The material warms up, converting the electrical energy into heat.

FORM OF ENERGY OBTAINED	EXAMPLES OF APPLICATIONS
Thermal energy	Ovens, kettles

PIEZOELECTRIC CRYSTALS

When an electric current is applied to a piezoelectric crystal, the crystal starts to vibrate.

FORM OF ENERGY OBTAINED	EXAMPLES OF APPLICATIONS
Mechanical energy or sound energy (vibrations)	Quartz watches, speakers

ELECTROMAGNETS

The electrons flow through a coil of electrical wire wrapped around an iron core. The current flow gives the iron a magnetic charge, creating a magnetic field.

FORM OF ENERGY OBTAINED	EXAMPLES OF APPLICATIONS
Magnetic energy	Tape recorders, equipment for sorting scrap metal

14.21 Electrical components used to transform energy

EST AST

6 Components with other functions

Electrical and electronic circuits contain components that enable them to perform other functions than those described in the previous pages. The next section presents some of these components.

EST AST 6.1 CAPACITORS

After resistors, capacitors are the second most common component in electronic circuits. Their role is similar to that of hydroelectric reservoirs: they store electrical energy. This ability to store energy is called *capacitance*. It is expressed in farads, represented by the letter *F*.

Capacitor comes from the Latin *capax*, meaning "spacious."

A capacitor is made up of two metal plates placed close to each other. The plates are separated by an insulating material, called the *dielectric,* which blocks the flow of electrons. The dielectric is made of ceramic, mica, plastic or even air.

A CAPACITOR is a device composed of two electrical surfaces separated by an insulating material. The device can store an electrical charge.

ELECTRICAL MIXUP

A battery (electrochemical cell) cannot be recharged. The object we commonly call a *rechargeable battery* should be called an *accumulator*. A battery such as a car battery actually unites several components of the same type (accumulators, electric cells, capacitors, etc).

When a power supply is connected to a capacitor, electrical charges accumulate on the metal plates. For example, let's look at Figure 14.22, which shows a simple electrical circuit made up of a battery and a capacitor. The plate on the left is connected to the negative terminal of the battery; it accepts electrons from the battery and becomes negatively charged. The plate on the right is connected to the positive terminal of the battery; it loses electrons, which are attracted to the battery. The plate thus becomes positively charged.

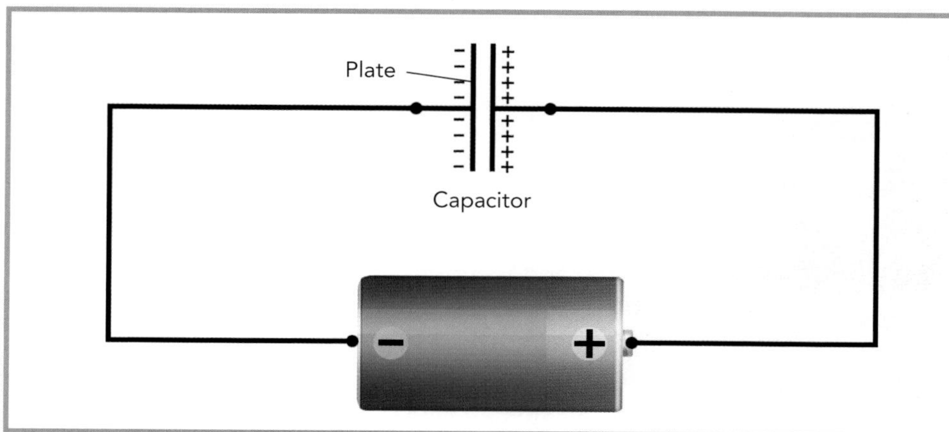

14.22 Electrical charges accumulate on the capacitor plates.

The electrons that accumulate on the plate to the left cannot move: they are strongly attracted to the plate on the right, but the insulator blocks the way. As soon as this obstacle is removed, an electrical discharge occurs.

While a battery is gradually emptied of its energy, a capacitor can release its stored charge almost instantly. It can thus provide a strong charge in a short period of time. In a camera flash, for example, a battery recharges the flash capacitor until an indicator lights up. When the photographer presses the shutter button to take a picture, the capacitor releases its full charge to the flash in a fraction of a second, producing a bright light.

Capacitors have other applications, such as stabilizing a fluctuating power supply. The capacitors release their charges when the power voltage drops and recharge when the voltage increases again.

14.23 One of the many forms of capacitors

EST AST 6.2 DIODES

A diode is a small device that, when inserted into an electrical circuit, allows the current to flow in one direction but not the other. It can be compared to a turnstile at the entrance to a subway station or department store: a person can either enter or exit through the turnstile but cannot do both. A diode is made of a semiconductor, usually silicon.

A DIODE is a device that allows electric current to flow in only one direction.

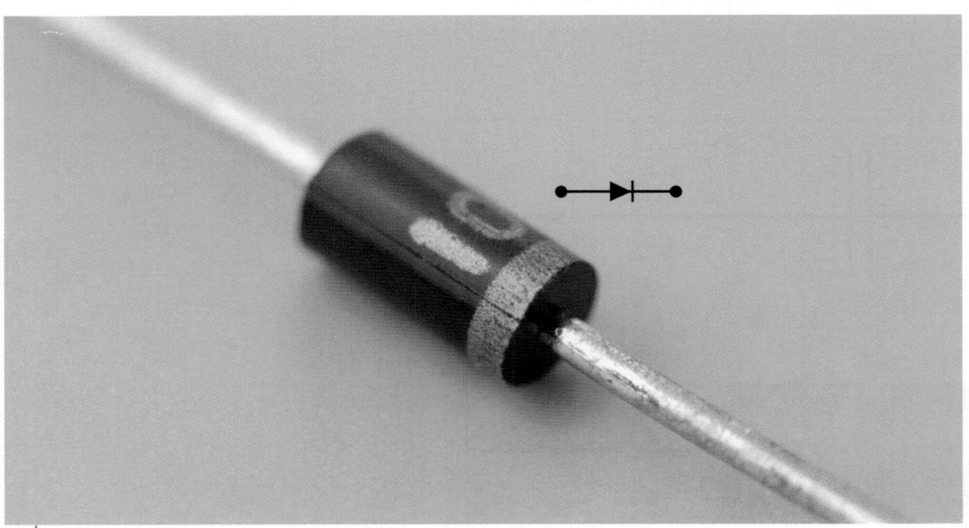

14.24 A diode and its electrical symbol. The arrow in the symbol shows that the current flows in only one direction.

There are many types of diodes. In a circuit, some diodes guide and block the current. Battery-operated electronic devices, such as television remote controls, all contain diodes. They prevent the electrons from moving when the user installs the battery upside down. They thus protect the fragile electronic parts inside the circuit.

Other diodes are used for rectification, which is the conversion of alternating current into direct current. Since they accept only those electrons that are flowing in one direction, the diodes prevent any back-and-forth movement.

Diodes may also be electroluminescent. These light-emitting diodes (LEDs) give off light when a current flows through them. They consume less energy than light bulbs do and are used increasingly in lighting systems.

Electroluminescent comes from the prefix *electro-*, meaning "relating to electricity," and the Latin word *lumen*, meaning "light."

1849
1945

John Ambrose Fleming

In 1904, this British physicist and electrical engineer invented and patented the first diode. It was nicknamed the "Fleming valve." The invention is commonly considered the starting point of electronics.

14.25 Light-emitting diodes (LEDs)

LET THERE BE LIGHT!

Before the year 2000, LEDs were mostly used for indicator lights on electrical appliances. In recent years, more powerful LEDs have been developed. According to researchers, LEDs could replace incandescent bulbs and fluorescent tubes in the future.

AST 6.3 TRANSISTORS

A transistor is a small semiconductor device (often made of silicon) widely used in electronic circuits. It works in two different ways: it can act as a switch, blocking the current, or it can alter the current, usually by amplifying it.

Transistor is a blend of the words *transfer* and *resistor*.

A TRANSISTOR is an electronic device used to block or amplify an electric current.

The operation of a transistor depends on three essential parts (Figure 14.27): the collector, the emitter and the base. Current flows from the collector to the emitter through the base, which acts like a door. It can either stop the current or facilitate its flow. This doorlike mechanism is controlled by a weak current (arriving from the left in Figure 14.27).

14.26 Different types of transistors

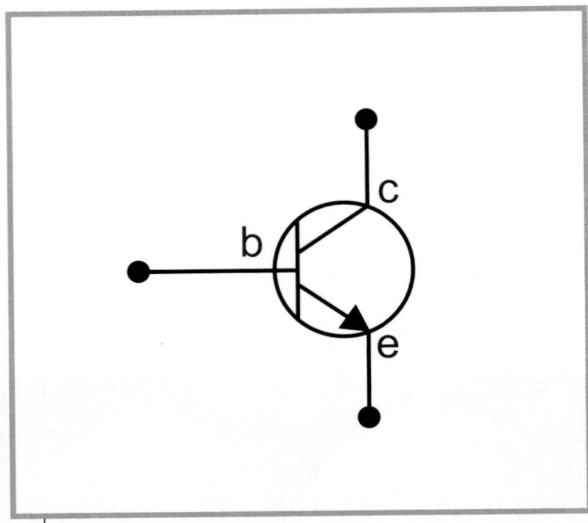

14.27 A transistor is made up of three parts: the collector (c), the base (b) and the emitter (e).

ENVIRONMENT EXTRA

Microcomputers, mega pollution

Personal computers, on which we have come to depend so much, have a greater impact on the environment than most of us might suspect.

Let's begin with the manufacture of a microprocessor (the central unit of a computer). Millions of transistors must be printed on a silicon wafer to make just one microprocessor. The procedure is complex, involving about 400 operations. It takes place in a sterile environment, where the wafer must be cleaned with distilled water and acid solutions. It takes an enormous amount of energy and raw materials.

Next, assembling a computer requires thousands of litres of water and dozens of kilograms of chemicals. The process generates large amounts of wastewater and garbage. Knowing that a factory can produce thousands of microprocessors each week, we can easily imagine the overall pressure that computer production puts on the environment. This high productivity is largely due to the short life span of computers: most users keep their machines for only a few years before replacing them.

Microprocessors are made with silicon wafers.

Transistors are particularly important in the field of electronics. Thanks to their invention, which dates back to 1947, computers have made spectacular progress in just a few decades. Computers make calculations by processing long series of 0's and 1's. The combinations are called *binary code*. A 0 corresponds to an absence of electric current (when a transistor blocks its path). A 1 indicates current flow (when the transistor acts as an amplifier).

> *Binary* comes from the Latin *binarius*, meaning "two together."

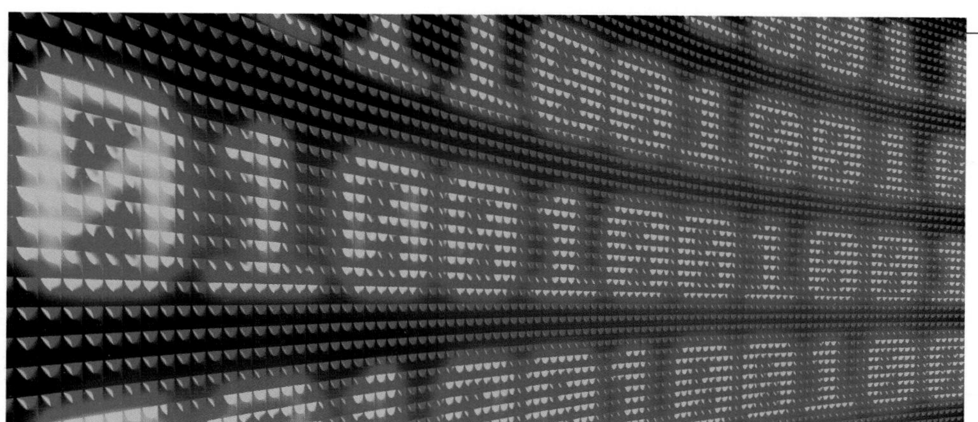

14.28 Binary code is a series of 0's and 1's, which corresponds to encoded data.

When we press on the "A" key of a computer keyboard, for example, several transistors are activated. The microprocessor decodes the corresponding series of 0's and 1's, and an *A* appears on the screen.

The microprocessor, the "brain" of the computer, may unite millions of transistors on a single silicon wafer of just a few square centimetres. Microprocessors are found not only in computers but also in any electronic equipment that processes data, such as cellphones, calculators, MP3 players and DVD players.

14.29 A modern microprocessor contains millions of miniature transistors.

AST 6.4 RELAYS

A relay is a component that opens or closes a circuit, using an electrical signal from another circuit. The signal can come from a switch, a computer or a photoelectric (light-sensitive) cell.

The advantage of using a relay is that the control circuit and the circuit to be controlled remain separate; there is no electrical contact between the two. A relay is made up of two parts (Figure 14.30, page 478): one part that receives the signal from the first circuit and sends a command, and another part that receives the command and starts the second circuit. These two parts are also isolated from each other.

Relays are used especially to control high-energy-consuming devices from a distance. Typical applications include the lighting system in a theatre, the heating system in a public building, industrial motors and high-voltage appliances.

A RELAY is a component used to control a high-voltage circuit from a distance with a low-voltage circuit.

Figure 14.30 shows an example of a relay application. The relay here controls an X-ray machine, a high-voltage apparatus (consuming approximately 50 000 V to 100 000 V) controlled from a distance by a computer (a low-voltage machine). In this way, the person operating the equipment avoids any risk of electric shock or exposure to high doses of radiation.

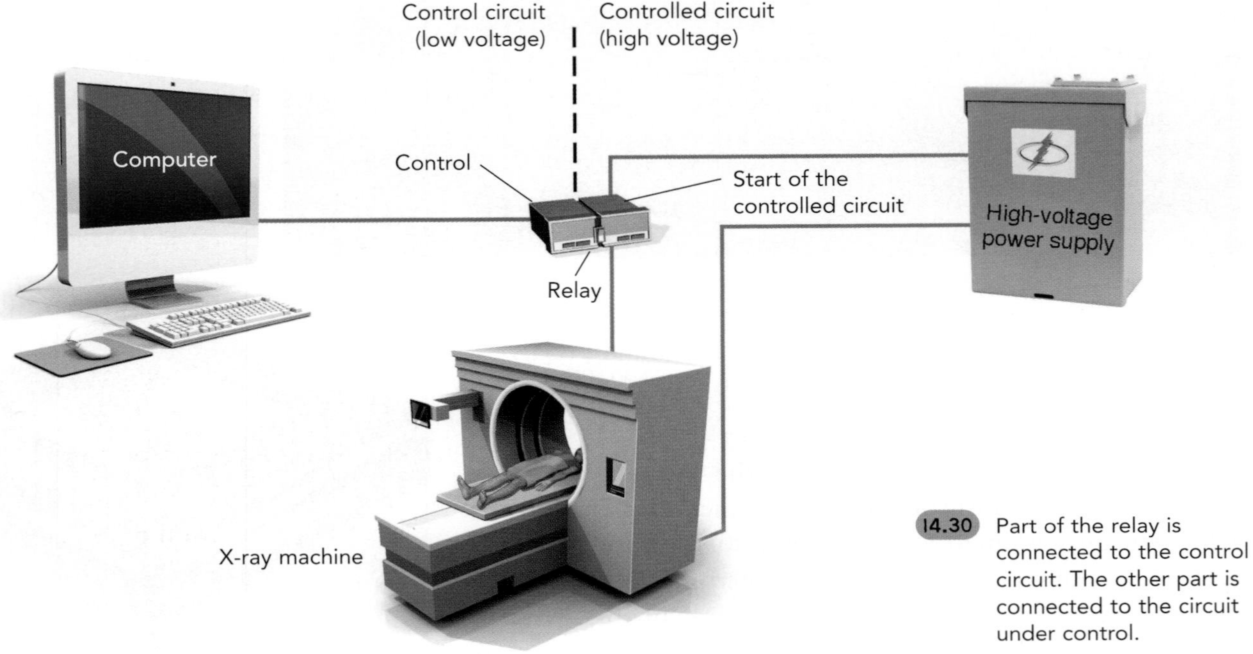

14.30 Part of the relay is connected to the control circuit. The other part is connected to the circuit under control.

There are electromechanical relays and solid-state relays (or *static relays*):

- In an electromechanical relay, the control depends on the magnetic field of an electromagnet, which causes metallic parts to move. In general, this type of relay has a shorter life span than a solid-state relay because it contains moving parts and is much bigger. However, it can control more powerful circuits.
- A solid-state relay does not contain any moving parts. Control is made possible by an LED and light-sensitive cells. This type of relay is usually airtight (this is not always the case for electromechanical relays, which may gather dust and corrode over time). In addition, solid-state relays are more compatible with digital circuits.

EVER SMALLER PARTS

Silicon, the most abundant element on Earth after iron and oxygen, is the basic material for electronic components. Manufacturers have been using it to make semiconductors for more than 40 years. However, the future belongs to molecular electronics, which uses much smaller components than integrated silicon circuits.

CHECKUP

ST 1–8, 10, 11, 13, 15, A and C. **AST** 1–21 and A–C.
EST 1–18, A and C. **SE** None.

1 What is electrical engineering? (pp. 458–462)

1. List five technical objects that you use every day and that could have been designed by an electrical engineer. Explain your choices.
2. What are the main differences between electrical components and electronic components?
3. How do electrical engineers represent circuits and related information?
4. Batteries are a source of direct current. Power plants generate alternating current. Explain the difference between these two types of current.
5. Explain why the following statements are false.
   a) Electrons flow from the positive terminal of a battery to the negative terminal.
   b) An electrical circuit contains only components designed to conduct current.

2 Power supply (pp. 462–463)

6. An electrical engineer must choose a power supply for various electrical material. What is the most suitable power source for each of the following projects?
   a) a communications tower to be built in the Far North of Québec, beyond access to the power grid
   b) a digital camera
   c) a photocopier
7. Name one advantage and one disadvantage for each of the power supplies mentioned in question 6.

3 Conduction, insulation and protection (pp. 464–468)

8. Which of the following is acting as a conductor in an electrical circuit? Explain your answer.
   a) the plastic casing of an electrical wire
   b) a metal screw wrapped with electrical wire, inside a switch
   c) the ceramic housing for an electrical outlet
   d) wiring connected to a battery
9. What kind of circuit is used to save space inside a computer?
10. Electrical wires are usually covered in plastic.
    a) Explain why.
    b) Which electrical function is performed by the plastic casing?
11. Fuses and breakers perform the same function in electrical circuits.
    a) What is this function called?
    b) Which of the two components—fuses or breakers—is the better option? Explain your answer.
12. Look at the electrical resistor below.

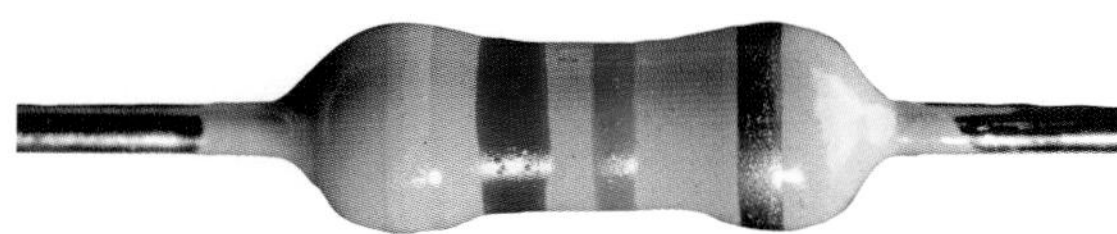

    a) What is its resistance value?
    b) What are the minimum and maximum values determined by the tolerance?
    c) Which unit of measurement is used to express resistance?
    d) Describe one advantage of using a resistor in an electrical circuit.

4 Control (pp. 469–471)

13. When a lamp is switched off, is the electrical circuit to the light bulb open or closed? Explain your answer.

14. Choose the appropriate type of switch for the following functions.
    a) opening or closing two contacts at once
    b) opening one or the other of two circuits

5 The transformation of energy (pp. 471–472)

15. In each of the appliances below, electrical energy is converted into another form of energy. What is the resulting form of energy?

A

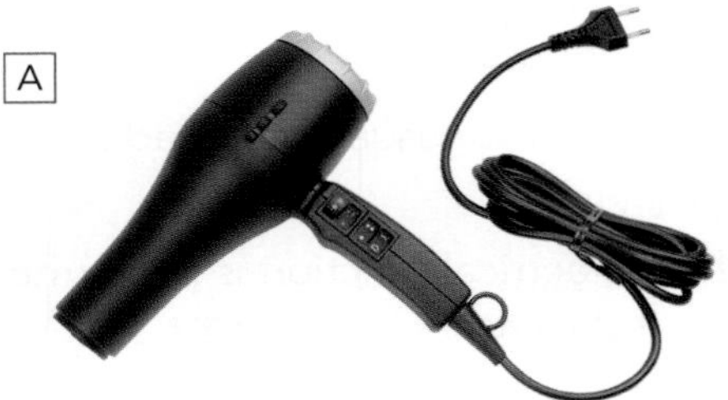

B

C

6 Components with other functions (pp. 473–478)

16. Anna designs an electrical circuit for a laptop computer. The parts for the circuit are fragile, so she wants to make sure that the current flow will remain stable even when the computer is plugged into an outlet where the power supply fluctuates slightly. Which electrical component should she place at the beginning of the circuit? Explain briefly how this component works.

17. Which unit of measurement is used to express capacitance?

18. Name three functions of diodes in electrical circuits.

19. The transistor revolutionized the field of electronics. Computers could not exist without them.
    a) What are the three main parts of a transistor?
    b) What are the two functions that a transistor can perform?
    c) What do the digits in binary code mean?

20. Do you think that the objects below contain transistors? Explain your answers.

A B

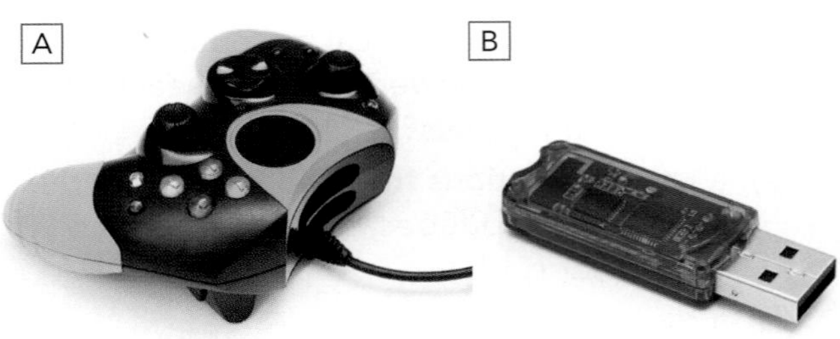

21. What is the purpose of a relay, whether electromagnetic or solid-state?

review questions

A. When you go to a friend's house and ring the doorbell, an electrical circuit is activated, and the doorbell rings.

a) When you press the button for the doorbell, you close an electrical circuit. Which function does the push button perform in the circuit?

b) The doorbell is covered in plastic. Why? Which function does this small round plastic cover perform?

c) When electrons start to flow in the circuit, they pass through a coil of electrical wire wrapped around a small iron bar. What is this device called?

d) What form of energy results from this transformation?

e) The iron core inside the wire coil is attracted to a metal bar (a *tone bar*). When they meet, the tone bar vibrates. What is the final form of energy produced by this device?

f) Back at your friend's house a week later, you have to knock on the door because the doorbell is not working. Your friend tells you that it has not been working since the night before, when he tried to plug in a string of lights to decorate his house. The lights came on for less than a second and then went out. What do you advise him to do?

B. An optical computer mouse contains a diode that shines a light on the flat surface where the mouse is placed. The light is reflected and then captured by an optical sensor. A microprocessor analyzes the data received and determines the movement of the mouse. A signal is sent to the computer, which moves the cursor accordingly.

a) What type of diode is used in the optical mouse?

b) In the mouse, which component acts as an insulator?

c) The microprocessor must process the data collected by the optical sensor and relay the results of the analysis to the computer in a series of 0's and 1's. Which component performs this information processing?

d) The resistors in the mouse are miniaturized and numbered. A resistor indicating 473 has a value of 47×1000, or 47 000 Ω. On a conventional resistor of this value, what colours would the first three bands be?

C. Prepare your own summary of Chapter 14 by building a concept map.

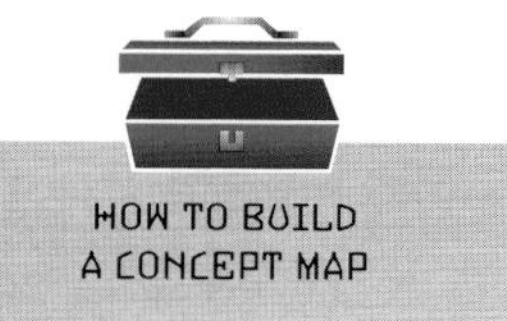

HOW TO BUILD A CONCEPT MAP

Electronic waste is piling up

THE TIME HAS COME TO RECYCLE

The amount of electronic waste is growing at an alarming rate. In 2006, the International Association of Electronics Recyclers estimated that one billion computers were then in operation around the world. Since the average life span of a computer is three to five years, three billion computers will be polluting nature by 2010. This figure does not even include other electronic waste, such as household appliances, MP3 players, televisions, cellphones and video game consoles. In Canada alone, more than 272 000 tonnes of electronic waste end up in landfills each year, a weight equivalent to that of 30 000 adult African elephants. Toxic substances in the waste, such as lead and mercury, make it hazardous to the environment.

RECYCLING AND EDUCATING AT THE SAME TIME

In Québec, recycling programs for electronic waste have been implanted, including those in the Centres de formation en entreprise et récupération (CFER) [Business and Recycling Training Centres], founded by Normand Maurice.

Normand Maurice is considered by many to be the father of recycling in Québec. A committed educator, he refused to accept that high-school dropouts were an inevitable fact of modern society. In 1970, he began offering cultural workshops to spark the interest of students in technical programs for more academic subjects such as French, Math and Ethics. Then he decided to try to help dropouts by teaching them about recycling. In 1990, in collaboration with some colleagues from a high school in Victoriaville (Polyvalente du Boisé), he opened the first CFER to train young people in all kinds of recycling: furniture, paint, paper, cardboard, etc. Finally, since there was no program for recycling computers at the time, Maurice decided to attack this problem as well.

Today, 9 of the 22 CFERs in the province of Québec recover electronic components. The students learn to rebuild computers and recycle metals, such as copper, aluminum and lead, which are melted down and resold. They recover plastic parts, which are ground and then used to manufacture new products. Once sorted, all these materials are sent out to recycling centres across North America.

Two CFERs, one in the city of Québec and the other in the Saguenay region, receive used computers through the Computers for Schools (CFS) program. CFS recovers computers from businesses, has the computers recycled and then donates them to schools in need.

Other projects,,similar to the CFERs, are underway in Québec. École-Entreprise du Centre Saint-Michel, in Sherbrooke, also takes part in the CFS program. The social business Insertech Angus, in Montréal, oversees the social and professional reintegration of more than 40 young adults each year by teaching them to build and recycle computers, which are then sold to the public.

Some of the metals in electronic equipment can be melted down and reused.

EVEN MORE RECYCLING

These recycling projects for electronic equipment are interesting and motivating, but they are still insufficient to meet present needs. To effectively deal with the growing problem of electronic waste management, it is vital to act quickly and organize more programs, on a much wider scale.

The Computers for Schools program gives new life to computers that businesses no longer use.

1. What do you think makes electronic equipment difficult to recycle?
2. What can you do in your own daily life to reduce the impact of electronic waste on the environment?

Science at work IN...

A BIOGAS POWER PLANT

For decades, tonnes of residual materials have been buried in various landfills. Unfortunately, when buried waste decomposes, it causes the formation of biogases, such as methane, which are powerful greenhouse gases. However, these gases also represent an important source of energy. For this reason, power plants are cropping up near dumps, taking advantage of the biogases to generate electricity.

Let's meet some of the people who work in biogas power plants.

Isabelle Simard,
electronic engineering technician

Martin Lapointe,
assistant operator in charge of equipment operation

Réal Cormier,
assistant operator in charge of workplace health and safety

Pierre Auger,
process operator

Barbara Lee,
mechanical engineer

Occupation	Education	Length of study	Main tasks
Electronic engineering technician	DCS in industrial electronics technology	3 years	• Assemble and adjust production equipment (alternators and turbines)
Assistant operator	DVS in industrial construction and maintenance mechanics	1800 hours	• Ensure that equipment is functioning properly
Process operator	DVS in industrial construction and maintenance mechanics	1800 hours	• Supervise the operation of a thermal power plant
Mechanical engineer (specializing in energy)	Bachelor's degree in electromechanical engineering	4 years	• Design power plants for generating electricity • Supervise the construction of power plants

environmental

ISSUES

CONTENTS

Climate change

Meteorologists have become accustomed to record-breaking firsts, as temperatures around the world rise year after year. Since the Industrial Revolution, and the beginning of detailed temperature records (around the year 1880), the mean temperature on Earth has risen by about 0.76°C. And there is no end in sight to this trend!

As the Earth heats up, extreme weather events, such as storms, torrential rains and coastal flooding, become more frequent.

EI.1 EVOLUTION OF MEAN TEMPERATURES ON EARTH FROM 1880 TO 2005

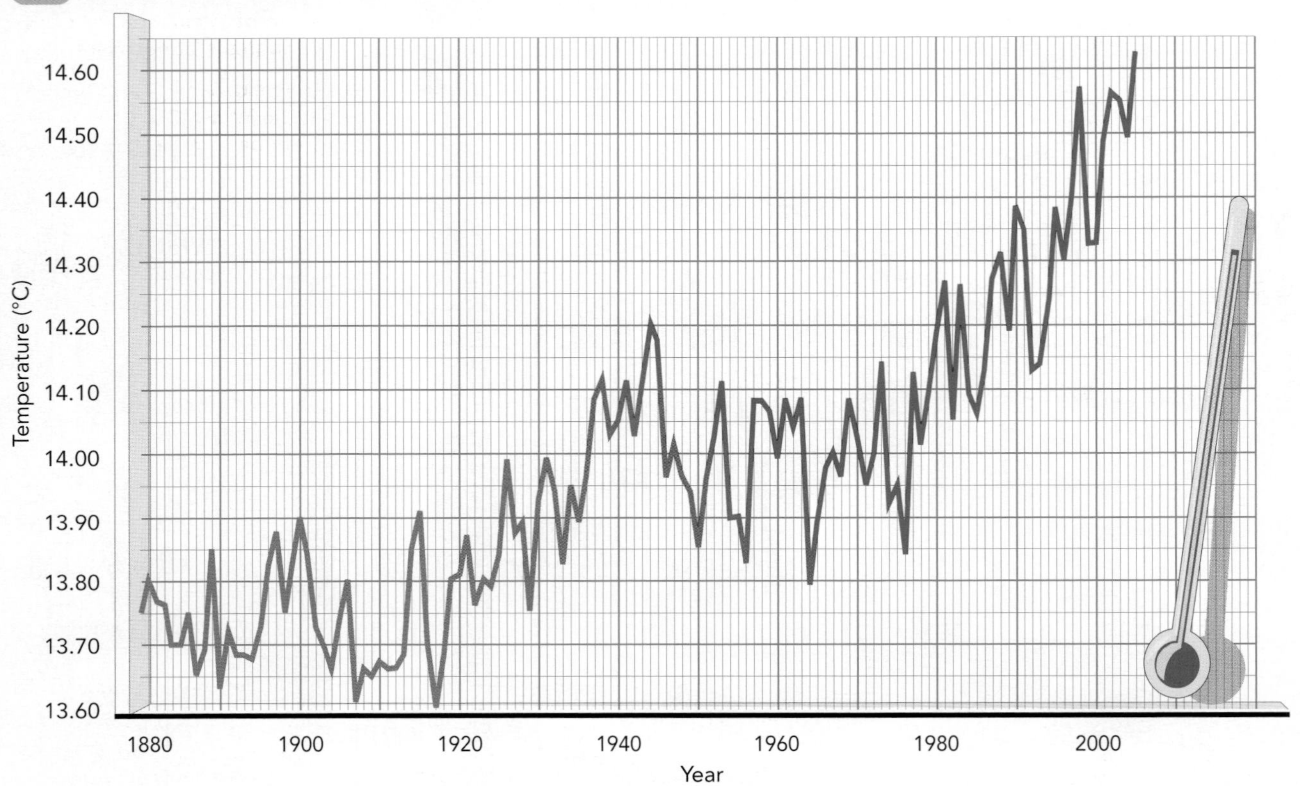

Source: World Resources Institute / Goddard Institute for Space Studies (GISS), 2006.

LEADING CAUSES

It is not mere coincidence that the Earth's climate has been warming up since the beginning of the industrial era. Until 1880, the concentration of carbon dioxide (CO_2) in the atmosphere remained relatively stable. CO_2 is the main by-product of fossil fuel combustion, however, so as humans burned more fossil fuels (oil, natural gas and coal) in the engines of industrial equipment and cars, CO_2 emissions increased.

CO_2 accumulates in the atmosphere, adding to the layer of **GREENHOUSE GASES** and contributing to the **GREENHOUSE EFFECT**. For thousands of years, this layer around the Earth has been trapping some of the **INFRARED** rays released by the planet (Figure EI.2, page 489).

Besides CO_2, other greenhouse gases that contribute to climate warming include methane (CH_4), produced mostly by livestock (during digestion) and by manure management, and nitrous oxide (N_2O), from industrial activity and fertilizer use. As you can see in Figure EI.3 (page 489), Canadians are heavy emitters of greenhouse gases.

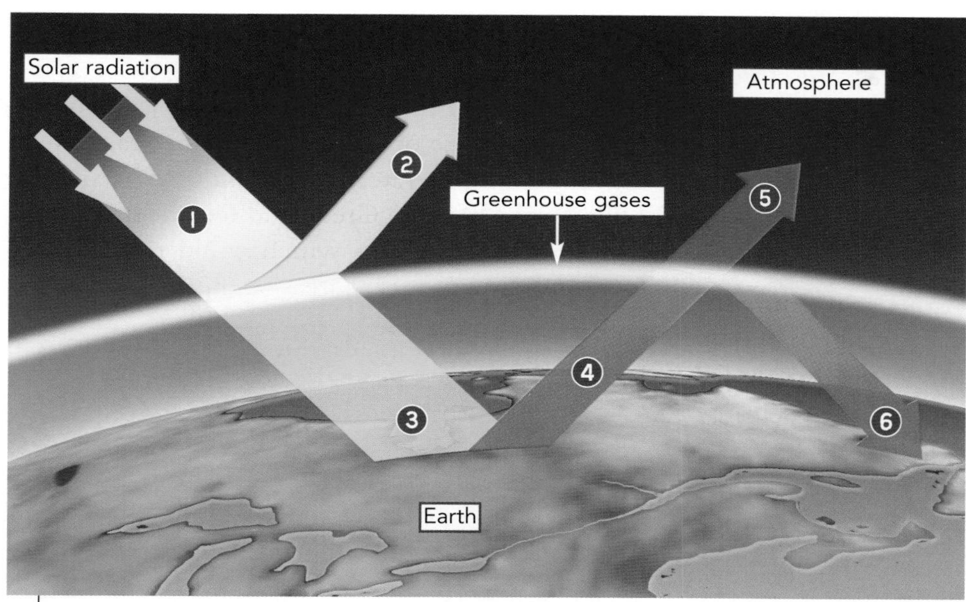

1. The sun's rays pass through the Earth's atmosphere.
2. Some of the rays are deflected by the greenhouse gases.
3. Solar energy is absorbed by the Earth's surface and warms it.
4. Part of the heat absorbed by the Earth is released into the atmosphere in the form of infrared rays.
5. Some of the infrared rays pass through the atmosphere.
6. Greenhouse gases trap some of the infrared rays and reflect them back to Earth.

EI.2 The greenhouse effect

EI.3 PER CAPITA CO_2 EMISSIONS FOR CERTAIN COUNTRIES IN 2004

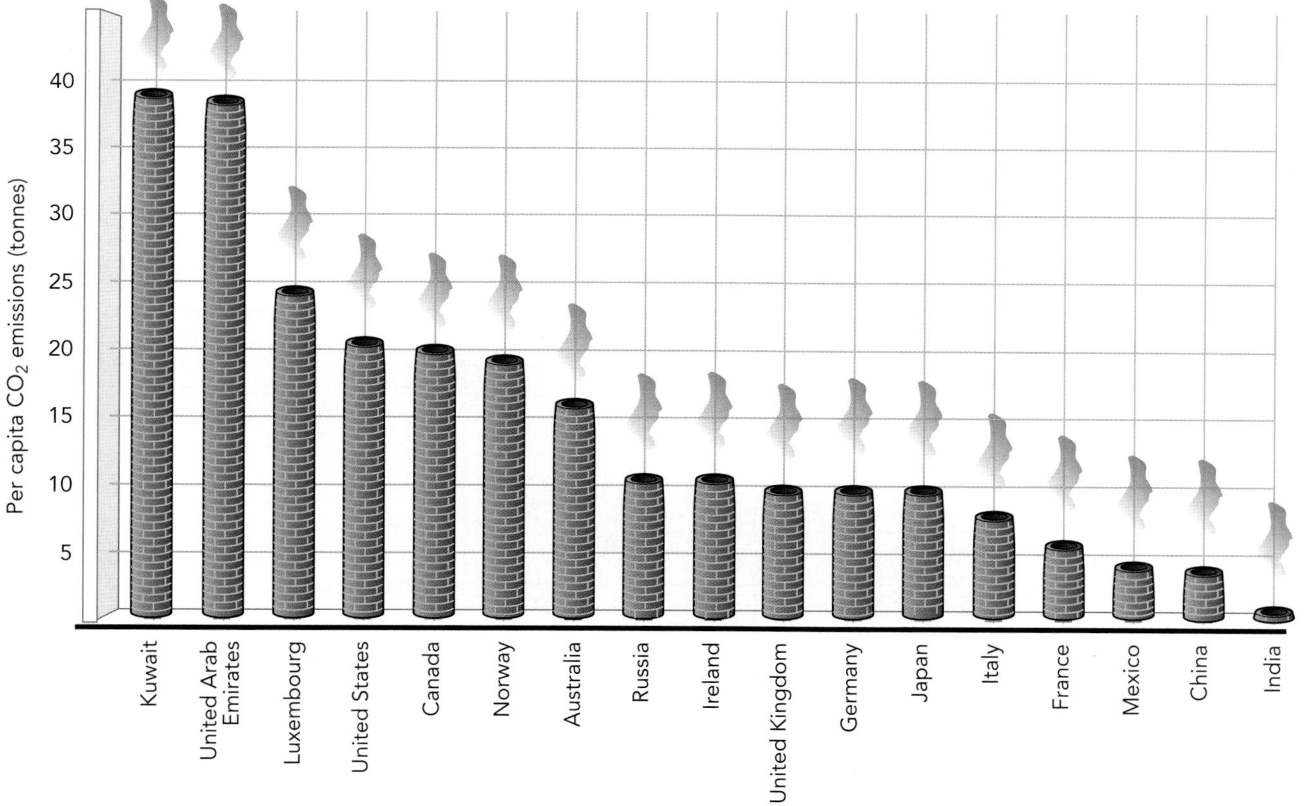

Source: World Resources Institute, 2005.

READING THE FUTURE

Uniting experts from 120 countries, the Intergovernmental Panel on Climate Change (IPCC) estimates that by the year 2100, the mean temperature on Earth could rise by three to five degrees Celsius compared to pre-industrial temperatures (Figure EI.4).

The IPCC makes these predictions using climatic models and complex computer programs that simulate future climate patterns based on thousands of mathematical equations representing atmospheric phenomena.

Temperatures a few degrees higher may sound appealing to residents of cold countries like Canada. However, scientists estimate that an increase of just two degrees could have disastrous consequences. For example, nearly a million species could disappear before mid-century. In addition, the rise in sea level could submerge coastal areas, swallowing up part of Florida.

THE IMPACT OF CLIMATE CHANGE

There is no need to wait for Florida to disappear under the waves to feel the impact of climate change. Many effects are already visible, including the examples described in the following paragraphs.

Melting ice in the North

In the Arctic, the temperature is rising twice as fast as elsewhere on the planet. The polar ice pack, an immense expanse of ice floating on the sea, is melting at an alarming rate, threatening wildlife and the Inuit way of life. The Greenland Ice Sheet is also in the process of melting, which could raise the sea level and drown coastal areas.

EI.5 Melting pack ice threatens the survival of the polar bear.

EI.4 PREDICTED TEMPERATURE INCREASE BY 2041-2060, COMPARED TO MEAN TEMPERATURES BETWEEN 1981 AND 2000

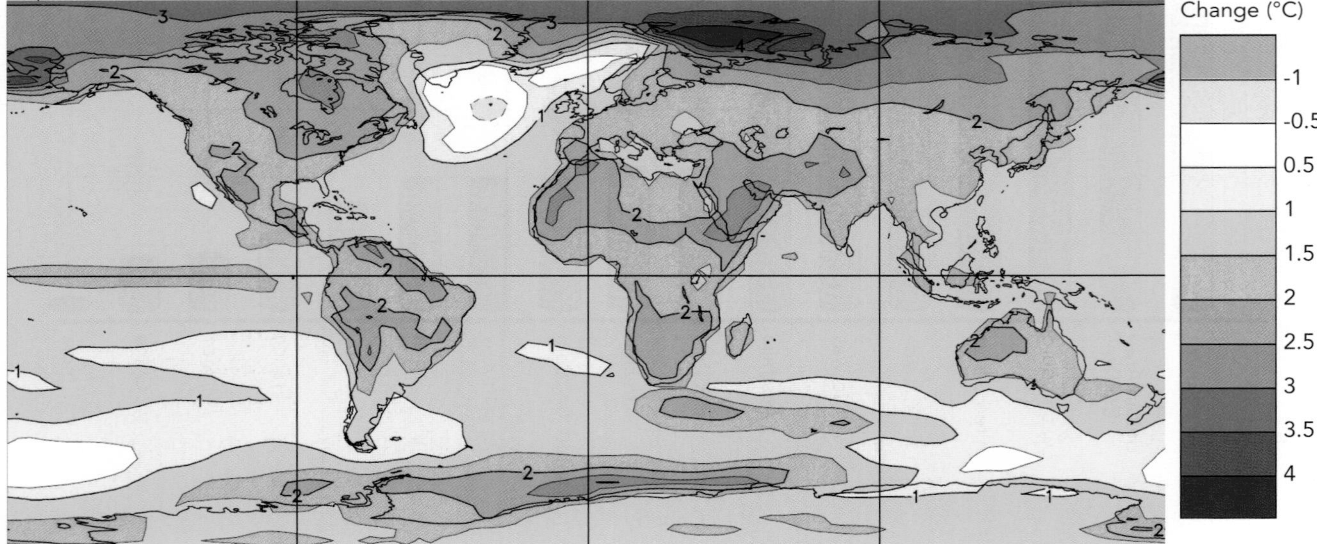

Source: Environment Canada, 2008.

The threat of malaria

Malaria is caused by a parasite transmitted to humans by a mosquito of the genus *Anopheles*. The heat-loving insect is not usually found in North America. As our climate becomes warmer, however, it could make a new home for itself on our continent by 2020.

Drought-stricken farms

Higher temperatures on land lead to higher rates of water evaporation. As a result, farmers struggle to irrigate their fields in certain regions of the world.

EI.6 Droughts are particularly severe in the Sahel (a region stretching across Africa, south of the Sahara Desert), where the people already suffer from malnutrition.

IN SEARCH OF A GLOBAL SOLUTION

Even if a country managed to eliminate its greenhouse gas emissions, it would still suffer from climate warming caused by emissions from other countries. To combat climate change effectively, the nations of the world must work together.

The United Nations Framework Convention

At the Earth Summit in Rio de Janeiro in 1992, 154 countries and the European Union adopted the United Nations Framework Convention on Climate Change. These countries, including Canada, thus recognized the urgent need for action. They committed to stabilizing greenhouse gas concentrations in the atmosphere to prevent any dangerous climate disruptions. However, no concrete goals were set for emission reductions.

The Kyoto Protocol

Since 1995, the countries committed to the UN Framework Convention on Climate Change have been meeting annually. These sessions are referred to as *Conferences of the Parties* (COP). COP 1 took place in Berlin in 1995.

In 1997, at COP 3 in Kyoto, Japan, many signatory countries committed to specific emission reduction targets. Generally, industrialized countries agreed to reduce their greenhouse gas emissions to levels five percent below their 1990 levels, with results to be measured during the first five-year commitment period, from 2008 to 2012. Canada, for its part, promised a six-percent reduction.

Beyond Kyoto

Ten years after the Kyoto meeting, Canadian greenhouse gas emissions are still on the rise. In 2007, they had increased by 25 percent compared to 1990 levels.

Emerging technologies may come to the rescue; for example, the carbon emissions from certain factories can be captured and stored deep underground. Authorities could also give higher priority to clean energy sources such as wind turbines (rather than coal-burning power plants) and to improved public transit.

Drinking water

More than any other resource, water is essential to human life. We need 1.5 litres of water each day to survive. After only four days without water, we would die. In comparison, we can survive for several weeks without eating.

A RARE RESOURCE

From the world map below, it is evident that water is abundant on Earth. It covers more than two thirds of the planet's surface. However, only a fraction of this water is available for human use and potable (safe to drink). In fact, 97.5 percent of the water on Earth is too saline for human consumption. Most of the remaining 2.5 percent is trapped in glaciers or inaccessible groundwater aquifers.

In addition, drinking water is unequally distributed throughout the world, with fewer than 10 countries sharing 60 percent of global reserves. Map EI.7 below shows what percentage of the population in each country had access to drinking water in 2004.

IS THE WATER SAFE TO DRINK?

To be considered potable, water must meet a series of quality criteria, which can be classified into different categories.

EI.8 QUALITY CRITERIA FOR DRINKING WATER

Quality criterion	Definition
Sensory properties	These include colour, turbidity (clarity), odour and taste. Failure to meet standards does not necessarily point to a health hazard, but consumer satisfaction will be greatly affected.
Physical and chemical parameters	The pH, temperature and salinity of the water must not exceed certain limits. If the water is too acidic, for example, the distribution pipes will be subject to corrosion.
Toxic substances	The concentrations of substances that are hazardous to human health, such as arsenic, pesticides or lead, must not exceed certain levels.
Microbiological parameters	The water must not contain viruses or bacteria that are likely to cause disease.

In industrialized countries, these parameters are government-regulated. In Québec, for example, all tap water must conform to the *Regulation respecting the quality of drinking water.*

EI.7 ACCESS TO DRINKING WATER

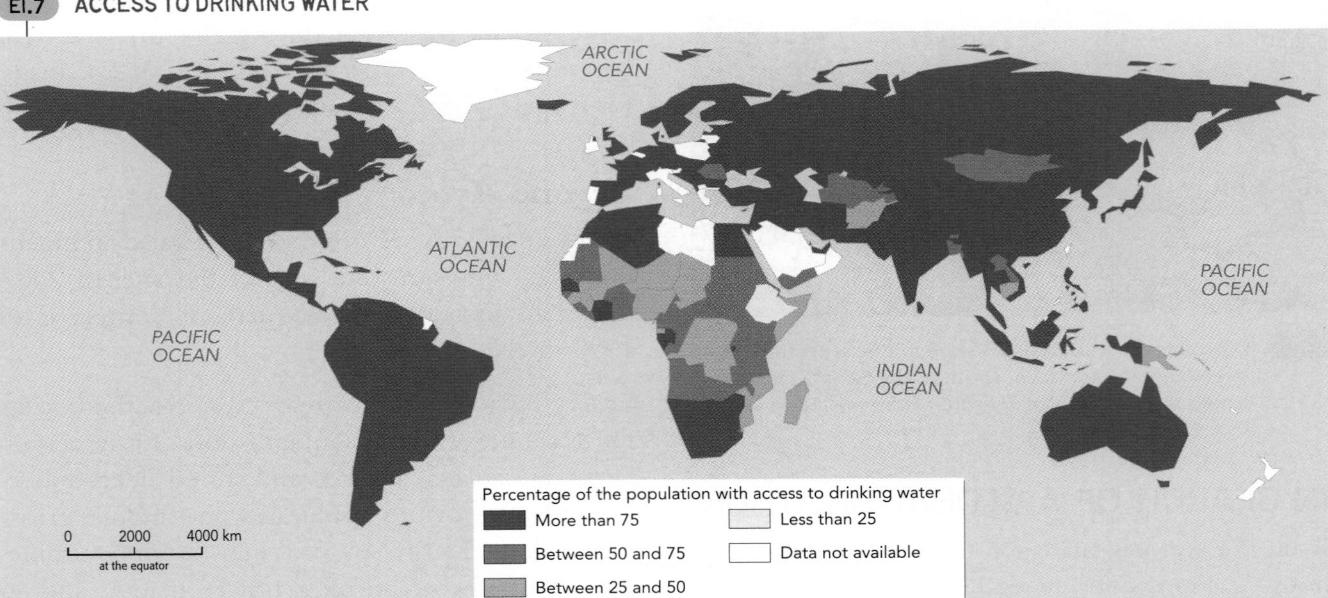

Source: United Nations Development Programme (UNDP), *Human Development Report 2007/2008* (2004 data).

EI.9 EXAMPLES OF LIMITS SET BY THE *REGULATION RESPECTING THE QUALITY OF DRINKING WATER*

Substance	Maximum concentration (ppm)
Arsenic	0.025
Benzene	0.005
Cyanides	0.2
Lead	0.01
Mercury	0.001
Trichloroethylene	0.05
Uranium	0.02

Source: Gouvernement du Québec, *Gazette officielle du 23 janvier 2008.*

WATER PURIFICATION

Water drawn from the natural environment rarely meets all the quality standards for consumer health and satisfaction. It is purified in a water treatment plant before it makes its way through a water supply system to homes, businesses and industries. Figure EI.10 illustrates the main equipment and processes in this type of plant.

Four billion people around the world do not have access to a system that purifies and distributes water. Every year, contaminated water claims five million lives, making it the world's leading cause of death.

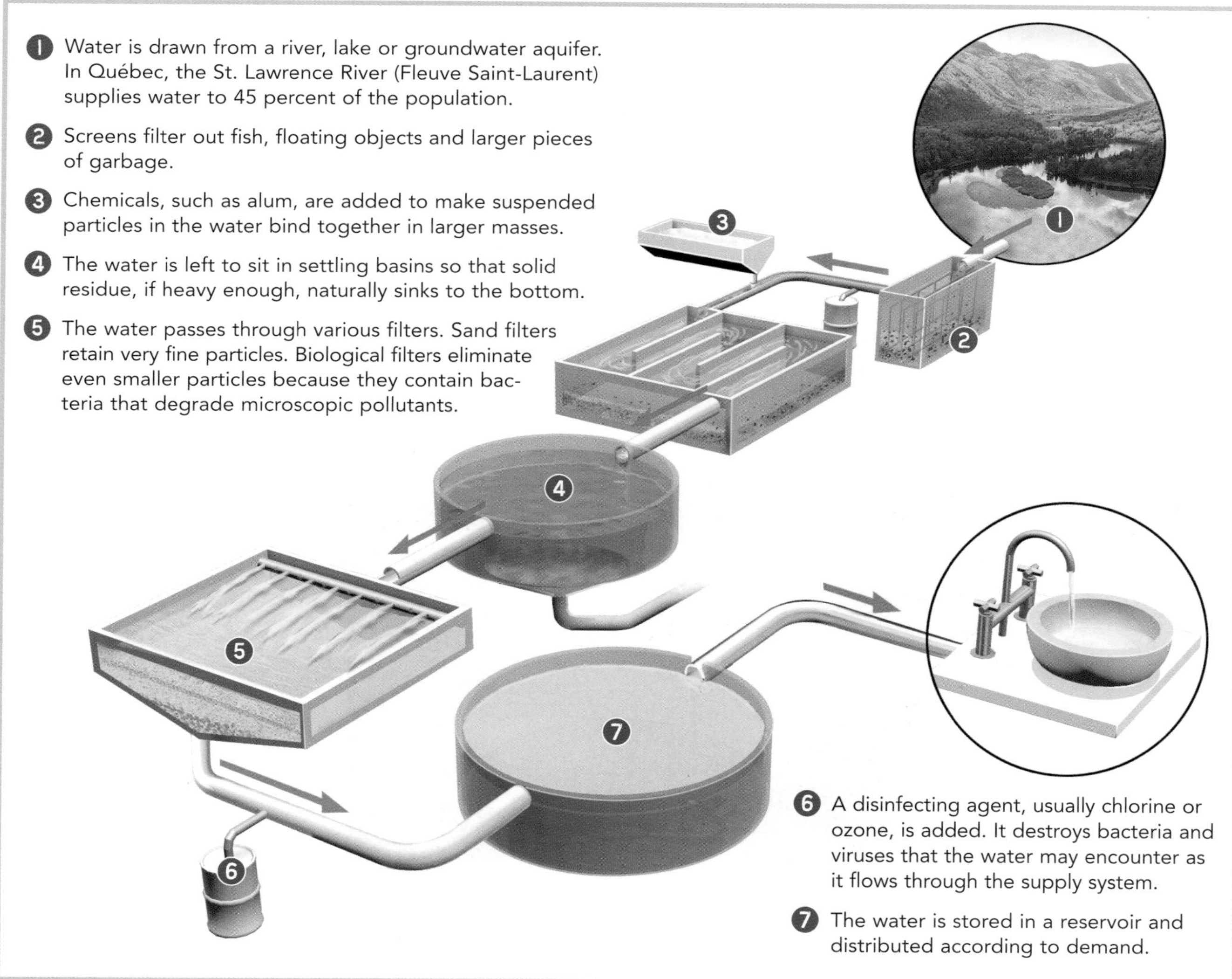

EI.10 Example of a water treatment process

SOURCES AT RISK

Many lakes and rivers that supply water treatment plants are threatened by human activities. Pollutants from industry, farms or homes contaminate the supply and can make treatment difficult, or even impossible.

Pollution

The most common pollutants include pesticides and fertilizers, used on farmland; heavy metals, discharged in wastewater from factories; and bacteria, found in domestic wastewater discharged into sewers. In many industrialized regions, treatment plants receive wastewater from sewers and clean it before discharging it into a nearby river. However, not all pollutants can be removed through treatment.

Climate change

In addition to the pollutants that find their way into lakes and rivers, other problems put water resources at risk. Climate change could cause the water level of the St. Lawrence River (Fleuve Saint-Laurent) to drop several metres by 2050. Should this occur, salt water from the Gulf of St. Lawrence (Golfe du Saint-Laurent) could flow farther upriver than at present. The water intakes for the cities of Lévis and Québec could become unusable in a matter of decades because the river there would be saline.

EXCESSIVE HUMAN CONSUMPTION

As the amount of used water entering wastewater treatment plants increases, the facilities become less effective at eliminating pollutants. Unfortunately, Canadians are huge consumers of drinking water. In homes across the country, each person uses 335 litres of water per day—more than double the per capita consumption in Europe. Filling swimming pools, using a powerful spray to wash cars, and excessive lawn watering figure among the causes of this heavy use.

EI.11 The water level of the St. Lawrence River (Fleuve Saint-Laurent) has been recorded annually since 1800, and the data shows that the level is falling. This photo shows a section of the river in the summer of 2001.

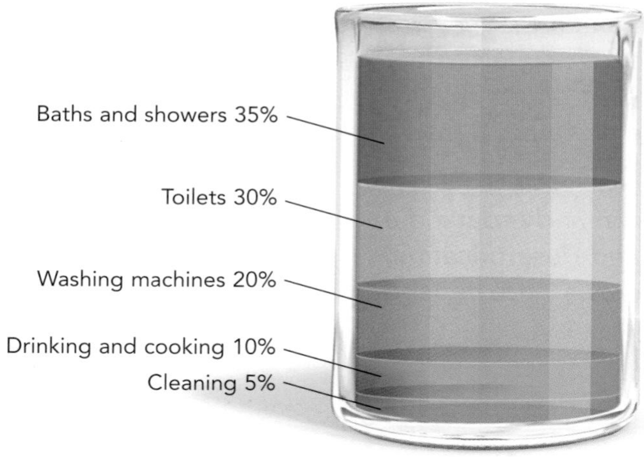

EI.12 Most of the water used in a household goes down the drains in the bathroom.

While individual water consumption in North America is high, the total amount used in Asia—with eight times the population of North America—is staggering. Figure EI.13 shows that Asian consumption is rapidly increasing and should exceed 3000 billion cubic metres annually by 2025. Meanwhile, North American consumption should level out under 1000 billion cubic metres.

TAKING PREVENTIVE ACTION

The Government of Québec adopted a water policy in 2002 to protect resources, public health and **ECOSYSTEMS** while applying principles of **SUSTAINABLE DEVELOPMENT** to its water management. The policy includes commitments in several areas, such as:

- watershed-based management
- research, especially on groundwater reserves
- improved drinking water and wastewater treatment facilities
- the prevention of agricultural and industrial pollution
- resource protection

The policy was the product of a huge consultation process and received unanimous support once adopted. Some areas have since been addressed, including the review of treatment facilities for drinking water and the management of certain **WATERSHEDS**, but much work remains to be done to meet policy objectives.

EI.13 WATER CONSUMPTION AROUND THE WORLD FROM 1900 TO 2025

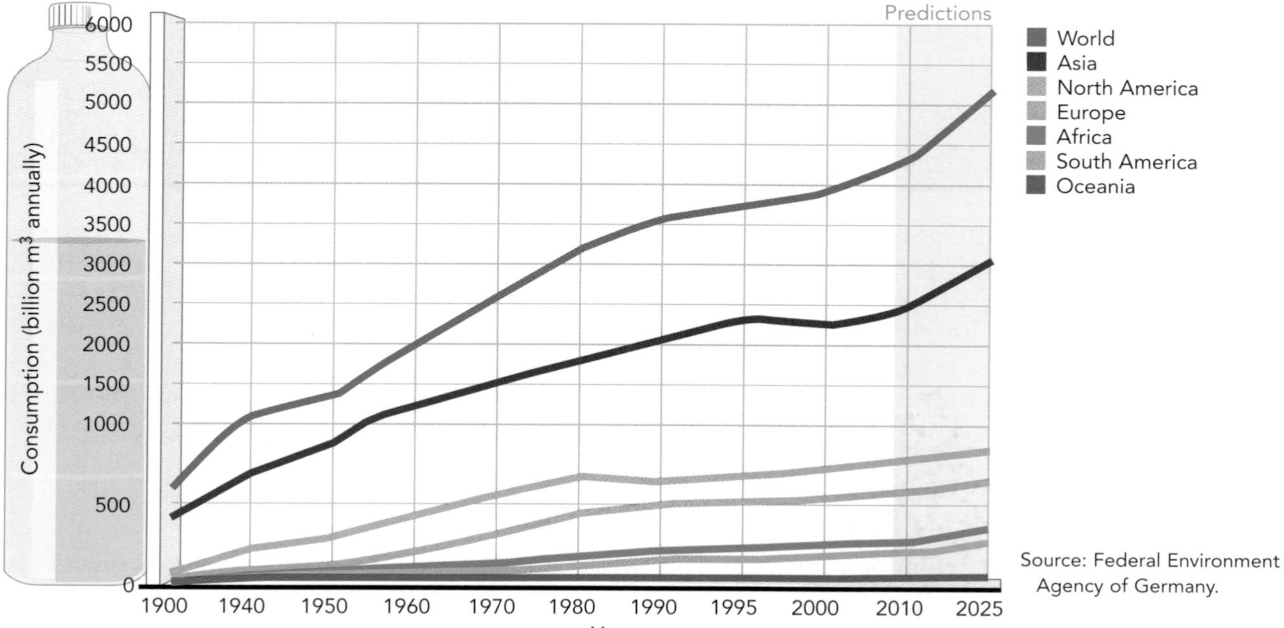

Deforestation

Forests are among the most precious natural resources on Earth. They are home to a large proportion of the planet's plants and animals. They also help to stabilize the climate because their abundant plant life captures carbon dioxide (CO_2), thus reducing the concentration of greenhouse gases in the atmosphere.

Forests provide other benefits: they prevent soil erosion and reduce the risks of natural disasters, such as floods, avalanches and desertification. Meanwhile, more than 300 million people live in forests and depend directly on their resources.

EI.14 CHANGES IN FOREST AREA FROM 1990 TO 2005

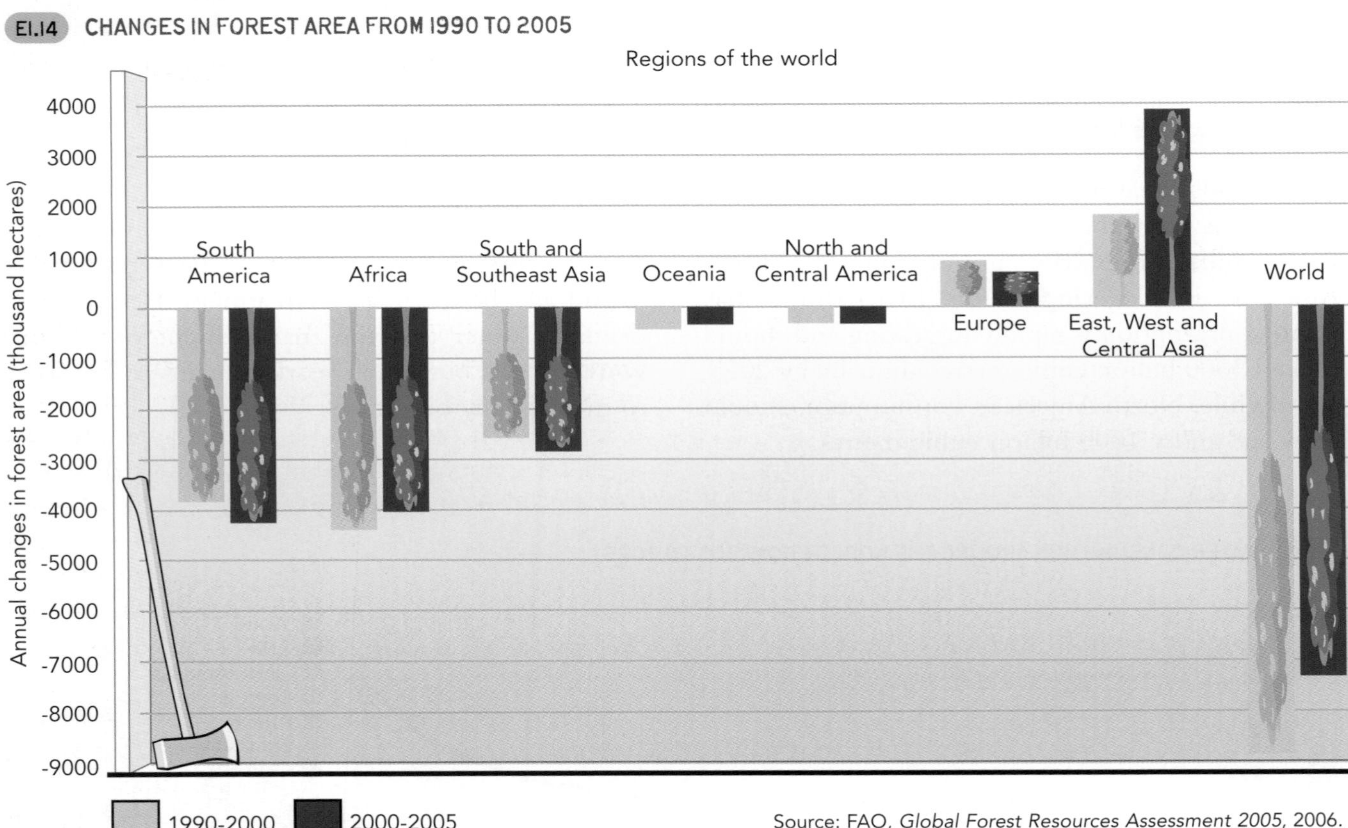

Source: FAO, *Global Forest Resources Assessment 2005*, 2006.

RECEDING FORESTS

Forests cover nearly four billion hectares—approximately 30 percent of dry land on Earth. More than half of the forests are concentrated in Russia, Brazil, Canada, the United States and China. However, forest area decreased at an average rate of 7.3 million hectares worldwide per year between 2000 and 2005. Since 1990, three percent of global forest cover has disappeared.

CAUSES

Many human activities, as well as natural causes, are responsible for the loss of forest area. The main factors are explained on the following page.

Clearing land for farming

In certain tropical regions, as much as 45 percent of deforestation is caused by migrant farmers who burn small areas of the forest to plant subsistence crops, such as soybean or sorghum. After a few years, the soil is no longer fertile enough to produce a good crop, so the farmers move on to a new area of the forest.

EI.15 In order to work the land, farmers in some African and South American countries burn large areas of the tropical forest. This is known as *slash-and-burn agriculture.*

Logging

Harvesting forests for the pulp-and-paper or lumber industries poses a serious threat to the resource. In the Québec forest industry alone, 33 million cubic metres of lumber are cut annually. Replanting cannot keep pace with the rate of harvesting. Of particular concern is the practice of clear-cutting, which involves cutting down all the trees in an area, completely destroying certain wildlife habitats.

EI.16 An example of clear-cutting

Monoculture

Monoculture is an agricultural or forestry practice in which a single crop or species of tree is planted over a large area. In warm climates, for example, huge stands of eucalyptus are planted to supply newsprint mills. Such plantations are sometimes called "green deserts," and their environmental impact is significant. Trees become more vulnerable to harmful insects because single-species planting does not encourage **BIODIVERSITY**, which would usually include the insects' natural predators. Monoculture also results in **SOIL DEPLETION** because the crop draws constantly on the same nutrients.

EI.17 Plantation of eucalyptus near Coimbra, Portugal

Urbanization

Until the end of the 19th century, Europe was almost entirely covered in forests. With the expansion of urban areas, the forests were gradually destroyed; only one percent of them now remains. In the St. Lawrence Valley (Vallée du Saint-Laurent), the forest has also given way to cities. And in countries with sustained population growth, like China, urbanization is putting constant pressure on forests.

Air pollution

Fossil fuel combustion releases pollutants into the atmosphere, including sulphur dioxide (SO_2) and nitrogen oxides (NO_x), which cause **ACID RAIN**. Soil exposed to acid rain can no longer retain the nutrients needed to support plant life. Tree growth declines and may even stop completely.

EI.18 The trees in this forest have been killed by acid rain.

Natural factors

Forests are also threatened by many natural factors, such as fires, landslides or disease caused by insects. In 1999, for example, violent storms uprooted thousands of trees in Europe.

EI.19 The ice storm in southwestern Québec in 1998 damaged nearly two million hectares of forest.

THE IMPACT OF DEFORESTATION

On biodiversity

Forests are among the most diverse ecosystems on Earth. They are home to 70 percent of living species, with their trees providing both a habitat and food for many birds, insects, plants, fungi and microorganisms. As a result of deforestation, thousands of these plant and animal species disappear each year. In Canada, many species at risk depend directly on the forest, including the spotted owl, the American marten (Newfoundland population), the woodland caribou, the wood bison and the American chestnut.

On the water cycle

Trees play an essential role in the water cycle by doing the following:

- reducing surface runoff. Forests actually absorb 10 times more rainwater than fields do.
- reducing soil erosion. Trees prevent soil from being carried away with surface runoff when it rains.
- releasing water into the air through **EVAPOTRANSPIRATION**. This process maintains a certain level of air humidity.

If the forest disappears, the water cycle is profoundly disrupted.

On the climate

The forests of the world store much of the Earth's carbon. When trees are cut down and then either decompose or are burned, the carbon is converted into CO_2. Deforestation is thus responsible for a quarter of global greenhouse gas emissions.

Deforestation also causes climate change on a local scale. Trees maintain air humidity through evapotranspiration and act as windbreaks. When land is cleared in tropical regions, the temperature can rise as much as 10°C.

SUSTAINABLE FOREST MANAGEMENT

Many agreements and international treaties have been adopted to protect forest environments around the world. For example, the Convention on Biological Diversity (1992) is a treaty for the conservation and sustainable use of natural resources. The United Nations Convention to Combat Desertification (1994) established an international plan of action against land degradation in arid, semi-arid and subtropical dry zones.

Sustainable forest management can be applied on a national level in a variety of ways, including the practices described below.

Selective cutting

This harvesting technique consists in cutting only mature trees of a certain type and quality. It is less detrimental to the forest environment than clear-cutting because soil erosion and surface runoff are reduced, natural habitats are disturbed to a lesser extent, and a substantial tree cover is left standing. From an economical point of view, however, this method is more expensive and therefore less competitive.

Eco-certified products thanks to the Forest Stewardship Council

The Forest Stewardship Council (FSC) is a non-governmental organization that promotes forest management that is environmentally, socially and economically responsible and sustainable. It issues certificates to logging companies around the world that meet council standards for good forest management. The certification guarantees consumers, retailers, investors and governments that the approved products come from forests under environmentally friendly management.

Protected areas

Protected areas are established to preserve biodiversity in natural environments and protect wilderness resources. All industrial activity is forbidden. In Québec, less than five percent of the province was protected in 2007. The objective is to extend protected areas to include eight percent of the province by 2010.

Energy

Access to energy is indispensable for satisfying basic human needs, such as food, heat and light. However, energy consumption has a considerable impact on the environment. Every source of energy has its advantages and disadvantages.

CONSUMPTION

Westerners, accustomed to a life of comfort, buy goods that require large amounts of energy to manufacture. The greatest impact on individual energy consumption has undoubtedly come from the invention of the automobile. Cars conquered North America, ensuring the population unequalled freedom of movement. Thanks to cars, people could live at a considerable distance from their workplaces. The result has been ever-increasing urban sprawl.

Graph EI.20 shows that Canada has one of the highest per capita rates of power consumption. This can be explained, at least partially, by the rigours of our climate.

"CLASSIC" SOURCES OF ENERGY

Traditionally, humans have used easily obtained fuels to produce energy. When they burn, almost all these fuels are transformed into carbon dioxide (CO_2), the principal gas behind climate change. Another disadvantage of these fuels is their limited supply.

Wood

In developing countries, people still use wood for cooking and for heating water. The practice is one of the causes of desertification, a serious problem in some of these countries. Cleared land no longer retains rainwater, which runs off into rivers, causing floods and sometimes even the contamination of drinking water sources.

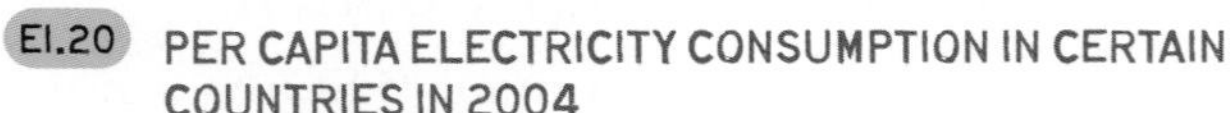
EI.20 PER CAPITA ELECTRICITY CONSUMPTION IN CERTAIN COUNTRIES IN 2004

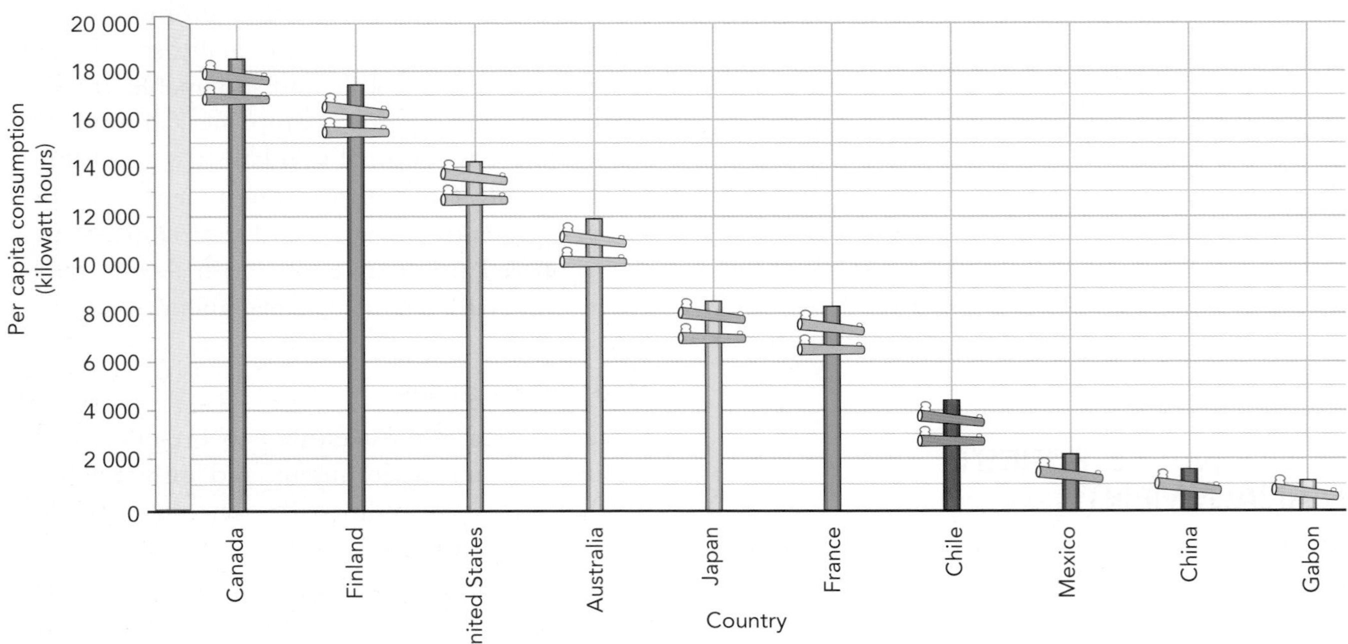

Source: United Nations Development Programme (UNDP), *Human Development Report 2007/2008* (2004 data).

Coal

Coal was the main source of energy in Canada at the beginning of the 20th century and is still widely used to produce electricity in various regions of the world. In addition to producing CO_2, coal combustion releases sulphur dioxide (SO_2) and nitrogen oxides (NO_x) into the atmosphere, causing acid rain. It also produces mercury emissions. The mercury eventually returns to the earth with rainwater, falling into lakes and rivers, where it is absorbed by fish—and later by humans who eat the fish.

EI.21 Burning coal releases pollutants into the air, specifically CO_2, one of the greenhouse gases responsible for climate change.

Oil

Oil wells draw petroleum (oil) from the depths of the Earth. The oil is then refined into a variety of products, including the gasoline we burn in our car engines. Like coal, its combustion generates CO_2, SO_2 and NO_x. In recent years, however, oil companies have reduced the concentration of sulphur in gasoline, to limit SO_2 emissions.

Using oil for fuel is not the only way in which it is harmful to the environment. Its extraction and transport can also be polluting. In Canada, for example, oil sand mines in Alberta produce a third of the country's greenhouse gas emissions. Huge quantities of steam are used to separate the oil from the grains of sand in a process that requires a lot of energy.

EI.22 Oil sands. It takes a lot of energy to separate the hydrocarbons from the grains of sand.

Natural gas

Natural gas is the second most widely used energy source in the world, after oil. It is used to heat homes and generate electricity, for example, and as fuel for gas stoves.

Natural gas combustion is generally a cleaner process than burning coal or oil. It generates little SO_2 and NO_x but just as much CO_2, one of the principal greenhouse gases.

Canada has plans to build liquefied natural gas (LNG) terminals on the East Coast to receive natural gas shipments by LNG tanker from Russia or Algeria. The projects are a source of controversy, however, because of the risks of accidents and spills.

EI.23 Liquefied natural gas terminals can store natural gas that arrives by tanker ship.

Nuclear power

When a uranium atom breaks up during **NUCLEAR FISSION**, it releases a large amount of energy in the form of heat, which can be transformed into electricity. The process does not generate greenhouse gases, but it does produce radioactive waste, which is hazardous to human health. Even though numerous precautions are taken to avoid radiation leakage into the environment, nuclear power generation is never completely accident-proof.

EI.24 Nuclear power plant in Saint-Laurent-des-Eaux, France

RENEWABLE SOURCES OF ENERGY

Scientists, engineers and representatives of both government and industry are caught up in an unprecedented race to discover and develop new sources of clean energy. Each of these sources presents different advantages and challenges.

Hydroelectricity

With its wealth of rivers, Québec produces almost all the power it needs in hydroelectric power plants. Huge dams block the rivers, causing their waters to accumulate upstream and put immense pressure on the dams. When large pipes under the dams are opened, the water rushes through them, spinning turbines along its way.

EI.25 Barrage Daniel-Johnson. It is the most famous dam in the hydroelectric complex called Manic-Outardes in the Côte-Nord region of Québec.

Wind power

When the wind hits the blades of a wind turbine, they turn, activating a power generator. Wind turbine towers can be as tall as 120 m. The largest ones can produce two megawatts of electricity—enough to supply 200 to 300 homes—when functioning at 30 percent of their full capacity (a realistic figure since the wind does not blow constantly).

EI.26 Wind turbines at Cap-Chat, in Gaspésie

Solar energy

It is estimated that the Earth receives enough solar energy in one hour to supply the energy needs of the planet for a whole year. Photovoltaic (solar) panels can convert part of this energy into electricity. They are made from materials that, on exposure to light, set electrons in motion, generating an electric current.

EI.27 Solar vehicles still have a long way to go before they can take to the roads.

Geothermal energy

The Earth's internal temperature rises with increasing depth below the surface. Engineers, geologists and other specialists have developed technologies to recover this energy—for example, by injecting fluids underground that can capture the heat and bring it back to the surface.

Tidal power

The movement of water in tides, as they ebb and flow, represents a significant source of energy. Engineers, hydrologists and other experts have developed technologies to transform this movement into electricity through the use of turbines.

REDUCING ENERGY DEMANDS

All energy production, however "green" the technology, has an impact on the environment. For this reason, the best way to meet the energy challenge is to reduce our demand.

The quest for **ENERGY EFFICIENCY** calls on us to reduce our energy consumption while continuing to meet our needs. Simple gestures in our daily lives can make a difference: turning off lights when we leave a room, turning down the heat when we leave the house or using energy-efficient light bulbs.

Emerging technologies may point the way to even greater efficiency. The following are some examples.

Energy-efficient cars

Automobile manufacturers are working on new models with greater fuel economy. Hybrid cars are at the forefront of this trend. They run on both gas and an electric motor, which reduces certain energy losses. During deceleration, for example, some of the dissipated kinetic energy is recovered and used to recharge the battery.

Hybrid cars are not the solution to all our energy problems. Hybrid SUVs ("sport utility vehicles") give consumers the impression they are making an environmentally friendly choice when these models actually burn more fuel than smaller cars with conventional gas engines.

Energy-efficient industries

Many factories emit water vapour (steam) in the manufacture of their products. The steam used to be released into the environment, but now it is captured and reused to heat the buildings during winter.

Energy-efficient homes

New homes are often built with maximal exposure to sunlight in order to reduce heating costs. Improved insulation helps conserve heat inside houses, for greater home comfort.

To encourage Québec home builders to use energy-efficient materials and techniques, the Agence de l'efficacité énergétique [the Agency for Energy Efficiency] has established the "Novoclimat" construction standards. Homes that meet these standards are better insulated, with energy-efficient ventilation and heating systems; they also cost less to run.

Residual materials

To satisfy their needs, humans have learned to draw on the Earth's natural resources and transform them into a variety of consumer goods, such as cellphones, laptops, cars and toys. The world's inhabitants have become avid consumers, and the more they consume, the more they pollute the environment with their waste.

EI.28 Canadians keep their cellphones for an average of 18 months before choosing a new model.

A GIANT GARBAGE CAN

People no longer buy goods simply to meet their needs; they buy objects that fulfill their desires. Garbage is piling up in landfills, putting ecosystems at risk. Graph EI.29 shows that the average Canadian produces 420 kg of garbage annually. That is less than a Spaniard, who generates 530 kg, but more than a Pole, with 170 kg. The amount of waste from discarded telecommunications equipment (telephones, cellphones, fax machines) in Canada exceeds 10 000 tonnes annually.

EI.29 ANNUAL PER CAPITA PRODUCTION OF HOUSEHOLD WASTE IN CERTAIN COUNTRIES, 1980-2005

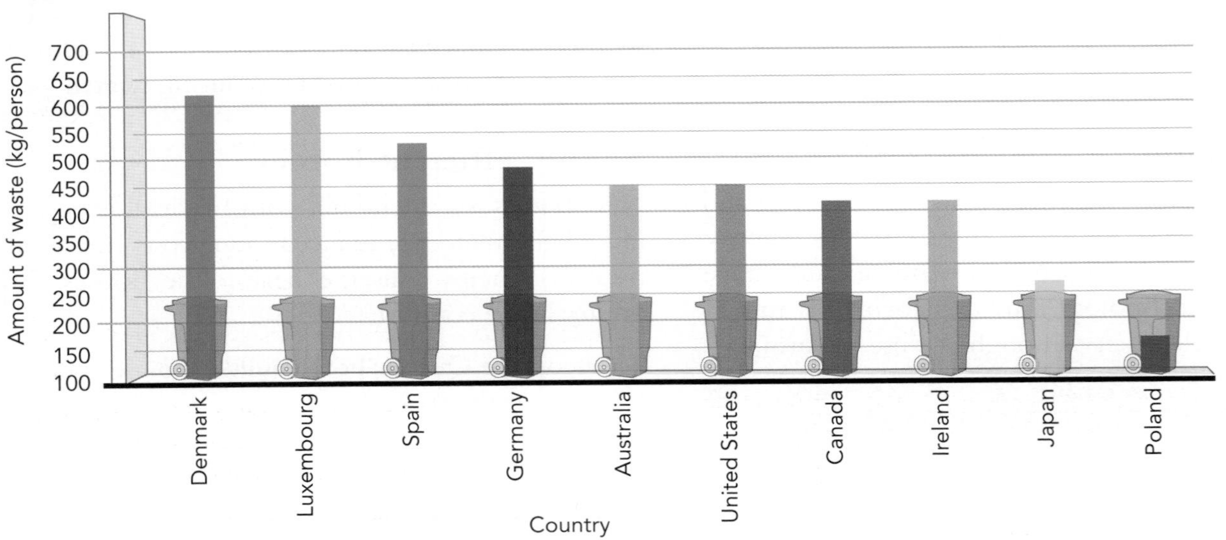

Source: *OECD Environmental Data: Compendium 2006/2007.*

WHERE DOES THE WASTE GO?

Household garbage is carried away to various disposal sites. In Québec, these sites are usually landfills. Cells are made by digging pits in the ground and lining them with waterproof membranes. Excavators dump the garbage in these cells and then cover it with a layer of earth; further layers of garbage and earth are added.

Landfills are not completely leakproof. Sometimes the cells are not fully sealed off, and the garbage mixes with rainwater. The contaminated water runs into the ground, infiltrating aquifers and bringing with it heavy metals and other pollutants it may have come in contact with. Once they reach the groundwater, pollutants can spread over large areas, threatening sources of drinking water wherever they go.

Another problem with landfills is that they are an important source of methane emissions. Methane (CH_4) is a greenhouse gas that is 21 times more powerful in trapping heat than carbon dioxide (CO_2). Methane is released into the atmosphere when anaerobic bacteria (which live in the absence of oxygen) decompose organic waste.

In most landfills in Québec, a system of pipes collects the methane and burns it, transforming it into CO_2 before it escapes into the atmosphere. Certain sites even make use of the methane to generate electricity by burning it to produce steam, which is then forced through turbines.

EI.30 Methane flares are often installed in landfills to burn off the gas released by waste decomposition before it can escape into the atmosphere.

NOT IN MY BACK YARD

The more a city expands, the more difficult it becomes to find nearby sites for garbage disposal. In Québec, landfills are overflowing, but people object strenuously to any plans for new disposal sites near their homes for fear of the stench of decomposing garbage.

THE 4R-D APPROACH

In its search for alternate solutions to overflowing landfills, the Québec government is promoting its own extended version of the classic three Rs of recycling (reduce, reuse and recycle). In the "4R-D" approach, waste management options should be considered in the following order: (source) reduction, reuse, recycling, resource recovery and disposal. To apply the four Rs, a consumer should think about the questions below (Table EI.31) before buying an object.

EI.31 THE 4R-D PRINCIPLES AND CONSUMER QUESTIONS

Principle	Questions
Reduce	Do I need this object?
Reuse	Do I already own an object similar to the one I am thinking about buying? Could I repair a similar object for reuse instead of buying a new one?
Recycle	Is this object easily recyclable? What about its packaging?
Recover (resource)	Could this object (and its packaging) have a second life, once discarded—for example, by being used to generate energy?

RECOVERY AND RECYCLING IN QUÉBEC

In 1998, the provincial government adopted the Québec Residual Materials Management Policy, 1998-2008. The overall objective of the policy was to divert at least 65 percent of waste from landfills to recycling or recovery operations.

Specific objectives for municipal waste recovery were as follows:

- 60 percent of glass, plastic, metal, fibres (paper and cardboard), bulky waste and putrescible material (kitchen and garden compostable waste)
- 80 percent of non-refillable beer and soft-drink containers
- 50 percent of textiles
- 20 percent of non-refundable aluminum
- 75 percent of oils, paints and pesticides (household hazardous materials)
- 60 percent of all other household hazardous materials

Paper, glass, metal and plastic are recovered through curbside collections and taken to sorting centres. There, they are separated and sold to recycling companies, who turn them into new products.

While paper recovery and recycling in 2006 met, and even surpassed, policy objectives, recovery rates for other materials were still well below target levels. (See the Recyc-Québec figures in Table EI.32.)

EI.32 RECOVERY RATES IN 2006

Residual material	Recovery rate	Goal
Paper and cardboard	75%	60%
Glass	40%	60%
Metal	24%	60%
Plastic	17%	60%
Total	48%	60%

Source: Recyc-Québec, *Bilan 2006 de la gestion des matières résiduelles au Québec.*

OTHER TYPES OF WASTE AND THEIR DISPOSAL

Certain other types of waste cannot be put in the recycling bin. Western governments, including the government of Québec, have set up programs to recover this waste for other uses or at least eliminate it safely. Some municipalities have eco-centres, where residents can dispose of waste that is not accepted in the regular garbage collection.

Compost

Waste material of animal or vegetable origin, such as table scraps, can be degraded by **DECOMPOSERS** and converted into compost, which is rich in nutrients that sustain plant life. The compost can be applied to gardens and farm crops.

Individual composters can be used in households to recover table scraps and garden waste and recycle them directly. Some municipalities have organized curbside collections of compostable material.

Household hazardous materials

Batteries, leftover paint, used oils, and medicines belong to a type of waste called *household hazardous materials*. They cannot be placed in recycling bins, but sending them to landfills may be harmful to the environment because they contain toxic substances.

Some municipalities organize collections of these materials several times a year. Residents are encouraged to hand over their hazardous waste, which is then recycled, or buried in specially designed landfill cells.

EI.33 EXAMPLES OF HOUSEHOLD HAZARDOUS MATERIALS

Place	Hazardous product	Corrosive	Flammable	Toxic	Explosive
Kitchen	Ammonia (glass cleaner)	✓		✓	
	Oven cleaner	✓			
Bathroom	Rubbing alcohol		✓	✓	
	Medicines			✓	
	Nail polish		✓	✓	
	Toilet cleaner	✓		✓	
Laundry room	Detergents and stain removers	✓			
	Bleach	✓		✓	
	Fabric softener	✓			
Basement and storage	Fluorescent light bulbs			✓	
	Batteries			✓	
	Latex paint	✓			
	Solvents	✓	✓	✓	
	Varnish	✓	✓	✓	
Garage or toolshed	Antifreeze		✓	✓	
	Car batteries	✓	✓	✓	
	Propane tanks				✓
	Pesticides	✓		✓	

Source: Adapted from Recyc-Québec.

Used tires

On May 16, 1990, in Saint-Amable, Québec, a pile of old tires caught fire. The fire burned for six days, consuming 3.5 million tires and spreading a thick black cloud of toxic smoke over the area. At that time, millions more tires lay abandoned in hundreds of storage sites across the province.

To prevent another such incident, the Government of Québec set up a recovery system for used tires. Today, vehicle owners must pay a tax of three dollars on each new tire they purchase in order to finance the system. Used tires are retreaded or recycled (into carpets, soundproofing panels or flower containers, for example) or used as fuel in cement plants.

EI.34 When tires burn, they release toxic smoke into the atmosphere.

Food production

By 2020, the Earth is expected to have a population of eight billion. How will the world's farms provide food for so many, when two billion people are already suffering from malnutrition today? The situation is further complicated by rising temperatures—the result of climate change—and by soil depletion from overuse.

AGRICULTURE IN THE INDUSTRIAL ERA

Agriculture has been revolutionized in recent decades to satisfy the growing demand for food. In industrialized countries, manual farm labour has practically disappeared, replaced by combine harvesters, electric milking machines and other farming technology. Producers aim for ever-higher yields, at ever-lower costs.

Many large agri-food companies are choosing monoculture, planting a single species of grain, fruit or vegetable over a vast area. Fields have become "factories," where the goal is mass production.

ENVIRONMENTAL IMPACT

The transition from traditional farming to industrial agriculture has taken its toll. The following paragraphs describe some of its effects on the environment.

Soil compaction

Heavy machinery compacts the soil on arable land. Once hardened, the ground does not absorb water as well, so the rain runs off the surface, carrying soil particles and useful nutrients into rivers and putting drinking water sources at risk.

EI.35 Fields of sunflowers stretch as far as the eye can see. In other places, similar fields are full of corn or apple trees. It is more profitable for producers to grow a single crop over a large area.

Soil depletion

Soil is fragile. Plants benefit from its micro-organisms, organic matter and minerals through the roots they put down. With its rapid crop rotation, intensive agriculture does not allow the soil enough time to recover between harvests and renew its supply of nutrients.

Fertilizers

The intensive use of chemical fertilizers to increase the productivity of farmland also has a considerable impact on the environment. Surplus fertilizers run off the ground with rainwater, making their way into groundwater, rivers and lakes. In lakes, they promote the rapid growth of algae, leading to **EUTROPHICATION**. The lakes suffer from a lack of oxygen, and "dead zones" gradually form. Fertilizer use is expected to continue increasing around the world and should reach almost 200 million tonnes by 2030 (Graph EI.36).

Pesticides

Farmers apply pesticides to their crops and fields to eliminate weeds and harmful insects. Pesticides can be divided into three main categories: insecticides, which kill insects; herbicides, which kill weeds; and fungicides, which eliminate fungi and mould. Unfortunately, these substances are not specific enough to act on only one type of organism. They are harmful, to varying extents, to many living organisms, including human beings.

Soil, groundwater, lakes, rivers and even the air can all be contaminated by pesticides used in farming. Once released into the environment, these harmful substances can stay there for years, upsetting the balance of ecosystems.

EI.36 EVOLUTION OF CHEMICAL FERTILIZER USE AROUND THE WORLD

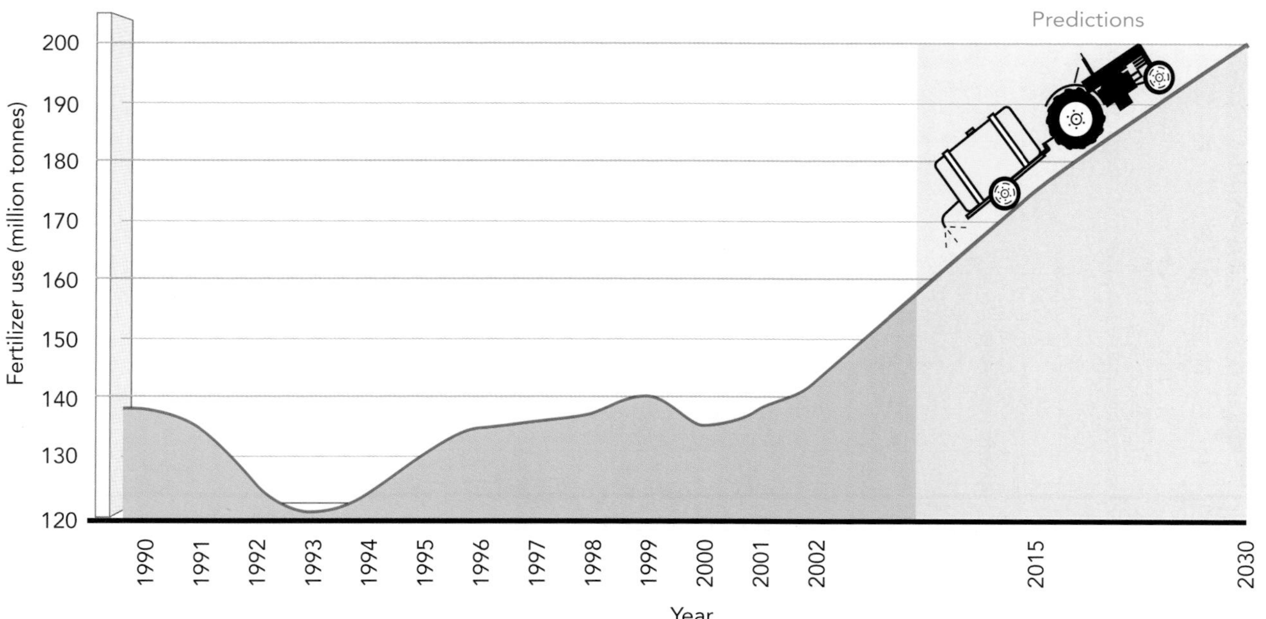

Source: Data from Earthtrends / World Resources Institute, 2006 and from FAO, *Fertilizer requirements in 2015 and 2030*, 2000.

GENETICALLY MODIFIED SEEDS

Since the earliest days of agriculture, farmers have selected the best plants to create **HYBRIDS** and the best animals to crossbreed. Hybridization ensures a strong genetic profile, resulting in healthy plants and animals.

Today, modern scientific advances make it possible to bypass certain stages of classic hybridization. Biochemists can now extract a DNA segment from a plant or animal cell, selecting a series of **GENES** that determine particularly desirable traits. The scientists can then insert this fragment into a host cell—a fertilized egg, for example. The selected genes enter the genetic code of the developing organism, which will display the desired traits. The resulting life form is called a *genetically modified organism* (GMO).

In their laboratories, scientists have perfected frost-resistant tomatoes by inserting a gene from certain arctic fish into the tomato cells. Other researchers have developed a drought-tolerant strain of wheat, using a gene from a scorpion.

Graph EI.37 shows that Canada is the fourth largest producer of GMOs in the world, after the United States, Argentina and Brazil. In 2007, Health Canada authorized 48 genetically modified food crops, including a herbicide-resistant strain of corn, a slow-ripening variety of tomato (which will stay red longer in grocery store displays) and a potato that is less vulnerable to the Colorado potato beetle, a pest that can severely damage potato crops. While genetically modified tomatoes and potatoes have been approved, Canadian grocery stores do not yet offer genetically modified fresh fruit and vegetables for sale. GMOs are present, however, in certain processed foods through the canola, grain corn and soybean among their ingredients.

EI.37 THE LARGEST PRODUCERS OF GMOs IN THE WORLD IN 2006

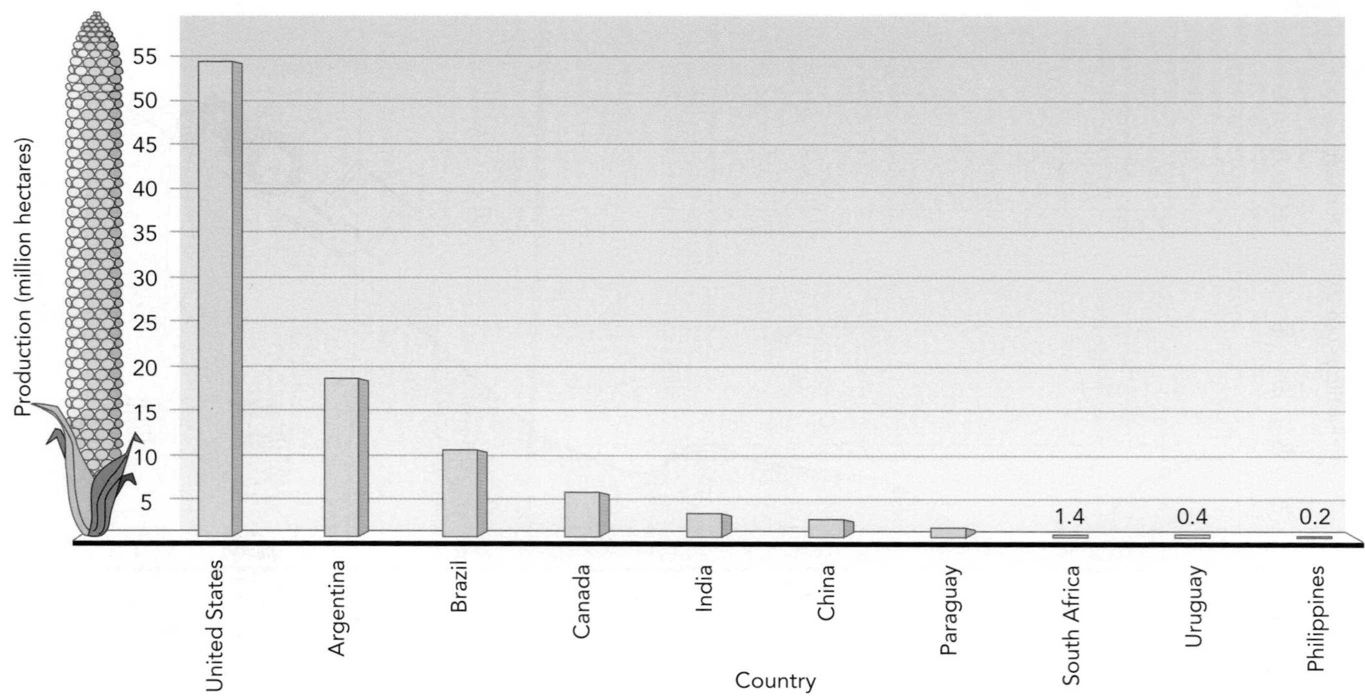

Source: International Service for the Acquisition of Agri-biotech Applications (ISAAA), 2006.

GMOs are not universally accepted; on the contrary, they are highly controversial. Many people believe that they represent a hazard to human health and an environmental risk. In the interest of public safety, they petition producers to put an end to GMO farming until it has been proven harmless.

POSSIBLE SOLUTIONS

To reduce the impact of agriculture on the environment and to guarantee high-quality foods, many environmentalists favour a return to traditional farming methods that are more respectful of nature.

Organic farming

Organic farmers choose not to use chemical fertilizers and pesticides on their fields. Instead, they use natural predators to control harmful insects, give the land time to recover between harvests and practise crop rotation to avoid depleting the soil of certain nutrients through repeated plantings of the same crop.

Organic farming takes more time and is more labour-intensive. That is why organic food is more expensive than non-organic products.

Local food

People can choose to buy as much of their food as possible from local farmers. In this way, the pollution caused by goods transport, especially the emission of greenhouse gases, is avoided.

Fair trade food

Fair trade ensures that food growers, especially those in developing countries, receive adequate compensation for their products and labour. Fair trade certification also guarantees that the originating farm respects the environment and assures the sustainability of resources in its production methods.

In Canada, certain brands of coffee, tea, sugar, cocoa, chocolate, bananas and rice have received fair trade certification.

EI.38 Consumers who buy a product with the fair trade logo can be sure that the producers have received a fair wage for their work. Opposite, a worker stands near a cacao, or cocoa tree.

APPENDIXES

CONTENTS

APPENDIX I

PERIODIC PROPERTIES OF THE ELEMENTS IN THE PERIODIC TABLE (AT 20°C AND 101.3 kPa)

Atomic number	Chemical symbol	Melting point (°C)	Boiling point (°C)	Density (g/mL)	Atomic radius (10^{-12} m)	First ionization energy (eV)	Electronegativity (Pauling scale)
1	H	-259	-253	0.000 084	79	13.60	2.1
2	He	-272	-269	0.000 17	89	24.58	-
3	Li	180	1342	0.53	179	5.39	1.0
4	Be	1278	2970	1.85	127	9.32	1.5
5	B	2300	2550	2.34	100	8.30	2.0
6	C	3650	4827	2.25	91	11.26	2.5
7	N	-210	-196	0.001 7	73	14.53	3.0
8	O	-219	-183	0.001 33	65	13.62	3.5
9	F	-219	-188	0.001 58	64	17.42	4.0
10	Ne	-249	-246	0.000 84	51	21.56	-
11	Na	98	883	0.97	188	5.14	0.9
12	Mg	649	1107	1.74	166	7.65	1.2
13	Al	660	2467	2.70	163	5.98	1.5
14	Si	1410	2355	2.32	132	8.15	1.8
15	P	44	280	1.82	108	10.48	2.1
16	S	113	444	2.5	107	10.36	2.5
17	Cl	-101	-35	0.002 95	97	12.97	3.0
18	Ar	-189	-186	0.001 66	131	15.76	-
19	K	63	760	0.86	252	4.34	0.8
20	Ca	839	1484	1.54	210	6.11	1.0
21	Sc	1541	2831	3.0	185	6.54	1.3
22	Ti	1660	3287	4.51	172	6.82	1.5
23	V	1890	3380	5.96	162	6.74	1.6
24	Cr	1857	2672	7.20	155	6.77	1.6
25	Mn	1244	1962	7.20	152	7.43	1.5
26	Fe	1535	2750	7.86	148	7.87	1.8
27	Co	1495	2870	8.90	146	7.86	1.8
28	Ni	1455	2730	8.90	143	7.63	1.8
29	Cu	1083	2567	8.92	142	7.73	1.9
30	Zn	419	907	7.14	143	9.39	1.6
31	Ga	30	2403	5.90	152	6.0	1.6
32	Ge	937	2830	5.35	137	7.90	1.8
33	As	613	817	5.72	129	9.81	2.0
34	Se	217	685	4.81	169	9.75	2.4
35	Br	-7	59	0.003 12	112	11.81	2.8
36	Kr	-157	-152	0.003 48	103	14.00	-

Atomic number	Chemical symbol	Melting point (°C)	Boiling point (°C)	Density (g/mL)	Atomic radius (10^{-12} m)	First ionization energy (eV)	Electronegativity (Pauling scale)
37	Rb	39	686	1.53	273	4.18	0.8
38	Sr	769	1384	2.60	230	5.69	1.0
39	Y	1522	3338	4.47	204	6.38	1.3
40	Zr	1852	4377	6.49	188	6.84	1.4
41	Nb	2468	4742	8.57	175	6.88	1.6
42	Mo	2610	5560	10.2	169	7.10	1.8
43	Tc	2172	4877	11.5	165	7.28	1.9
44	Ru	2310	3900	12.3	162	7.37	2.2
45	Rh	1966	3727	12.4	159	7.46	2.2
46	Pd	1554	2970	12.0	158	8.34	2.2
47	Ag	962	2212	10.5	160	7.57	1.9
48	Cd	321	765	8.65	160	8.99	1.7
49	In	156	2080	7.30	181	5.78	1.7
50	Sn	232	2270	7.30	156	7.34	1.8
51	Sb	630	1750	6.68	168	8.64	1.9
52	Te	449	990	6.00	143	9.01	2.1
53	I	113	184	4.93	132	10.45	2.5
54	Xe	-112	-107	0.005 49	171	12.13	-
55	Cs	28	669	1.88	300	3.89	0.7
56	Ba	725	1640	3.51	248	5.21	0.9
57	La	921	3457	6.17	231	5.58	1.1
58	Ce	799	3426	6.65	226	5.47	1.1
59	Pr	931	3512	6.77	225	5.42	1.1
60	Nd	1024	3027	7.00	223	5.49	1.1
61	Pm	1168	2460	7.22	222	5.55	1.1
62	Sm	1077	1791	7.52	220	5.64	1.2
63	Eu	822	1597	5.24	230	5.67	1.2
64	Gd	1313	3266	7.90	217	6.14	1.2
65	Tb	1360	3123	8.23	215	5.85	1.2
66	Dy	1412	2562	8.55	213	5.93	1.2
67	Ho	1474	2695	8.79	212	6.02	1.2
68	Er	1529	2863	9.06	210	6.10	1.2
69	Tm	1545	1947	9.32	208	6.18	1.2
70	Yb	819	1194	6.96	217	6.25	1.1
71	Lu	1663	3395	9.84	199	5.43	1.2
72	Hf	2227	4602	13.3	186	7.0	1.3
73	Ta	2996	5425	16.6	176	7.89	1.5
74	W	3410	5660	19.3	170	7.98	1.7
75	Re	3180	5627	20.5	167	7.88	1.9
76	Os	2700	5300	22.5	164	8.7	2.2
77	Ir	2410	4130	22.4	161	9.1	2.2
78	Pt	1772	3827	21.4	161	9.0	2.2
79	Au	1064	3080	18.9	162	9.22	2.4
80	Hg	-39	356	13.6	168	10.4	1.9
81	Tl	303	1457	11.8	189	6.11	1.8
82	Pb	327	1740	11.4	178	7.41	1.8
83	Bi	271	1560	9.8	159	7.29	1.9
84	Po	254	962	9.4	160	8.42	2.0
85	At	302	337	unknown	143	unknown	2.2
86	Rn	-71	-62	0.009 23	134	10.75	-

APPENDIX 2

PROPERTIES OF COMMON SUBSTANCES

SUBSTANCES THAT ARE GASES AT 20°C

Substance (chemical formula)	Description	Uses and characteristics	Hazards and precautions	Physical properties				Chemical properties
				MP (°C)	BP (°C)	ρ (g/mL at 20°C)	Solubility (g/L of water at 20°C)	
Ammonia (NH_3)	• Colourless • Characteristic odour	• Manufacture of cleaning products and fertilizers • Refrigeration	• Highly toxic, irritating and corrosive • Can cause burns	-78	-33	0.000 75	531	• Produces white smoke in reaction with hydrochloric acid • Extinguishes flames • Colours litmus paper blue[1]
Carbon dioxide (CO_2)	• Colourless • Odourless • Nonexistent in liquid form	• Product of combustion • Soft drinks • Dry ice (in solid form)	• Causes the greenhouse effect	-79[2]	n/a	0.001 98	1.6	• Extinguishes flames • Clouds limewater • Colours litmus paper red[1]
Carbon monoxide (CO)	• Colourless • Odourless	• By-product of incomplete combustion	• Lethal if inhaled • Flammable	-207	-192	0.001 25	0.26	• Produces a bright blue flame
Chlorine (Cl_2)	• Greenish yellow • Suffocating odour	• Disinfectant • Drinking water treatment • Bleaching agent	• Highly toxic • Irritant to the airways, eyes and skin	-102	-35	0.002 94	7.3	• Reignites a glowing splint
Helium (He)	• Colourless • Odourless	• Balloon inflation • Cryogenics • Welding • Refrigeration	• Usually non-toxic, but can cause asphyxia if inhaled in large amounts	-272	-269	0.000 18	0.0017	• Inert (does not react) • Extinguishes flames
Hydrochloric acid (HCl)	• Colourless • Sharp odour	• Metal cleaning • Rubber and cotton processing	• Highly toxic and corrosive • Can cause burns, coughing, etc.	-114	-85	0.001 64	420	• Produces white smoke in reaction with ammonia • Extinguishes flames • Colours litmus paper red[1]

Hydrogen gas (H_2)	• Colourless • Odourless	• Manufacture of certain substances (ammonia, hydrogenated vegetable oil, etc.) • Rocket fuel	• Explosive in the presence of a flame • Can cause asphyxia	-259	-253	0.000 09	0.002	• Explodes in the presence of a burning splint
Hydrogen sulphide (H_2S)	• Colourless • Characteristic odour of rotten eggs	• Protection of iron	• Toxic • Can damage the sense of smell • Flammable	-83	-60	0.001 54	4.13	• Colours lead acetate paper black • Explodes in the presence of a flame
Methane or natural gas (CH_4)	• Colourless • Odourless	• Fuel	• Flammable	-183	-162	0.000 72	0.025	• Explodes in the presence of a flame
Molecular nitrogen (N_2)	• Colourless • Odourless	• Main component of air (78%) • Freezing of living cells (cryogenics)	• Usually non-toxic, but can cause asphyxia if inhaled in large amounts	-210	-196	0.001 25	0.02	• Extinguishes flames
Molecular oxygen (O_2)	• Colourless • Odourless	• Component of air (21%) • Welding • Medicine	• Maintains combustion	-218	-183	0.001 43	0.04	• Reignites a glowing splint
Ozone (O_3)	• Pale blue • Slight odour	• Protection of the Earth's inhabitants from UV rays at high altitude • Pollutant at low altitude	• Highly toxic if inhaled • Explosive	-193	-111	0.002 14	0.57	• Reignites a glowing splint
Propane (C_3H_8)	• Colourless • Odourless	• Barbecue fuel	• Flammable	-188	-42	0.001 83	0.119	• Produces a blue flame

MP: melting point **BP: boiling point** **ρ: density** **n/a: not applicable**

1. This property becomes apparent when the substance is dissolved in water.
2. This temperature corresponds to the sublimation point.

SUBSTANCES THAT ARE LIQUIDS AT 20°C

Substance (chemical formula)	Description	Uses and characteristics	Hazards and precautions	Physical properties					Chemical properties
				MP (°C)	BP (°C)	ρ (g/mL)	EC	Solubility in water	
Acetic acid (CH_3COOH)	• Colourless • Characteristic odour of vinegar	• Food (produces vinegar when diluted in water) • Antiseptic • Disinfectant	• Corrosive • Irritating fumes • Can cause burns	17	118	1.05	Yes	Yes	• Colours litmus paper red
Ethanol or ethyl alcohol (C_2H_6O)	• Colourless • Characteristic odour	• Product of sugar fermentation	• If ingested, can cause inebriation, nausea, vomiting • Hazardous to the eyes • Flammable	-114	78	0.79	No	Yes	• Produces a pale blue flame
Ethylene glycol ($HOCH_2CH_2OH$)	• Colourless • Slightly sweet odour	• Antifreeze • Manufacture of vaccines	• Irritating fumes • Can cause vomiting and paralysis	-13	198	1.11	No	Yes	• Flammable
Glycerin or glycerol ($C_3H_8O_3$)	• Colourless • Odourless • Viscous • Sweet-tasting	• Lubricating agent in medicines and cosmetics • Bubbling liquid	• Explosive under certain conditions	18	290	1.26	No	Yes	• Explodes in the presence of some substances
Mercury (Hg)	• Silvery grey • Shiny	• Thermometers • Barometers • Mirrors • UV lamps	• Highly toxic • Can cause neurological disorders	-39	357	13.55	Yes	No	• Reacts with nitric acid (HNO_3) • Oxidizes to form a black solid
Methanol or methyl alcohol (CH_3OH)	• Colourless • Characteristic odour	• Antifreeze • Fuel • Solvent	• Toxic if ingested • Can be lethal • Dries the skin • Causes blindness • Flammable	-98	65	0.79	No	Yes	• Produces a pale blue flame
Water (H_2O)	• Colourless • Odourless	• Basic necessity of life • Food • Solvent	• None	0	100	1.00	No	n/a	• Colours cobalt chloride paper pink • Colours litmus paper purple

MP: melting point **BP:** boiling point **ρ:** density **EC:** electrical conductivity **n/a:** not applicable

SUBSTANCES THAT ARE SOLIDS AT 20°C

Substance (chemical formula)	Description	Uses and characteristics	Hazards and precautions	Physical properties					Chemical properties
				MP (°C)	BP (°C)	ρ (g/mL)	EC	Solubility (g/L of water at 20°C)	
Aluminum (Al)	• Grey-white • Odourless • Shiny • Malleable	• Outer wall coverings • Cans for preserving food • Automobiles	• Toxic in large amounts	660	2467	2.7	Yes (good conductor)	0	• Oxidizes to form a white solid
Barium chloride ($BaCl_2$)	• White or colourless crystals • Odourless	• Fireworks • Manufacture of pigments	• Toxic if ingested • Avoid contact with skin	963	1560	3.90	Yes[1]	360	• Produces a yellowish-green flame
Barium nitrate ($Ba(NO_3)_2$)	• White crystals • Odourless	• Fireworks • Ceramics manufacture • Green traffic lights	• Highly toxic if inhaled or ingested	590	n/a[2]	3.24	Yes[1]	87	• Produces a yellowish-green flame
Calcium carbonate ($CaCO_3$)	• White • Odourless	• Component of chalk • Component of marble	• Produces a dust that irritates the eyes and airways	n/a[2]	n/a	2.83	Yes[1]	0.0153	• Releases carbon dioxide in the presence of an acid • Colours litmus paper blue[1]
Calcium chloride ($CaCl_2$)	• White crystals • Odourless	• Food • Deicer for roads • Concrete hardener	• Eye irritant	772	1935	2.15	Yes[1]	425	• Produces an orange-red flame
Calcium hydroxide ($Ca(OH)_2$)	• White • Odourless	• Forms limewater when diluted in water	• Avoid contact with eyes	n/a[2]	n/a	2.24	Yes[1]	1.59	• Colours litmus paper blue[1]

MP: melting point BP: boiling point ρ: density EC: electrical conductivity n/a: not applicable

1. This property becomes apparent when the substance is dissolved in water.
2. Not applicable because this substance decomposes before reaching its melting or boiling point.

Substance (chemical formula)	Description	Uses and characteristics	Hazards and precautions	Physical properties					Chemical properties
				MP (°C)	BP (°C)	ρ (g/mL)	EC	Solubility (g/L of water at 20°C)	
Carbon (diamond) (C)	• Colourless crystals • Odourless	• Jewellery • Drilling	• n/a	3547	4200	3.52	Yes (but poor conductor)	0	• Oxidizes to form carbon dioxide
Carbon (graphite) (C)	• Grey-black • Odourless	• Good fuel • Essential element to life • Pencil leads • Steel	• If burned, produces a greenhouse gas • Irritating dust	3652	4200	2.09	Yes (but poor conductor)	0	• Oxidizes to form carbon dioxide
Copper (Cu)	• Reddish brown • Odourless • Shiny	• Essential element to life, in small doses • Electrical wires • Pipes for plumbing • Coins	• Dust that irritates the eyes and stomach	1083	2595	8.94	Yes (excellent conductor)	0	• Oxidizes to form a greenish or black solid • Produces a green flame
Copper oxide (CuO)	• Black powder • Odourless	• Green pigment • Fireworks	• Toxic if ingested	1446	n/a[2]	6.32	Yes[1]	0	• Reacts with certain metals • Produces a blue-green flame
Copper sulphate ($CuSO_4$)	• Blue crystals • Odourless	• Fungicides • Bactericides • Pesticides • Dietary supplement for hogs	• Highly toxic • Avoid contact with skin	n/a[2]	n/a	3.60	Yes[1]	220	• Produces a blue-green flame
Glucose ($C_6H_{22}O_{11}$)	• White • Slightly sweet odour • Sometimes sticky texture	• Product of photosynthesis by plants • Food	• Dust that irritates the eyes	146	n/a[2]	1.56	No	1000	• Turns golden in colour when heated
Gold (Au)	• Golden • Odourless • Shiny • Malleable	• Jewellery • Coins • Electronic circuits	• n/a	1064	2807	19.32	Yes (good conductor)	0	• Does not oxidize • Reacts with ammonia

Iodine (I_2)	• Black-purple crystals • Acrid odour	• Essential element to life, in small doses • Antiseptic • Halogen lamps • Pharmaceutical products	• Releases toxic vapours	114	184	4.93	No	0.29	• Reacts in the presence of starch
Iron (Fe)	• Grey-white • Odourless • Shiny	• Essential element to life • Steel • Construction • Automobiles • Magnetic tape • Vitamin supplements	• Irritating dust	1535	3000	7.86	Yes (good conductor)	0	• Oxidizes to form a reddish-brown solid
Lead (Pb)	• Bluish grey • Odourless • Highly malleable • Shiny	• Protection from radiation • Batteries	• Highly toxic if ingested • Causes neurological disorders	327	1740	11.34	Yes (good conductor)	0	• Oxidizes to form a black solid
Lithium chloride (LiCl)	• White powder • Odourless	• Fireworks • Refrigeration • Antidepressants	• Can cause kidney problems in the long term	605	1360	2.07	Yes[1]	454	• Produces a bright red flame
Lithium nitrate ($LiNO_3$)	• White powder • Odourless	• Fireworks	• Toxic if ingested • Avoid contact with skin	255	n/a[2]	2.38	Yes[1]	430	• Produces a bright red flame
Magnesium (Mg)	• Grey-white • Odourless • Shiny	• Essential element to life, in small doses • Computer casings • Pharmaceutical products	• Flammable in small pieces	650	1100	1.74	Yes (good conductor)	0	• Oxidizes to form a white solid • Produces a very intense white flame
Nickel (Ni)	• Grey-white • Odourless • Shiny	• Coins • Stainless steel • Television screens	• Can cause lung cancer, in high doses • Can irritate the skin	1455	2730	8.90	Yes (good conductor)	0	• Oxidizes slightly to form a green solid

MP: melting point **BP: boiling point** **ρ: density** **EC: electrical conductivity** **n/a: not applicable**

1. This property becomes apparent when the substance is dissolved in water.
2. Not applicable because this substance decomposes before reaching its melting or boiling point.

Substance (chemical formula)	Description	Uses and characteristics	Hazards and precautions	Physical properties					Chemical properties
				MP (°C)	BP (°C)	ρ (g/mL)	EC	Solubility (g/L of water at 20°C)	
Nickel chloride ($NiCl_2$)	• Green crystals • Odourless	• Ink • Gas masks	• Irritant • Avoid contact with skin	1001	n/a	3.55	Yes[1]	642	• Colours litmus paper red[1] • Produces a green flame
Para-dichloro-benzene ($C_6H_4Cl_2$)	• Colourless or white crystals • Characteristic odour	• Insecticides • Mothballs	• Fumes that irritate the skin, throat and eyes	54	174	1.46	No	0.08	• Reacts with aluminum
Potassium chloride (KCl)	• White crystals • Odourless	• Photography • Batteries	• Toxic if ingested	774	1411	1.99	Yes[1]	344	• Produces a purple flame
Potassium nitrate (KNO_3)	• White crystals • Odourless	• Fertilizers	• Toxic if ingested • Do not pour down drains	334	n/a[2]	2.11	Yes[1]	357	• Produces a purple flame
Silver (Ar)	• Silvery white • Odourless • Shiny • Malleable	• Jewellery • Photography • Electrical components	• Moderately toxic if ingested	961	2212	10.40	Yes (excellent conductor)	0	• Oxidizes to form a black solid • Produces a silvery-white flame
Sodium chloride (table salt) (NaCl)	• White cubic crystals • Odourless	• Food • Deicer for roads	• Can cause high blood pressure	801	1413	2.17	Yes[1]	357	• Produces an orange-yellow flame
Sodium hydroxide (NaOH)	• White crystals • Odourless	• Manufacture of plastics, detergents, soaps, etc.	• Avoid contact with skin • Corrosive	318	1390	2.13	Yes[1]	1111	• Colours litmus paper blue[1]
Strontium chloride ($SrCl_2$)	• White crystals • Odourless	• Fireworks	• Toxic if ingested • Avoid contact with skin	875	1250	3.05	Yes[1]	538	• Produces a red flame

Strontium nitrate ($Sr(NO_3)_2$)	• White crystals • Odourless	• Fireworks • Red traffic lights	• Toxic if ingested • Avoid contact with skin	570	645	2.99	Yes[1]	700	• Produces a red flame
Sulphur (S)	• Yellow • Characteristic odour	• Essential element to life, in small doses • Fungicides • Matches • Fireworks	• Causes acid rain • Irritant to the skin, eyes and airways	115	445	1.96	No	0	• Produces a blue flame
Tungsten (W)	• Grey • Odourless • Shiny	• Filament for light bulbs • Heating elements	• Can irritate the airways	3410	5900	19.35	Yes (good conductor)	0	• Oxidizes slightly • Reacts with nitric acid

MP: melting point BP: boiling point ρ: density EC: electrical conductivity n/a: not applicable

1. This property becomes apparent when the substance is dissolved in water.
2. Not applicable because this substance decomposes before reaching its melting or boiling point.

APPENDIX 3

UNITS OF MEASUREMENT AND MATHEMATICAL FORMULAS

UNITS OF MEASUREMENT

Measure	Symbol	Unit of measurement	Symbol of the unit of measurement	Some equivalencies
Area	A	• Square metre (square centimetre)	m^2 (cm^2)	$1\ m^2 = 10\ 000\ cm^2$
Concentration	C	• Gram of solute per litre of solution • Part per million	$\frac{g}{L}$ ppm	$\frac{1\ g}{1\ L} = \frac{1\ g}{1000\ mL}$ $1\ ppm = \frac{1\ mg}{1000\ g}$ Aqueous solution: $1\ ppm \simeq \frac{1\ mg}{1\ L}$
Current intensity	I	• Ampere	A	$1\ A = \frac{1\ C}{1\ s}$ $1\ A = \frac{1\ V}{1\ \Omega}$
Distance travelled	d	• Metre (kilometre)	m (km)	1 km = 1000 m
Electrical charge	q or Q	• Coulomb	C	$1\ C = 6.25 \times 10^{18}$ elementary charges
Electrical power	P_e	• Watt (kilowatt)	W (kW)	1 kW = 1000 W $1\ W = \frac{1\ J}{1\ s}$ $1\ W = 1\ A \times 1\ V$
Electrical resistance	R	• Ohm	Ω	$1\ \Omega = \frac{1\ V}{1\ A}$
Energy – Kinetic energy – Mechanical energy – Gravitational potential energy – Thermal energy – Electrical energy	E E_k E_m E_p E_t	• Joule (kilojoule) • Kilowatt hour	J (kJ) kWh	$1\ J = 1\ N \times 1\ m$ $1\ J = 1\ \frac{kg \times m^2}{s^2}$ 1 kJ = 1000 J 1 kWh = 3600 kJ
Force – Electrical force – Gravitational force – Buoyant force	F F_e F_g F_b	• Newton	N	$1\ N = 1\ \frac{kg \times m}{s^2}$ On Earth: $1\ N \simeq 100\ g$
Heat	Q	• Joule	J	1 kJ = 1000 J
Height	h	• Metre (kilometre)	m (km)	1 km = 1000 m

Measure	Symbol	Unit of measurement	Symbol of the unit of measurement	Some equivalencies
Intensity of the gravitational field or gravitational acceleration	g	• Newton per kilogram • Metre per second squared	$\frac{N}{kg}$ $\frac{m}{s^2}$	$1\ \frac{N}{kg} = 1\ \frac{m}{s^2}$
Length	L	• Metre (kilometre)	m (km)	1 km = 1000 m
Mass	m	• Gram (milligram, kilogram) • Tonne	g (mg, kg)	1 kg = 1000 g 1 tonne = 1000 kg
Molar concentration	C	• Mole of solute per litre of solution	$\frac{mol}{L}$	$\frac{1\ mol}{1\ L} = \frac{6.02 \times 10^{23}\ entities}{1\ L}$
Molar mass	M	• Gram per mole	$\frac{g}{mol}$	$\frac{1\ g}{1\ mol} = \frac{1\ g}{6.02 \times 10^{23}\ entities}$
Number of moles	n	• Mole	mol	1 mol = 6.02×10^{23} entities
Potential difference or voltage	V	• Volt	V	$1\ V = \frac{1\ J}{1\ C}$ $1\ V = 1\ A \times 1\ \Omega$
Pressure	P	• Pascal (kilopascal) • Millimetre of mercury	Pa (kPa) mm Hg	$1\ Pa = \frac{1\ N}{1\ m^2}$ 1 kPa = 1000 Pa 1 mm Hg = 0.13 kPa
Specific heat capacity[1]	c	• Joule per gram per degree Celsius	$\frac{J}{g°C}$	$1\ \frac{J}{g°C} = 1\ \frac{1\ kJ}{kg°C}$
Temperature[1]	T	• Degree Celsius • Kelvin	°C K	0°C = 273 K
Time	t	• Second • Minute • Hour	s min h	1 min = 60 s 1 h = 60 min 1 h = 3600 s
Velocity / speed	v	• Metre per second • Kilometre per hour	$\frac{m}{s}$ $\frac{km}{h}$	$1\ \frac{m}{s} = 3.6\ \frac{km}{h}$
Volume	V	• Cubic metre (cubic centimetre, cubic decimetre) • Litre (millilitre)	m^3 (cm^3, dm^3) L (mL)	1 mL = 1 cm^3 1 L = 1 dm^3 1 L = 1000 mL
Weight	w	• Newton	N	$1\ N = 1\ \frac{kg \times m}{s^2}$
Work	W	• Joule	J	$1\ J = 1\ N \times 1\ m$

1. In this textbook, we use the degree Celsius (°C) rather than the kelvin, which is the SI base unit.

MATHEMATICAL FORMULAS

THE MATERIAL WORLD

AVERAGE SPEED

$v = \frac{d}{\Delta t}$ where v is the average speed (in m/s)
d is the distance travelled (in m)
Δt is the time variation—in other words, the travelling time (in s)

CONCENTRATION

$C = \frac{m}{V}$ where C is the concentration (in g/L)
m is the mass of the solute (in g)
V is the volume of solution (in L)

$C = \frac{n}{V}$ where C is the concentration (in mol/L)
n is the amount of solute (in mol)
V is the volume of solution (in L)

COULOMB'S LAW

$F_e = \frac{kq_1q_2}{r^2}$ where F_e is the electrical force (in N)
k is Coulomb's constant, which is 9×10^9 Nm^2/C^2
q_1 is the charge of the first particle (in C)
q_2 is the charge of the second particle (in C)
r is the distance between the two particles (in m)

CURRENT INTENSITY

$I = \frac{q}{\Delta t}$ where I is the current intensity (in A)
q is the charge (in C)
Δt is the time interval (in s)

EFFECTIVE FORCE (USEFUL TRIGONOMETRIC FUNCTIONS)

$$\text{Sin } A = \frac{\text{side opposite to angle } A}{\text{hypotenuse}}$$

$$\text{Cos } A = \frac{\text{side adjacent to angle } A}{\text{hypotenuse}}$$

$$\text{Tan } A = \frac{\text{side opposite to angle } A}{\text{side adjacent to angle } A}$$

Note: Most scientific calculators immediately give the sine (sin), cosine (cos) and tangent (tan or tg) values of any angle. However, make sure the calculator measures angles in degrees (and not in radians or grads).

ELECTRICAL ENERGY USED

$E = P_e \Delta t$ where E is the electrical energy used (in J or kWh)
P_e is the electrical power (in W or kW)
Δt is the time interval (in s or h)

ELECTRICAL POWER

$P_e = \frac{W}{\Delta t}$ where P_e is the electrical power (in W)
W is the work (in J)
Δt is the time required (in s)

$P_e = VI$ where P_e is the electrical power (in W)
V is the potential difference (in V)
I is the current intensity (in A)

GRAVITATIONAL POTENTIAL ENERGY

$E_p = mgh$ where E_p is the gravitational potential energy (in J)
m is the mass of the object (in kg)
g is the gravitational field intensity (in N/kg)
h is the height of the object above the reference surface (in m)

HEAT AND THERMAL ENERGY

$Q = \Delta E_t$ where Q is the heat (in J)
ΔE_t is the variation in thermal energy (in J)

$Q = mc\Delta T$ where Q is the heat (in J)
m is the mass (in g)
c is the specific heat capacity (in J/g°C)
ΔT is the temperature variation (in °C)

$\Delta T = T_f - T_i$ where T_f is the final temperature (in °C)
T_i is the initial temperature (in °C)

KINETIC ENERGY

$E_k = \frac{1}{2} mv^2$ where E_k is the kinetic energy of the object (in J)
m is the mass of the object (in kg)
v is the velocity of the object (in m/s)

MECHANICAL ENERGY

$E_m = E_k + E_p$ where E_m is the mechanical energy (in J)
E_k is the kinetic energy (in J)
E_p is the potential energy (in J)

MOLAR MASS

$M = \frac{m}{n}$ where M is the molar mass (in g/mol)
m is the mass (in g)
n is the number of moles (in mol)

OHM'S LAW

$V = RI$ where V is the potential difference (in V)
R is the resistance (in Ω)
I is the current intensity (in A)

POTENTIAL DIFFERENCE

$V = \frac{E}{q}$ where V is the potential difference (in V)
E is the energy transferred (in J)
q is the charge (in C)

PRESSURE

$P = \frac{F}{A}$ where P is the pressure (in Pa)
F is the force perpendicular to the surface (in N)
A is the surface area subjected to the force (in m^2)

WEIGHT AND GRAVITATIONAL FORCE

$w = F_g = mg$ where w is the weight (in N)
F_g is the gravitational force (in N)
m is the mass (in kg)
g is the gravitational field intensity (in N/kg)

WORK

$W = \Delta E$ where W is the work (in J)
ΔE is the variation in energy in an object or a system (in J)

$W = F_{//}d$ where W is the work (in J)
$F_{//}$ is the force or the force component parallel to the direction of travel (in N)
d is the distance travelled by the object (in m)

THE LIVING WORLD

POPULATION DENSITY

$$\text{Population density} = \frac{\text{Number of individuals}}{\text{Space (area or volume) occupied}}$$

POPULATION SIZE, ESTIMATED USING SAMPLE AREAS

$$\text{Population size} = \frac{\text{Average number of individuals per section} \times \text{Total study area}}{\text{Area of a section}}$$

POPULATION SIZE, ESTIMATED USING THE MARK-RECAPTURE METHOD

$$\text{Population size} = \frac{\text{Number of marked animals} \times \text{Total number of animals captured the second time}}{\text{Number of marked animals recaptured}}$$

APPENDIX 4

AMINO ACIDS IN PROTEIN COMPOSITION AND THE GENETIC CODE

Amino acid	Abbreviation	Amino acid	Abbreviation	Amino acid	Abbreviation
Alanine	Ala	Glycine	Gly	Proline	Pro
Arginine	Arg	Histidine	His	Serine	Ser
Asparagine	Asn	Isoleucine	Ile	Threonine	Thr
Aspartic acid	Asp	Leucine	Leu	Tryptophan	Trp
Cysteine	Cys	Lysine	Lys	Tyrosine	Tyr
Glutamic acid	Glu	Methionine	Met	Valine	Val
Glutamine	Gln	Phenylalanine	Phe		

THE GENETIC CODE

The genetic code indicates how each nucleotide triplet (codon) carried by the mRNA should be translated during protein synthesis. In the example below, the amino acid trytophan (Trp) is encoded by the codon UGG, while the amino acid phenylalanine (Phe) is encoded by the codon UUU.

The codon AUG not only encodes the amino acid methionine (Met) but also acts as the start codon, initiating the protein synthesis. Codons UAA, UAG and UGA (stop codons) signal the end of the protein synthesis.

GENETIC CODE

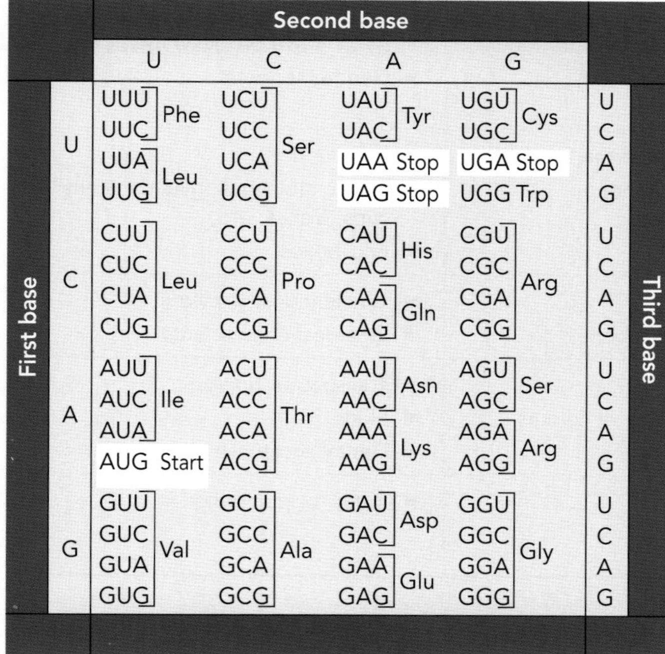

First base	Second base: U	C	A	G	Third base
U	UUU Phe	UCU Ser	UAU Tyr	UGU Cys	U
	UUC Phe	UCC Ser	UAC Tyr	UGC Cys	C
	UUA Leu	UCA Ser	UAA Stop	UGA Stop	A
	UUG Leu	UCG Ser	UAG Stop	UGG Trp	G
C	CUU Leu	CCU Pro	CAU His	CGU Arg	U
	CUC Leu	CCC Pro	CAC His	CGC Arg	C
	CUA Leu	CCA Pro	CAA Gln	CGA Arg	A
	CUG Leu	CCG Pro	CAG Gln	CGG Arg	G
A	AUU Ile	ACU Thr	AAU Asn	AGU Ser	U
	AUC Ile	ACC Thr	AAC Asn	AGC Ser	C
	AUA Ile	ACA Thr	AAA Lys	AGA Arg	A
	AUG Start	ACG Thr	AAG Lys	AGG Arg	G
G	GUU Val	GCU Ala	GAU Asp	GGU Gly	U
	GUC Val	GCC Ala	GAC Asp	GGC Gly	C
	GUA Val	GCA Ala	GAA Glu	GGA Gly	A
	GUG Val	GCG Ala	GAG Glu	GGG Gly	G

EXAMPLE OF TRANSLATION

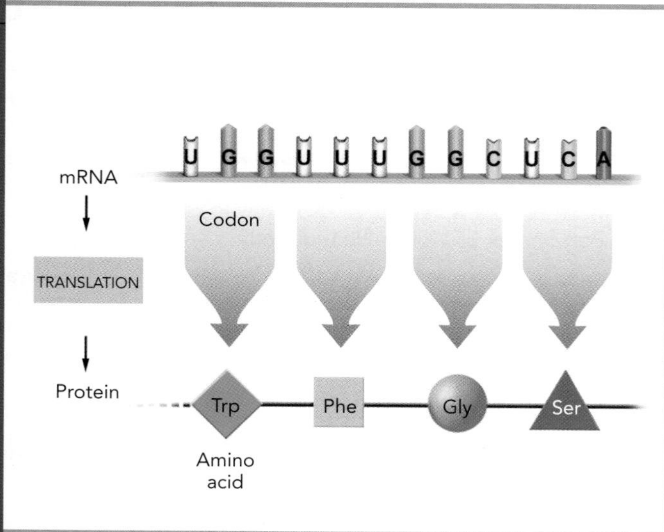

APPENDIX 5

THE MOST COMMONLY USED PLASTICS, METALS AND ALLOYS

THE MOST COMMONLY USED PLASTICS

		Recycling code	Properties	Uses
Thermoplastics	Polyethylene terephthalate	1 PETE	• Resilient • Impervious to gases and humidity • Relatively heat-resistant	• Bottles (soft drinks, sports drinks, etc.) • Containers (peanut butter, jam, etc.) • Oven-proof packaging
	Polyethylenes	2 HDPE 4 LDPE	• Flexible • Easy to cut • Easy to shape • Impervious to humidity	• Compressible bottles (mustard, dishwashing liquid, etc.) • Garbage bags • Grocery bags • Plastic film for wrapping food • Beach balls
	Polyvinyl chloride (PVC)	3 V	• Hard • Resistant to penetration by grease, oil and many chemicals	• Tubes for medications • Patio furniture • Cassette cases • Building materials (pipes, plumbing connections, window edging)
	Polypropylene	5 PP	• Resilient • Heat-resistant • Resistant to penetration by oil and grease • Waterproof	• Containers (margarine, yogurt) • Water bottles • Automotive products (bumpers) • Geomembranes
	Polystyrene	6 PS	• Excellent thermal insulator • Can be a foam or a rigid plastic	• Insulation • Plastic tableware (glasses, utensils, cups, dishes, etc.) • Egg boxes
	Polyamides	Not currently recyclable	• Elastic • Water-absorbent	• Textile industry (nylon) • Electrical components
	Polymethyl methacrylate (also called *acrylic*)	Not currently recyclable	• Very rigid • Wide variety of colours	• Transparent bowls • Signs • Dental prostheses
	Acrylonitrile butadiene styrene (ABS)	Not currently recyclable	• Resilient	• Pipes for plumbing

		Recycling code	Properties	Uses
Thermosetting plastics	Phenol formaldehyde (often called *Bakelite*)	Not currently recyclable	• Heat-resistant • Electrical insulator	• Electrical components • Casings • Jewellery
	Melamine formaldehyde (often simply called *melamine*)	Not currently recyclable	• Heat-resistant • Abrasion-resistant • Wide variety of colours	• Furniture coverings, cabinets and countertops • Unbreakable plates and cups
	Polyesters	Not currently recyclable	• Electrical insulators • Hard • Resilient	• Boat hulls • Cafeteria trays • Fishing rods

THE MOST COMMONLY USED METALS

Metal (chemical symbol)	Description and characteristics	Useful properties	Uses
Aluminum (Al)	• White • Soft • Very abundant in nature • Most commonly used metal after iron	• Malleability • Lightness • Resistance to corrosion • Very good electrical conductivity	• Watercraft • Aluminum foil • Cans • Electrical products
Chromium (Cr)	• White, slightly bluish	• High degree of hardness • Resistance to corrosion	• Coatings
Copper (Cu)	• Reddish brown • One of the best electrical conductors	• Ductility • Malleability • Excellent electrical conductivity	• Electrical wires • Musical instruments • One-cent coins
Iron (Fe)	• Silvery • Soft • Can rust in the presence of oxygen • Most commonly used metal	• Ductility • Malleability	• Automobiles • Building structures • Utensils • Cables • Nails
Magnesium (Mg)	• Silvery white • May burn on contact with air	• Lightness • Flammability	• Fireworks and flares • Cans
Nickel (Ni)	• Grey	• Hardness • Malleability • Resistance to corrosion	• Heating elements • Coins
Tin (Sn)	• Silvery white	• Ductility • Malleability • Relatively low melting point	• Welding • Utensils
Zinc (Zn)	• White, slightly bluish	• Ductility • Malleability • Resistance to corrosion	• Electrical wires • Eavestroughs • Coatings

THE MOST COMMONLY USED ALLOYS

	Alloy	Composition and description	Useful properties	Uses
Ferrous alloys	Cast iron	• Mixture of iron and carbon (more than 2% carbon)	• Hardness	• Cooking pots • Wood stoves • Engine blocks
	Steel	• Mixture of iron and carbon (less than 1.5% carbon) • Nickel, chromium and zinc are often added.	• Hardness • Resilience • Malleability	• Building tools • Building structures • Automotive industry
Nonferrous alloys	Aluminum alloys	• Aluminum alloys are numerous and contain small amounts of one or more other substances (copper, manganese, silicon, zinc, magnesium, etc.).	• Malleability • Low density • Resistance to corrosion • Lightness	• Car parts • Airplane parts • Electronic parts
	Brass	• Mixture of copper and zinc • Its colour varies (white, grey, pink or golden) depending on its composition.	• Ductility • Malleability • Resistance to corrosion • Excellent electrical conductivity	• Decoration • Automotive industry • Electrical components
	Bronze	• Mixture of copper and tin • Its colour varies from yellow to red to brown.	• Hardness • Malleability • High density • Resistance to wear and corrosion	• Works of art • Olympic medals • Boat propellers

GLOSSARY

A page number in bold type indicates that the same definition can be found on that page.

A

Abiotic factors: ecological factors of physical or chemical origin. (p. **300**)

Acid: substance that releases H^+ ions in an aqueous solution. (pp. **58**, 394)

Acid-base neutralization: chemical change involving the reaction of an acid with a base, producing a salt and water. (p. **119**)

Acid rain: rainwater with a very low pH (lower than 5.6) caused mainly by the transformation of sulphur dioxide and nitrogen oxides. (pp. 197, 200, 235, 498)

Adhesion: the phenomenon by which two surfaces tend to remain in contact with each other without slipping. (p. **433**)

Air: the mixture of gases, especially nitrogen and oxygen, that makes up the atmosphere. (p. **222**)

Air mass: large expanse of the atmosphere with relatively uniform temperature and humidity. (p. **229**)

Allele: possible form of a gene. Different alleles have different nucleotide sequences. (p. **362**)

Alloy: mixture of a metal with one or more other substances, which may be metallic or nonmetallic. (p. **394**)

Alternating current: electric current in which the electrons move back and forth in a regular pattern. (p. **461**)

Amino acid: molecule that can combine with other amino acids to form proteins. (p. **356**)

Annealing: heat treatment that restores the original properties of steel after it has been deformed, for example, after welding. (p. 395)

Anticyclone: area of atmospheric circulation surrounding a high-pressure centre. The air turns clockwise in the Northern Hemisphere and counterclockwise in the Southern Hemisphere. (p. **231**)

Aqueous solution: solution in which the solvent is water. (p. **51**)

Archimedes' principle: principle stating that an object immersed in a fluid is subjected to a buoyant force equal to the weight of the fluid displaced by the object. (p. **95**)

Assembling: set of techniques by which various parts are united to form a complete technical object. (p. **417**)

Atmosphere: the layer of air surrounding the Earth. (pp. **222**, 254)

Atmospheric circulation: the global-scale movement of the layer of air surrounding the Earth. (p. **226**)

Atmospheric pressure: the pressure of the air in the atmosphere. (p. **224**)

Atom: the smallest particle of matter. It cannot be divided chemically. (p. **7**)

Atomic number: number representing the number of protons in the nucleus of an atom. It distinguishes one element from another. (p. **24**)

Autotroph: organism that can feed itself without ingesting other organisms. Autotrophs are the base of any food chain. (p. 320)

Avogadro's number: number representing the number of entities in a mole. It equals 6.02×10^{23} of those entities. (pp. **31**, 54)

B

Balancing a chemical equation: process consisting in placing a coefficient before each reactant and product so that the number of atoms of each element on the reactant side is equal to the number of atoms of each element on the product side. (p. **111**)

Base: substance that releases OH^- ions in an aqueous solution. (pp. **59**, 394)

Bending: machining technique in which a material is curved into a certain shape. (p. **415**)

Bernoulli's principle: principle stating that the higher the speed of a fluid, the lower its pressure, and vice versa. (p. **98**)

Bioaccumulation: the tendency among certain contaminants to accumulate over time in the tissues of living organisms. (p. **335**)

Bioconcentration: (also *bioamplification*) phenomenon by which the concentration of a contaminant in the tissues of living organisms tends to increase with each trophic level. (p. **336**)

Biodegradation: the breaking down of organic matter into inorganic matter by microorganisms. (p. **337**)

Biodiversity: term describing the variety of species living in a community. (pp. 200, 265, **303**, 497)

Biogeochemical cycle: set of processes by which an element passes from one environment to the next and eventually returns to its original environment, in an infinite loop of recycling. (p. **255**)

Biological cycle: cycle composed of alternating periods of rise and fall in the size of a population. These periods are of fixed duration and are repeated continually. (p. **301**)

Biomass: the total mass of organic matter in an ecosystem at any given time. (p. **326**)

Biomes: large regions of the world with distinctive climates, wildlife and vegetation. (p. **262**)

Bioremediation: biotechnology for cleaning up a polluted site, using microorganisms that decompose the contaminants. (p. **337**)

Biosphere: the layer around the Earth containing all living organisms. (p. **254**)

Biotechnology: set of techniques in which living organisms, or substances derived from them, are used to meet a need or desire. (p. 337)

Biotic factors: ecological factors related to the actions of living organisms. (p. **300**)

Buffering capacity: the ability of a soil to resist changes in its pH when acidic or alkaline compounds are added to it. (p. **193**)

C

Capacitor: device composed of two electrical surfaces separated by an insulating material. The device can store an electrical charge. (p. **473**)

Carbon cycle: biogeochemical cycle involving all the exchanges of carbon on Earth. (p. **257**)

Cellular respiration: chemical change in which glucose and oxygen are used to generate energy. The reaction also produces carbon dioxide and water. (pp. **123**, 222)

Ceramic: solid material obtained by heating inorganic matter containing various compounds, usually oxides. (p. **392**)

Characteristic property: chemical or physical property that identifies a pure substance or the group of substances to which it belongs. (p. 108)

Character trait: physical, psychological or physiological attribute that may vary from one individual to another within the same species. (p. **350**)

Charging: process of creating an imbalance in the electrical charge of an object. (p. **142**)

Chemical bond: the union of two atoms through the transfer or sharing of one or more electrons. (p. **45**)

Chemical change: (also *chemical reaction*) change altering the nature and characteristic properties of matter. The bonds between atoms are rearranged, and new molecules are formed. (p. **108**)

Chemical recycling: natural phenomenon by which decomposers make inorganic matter available in an ecosystem by breaking down organic matter. (p. **324**)

Chromatin: mass of DNA and proteins within the nucleus of most cells not undergoing division. (p. **351**)

Chromosome: structure that is formed when chromatin contracts. It is visible under the microscope. (p. **352**)

Circuit breaker: protective device that cuts the electric current in a circuit in the event of an overload. The breaker can be reset. (pp. 158, 467)

Climate change: the abnormal modification of climatic conditions on Earth, caused by human activity. (p. **234**)

Cloning: the reproduction of an individual, part of that individual or one of its genes in order to obtain an exact copy. (p. **369**)

Closed circuit: circuit in which electric current flows in a loop. (p. **469**)

Combustion: form of oxidation that releases a large amount of energy. (pp. **122**, 233)

Commensalism: the interaction between two living organisms in which one organism benefits from the relationship, while the other remains unaffected. (p. **308**)

Community: set of populations of different species sharing the same habitat. (pp. **303**, 318)

Competition: the interaction between living organisms that seek access to the same resource in their habitat. (p. **306**)

Component: in mechanics, part or fluid that performs a mechanical function. (p. **427**)

Composite: material formed by combining materials from different categories to obtain a new product with enhanced properties. (p. **399**)

Compound: pure substance containing at least two different elements that are bonded chemically. (p. 22)

Compressible fluid: fluid whose volume may vary. Gases are compressible fluids. (p. 224)

Concentration: the amount of solute in a given amount of solution. (p. **52**)

Concentration in ppm: the number of parts of solute in a million parts of solution. (p. **53**)

Conduction: the electrical function performed by any component that can transmit electric current from one part of a circuit to another. (p. **464**)

Conductor: substance that permits the free flow of electrical charges. (pp. **143**, 459)

Constraint: term describing the effect of external forces on a material. (p. **387**)

Consumers: heterotrophic organisms that feed on other living organisms. (p. **321**)

Contaminant: any type of substance or radiation that is likely to cause harm to one or more ecosystems. (pp. 235, 275, **332**)

Contamination: the abnormal presence of a harmful substance in an environment. (pp. **200**, 236)

Control: the electrical function performed by any component that can open and close a circuit. (p. **469**)

Convection: transfer of heat through the motion of a fluid, such as air or water. (p. 226)

Conventional current direction: the direction in which a positive particle would flow in an electrical circuit. For this reason, the direction goes from the positive terminal of the power supply to its negative terminal. (pp. **150**, 459)

Coriolis effect: deviation of the trajectory of a body in motion in a rotational system. The Coriolis effect causes winds to deviate to the right in the Northern Hemisphere and to the left in the Southern Hemisphere. (p. 226)

Coulomb: the unit of measurement for electrical charge. One coulomb is equal to the charge of 6.25×10^{18} electrons or protons. (p. **141**)

Coulomb's law: law stating that the magnitude of the force between two immobile and electrically charged particles is directly proportional to the product of their charges and inversely proportional to the square of the distance between them. (p. **149**)

Covalent bond: the result of the sharing of one or more electron pairs between two atoms (usually two nonmetals). (p. **46**)

Crossbreeding: the exchange of gametes between two different individuals during sexual reproduction. (p. **360**)

Cryosphere: layer consisting of all the frozen water on the Earth's surface. (p. **207**)

Current intensity: the number of charges that flow past a given point in an electrical circuit every second. (p. **151**)

Cutting: act of giving a material a desired shape. (p. **414**)

Cyclone: tropical storm characterized by violent winds revolving around an area of low pressure. (p. **232**)

D

Decomposers: organisms that feed on the waste and remains of other living organisms. (pp. **322**, 506)

Decomposition: reaction in which a compound separates into two or more compounds or elements. (p. 118)

Deformation: change in shape of an object. (p. 387)

Degradation of a material: the decline in some of its properties due to the effects of the surrounding environment. (p. **389**)

Degrees of freedom: the set of independent movements that are possible for a given part in a technical object. (p. **430**)

Density: mass of a substance per unit of volume. (p. 224)

Depression: area of atmospheric circulation surrounding a low-pressure centre. The air turns counterclockwise in the Northern Hemisphere and clockwise in the Southern Hemisphere. (p. **231**)

Detail drawing: drawing specifying all the relevant information for manufacturing a part. (p. **405**)

Detritivore: organism that feeds on detritus, which is dead organic matter, such as fallen leaves, the wood of dead trees, animal remains and excrement. (p. 322)

Development: the representation of the surface area required to make a part by bending. (p. **407**)

Diagram: simplified representation of an object, a part of an object, or a system. (p. **408**)

Dimension: indication, on a drawing, of the finished measurements and the position of various parts of a technical object. (p. 405)

Dimensional tolerance: indicator of the maximum acceptable difference between a specified measurement and the actual measurement on the finished object. (p. **406**)

Diode: device that allows electric current to flow in only one direction. (p. **474**)

Direct current: electric current in which the electrons are continuously moving in the same direction. (p. **460**)

Disturbance: event that damages an ecosystem. It can lead to the elimination of organisms and alter the availability of resources. (p. **327**)

DNA (deoxyribonucleic acid): double-helix-shaped molecule found in all the cells of living organisms and in certain viruses. (pp. 258, 353)

Dominant allele: allele that is expressed when an individual carries two different alleles for a given gene. (p. **364**)

Double bond: bond between two atoms resulting from the sharing or transfer of two pairs of electrons. (pp. 47, 115)

Drilling: act of making a hole in a material. (p. **414**)

Dynamic electricity: term encompassing all the phenomena related to electrical charges in motion. (p. **150**)

E

Ecological carrying capacity: the number of individuals that can be supported by the resources of a given habitat. (p. 330)

Ecological factor: aspect of a habitat that can affect the organisms living there. (p. **299**)

Ecological footprints: estimates of the surface area individual humans or populations require to obtain the resources for satisfying all their needs and to ensure the disposal of their waste. (p. **330**)

Ecological succession: the series of changes that occur in an ecosystem after a disturbance and that continue until the balance of the ecosystem is restored. (p. **329**)

Ecosystem: community of living organisms interacting with one another and with the nonliving components of the environment they inhabit. (pp. 200, 269, **318**, 495)

Ecotoxicology: the study of the ecological consequences of polluting the environment with various substances and radiation, released by human activity. (p. **331**)

Effective force: the force component that alters the motion of an object. It is the component that is parallel to the movement of the object. (p. **88**)

Electrical charge: property of protons and electrons. A proton carries a positive charge, while an electron carries a negative charge. (pp. 84, **141**)

Electrical circuit: network in which electrical charges can flow continuously in a loop. (pp. **156**, 458)

Electrical conductivity: the ability of a substance to allow an electric current to flow through it. (pp. **55**, 391)

Electrical field: the area of space in which the electrical force of a charged body can act on another charged body. (p. **144**)

Electrical function: the role that a component plays in the control or transformation of electric current. (p. **462**)

Electrical power: the amount of work an electrical device can perform per second. (p. **155**)

Electrical resistance: the ability of a material to hinder the flow of electric current. (p. **153**)

Electric current: the orderly flow of negative charges carried by electrons. (pp. **150**, 459)

Electricity: term encompassing all the phenomena caused by positive and negative charges. (p. **140**)

Electrolyte: substance that, when dissolved in water, allows an electric current to flow through the solution. (p. **55**)

Electrolytic dissociation: the separation of a dissolved compound into two ions of opposite charges. (p. **55**)

Electrolytic solution: solution containing an electrolyte that has dissociated into ions, allowing electric current to flow through the solution. (pp. 55, 142)

Electromagnetic induction: process consisting in generating an electric current in a conductor by varying a magnetic field around that conductor. (p. **171**)

Electromagnetic spectrum: image representing all the wavelengths of a light source. (pp. 14, 240)

Electromagnetism: term encompassing all the phenomena resulting from the interaction between electricity and magnetism. (p. **167**)

Electron: one of the particles that make up an atom. It is negatively charged. (pp. **11**, 241, 460)

Elementary charge: the charge carried by a single electron or proton. It has a value of 1.602×10^{-19} C. (p. **141**)

Endothermic reaction: chemical change that absorbs energy. (p. **114**)

Energy: the ability to do work or effect change. (p. **71**)

Energy efficiency: the percentage of energy consumed by a machine or system that was transformed into useful energy. (pp. **72**, 503)

Energy transfer: the movement of energy from one place to another. (p. **71**)

Energy transformation: the changing of energy from one form to another. (p. **71**)

Engine torque: torque that increases the rotational speed of components in mechanical systems. (p. **445**)

Equilibrium of two forces: state achieved when the resultant force applied to an object is zero. The motion of the object therefore remains constant. (p. **87**)

Eukaryotic: describes a cell with a nucleus containing DNA. (p. 351)

Eutrophication: the process by which natural waters lose their oxygen because of an excessive accumulation of organic matter and nutrients. (pp. **212**, 261, 509)

Evapotranspiration: phenomenon of water transfer from the Earth to the atmosphere through the evaporation of surface and ground water and through plant transpiration. (p. 499)

Exothermic reaction: chemical change that releases energy. (p. 114)

Exploded view: drawing in which the various parts of the object are separated from one another. (p. **404**)

F

Ferromagnetic substance: substance with the ability to acquire magnetic properties. (p. **167**)

Ferrous alloy: alloy whose main component is iron. (p. 394)

Finishing: set of techniques that complete the manufacture of the parts of a technical object. (p. **417**)

Food chain: series of living organisms in which each organism feeds on the one preceding it in the chain. (pp. 124, 319)

Force: action that can change the motion of an object, or deform the object, by pushing or pulling on it. (pp. **80**, 386, 433)

Fossil energy: energy derived from fossil fuels. (p. 196)

Fossil fuels: fuels resulting from the transformation of organic residue. These energy sources consist of oil, natural gas and coal. (pp. **196**, 257, 396)

Friction: (physics) force that prevents two objects from slipping over each other when they come into contact. (p. **85**)

Friction: (mechanics) force that resists the slipping of one moving part over another. (p. **433**)

Functional dimensioning: inclusion, in a technical drawing, of information required for the object to work. (p. **406**)

Fuse: protective device that cuts the electric current in a circuit in the event of an overload. The fuse filament melts, so the fuse cannot be reused. (pp. 158, 467)

G

Gamete: cell involved in sexual reproduction. Female gametes are usually called *ova* in both plants and animals, while male gametes are usually called *sperm* in animals and *pollen* in plants. (p. 360)

Gene: DNA segment that contains information for making proteins. (pp. **354**, 510)

General arrangement: technical drawing representing the overall appearance of an object. (p. **403**)

Generation: group of individuals descended from common parents. (p. **361**)

Genome: an individual's complete set of genes. (p. 354)

Genotype: an individual's genetic inheritance. It describes all of an individual's alleles for specific genes. (p. **365**)

Geothermal energy: the energy that comes from the internal heat of the Earth. (p. **198**)

Glacier: mass of ice on land, formed by compressed snow. (p. **208**)

Gravitational force: force of attraction between all objects due to their masses and the distances between them. (pp. 81, 239)

Gravitational potential energy: the energy reserve of an object based on its mass and its height above a reference surface. (p. **77**)

Greenhouse effect: natural process that allows the Earth to retain some of the heat it receives from the Sun. (pp. **233**, 488)

Greenhouse gas: gas suspended in the Earth's atmosphere, trapping some of the infrared rays emitted from the surface. (pp. 197, 233, 488)

Group: set of elements corresponding to a column of the periodic table. The elements in a particular group have similar chemical properties because they all have the same number of valence electrons. (pp. **21**, 40)

Guiding: the mechanical function performed by any component that controls the motion of one or more moving parts. (p. **431**)

Guiding component: (also *guiding control*) component whose mechanical function is to guide the motion of moving parts. (p. **431**)

H

Half-life: the time it takes for half of the nuclei in a sample of radioactive material to decay. (p. **128**)

Heat: the transfer of thermal energy between two environments with different temperatures. Heat always passes from the warmer to the cooler environment. (p. **73**)

Helical guiding: guiding that ensures the translational motion of a moving part while it rotates about the same axis. (p. **432**)

Heredity: the transmission of parents' character traits to their offspring. (p. **359**)

Heterotroph: living organism that cannot produce its own food. (p. 321)

Heterozygote: individual with two different alleles for a given character trait. (p. **363**)

Homozygote: individual with two identical alleles for a given character trait. (p. **363**)

Hybrid: individual obtained by the crossbreeding of two genetically different individuals. (pp. **361**, 510)

Hydraulic energy: the energy that can be derived from moving water. (p. **209**)

Hydroelectric dam: structure built to convert a river's hydraulic energy into electrical power. (p. **210**)

Hydrosphere: the Earth's outer layer of water, uniting water in all its states: liquid, solid and gas. (pp. **201**, 254)

I

Igneous rocks: rocks formed when magma cools and solidifies. (p. **190**)

Infrared: describing rays in the electromagnetic spectrum with a frequency lower than that of red light. They are invisible but transmit heat. (pp. 233, 488)

Inland waters: all the freshwater bodies found on continents, uniting rivers, lakes and groundwater. (p. **201**)

Inorganic matter: matter not necessarily produced by living organisms. (p. 320)

Insulation: the electrical function performed by any component that prevents an electric current from flowing. (p. **466**)

Insulator: substance that impedes the free flow of electrical charges. (pp. **143**, 466)

Ion: atom that has become electrically charged by losing or gaining one or more electrons. (pp. **42**, 142)

Ionic bond: the result of a transfer of one or more electrons from one atom (usually a metal) to another atom (usually a nonmetal). (p. **46**)

Ionic compound: compound containing at least one ionic bond. Ionic compounds are usually composed of a metal and a nonmetal. (p. 118)

Isotope: atom of an element with the same number of protons as another atom of the same element but with a different number of neutrons. (pp. **26**, 126)

K

Karyotype: ordered representation of an individual's chromosomes, obtained by grouping them into pairs according to size. (p. **352**)

Kinetic energy: the energy an object possesses due to its motion. (p. **76**)

Kirchhoff's first law: law stating that the intensity of a current that flows into an element or a node of an electrical circuit is always equal to the intensity of the current that flows out of the element or node. (p. **159**)

Kirchhoff's second law: law stating that in an electrical circuit, the total energy acquired by the charges from the power supply is always equal to the total energy transferred by these charges, whatever pathway they may take in the circuit. (p. **160**)

L

Law of conservation of energy: law stating that energy can be neither created nor destroyed; it can only be transferred or transformed. The total amount of energy in an isolated system always remains constant. (p. **71**)

Law of conservation of mass: law stating that the total mass of reactants is always equal to the total mass of products. (pp. **111**, 323)

Laying out: the act of tracing markings or reference points onto a material. (p. **412**)

Lethal dose: single amount of a contaminant that, if ingested, will cause death in an organism. (p. 334)

Lewis notation: simplified representation of the atom, in which only the valence electrons are illustrated. (p. **27**)

Lewis structure: representation of a given atom in Lewis notation. (p. 46)

Limiting factor: ecological factor that causes the density of a population to decrease. (p. **300**)

Linking: the mechanical function performed by any component that connects different parts of a technical object. (p. **427**)

Linking component: part or fluid that performs the mechanical function of linking. (p. 427)

Lithosphere: the hard shell of the Earth, consisting of the crust and the topmost part of the upper mantle. (pp. **184**, 254)

Lubrication: the mechanical function performed by any component that reduces friction between two parts. (p. **434**)

M

Machine tool: tool that is held and operated by forces other than human force. (p. **411**)

Machining: act of shaping a material into a desired configuration. (p. **413**)

Magnet: object that can attract other objects containing iron, cobalt or nickel. (p. **163**)

Magnetic field: the area of space in which the magnetic force of a magnet can act on another magnet. (p. **166**)

Magnetic pole: See *North pole*. (p. 84)

Magnetic remanence: property describing the ability of a material to acquire and conserve magnetic properties. (p. **167**)

Magnetism: term encompassing all the phenomena caused by magnets. (p. **163**)

Manufacturing: series of operations resulting in the creation of a technical object. (p. **410**)

Manufacturing process sheet: document describing a series of operations to perform in the manufacture of a given part and listing the materials and tools required. (p. 412)

Mass: measure of the quantity of matter in an object. (p. **83**)

Material and energy flow: the exchange of matter and energy between the living organisms in an ecosystem and between those organisms and their environment. (p. **323**)

Measuring: the act of determining the size or position of a marking. (p. **412**)

Mechanical energy: energy resulting from the velocity of an object, its mass and its position in relation to surrounding objects—in other words, the sum of the kinetic and potential energy of an object. (pp. 78, 153, 197, 238)

Mechanical engineering: branch of engineering that focuses on the design, production, analysis, working and improvement of technical objects with moving parts. (p. **426**)

Mechanical properties: properties describing how a material reacts when subjected to one or more constraints. (p. **388**)

Meiosis: process of cell division producing male and female gametes for sexual reproduction. (p. 366)

Metal: material extracted from a mineral ore. Metals are usually shiny in appearance and are good conductors of electricity and heat. (pp. 20, **394**)

Metalloid: element with properties of both metals and nonmetals. Metalloids are found along both sides of the staircase in the periodic table. (pp. 21, 143)

Metamorphic rocks: former igneous or sedimentary rocks that have been transformed by heat or pressure. (p. **191**)

Mineral ore: rock containing a mineral with mining potential. (pp. 187, 394)

Minerals: solid inorganic substances with clearly defined composition and properties. (p. **185**)

Modified wood: treated wood or a material made from wood mixed with other substances. (p. **391**)

Molar concentration: the number of moles of solute in a litre of solution. (p. **54**)

Molar mass: the mass of one mole of a given substance. (p. **30**)

Mole: quantity equal to the number of atoms in exactly 12 g of carbon-12. Its symbol is mol. (p. **30**)

Molecular cloning: the production of multiple copies of the same gene. (p. **373**)

Molecule: group of two or more chemically bonded atoms. (p. **40**)

Motion transformation: the mechanical function of relaying a motion from one part to another while altering the nature of the motion. (p. **445**)

Motion transmission: the mechanical function of relaying a motion from one part to another without altering the nature of the motion. (p. **435**)

Motion transmission system: set of components that perform the function of transmitting motion. (p. **436**)

Mutualism: the interaction between two living organisms that benefits both organisms. (p. **308**)

N

Natural cloning: process of asexual reproduction producing genetically identical individuals. (p. **369**)

Negatively charged body: body containing more electrons than protons. (p. **141**)

Neutron: one of the particles that make up an atom. With the proton, it forms the nucleus. It has no electrical charge, so it is neutral. (p. **16**)

Nitrogen cycle: biogeochemical cycle involving all the exchanges of nitrogen on Earth. (p. **259**)

Noble gas: (also *rare gas* or *inert gas*) extremely stable element belonging to the last column of the periodic table. (pp. 22, 40)

Nonferrous alloy: alloy whose main component is a metal other than iron. (p. 394)

Nonmetal: element that is usually a poor conductor of heat and electricity. Nonmetals are found to the right of the staircase in the periodic table, except hydrogen. (pp. 20, 143)

North pole: the end of a magnet that naturally seeks the Earth's magnetic pole near the geographic North Pole. The other end of the magnet is its **south pole**. (p. **166**)

Nuclear energy: the energy stored in the bonds between the particles in the nucleus of an atom. (p. **198**)

Nuclear fission: nuclear reaction in which the nucleus of a large atom is split to form two or more lighter atomic nuclei. (pp. **129**, 502)

Nuclear fusion: nuclear reaction in which two small atomic nuclei join together to form one heavier nucleus. (p. **131**)

Nuclear reaction: See *nuclear transformation*. (p. 239)

Nuclear stability: the state of a nucleus in which the nuclear force is greater than the forces of electrical repulsion between protons. (p. **125**)

Nuclear transformation: change in which the particles making up an atomic nucleus are rearranged, and new elements are formed. (p. **108**)

O

Ocean circulation: the combined effect of all the currents that move across the oceans. (p. **205**)

Ocean current: the movement of seawater in a certain direction. (p. **205**)

Ohm's law: law stating that, for a given resistance, the potential difference in an electrical circuit is directly proportional to the current intensity. (p. **154**)

Open circuit: circuit in which electric current cannot flow in a loop. (p. **469**)

Organic matter: matter that enters into the composition of living organisms and that is usually created by them. (p. 320)

Oxidation: chemical change involving oxygen or a substance with properties similar to those of oxygen. (pp. **120**, 395)

Oxide: compound formed by the combination of oxygen with one other element. (p. 392)

Ozone layer: part of the atmosphere with a high concentration of ozone molecules, which absorb some of the ultraviolet rays from the sun. (p. **236**)

P

Pack ice: the ice floating on the oceans near the North and South poles. (p. **207**)

Parallel circuit: circuit that contains at least one branch. (p. **158**)

Parent rock: solid part of the Earth's crust and original rock from which soil is eventually formed. (p. 192)

Pascal's principle: principle stating that an increase in the pressure of an enclosed fluid is transmitted uniformly in all directions. (p. **94**)

Period: set of elements corresponding to a row of the periodic table. All the elements in a period have the same number of electron shells. (p. **23**)

Periodic classification: way to group the elements according to certain properties. (p. **17**)

Periodicity of properties: the repetition of patterns in properties from one period to another. (p. **24**)

Periodic table of the elements: visual presentation of the elements in groups according to their physical and chemical properties. (p. **17**)

Permafrost: ground whose temperature has been 0°C or lower for at least two years. (pp. **194**, 269)

Perspective: representation of all three dimensions of an object in a single view. (p. 403)

Phenotype: the way in which a genotype expresses itself. It describes the appearance or state of the individual for one or more character traits. (p. **365**)

Phosphorus cycle: biogeochemical cycle involving all the exchanges of phosphorus on Earth. (p. **260**)

Photosynthesis: chemical change that produces glucose and oxygen from solar energy, carbon dioxide and water. (pp. 71, **124**, 222, 301, 321)

Physical change: change altering neither the nature nor the characteristic properties of matter. The atoms and molecules of the substance do not change. (p. **108**)

Phytoremediation: biotechnology that uses plants or algae to eliminate contaminants from a site. (p. **338**)

Plastic: material made of polymers, to which other substances may be added to obtain certain desirable properties. (p. **397**)

Polyatomic ion: group of two or more chemically bonded atoms that has become electrically charged by losing or gaining one or more electrons. (p. **44**)

Population: group of individuals of the same species, living in a shared space at a specific point in time. (pp. **292**, 318)

Population density: the number of individuals per unit of area or volume. (p. **297**)

Population distribution: the way in which individuals are dispersed within their habitat. (p. **298**)

Population size: the number of individuals in a population. (p. **293**)

Positively charged body: body containing fewer electrons than protons. (p. **141**)

Potential difference: the amount of energy transferred between two points in an electrical circuit. (p. **152**)

Power supply: the electrical function performed by any component that can generate or provide an electric current in a circuit. (p. **463**)

Precipitation: reaction of two solutions in which an insoluble, or only slightly soluble, solid (precipitate) is formed. (p. 118)

Predation: the interaction between two living organisms in which one feeds on the other. (p. **307**)

Prevailing winds: major atmospheric currents that blow in a given direction according to global patterns of movement. (p. **228**)

Primary productivity: the amount of new biomass in an ecosystem, generated by its producers. (p. **326**)

Printed circuit: electrical circuit printed on a solid support called a *circuit board*. (p. **465**)

Producers: autotrophic organisms with the ability to create organic matter from inorganic matter in an ecosystem. (pp. 124, **320**)

Projection: the representation of a three-dimensional object on a two-dimensional surface. (p. **402**)

Protection: the electrical function performed by any component that can automatically cut current flow in the event of a power surge. (p. **467**)

Protection of a material: the application of procedures that prevent or delay its degradation. (p. **390**)

Protein: molecule that plays a specific role in the functioning of an organism and in the expression of its character traits. (p. **355**)

Protein synthesis: the creation of proteins by cells. (p. **357**)

Proton: one of the particles that make up an atom. It is found in the nucleus and carries a positive charge. (p. **13**)

Pure line: group of individuals of the same species, which, for a specific character trait, produces only offspring with the same trait, without variation. (p. **360**)

Q

Quench hardening: heat treatment that makes steel harder, but more brittle. (p. 395)

R

Radioactivity: natural process in which an unstable atom spontaneously transforms into a more stable atom, or several more stable atoms, while releasing energy in the form of radiation. (p. **126**)

Recessive allele: allele that is not expressed when an individual carries two different alleles for a given gene. (p. **364**)

Relative atomic mass: the mass of an atom measured by comparison with a reference element, carbon-12. (p. **25**)

Relay: component used to control a high-voltage circuit from a distance with a low-voltage circuit. (p. **478**)

Reproductive cloning: the application of cloning techniques to obtain a new individual genetically identical to the one being cloned. (p. **373**)

Resisting torque: torque that slows or stops the rotation of components in mechanical systems. (p. **445**)

Resistor: component designed to limit the flow of electrons through an electrical circuit. (p. **467**)

Resultant force: virtual force whose action is equal to the combination of all the forces applied simultaneously to an object. (p. **86**)

Rocks: heterogeneous solids composed of many minerals. (p. **189**)

Rotational guiding: guiding that ensures the rotational motion of a moving part. (p. **432**)

Roughing: first step in machining a part, in which a rough shape of the object is cut out of the material. (p. 413)

Rutherford-Bohr atomic model: representation of the atom as a very small nucleus made up of positively charged protons, surrounded by negatively charged electrons moving in defined orbits. (p. **15**)

S

Salinity: measure of the amount of salt dissolved in a liquid. (p. **204**)

Salt: substance produced by the chemical bonding of a metallic ion and a nonmetallic ion (other than H^+ and OH^- ions). (p. **59**)

Scale: ratio between the measurements of an object in a technical drawing and the actual measurements of the finished object. (p. 403)

Sedimentary rocks: rocks formed by the accumulation and compaction of debris. (p. **191**)

Self-pollination: pollination of the flower of a plant with pollen from the same flower. (p. 360)

Semiconductor: material with electrical conductivity between that of conductors and insulators, allowing it to control the amount and direction of current flowing through it. (pp. 21, 459)

Separation techniques: techniques for physically separating the components of a mixture without altering the nature of the substances involved. (p. 50)

Series circuit: circuit in which the elements are connected end to end. (p. **158**)

Sexual reproduction: reproduction through the union of a male and a female gamete. (p. 360)

Short circuit: connection of two points of different voltages in an electrical circuit, causing the charge to flow along a different path from the one intended. (p. 464)

Simplified atomic model: representation of the atom indicating the number of protons and neutrons in the nucleus and the number of electrons in each of the electron shells. (p. **16**)

Single bond: bond between two atoms resulting from the sharing or transfer of a pair of electrons. (p. 115)

Smog: thick mixture of fog, smoke and atmospheric pollutants. (p. **237**)

Soil depletion: the loss of soil fertility. (pp. **199**, 497)

Soil horizons: differentiated layers running roughly parallel to the surface of the ground. (p. **192**)

Solar energy: the energy that comes from the sun in the form of radiation through the atmosphere. (p. **241**)

Solenoid: cylindrical coil of live wire. (p. **169**)

Solubility: the maximum amount of solute that can be dissolved in a certain volume of solvent. (p. **52**)

Solute: one of the components of a solution. It is dissolved in another substance, the solvent. (p. 51)

Solution: homogeneous mixture whose component substances cannot be distinguished, even with the aid of a magnifying instrument. (p. **51**)

Solvent: one of the components of a solution. Another substance, the solute, is dissolved in it. (p. 51)

Species: set of individuals with common characteristics, able to reproduce among themselves and bearing offspring that are also able to reproduce. (p. 292)

Specific heat capacity: property corresponding to the amount of thermal energy required to raise the temperature of one gram of a substance by one degree Celsius. (p. **74**)

Speed change: phenomenon that occurs in a motion transmission system when the driver does not turn at the same speed as the driven component or components. (p. **442**)

Static electricity: term encompassing all the phenomena related to electrical charges at rest. (p. **145**)

Steel heat treatments: methods of enhancing certain mechanical properties of steel through periods of heating. (p. **395**)

Stoichiometry: the study of the quantities of reactants required for chemical reactions to occur and of the quantities of products that are thus formed. (p. **112**)

Strength of an electrolyte: the degree to which an electrolyte dissociates into ions. The higher the degree of dissociation, the stronger the electrolyte. (p. **58**)

Sustainable development: development that meets the needs of the present population without compromising the needs of future generations. Sustainable development implies a balance between social development, economic development and environmental protection (Brundtland Commission, 1987). (p. 495)

Synthesis: reaction in which two or more reactants combine to form a new product. (p. 118)

T

Tapping: machining technique in which screw threads are formed inside holes drilled into a material. (p. **415**)

Temperature: measure of the degree of agitation of the particles of a substance. (p. **74**)

Tempering: heat treatment that makes steel less brittle. (p. 395)

Therapeutic cloning: the application of cloning techniques to obtain tissues or organs genetically identical to those of a person in need of a transplant or medical grafting. (p. **373**)

Thermal energy: the energy contained in a substance, determined by the number of particles in the substance and their temperature. (pp. **73**, 153, 197)

Thermohaline circulation: circulation of surface and subsurface currents moving ocean waters in a vast loop all over the world. (p. 206)

Thermoplastic: plastic that becomes soft enough when heated to be moulded or remoulded and that hardens enough when cooled to hold its shape. (p. **397**)

Thermosetting plastic: plastic that remains permanently hard, even when heated. (p. **397**)

Threading: machining technique in which screw threads are formed around a rod. (p. **415**)

Tidal energy: the energy obtained from the ebb and flow of tides. (p. **245**)

Tide: the rise and fall of water in the seas and oceans. It is caused by the gravitational force of the Moon and, to a lesser extent, of the Sun. (p. **244**)

Title block: section at the bottom of a technical drawing, containing the drawing references (drafter, title, date and scale). (p. 403)

Tolerance: indicator of the maximum acceptable variation in resistance in a resistor in an electrical circuit. (p. 468)

Tool: instrument used in the manufacture of an object. (p. **411**)

Torque: Torque involves two forces of equal strength but applied in opposite directions, which cause a component to rotate about an axis. (p. **445**)

Toxicity threshold: the level of concentration above which a contaminant causes one or more harmful effects in an organism. (p. **334**)

Transformation of energy: the electrical function performed by any component that can convert electrical energy into another form of energy. (p. **471**)

Transistor: electronic device used to block or amplify an electric current. (p. **475**)

Translational guiding: guiding that ensures the straight translational motion of a moving part. (p. **431**)

Trophic level: position of a living organism in a food chain. Food chains contain three main trophic levels: producers, consumers and decomposers. (p. 319)

Trophic network: (also *food web*) representation of the trophic relationships in an ecosystem. (p. 322)

Trophic relationships: the feeding connections among the living organisms in an ecosystem. (p. **319**)

Valence electron: electron in the outermost shell of an atom. (pp. **21**, 40, 141)

Wastewater: water that is discharged after household or industrial use and that is polluted as a result of human activities. (p. **339**)

Watershed: area of land in which all inland waters drain into the same larger body of water. (pp. **202**, 275, 495)

Weight: measure of the gravitational force acting on an object. (p. **83**)

Wind energy: the energy that can be drawn from the wind. (p. **238**)

Wood: material obtained by harvesting and processing trees. (p. **390**)

Work: Work is done when a force applied to an object causes it to move—or causes part of it to move—in the same direction as the force or one of the force components. (p. **90**)

INDEX

D

E

F

G

H

I

O

P

R

S

T

U

V

W

PHOTO CREDITS

ALAMY
p. 10 (1.7): The Print Collector
p. 53 (2.23): D. R. Frazier Photolibrary, Inc.
p. 60: Liquid Light
p. 96: E. Reschke, Peter Arnold Inc.
p. 121 (bottom): A. Cooper
p. 140 (5.1): Natural Visions
p. 143 (right): Interfoto Pressebildagentur
p. 144 (5.10): Phototake Inc.
p. 146 (5.13): D. O'Dell
p. 155: Pictorial Press Ltd.
p. 198 (6.24): R1
p. 208 (6.33): B. & C. Alexander Photography
p. 217 (top): P. Blake
p. 238 (7.22): R. Abboud
p. 249: Camera Lucida Environment
p. 263 (8.7): D. Hosking
p. 266 (8.11): J. E. Marriott
p. 266 (bottom): J. T. Fowler
p. 267 (8.13): blickwinkel
p. 279 (8.29): Profimedia International s. r. o.
p. 282 (bottom left): ImageState
p. 282 (bottom right): J. Gould
p. 282 (top left): Robert Harding Picture Library Ltd.
p. 283 (top): Alaska Stock LLC
p. 284: F. Lépine
pp. 290–291: G. Vallée
p. 298 (9.10) (centre): Alt-6
p. 313 (bottom): R. McGouey
p. 315: blickwinkel
p. 323: G. Corney
p. 353: K. Bain
p. 360 (11.12): R. Walls
p. 379: blickwinkel
p. 386 (12.2): plainpicture GmbH & Co. KG
p. 398 (12.22): A. Arthur
p. 416 (bottom): T. Hertz
p. 423: B. Parsons
p. 430 (13.9): M. Griffin
p. 431 (13.11): F. Naylor
p. 434 (13.15): L. Smak
p. 436 (13.19): www.gerardbrown.co.uk
p. 439: North Wind Picture Archives
p. 439 (13.24) (left): tbkmedia.de
p. 439 (13.25): DIOMEDIA
p. 440 (13.26): P. Broadbent
p. 441 (13.29): S. Cooper
p. 447 (13.38): P. Lewis
p. 447 (13.39): D. Hoffman Photo Library
p. 448 (13.40) (right): Vivid Pixels
p. 455: Transtock Inc.
p. 459 (14.3): M. Cardy
p. 465 (14.10): STOCKFOLIO
p. 466 (right): Mary Evans Picture Library
p. 467 (14.12) (left): Leslie Garland Picture Library
p. 467 (14.12) (right): Lyroky
p. 468 (14.13): INSADCO Photography
p. 471 (14.20) (bottom): Cn Boon
p. 471 (14.20) (right): M. Broughton
p. 472 (14.21) (bottom left): D. R. Frazier Photolibrary, Inc.
p. 472 (14.21) (bottom right): imagebroker
p. 474 (14.23): J. Hallin
p. 476 (bottom): Stock Connection Blue
p. 477 (14.29): WoodyStock
p. 483 (bottom): I. Shaw
p. 490 (EI.5)
p. 498 (EI.19): D. MacDonald
p. 504 (EI.28): G. W. Williams
p. 505 (EI.30): J. West

ALEX LEGAULT
p. 105

ALT-6
p. 502 (EI.25): A. Caty
p. 502 (EI.26): Y. Beaulieu

ART RESOURCE
p. 408 (12.36)

BETHLEHEM STEEL CORPORATION
p. 148

BRITISH COLUMBIA PHOTOS
pp. 182–183: C. Joseph

CHARLES CORMIER
p. 287 (centre)

CORBIS
p. 2: Firefly Productions
p. 3: Firefly Productions
p. 9 (right): BBC
p. 10 (top): A. Della, epa
p. 16: Digital Art
p. 35 (bottom): R. McMahon
p. 35 (top): G. Schuster, zefa
pp. 38–39: Rainman, zefa
p. 47: Car Culture
p. 55 (bottom): Hulton-Deutsch Collection
pp. 68–69: F. Lanting
p. 73 (3.5): Bury, Photocuisine
p. 77 (3.7): T. Lang
p. 78 (3.9): L. Lefkowitz
p. 80 (3.10): J. Sugar
p. 83 (3.16)
p. 84 (3.17): M. S. Yamashita
p. 87 (3.24): A. West
p. 93 (3.29): S. Westmorland
p. 97 (3.37): S. Kaufman
p. 99 (D): K. Nomachi
p. 120: K. Schafer
p. 122 (4.20): D. Siracusa, Transtock

p. 123 (4.22): M. Chivers, Robert Harding World Imagery
p. 129
p. 131 (4.32): D. Scott
p. 131 (4.33): Xinhua, Xinhua Press
p. 132 (D): C. Hussey, Solus-Veer
p. 135 (bottom): Visuals Unlimited
p. 135 (top): JLP, Deimos
pp. 138–139: Arctic – Images
p. 157: L. Lefkowitz
p. 165 (top): K. Su
p. 176: Jason, zefa
p. 180: D. Woods
p. 181: D. Woods
p. 188 (6.10): E. Collis
p. 189 (6.11): Gaetano
p. 190 (6.13): S. T. Smith
p. 191 (6.14) (left): Visuals Unlimited
p. 195 (6.21): B. Fleumer, zefa
p. 197: B. Krist
p. 208 (6.34): R. A. Clevenger
p. 212 (6.39): P. A. Souders
p. 213 (6.40): I. Salas, epa
p. 215: J. Richardson
p. 216 (B): L. Neubauer
p. 217 (bottom): P. Souders
pp. 220–221: Eugen, zefa
p. 228 (7.8): A. Cooper
p. 228 (7.9)
p. 232 (bottom): NASA
p. 234 (7.17): Benelux, zefa
p. 234 (7.18): F. Muntada
p. 237 (7.20): NASA
p. 240 (7.26): NASA
p. 241 (7.27): NASA handout, dpa
p. 242 (7.28): D. Rose, zefa
p. 242 (bottom): Construction Photography
p. 246 (left): M. M. Lawrence
p. 248 (left): Benelux, zefa
pp. 252–253: D. Gulin
p. 264 (8.9): R. Clevenger
p. 267 (8.12): H. D. Seawell
p. 268 (8.15): H. Beral
p. 270 (8.18): F. Lukasseck
p. 271: F. Lemmens, zefa
p. 274 (8.22): A. & S. Carey, zefa
p. 275 (8.23): S. Terrill
p. 276 (8.24): J. Jamsen, zefa
p. 278 (8.27): T. Davis
p. 278 (8.28): S. Westmorland
p. 280 (right): E. Poupinet, zefa
p. 280 (top left)
p. 281: D. Lamont
p. 282 (top right): D. Muench
p. 283 (bottom): S. T. Smith
p. 288: S. Frink
p. 289: S. Frink
p. 293 (9.4): A. & S. Carey, zefa
p. 295 (9.7): S. Terrill
p. 296 (9.8): L. Kennedy
p. 298 (9.10) (bottom): W. Manning
p. 298 (9.10) (top): S. Frink
p. 301 (9.13): T. Brakefield
p. 301 (top): Y. Arthus-Bertrand
p. 302: R. Gehman
p. 306 (9.17): G. H. H. Huey
p. 307 (9.18): Gallo Images
p. 307 (9.19): H. Reinhard, zefa
p. 308 (9.20): R. Yin
p. 308 (9.21): R. Morsch
p. 310 (B): A. Morris
p. 312: W. Manning
p. 313 (top): T. Brakefield
p. 314: E. & D. Hosking
p. 318 (10.2): B. Gardel, Hemis
p. 320 (10.5) (left): F. Lanting
p. 320 (10.5) (right): S. Westmorland
p. 321 (10.6): A. Morris
p. 322 (10.7): A. & S. Carey, zefa
p. 326 (10.11) (left): Momatiuk – Eastcott
p. 327 (10.12): M. Harvey
p. 328 (10.14): Atlantide Phototravel
p. 331 (10.18): P. Turnley
p. 334 (10.22): R. Ressmeyer
p. 335 (10.24): J. E. Ross
p. 339 (10.27): W. H. Mueller, zefa
p. 342 (1): N. Benvie
p. 342 (2): M. Grandmaison
p. 342 (3): S. Smith
p. 342 (4): D. C. Spartas
pp. 348–349: F. Lanting
p. 350 (11.1): T. Davis
p. 351 (11.3) (centre): P. M. Fisher
p. 359 (11.11): A. Skelley
p. 362 (11.15): Moodboard
p. 368: B. Allig, zefa
p. 370
p. 382: I. Wagner, dpa
p. 383: I. Wagner, dpa
pp. 384–385: D. Boschung, zefa
p. 386 (12.1): K. Kinne, zefa
p. 389 (12.10): Owaki, Kulla
p. 390 (12.12): C. Gryniewicz, Ecoscene
p. 392 (12.16): F. Lukasseck
p. 400 (12.25) (left): D. Pu'u
p. 400 (12.25) (right): O. Van der Wall
p. 401 (12.26): Atlantide Phototravel
p. 413 (12.42): J. Tomter, zefa
p. 418 (D): R. Farris
p. 420: B. Allig, zefa
pp. 424–425: L. Manning
p. 429 (13.6): C. Wilhelm
p. 430 (13.8): Fernando Bengoechea, Beateworks
p. 431 (13.10): A. Rugg Photography, Beateworks
p. 432 (right): Bettmann
p. 433 (13.14): T. Tadder
p. 434 (bottom): Schlegelmilch
p. 454: P. Souders
pp. 456–457: G. B. Diebold
p. 458 (14.1): J. Richardson
p. 466 (14.11): A. Williams, zefa
p. 471 (14.20) (left): Pinto, zefa
p. 475 (top): Hulton-Deutsch Collection
p. 497 (EI.15): W. Kaehler
p. 497 (EI.16): G. Braasch
p. 497 (EI.17): T. Arruza
p. 498 (EI.18): R. Hackenberg, zefa
p. 501 (EI.21): L. Lefkowitz
p. 501 (EI.22): L. Solt, Dallas Morning News
p. 501 (EI.23)
p. 502 (EI.24): B. Barbier, Robert Harding World Imagery
p. 508 (EI.35): T. Bean

CORBIS BETTMANN
p. 17
p. 26
p. 45
p. 86
p. 241
p. 306 (top)

CORBIS REUTERS
p. 93 (3.30)
p. 137 (top)
p. 503 (EI.27): K. Mayama

CORBIS SYGMA
p. 37: C. Herve
p. 136: I. Kostin
p. 292 (9.1): J. Langevin
p. 482: B. Bisson
p. 511 (EI.38): C. Carrion

CP IMAGES
p. 29: V. Dargent, Abacapress.com
p. 66: J. McKnight, AP Photo
p. 74 (top): M. Evans, Picture Library 2006
p. 98: M. Evans, Picture Library 2006
p. 123 (4.21): Abaca Press (2004)
p. 128 (bottom): Mary Evans Picture Library
p. 209 (6.35): R. K. Singh, AP Photo
p. 218: J. Hayward
p. 219: J. Thompson
p. 246 (right): Lehtikuva-Ari-Matti Ruuska, AP Photo
p. 336
p. 372 (11.24) (circular inset): P. Chiasson

DANIEL ROUSSEL
p. 178
p. 179

DON PEROVICH
p. 216 (A)

DORLING KINDERSLEY
p. 9 (1.6)
p. 55 (2.24)

p. 114 (4.11)
p. 147 (5.16)
p. 170 (5.38)
p. 184 (6.1)
p. 185 (6.3)
p. 186 (6.4) (far left)
p. 186 (6.4) (far right)
p. 186 (6.4) (left)
p. 186 (6.5) (right)
p. 186 (6.6)
p. 187 (6.7)
p. 190 (6.12)
p. 191 (6.14) (right)
p. 192 (6.16)
p. 193 (6.18)
p. 206 (6.31)
p. 214 (left)
p. 214 (right)
p. 225 (7.4)
p. 226 (7.6)
p. 227 (7.7)
p. 229 (7.11)
p. 230 (7.12)
p. 231 (7.13)
p. 232 (7.15)
p. 233 (7.16)
p. 426 (13.1)

ÈVE-LUCIE BOURQUE
p. 494 (EI.11)

EXXON MOBIL CORPORATION
p. 337 (10.26)

FIRSTLIGHT
p. 485 (right): Jupiterimages

FRANÇOIS PRÉVOST
pp. 286–287 (background)

FUNDAMENTAL PHOTOGRAPH, NYC
p. 22 (1.24): R. Megna
p. 57 (2.26 to 2.28): R. Megna
p. 82 (3.13): Peticolas, Megna
p. 114 (4.10): R. Megna
p. 143 (5.7)
p. 166 (5.32)
p. 175

GETTY IMAGES
p. 65 (bottom): B. Hall / The Image Bank
p. 121 (4.18): G. Symon, The Image Bank
p. 128 (4.27): H. Sieplinga, HMS Images
p. 131 (4.34): P. Ginter, Science Faction
p. 222 (7.1): Michael Dunning, Photographer's Choice
p. 248 (right): Steve Satushek / Riser
p. 251: Y. Marcoux, Riser
p. 254 (8.1): C. Cheadle, All Canada Photos
p. 263 (8.6)
p. 268 (8.14): P. & K. Smith, Iconica
p. 269 (8.16): J. E Marriott, All Canada Photos
p. 272 (8.19): Travel Ink, Gallo Images
p. 277 (8.25): D. Allan, The Image Bank
p. 280 (bottom left): F. Nicklin, Minden Pictures
p. 295 (9.6): B. Haas, National Geographic
p. 299 (9.11): A. Bailey, Aurora
p. 300: F. Whitney, The Image Bank
p. 303 (9.15): J. Van Os, The Image Bank
p. 311: M. Moffett, Science Faction
pp. 316–317: M. Everton, Riser
p. 328 (10.13): J. Reed, Science Faction
p. 329: J. Hobbs, All Canada Photos
p. 413 (12.43): ColorBlind Images, Iconica
p. 483 (top): AFP

ISTOCKPHOTO
p. 6 (bottom): D. Gargano
p. 67
p. 80 (3.11): C. Gering
p. 84 (3.18): J. Delgado
p. 85 (3.20): C. Dagenais
p. 99 (A): A. Prill
p. 99 (B)
p. 99 (C): K. Steiner
p. 165 (5.31): G. Teitell
p. 188 (bottom): M. Evans
p. 265 (8.10): G. Clerk
p. 269 (8.17)
p. 285 (bottom)
p. 285 (top): A. Gingerich
p. 310 (A): C.A. Meyer
p. 333 (10.21): K. Tanir
p. 347 (bottom)
p. 351 (11.3) (left): E. Isselée
p. 351 (11.3) (right): S. Yagci
p. 389 (12.11)
p. 389 (12.9): S. Yagci
p. 391 (12.14) (centre)
p. 391 (12.14) (left): P. Robbins
p. 392 (12.15): K. Brynildsen
p. 393 (12.17)
p. 396: R. Whiteway
p. 418 (C): J. Verschoor
p. 419: M. Hilverda
p. 427 (13.2)
p. 428 (13.4) (left): M. Princigalli
p. 428 (13.4) (right): C. Hansen
p. 429 (13.7): L. C. Torres
p. 432 (13.12)
p. 435 (13.17) (left): I. Montero
p. 439 (13.24) (right): M. Sonnenberg
p. 448 (13.40) (left): D. Nichols
p. 450 (left): D. Morgan
p. 451: Alan Reinhart
p. 452
p. 453: L. Chapman
p. 463 (centre): S. Kessler
p. 463 (top): A. Veluscek
p. 472 (14.21) (top left): B. Mason
p. 472 (14.21) (top right): S. Larina
p. 475 (14.25): M. Tihelka
p. 476 (14.26): A. Khromtsov
p. 477 (14.28): A. Khlobystov
p. 479: O. Lantzendörffer
p. 480 (left) (A): A. Smirnov
p. 480 (left) (B): J. Smith
p. 480 (left) (C)
p. 480 (right) (A)
p. 480 (right) (B): M. Braze
p. 481: C. Pickens

JEAN-CLAUDE MARESCHAL
p. 394: Université de Montréal

JÉRÔME DUBÉ
p. 104: KEYSTONE
p. 427 (right)

LE SOLEIL
p. 399: P. Laroche

MARTIN LECLERC
p. 286 (left)
p. 287 (right)

MASTERFILE
pp. 106–107: J. Foster
p. 179 (bottom centre)
p. 305: M. Tomalty
p. 422: A. Birnbach

MAXX IMAGES
p. 418 (A): V. Bider

MÉGAPRESS
p. 195 (6.20)

MIT
p. 412

NASA
p. 207 (6.32)
p. 325

NATIONAL ARCHIVES OF CANADA
p. 417 (top): nlc010225-v6

NATIONAL PORTRAIT GALLERY, LONDON
p. 81
p. 319

PARC OLYMPIQUE DE MONTRÉAL
p. 13 (1.15)

PASCALE OTIS
p. 286 (centre)
p. 286 (right)

PEARSON EDUCATION
p. 64: PH College
p. 168

PHOTO STUDIO
p. 406 (12.33)
p. 409 (12.37)
p. 415 (12.46)
p. 415 (12.47)
p. 421
p. 432 (13.12)

PHOTOS.COM
p. 391 (12.13)

PHOTOSHOT
p. 335 (10.23): UPPA

PHOTOTHÈQUE ERPI
p. 6 (top)
p. 20
p. 36
p. 95
p. 109 (4.2)
p. 132 (A)
p. 158 (5.24)
p. 247
p. 255
p. 265 (top)
p. 274 (8.21)
p. 310 (C)
p. 356
p. 380 (centre)
p. 388 (12.6)
p. 388 (12.7)
p. 411 (12.41)
p. 414 (12.44)
p. 418 (B)
p. 418 (E)
p. 445 (13.35)
p. 450 (right)
p. 459 (14.2)
p. 462
p. 464 (14.9)
p. 465 (bottom)
p. 471 (14.20) (centre)
p. 474 (14.24)
p. 484 (left)
p. 493 (EI.9)

PIERRE-MARIE PAQUIN
p. 391 (12.14) (right)

POINT DU JOUR AVIATION LTÉE
p. 332 (10.20): J.-D. Cossette

PRENTICE HALL
p. 146 (5.12)
p. 158 (5.23)
p. 159 (5.25)

PUBLIC WORKS AND GOVERNMENT SERVICES CANADA
p. 490 (EI.4): Canadian Centre for Climate Modelling and Analysis, Environment Canada, 2008

PUBLIPHOTO
p. 74 (bottom): P. G. Adam
p. 193 (6.17): D. Lévesque
p. 211: P. G. Adam
p. 213 (bottom): P. G. Adam
p. 235: P. G. Adam
p. 236 (7.19): Y. Hamel
p. 237 (7.21): Y. Marcoux
p. 244 (7.30): P. G. Adam
p. 245 (7.32): Y. Derome
p. 250: F. Newman
p. 277 (8.26): P. G. Adam
p. 304: Jardin Botanique de Montréal
p. 309: P. Obendrauf
p. 327 (bottom): P. G. Adam
p. 330 (10.16): D. Ouellette
p. 340 (10.29): P. G. Adam
p. 346: L. Lisabelle
p. 347 (top): P. G. Adam
p. 352 (11.4) (right): Joubert, Phanie
p. 507 (EI.34): A. Masson

PUBLIPHOTO PHOTO RESEARCHERS
p. 25: M. Kulyk
p. 65 (top): Fletcher & Baylis
p. 132 (B): C. D. Winter
p. 132 (C): C. D. Winter
p. 186 (6.4) (centre right): D. Wiersma
p. 186 (6.5) (centre): Mark A. Schneider
p. 186 (6.5) (left): C. D. Winters
p. 326 (10.11) (right): M. P. Gadomski
p. 333 (bottom): G. D. McMichael
p. 361: Science Source
p. 375: Science Source
p. 395: Science Source

PUBLIPHOTO SPL
p. 85 (3.19): Dr. J. Burgess
p. 111
p. 124: American Institute of Physics
p. 164: S. Hill, NASA
p. 170 (right): S. Terry
p. 205: G. Bernard
p. 223: D. Ducros
p. 239 (7.24)
p. 276 (bottom): Dr. J. Burgess
p. 351 (11.2) (right): CNRI
p. 352 (11.4) (left): CNRI
p. 352 (top)
p. 366: National Library of Medicine
p. 373 (11.25): S. Fraser, RVI, Newcastle-Upon-Tyne
p. 374: A. Syred
p. 377: C. Coffrey
p. 397
p. 435 (13.17) (right)
p. 449
p. 463 (bottom): Rosenfeld Images Ltd.

REUTERS
p. 364 (11.17): R. Sigheti
p. 372 (bottom): R. Sprich

SÉJOUR SANTÉ ENFANTS TCHERNOBYL
p. 137 (bottom)

SHUTTERSTOCK
pp. 4–5: B. Wheadon
p. 102: Oleksii
pp. 486–487: V. Potapova

SUPERSTOCK
p. 417 (12.49): C. Orrico

TANGO
p. 32
p. 151
p. 152
p. 380 (top)
p. 380 (background)
p. 381 (centre)
p. 416 (12.48)
p. 432 (13.13)
p. 484 (centre right)

THE GRANGER COLLECTION
p. 149

THOM VOLK
p. 338

TIPS IMAGES
p. 43: G. A. Rossi

TOYOTA MOTOR
p. 430 (bottom): AFP

UNIVERSITÉ DE MONTRÉAL
pp. 484–485 (background)

UNIVERSITÉ DE SHERBROOKE
p. 154

UNIVERSITY OF OTTAWA (ARCHIVES)
p. 153

UNIVERSITY OF TORONTO (ARCHIVES)
p. 405

UNIVERSITY OF WASHINGTON
p. 461

VERDANT POWER, INC. 2006
p. 210 (6.37): J. Wuilliez, Ripe Studios

VISUALS UNLIMITED
p. 351 (11.2) (left): Dr. R. Calentine
p. 297 (9.9): M. Durham
p. 378: I. Spence